FRESHWATER QUALITY:
DEFINING THE INDEFINABLE?

FRESHWATER QUALITY: DEFINING THE INDEFINABLE?

Edited by

P. J. Boon and D. L. Howell

SCOTTISH
NATURAL
HERITAGE

EDINBURGH: THE STATIONERY OFFICE

The Stationery Office, South Gyle Crescent
Edinburgh EH12 9EB

Application for reproduction should be made to The Stationery Office

First published 1997

British Library Cataloguing in Publication Data
A catalogue record for this book is available from the British Library

Cover photography by L. Gill and J. MacPherson
ISBN 0 11 495 270 1

PREFACE

The Research and Advisory Services Directorate of Scottish Natural Heritage (SNH) held its fourth annual conference at the University of Stirling on 6 and 7 September 1995. These conferences are SNH's research 'shop window'. They are intended primarily to provide a forum for debating issues of particular interest to us, and thereby create an opportunity for our staff to present some of their work to a wider audience. Previous conferences in the series have taken a detailed look at particular aspects of the natural heritage of Scotland, namely: the marine environment of its islands (Baxter and Usher, 1993); its heaths and moorlands (Thompson *et al.*, 1995); and its soils (Taylor *et al.*, 1996). As the fresh waters of Scotland have recently been reviewed extensively elsewhere (Maitland *et al.*, 1994), we made a conscious decision to take a different approach. The theme for the 1995 conference, *Freshwater Quality: Defining the Indefinable?*, was chosen for three principal reasons.

First, the whole area of freshwater 'quality' is at times both confused and confusing. For example, the editors' involvement in the SERCON project (Boon *et al.*, this volume) had revealed a distinct difference in opinion between those who took a broad view of the meaning of 'quality', and those who regarded it as narrower in scope and equated it rather more with pollution status. The time seemed right to open up the topic for much wider debate, to discuss what 'quality' means, and how it might be defined. As the title suggests, we were prepared, if necessary, to conclude that attempts at definitions might not succeed, and that quality is primarily a subjective notion and in essence indefinable.

Second, the last five years has marked an intense period of activity in the UK in developing new techniques for assessing freshwater quality, and we were aware that this was being matched by developments in Europe and elsewhere. The traditional approaches to freshwater monitoring and quality assessment have usually focused on areas such as chemical analysis, and the enumeration and classification of invertebrate and algal populations. These and other approaches are now increasingly being combined with emerging technologies such as Decision Support Systems, remote sensing, Geographic Information Systems, and palaeo-limnological analysis, to shed new light on what is meant by 'freshwater quality'. It seemed an appropriate time to review the range of methods now available.

Third, several pertinent changes and developments in organizational structures and legislation have taken place recently, both in the UK and abroad. From 1 April 1996 the water regulatory authorities in England and Wales (National Rivers Authority) and Scotland (River Purification Authorities) have become part of larger organizations (the Environment Agency and Scottish Environment Protection Agency, respectively); similarly, in Copenhagen a headquarters has been set up for the new European Environment Agency. A wide-ranging 'framework Directive' on water policy has recently been proposed by the European Commission which would subsume several water-related Directives, including the draft Directive on the Ecological Quality of Water. In addition, national and international obligations, such as those under the EC Habitats Directive, or arising from the Biodiversity Convention signed at the Rio summit in 1992, point to the need for better ways of describing and monitoring a wider range of freshwater attributes.

The book is divided into five parts, with chapters arranged thematically. Each part contains chapters derived from oral presentations at the conference, as well as shorter chapters based on poster presentations. In Part 1, we explore the way in which 'freshwater quality' is understood and used, both here and abroad, by organizations, in scientific literature, and by the general public. Parts 2, 3 and 4 comprise much of what might be described as the 'meat' of the book. They contain descriptions of a wide array of methods and approaches in freshwater quality assessment, some of which are new and published here in detail for the first time.

Part 5 looks briefly at mechanisms for improving freshwater quality, focusing on areas such as the roles of legislation and Integrated Catchment Management. In our final chapter, we look again at some of the main themes running through the book, and draw conclusions based not just on our own ideas, but also on views expressed through a questionnaire completed by delegates attending the Stirling conference.

We are conscious that the balance of the book is heavily skewed to the natural attributes of fresh waters, and perhaps a reflection of our own personal expertise and experience. However, evidence from the book's chapters concerned with the more anthropocentric aspects of freshwater quality (for example, recreation value, aesthetic preferences and landscape appreciation) suggests that these fields are far less active in terms of freshwater research than the fields of ecology, chemistry, hydrology and geomorphology. To that extent perhaps the uneven balance of the book is justified.

We were delighted that the Stirling conference ran so smoothly. Much of that is due to our colleagues on the Conference Organizing Committee, and here we must express our thanks to Sheila Burr, Joanna Drewitt, Willie Duncan, Olivia Lassière, Peter Maitland and Nikki Wood for their unstinting efforts and cheerfulness in the face of what were often very busy times. We also owe a debt of thanks to all the staff at Stirling University and the Stirling Management Centre who contributed their part to the success of the conference. The conference poster session attracted 59 papers which stimulated much interest and discussion. We are grateful to all poster authors for the effort they put into preparing their displays; regrettably, space limitations in this book have prevented us from publishing them all.

Finally, we have brought the book to publication with assistance from numerous individuals. We thank especially the referees whose comments have improved the quality of the chapters, Lorne Gill and George Logan of SNH for their assistance in choosing the photographs for the colour plates, Nikki Wood for re-drawing figures, and the various staff at The Stationery Office—Angus McKinnon, Penny Clarke and Alastair Holmes—for seeing us through so capably to the final product.

References

Baxter, J. M. and Usher, M. B. (Eds) (1994). *The Islands of Scotland: A Living Marine Heritage*. HMSO, Edinburgh.

Boon, P. J., Holmes, N. T. H., Maitland, P. S., Rowell, T. A. and Davies, J. (This volume). A system for evaluating rivers for conservation (SERCON): development, structure and function.

Maitland, P. S., Boon, P. J. and McLusky, D. S. (Eds) (1994). *The Fresh Waters of Scotland: a National Resource of International Significance*. John Wiley, Chichester.

Taylor, A. G., Gordon, J. E. and Usher, M. B. (Eds) (1996). *Soils, Sustainability and the Natural Heritage*. HMSO, Edinburgh.

Thompson, D. B. A., Hester, A. J. and Usher, M. B. (Eds) (1995). *Heaths and Moorlands: Cultural Landscapes*. HMSO, Edinburgh.

P. J. Boon and D. L. Howell
Edinburgh, June 1996

CONTENTS

LIST OF CONTRIBUTORS

B. Andersson, Department of Environmental Assessment, Swedish University of Agricultural Sciences, Box 7050, S-75007 Uppsala, Sweden

H. S. Baral, Bird Conservation Nepal, P.O. Box 536, Kathmandu, Nepal

R. W. Battarbee, Environmental Change Research Centre, University College London, 26 Bedford Way, London WC1H 0AP

S. Bennett, Department of Geography, Drummond Street, University of Edinburgh, Edinburgh EH8 9XP

P. J. Boon, Scottish Natural Heritage, 2 Anderson Place, Edinburgh EH6 5NP

V. Brazier, Scottish Natural Heritage, 2 Anderson Place, Edinburgh EH6 5NP

P. A. Brewin, Catchment Research Group, School of Pure and Applied Biology, University of Wales, Cardiff CF1 3TL

S. T. Buckton, Catchment Research Group, School of Pure and Applied Biology, University of Wales, Cardiff CF1 3TL

R. T. Clarke, Institute of Terrestrial Ecology, Furzebrook Research Station, Furzebrook Road, Wareham, Dorset BH20 5AS

D. Cydzik, Institute of Environmental Protection, Lake Quality Division, 01-692 Warsaw, Kolektorska 4, Poland

M. Davidson, North East River Purification Board (Present address: Scottish Environment Protection Agency, Greyhope House, Greyhope Road, Torry, Aberdeen AB1 3RD)

J. Davies, 22 Hamilton Place, Edinburgh EH3 5UA

F. H. Dawson, Institute of Freshwater Ecology, River Laboratory, East Stoke, Wareham, Dorset BH20 6BB

Y. de Lafontaine, Centre Saint-Laurent, Environment Canada, 105 McGill, Montreal, Quebec, Canada H2Y 2E7

N. De Pauw, Laboratory of Biological Research, University of Gent, J. Plateaustraat 22, B-9000 Gent, Belgium

C. R. Doughty, Clyde River Purification Board (Present address: Scottish Environment Protection Agency, Rivers House, Murray Road, East Kilbride, Glasgow G75 0LA)

W. M. Duncan, Scottish Natural Heritage, 2 Anderson Place, Edinburgh EH6 5NP

J. M. Eadie, Wildlife, Fish and Conservation Biology, University of California, Davis, California 95616-8751, USA

A. C. Edwards, Macaulay Land Use Research Institute, Craigiebuckler, Aberdeen AB9 2QJ

R. W. Edwards, National Rivers Authority (Present address: Environment Agency, Rivers House, St. Mellons Business Park, St. Mellons, Cardiff CF3 0LT)

E. S. Edwards-Jones, Department of Civil and Offshore Engineering, Heriot-Watt University, Riccarton, Edinburgh EH14 4AS

G. Edwards-Jones, Rural Resource Management Department, SAC, Edinburgh EH9 3JG

M. Everard, National Rivers Authority (Present address: Environment Agency, Rio House, Waterside Drive, Aztec West, Almondsbury, Bristol BS12 4UD)

R. C. Ferrier, Macaulay Land Use Research Institute, Craigiebuckler, Aberdeen AB9 2QJ

M. Fordham, Anglia Polytechnic University, East Road, Cambridge CB1 4PT

P. Fox, National Rivers Authority (Present address: Environment Agency, Richard Fairclough House, Knutsford Road, Warrington WA4 1HQ)

I. R. Fozzard, Forth River Purification Board (Present address: Scottish Environment Protection Agency, Clearwater House, Heriot-Watt Research Park, Avenue North, Riccarton, Edinburgh EH14 4AP)

M. T. Furse, Institute of Freshwater Ecology, River Laboratory, East Stoke, Wareham, Dorset BH20 6BB

J. H. R. Gee, Institute of Biological Sciences, University of Wales, Aberystwyth SY23 3DA

J. E. Gordon, Scottish Natural Heritage, 2 Anderson Place, Edinburgh EH6 5NP

J. A. Gore, The Conservancy (Florida) (Present address: Environmental Science Program, School of Science, Columbus State University, Columbus, GA 31907, USA)

C. Green, Middlesex University Flood Hazard Research Centre, Queensway, Enfield, Middlesex EN3 4SF

R. D. Gregory, British Trust for Ornithology, Thetford, Norfolk IP24 2PU

S. W. Griffiths, Institute of Biological Sciences, University of Wales, Aberystwyth SY23 3DA

N. Hanley, Environmental Economics Research Group, University of Stirling, Stirling FK9 4LA

J. H. Hartig, International Joint Commission, Great Lakes Regional Office, 100 Ouellette Avenue, Windsor, Ontario, Canada N9A 6T3

J. M. Hellawell, Anglian Environmental Consultants Ltd, Engaine, Orton Longueville, Peterborough PE2 7QA

L. W. G. Higler, Department of Aquatic Ecology, Institute for Forestry and Nature Research (IBN-DLO), PO Box 23, NL-6700 AA Wageningen, The Netherlands

I. D. Hogg, Centre Saint-Laurent, Environment Canada, 105 McGill, Montreal, Quebec, Canada H2Y 2E7

N. T. H. Holmes, Alconbury Environmental Consultants, 57 Ramsey Road, Warboys, Huntingdon PE17 2RW

M. House, Middlesex University Flood Hazard Research Centre, Queensway, Enfield, Middlesex EN3 4SF

D. L. Howell, Scottish Natural Heritage, 2 Anderson Place, Edinburgh EH6 5NP

P. Johnes, Department of Geography, University of Reading, Whiteknights, Reading RG6 2AB

I. Jüttner, GSF-Forschungszentrum für Umwelt und Gesundheit, Institut für Ökologische Chemie, Neuherberg, 85758 Oberschleissheim, Germany

D. Kudelska, Institute of Environmental Protection, Lake Quality Division, 01-692 Warsaw, Kolektorska 4, Poland

R. H. W. Langston, British Trust for Ornithology, Thetford, Norfolk IP24 2PU

O. L. Lassière, Scottish Natural Heritage, 2 Anderson Place, Edinburgh EH6 5NP

T. M. Leatherland, Forth River Purification Board (Present address: Scottish Environment Protection Agency, Heriot-Watt Research Park, Riccarton, Edinburgh EH14 4AP)

K. M. Lee, Institute of Biological Sciences, University of Wales, Aberystwyth SY23 3DA

L. J. McEwen, Department of Geography and Geology, Cheltenham and Gloucester College of Higher Education, Francis Close Hall, Swindon Road, Cheltenham GL50 4AZ

D. W. Mackay, North East River Purification Board (Present address: Scottish Environment Protection Agency, Graesser House, Fodderty Way, Dingwall IV15 9XB)

P. S. Maitland, Fish Conservation Centre, Easter Cringate, Stirling FK7 9QX

A. Malcolm, Macaulay Land Use Research Institute, Craigiebuckler, Aberdeen AB9 2QJ

T. J. Malthus, Department of Geography, Drummond Street, University of Edinburgh, Edinburgh EH8 9XP

J. H. Marchant, British Trust for Ornithology, Thetford, Norfolk IP24 2PU

G. Moffett, Tay River Purification Board (Present address: Countryside Council for Wales, Plas Penrhos, Ffordd Penrhos, Bangor, Gwynedd LL57 2LQ)

I. Moreira, Instituto Superior de Agronomia, Universidade Técnica de Lisboa, 1399 Lisboa Codex, Portugal

J. G. Morrice, Macaulay Land Use Research Institute, Craigiebuckler, Aberdeen AB9 2QJ

B. Moss, Department of Environmental and Evolutionary Biology, University of Liverpool, Liverpool L69 3BX

D. Moss, Institute of Terrestrial Ecology, Monks Wood, Abbots Ripton, Huntingdon PE17 2LS

S. North, Department of Geography, Drummond Street, University of Edinburgh, Edinburgh EH8 9XP

J. O'Keeffe, Institute for Water Research, Rhodes University, Grahamstown, South Africa

S. J. Ormerod, Catchment Research Group, School of Pure and Applied Biology, University of Wales, Cardiff CF1 3TL

R. Owen, North East River Purification Board (Present address: Scottish Environment Protection Agency, Greyhope House, Greyhope Road, Torry, Aberdeen AB1 3RD

C. L. Padmore, Department of Geography, University of Newcastle, Newcastle upon Tyne NE1 7RU

G. Phillips, National Rivers Authority (Present address: Environment Agency, Cobham Road, Ipswich, Suffolk IP3 9JE)

P. Pinto, Dept. Biologia, Universidade de Evora, 7001 Evora Codex, Portugal

C. J. Place, Department of Geography, University of Edinburgh, Drummond Street, Edinburgh EH8 9XP

K. B. Pugh, North East River Purification Board (Present address: Scottish Environment Protection Agency, Graesser House, Fodderty Way, Dingwall IV15 9XB)

P. Raven, National Rivers Authority (Present address: Environment Agency, Rio House, Waterside Drive, Aztec West, Almondsbury, Bristol BS12 4UD)

H. Rothfritz, Catchment Research Group, School of Pure and Applied Biology, University of Wales, Cardiff CF1 3TL

T. A. Rowell, Conservation Data Services, Bryn Einon, Penffordd, Llanwenog, Llanybydder, Dyfed SA40 9XD

M. G. Saraiva, Instituto Superior de Agronomia, Universidade Técnica de Lisboa, 1399 Lisboa Codex, Portugal

A. Schneiders, Department of Biology, University of Antwerp, Universiteitsplein 1, B-2610 Wilrijk, Belgium

C. Sloan, Rural Resource Management Department, SAC, Edinburgh EH9 3JG

B. D. Smith, Institute of Biological Sciences, University of Wales, Aberystwyth SY23 3DA

I. R. Smith, 2 New Mill Cottages, New Mill on Slitrig, by Hawick TD9 9UQ

B. Söderbäck, Department of Environmental Assessment, Swedish University of Agricultural Sciences, Box 7050, S-75007 Uppsala, Sweden

H. Soszka, Institute of Environmental Protection, Lake Quality Division, 01-692 Warsaw, Kolektorska 4, Poland

C. J. Spray, Northumbrian Water, Abbey Road, Pity Me, Durham DH1 5FJ

A. M. Suren, New Zealand Institute of Water and Atmospheric Research, Kyle Street, Riccarton, Christchurch, New Zealand

C. Swanwick, Department of Landscape, University of Sheffield, Sheffield S10 2TN

Y. Trihadiningrum, Department of Environmental Engineering, FTSP-ITS, Kampus ITS Keputih Sukolilo, JL. A R Hakim, Surabaya 60111, Indonesia

S. Tunstall, Middlesex University Flood Hazard Research Centre, Queensway, Enfield, Middlesex EN3 4SF

M. B. Usher, Scottish Natural Heritage, 2 Anderson Place, Edinburgh EH6 5NP

L. van Liere, Department of Aquatic Ecology, Institute for Forestry and Nature Research (IBN-DLO), PO Box 23, NL-6700 AA Wageningen, The Netherlands

R. F. Verheyen, Department of Biology, University of Antwerp, Universiteitsplein 1, B-2610 Wilrijk, Belgium

A. Werritty, Department of Geography, University of Dundee, Dundee DD1 4HN

T. Wiederholm, Department of Environmental Assessment, Swedish University of Agricultural Sciences, Box 7050, S-75007 Uppsala, Sweden

E. Willén, Department of Environmental Assessment, Swedish University of Agricultural Sciences, Box 7050, S-75007 Uppsala, Sweden

D. D. Williams, Division of Life Sciences, Scarborough Campus, University of Toronto, 1265 Military Trail, Scarborough, Ontario, Canada M1C 1A4

N. E. Williams, Division of Physical Sciences, Scarborough Campus, University of Toronto, 1265 Military Trail, Scarborough, Ontario, Canada M1C 1A4

C. Wils, Department of Biology, University of Antwerp, Universiteitsplein 1, B-2610 Wilrijk, Belgium

J. F. Wright, Institute of Freshwater Ecology, River Laboratory, East Stoke, Wareham, Dorset BH20 6BB

M. A. Zarull, Aquatic Ecosystem Restoration Branch, National Water Research Institute, 867 Lakeshore Road, Burlington, Ontario, Canada L7R 4A6

FOREWORD

In the UK we have taken fresh water for granted for a long time. Its exploitation was fundamental to the Industrial Revolution, particularly in its use for steam power, for canal transport, for industry, and for disposing of industrial and human wastes. However, 200 years later we find ourselves at a point in our history when extremes of flood and drought are afflicting us with increasing frequency, and the costs of cleaning up and restoring polluted and re-engineered waters are proving very difficult to meet.

These are issues which confront us in a small, densely-populated island nation, at a stage in its economic development which has brought conflicts with what should be plentiful, clean freshwater resources. Even as progress continues to be made in cleaning pollution from our worst point sources, we continue to be challenged by pollution from diffuse sources, and from novel compounds present in fresh waters in minuscule concentrations—such as hormone analogues—which in turn may alter our present perceptions of the term 'freshwater quality'. One of the lessons emerging from the sustainable development debates of the last quarter of a century is that the current path of global economic development—which the UK virtually instigated through the Industrial Revolution—has already cost far more than we should expect the generations succeeding us to pay for.

This book is the result of a conference organized by a few inhabitants of what is often thought of as a nation plagued by insularity. Whilst many of the written contributions adopt an understandable UK bias, they also look outward to our European neighbours and to those further afield. Furthermore, one of the book's strengths is the international flavour imparted by contributions from authors from four continents. The conference itself was attended by 270 delegates from 17 countries around the world, and, through the post-conference questionnaire exercise reported in the editors' closing chapter, nearly 50% of them can see their views reflected in print. As chairman of a body which is required to represent the views of the UK's statutory conservation agencies to the rest of the world, I take all of this as encouraging evidence that, not only are UK freshwater specialists prepared to look around the globe for inspiration and ideas, but also, judging by the reaction to the conference, they enjoy themselves when they do so!

I find further encouragement in the extent to which those contributors to the book from backgrounds in what we might call the 'natural sciences' (e.g. geomorphology, hydrology, ecology, chemistry) are increasingly willing to focus their attentions on the complexities of human behaviour. The book also contains contributions from the 'human sciences'—such as economics and psychology—which consider human behaviour patterns at a range of scales, from the individual to the governmental. These contributions examine the factors which shape our perceptions of freshwater quality, and they demonstrate an accomplished willingness to enter the realm of the natural scientist. This interdisciplinary welding of expertise is a joy to behold, but if it is to succeed in its principal aim—which I hope I can summarize as to improve freshwater quality (having first defined it)—the specialists must continue to find new ways of conveying their findings to politicians and electorates. This book is but one medium for delivering what is an increasingly important message.

I hope (as I know do the editors and their employers) that the techniques, ideas and opinions expressed in the pages which follow provide inspiration for its readers, whether they are students, water practitioners, academics, politicians, or interested lay observers. The question of what is appropriate water quality—and what 'freshwater quality' actually means—is central to contemporary debates about sustainable development, as water availability and quality are vital both to human life and to the well-being of the natural world. This brings me, finally, to my own humble attempt to answer in a few lines what this book sets out to do in its 42 chapters—to 'define the indefinable'.

Water quality, surely, is quality of life for everything that lives on the planet. It is axiomatic, therefore, that a good quality of life for our fellow species is fundamental to a good quality of life for ourselves. The underlying complexity of this simple truth is something we have only recently begun to appreciate. The wonders of some of that complexity are expressed in many of the contributions which follow my own, so with that, I invite you to read on.

The Earl of Selborne
Peterborough, June 1996

1 INTRODUCTION

R. W. Edwards

Summary

1. Water quality only has meaning when judged against clear, objective criteria, and these are best established in relation to specific uses, both abstracted and *in situ*.

2. Water quality is a consequence not only of direct, discrete discharges to watercourses, but of catchment processes often influenced by global events and activity.

3. Water quality is only one aspect of environmental quality, and for *in situ* uses those wider aspects relating to physical and biological features are also important.

The title of this book reads rather like one of those enigmatic essay questions which Oxbridge dons delight in setting—searching for the imaginative, the conceptual and the lateral thinker. Yet the editors (and the organizers of the conference on which the book is based) presumably had more prosaic considerations in mind when questioning whether water quality is definable.

Even at one site on an individual river, conditions can vary widely and rapidly. Oxygen concentrations in some lowland rivers can range between 20 and 150% air saturation in a few hours through diurnal respiratory and photosynthetic processes, and suspended solids concentrations can increase by orders of magnitude during a brief storm event. The Greek philosopher Heraclitus seemed to recognize this highly variable quality of rivers when he wrote 'Everything is in flux—you cannot step into the same river twice'. Statistical descriptions have therefore become an integral aspect of most quality definitions.

There are, however, more basic issues, for quality implies a degree or scale of excellence, arguably relevant only when judged in relation to specific uses or purposes. With abstracted uses of water, such as for potable supply, relevant chemical and microbiological attributes defining quality are widely accepted and form the basis of use-related standards or Directives by international organizations such as the World Health Organization and the European Community. This approach also extends to some *in situ* uses for water, such as fisheries and water-based recreation. Some difference of opinion still exists about the universal validity of the use-driven quality description, the degree of departure of water quality from its 'natural state' being regarded as a possible alternative descriptor and one which has particular relevance to wildlife conservation. This book, at least in part, explores such philosophical issues.

Further problems arise when moving from establishing a use requiring quality standards—first in identifying the attributes relevant to protecting that use, and second in determining quantitative values for these standards. These problems occur, for example, in determining safety standards for drinking water. There is a high degree of confidence that, in relation to acute effects, quality standards are comprehensive and high. Confidence decreases to some degree, however, with long-term effects—particularly during periods of speculation about links between aluminium and Alzheimer's disease, pesticides and cancer, oestrogen analogues and fertility. Such speculation frequently proves to be unfounded. Nevertheless, nature has a nasty habit of delivering surprises and, however assiduous the attempts of experts, a quality definition will never be all-embracing. Consequently, safety factors and the precautionary principle will remain important; they seek to compensate for our ignorance, at a cost of course. In setting such safety factors there is an important distinction between protecting humans where concern is for the *individual*, and generally the most vulnerable, whereas with other species it is usually the far less exacting *population* viability which is protected.

One problem which arises in setting quantitative standards is the tendency to ignore interactions between pollutants and assume that they act singly, generally because toxicological studies have been conducted on single poisons. In practice, the spectrum of pollutants is wide and stresses are multiple, and in such situations there is frequent but inadequate dependence on large safety factors. The following example illustrates that in establishing water quality standards for fisheries, attempts have been made to take into account component effects of individual poisons in assessing the total toxicity of Willow Brook, an industrial river in England (Solbé, 1973). From chemical analytical data taken at many sites in the catchment over a substantial period and a knowledge of the toxicity of the major pollutants, an integrated measure of toxicity at each site was calculated. In Figure 1.1 each line reflects this total toxicity as a statistical distribution over time, and there is a quality separation between those sites with thriving fisheries and those where fisheries were marginal. Assessing the effects of single pollutants generally gives grossly optimistic pictures. The direct measurement of toxicity is only feasible in the most polluted rivers where acute effects occur but the wider use of direct toxicity tests of effluents, rather than reliance on chemical information on a few constituents, is to be greatly welcomed, particularly where such effluents are complex or variable.

In contrast to abstracted use, the definition of freshwater quality for *in situ* uses (fisheries, recreation, conservation) must embrace physical habitat qualities of the water bodies too. With respect to fisheries, and particularly salmonid fisheries, this physical quality definition has made great strides in recent years in the UK through the development and testing of such models as HABSCORE. In some geographical areas this can explain up to 95% of the spatial variation in fish

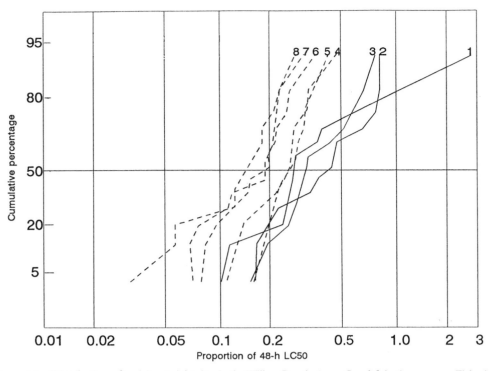

Figure 1.1   Distribution of toxicity at eight sites in the Willow Brook. (– – – Good fisheries; ——— Fisheries marginal.) (Reproduced from Solbé, 1973, with permission).

density (Milner *et al.*, 1985). Most freshwater invertebrates in rivers are closely associated with substrate, and physical habitat features are critically important. Studies in the Upper Wye catchment (mid-Wales), for example, have demonstrated the remarkable contrast in distribution of some species between riffles and marginal areas (Ormerod, 1985) (Figure 1.2). Nevertheless, predictive models have not generally been developed for river invertebrates despite their importance in biological monitoring programmes, past reliance being placed on the selection of a single habitat—the 'uniform riffle'. Sampling procedures introduced by the National Rivers Authority using the RIVPACS system for water quality assessment (Wright *et al.*, 1989) embrace all the accessible river habitats and give a much more comprehensive description of the faunal complement. However, the system is not ideal for conservation assessment without extending the taxonomic penetration beyond the family level, to which identification is normally taken for water quality purposes. Surveillance systems designed specifically for conservation value, and based on the distribution of natural and man-made features, are described later in the book (Raven *et al.*, this volume): their validation in terms of wildlife diversity is eagerly awaited.

There has been a tendency in the UK, unlike in many other parts of the world, to focus freshwater quality descriptions on rivers rather than lakes, principally

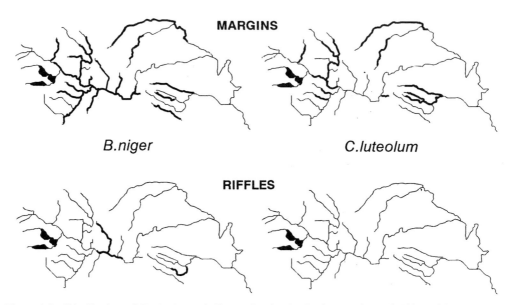

MARGINS

B.niger   *C.luteolum*

RIFFLES

Figure 1.2   Distribution of *Baetis niger* and *Centroptilum luteolum* in the margins and riffles of the River Wye catchment.

because the ravages caused by industrial and population growth have affected many rivers dramatically—rivers which are used for a variety of purposes. Most lakes are in the uplands and generally unaffected by man—except, of course, through the more subtle changes in land use and by acid rain. A further factor has been the small extent to which natural lakes have been utilized for water supply, reservoirs having been built for this purpose, many during the late nineteenth century. Only now is consideration being given to a more systematic description of lake quality and lake classification; this long gestation period during a period of increasing understanding of lake behaviour (particularly plant nutrients and food-chain dynamics) provides an opportunity for a thorough review of options for classification. One advantage which lakes have over rivers is the retention of their histories in sediments (rivers lose theirs downstream) and the opportunity this affords for time-based as well as spatial comparisons. On the other hand there are difficulties in providing simple quality descriptions created by the frequent heterogeneity of water columns and problems in sampling such heterogeneous systems.

The development of classification systems from quality descriptions is not confined to lakes but is occurring over a wide front and even venturing into the field of aesthetics of river corridors. For single uses quality classifications can generally be fairly rigorous (or at least defensible), but the broader such classification systems become the more rigour is sacrificed for utility, purity for pragmatism. The determination of class boundaries is itself a field for torrid argument. Nevertheless, for general management purposes, and particularly for reporting to the wider public, such general classification schemes are useful and help convey broad patterns of environmental quality in space and time, complementing the schemes devised for the expert and specialist user.

Whilst it might be argued that quality descriptions need not extend beyond river margins or lake shores for most purposes, it is important that riparian and catchment processes, and even those extending over much wider areas, are understood as they have profound effects on water quality. The National Rivers Authority (now part of the Environment Agency) has made formal the significance of these influences through the widespread adoption of catchment management plans.

Perhaps the most dramatic impacts of land management on water quality have been described for the Hubbards Brook wooded catchments on the eastern seaboard of the USA. In one field experiment trees were felled but not cleared and there were substantial changes to the ionic composition of the stream draining the catchment, which continued for several years (Likens *et al.*, 1977). There are many other examples of the impact which land use and land management have on river and lake quality, some determined from historical studies of lake sediments and others using experimental procedures. Observations on the acidification of fresh waters have revealed the interplay between the long-range transportation of contaminants and catchment vegetation and soils. Modelling the impact of these processes on river and lake communities has been useful in developing national and catchment strategies for recovery. Such strategies may differ, however, depending on which uses are regarded as important: catchment liming restores pH neutrality and protects fisheries but creates calcium-rich streams unnatural for many of these upland areas and for the flora and fauna which would normally occur there. This example demonstrates a much wider dilemma in water quality management which can be solved only on a case by case basis after priorities have been clearly established.

In summary, defining water quality can be meaningful but only where it is related to specific uses, for each use has its own spectrum of relevant criteria. Definitions will never be comprehensive, embracing all such relevant criteria, but there are ways of improving the historical reductionist approach based on a few key chemical variables supported by safety factors to reflect ignorance. For in-stream uses, which are gaining in significance, freshwater quality is as much about the physical as the chemical environment. Moreover, in whatever way freshwater quality is defined, processes far from the freshwater boundaries must be understood and managed or influenced if the uses to which freshwater systems are put can be protected effectively.

References

Likens, G. E., Bormann, F., Pierce, R. S., Eaton, J. S. and Johnson, N. M. (1977). *Biogeochemistry of a Forested Ecosystem*. Springer-Verlag, New York.

Milner, N. J., Hemsworth, R. J. and Jones, B. E. (1985). Habitat evaluation as a fisheries management tool. *Journal of Fish Biology*, **27**(Suppl. A), 85–108.

Ormerod, S. J. (1985). 'The Distribution of Macroinvertebrates in the Upper Catchment of the River Wye in Relation to Ionic Composition'. Unpublished Ph.D. thesis, University of Wales, Cardiff.

Raven, P. J., Fox, P., Everard, M., Holmes, N. T. H. and Dawson, F. H. (This volume). River Habitat Survey: a new system for classifying rivers according to their habitat quality.

Solbé, J. F. de L. G. (1973). The relation between water quality and the status of fish populations. *Water Treatment and Examination,* **22,** 41–61.

Wright, J. F., Armitage, P. D., Furse, M. T. and Moss, D. (1989). Prediction of invertebrate communities using stream measurements. *Regulated Rivers: Research and Management,* **4,** 147–155.

PART ONE
'FRESHWATER QUALITY': PRESENT USE OF THE TERM

2 ORGANIZATIONAL USE OF THE TERM 'FRESHWATER QUALITY' IN BRITAIN

K. B. Pugh

Summary

1. More than 80 organizations in Britain with an interest in the aquatic environment were asked how they defined, described and presented information about freshwater quality. Most acknowledged the difficulty of giving a succinct definition and wrote in terms of freshwater use and fitness for use, of legislative standards and controls, or of classification schemes. The summarized responses are presented.

2. A short list of specific freshwater uses and associated quality descriptors is given. Since many of these quality descriptors and their numerical standards have been subsumed into statutory instruments, the relevant pieces of specific legislation concerning fresh water are considered.

3. Concern over the maintenance of the water resource increasingly requires a more holistic assessment of the generality of water quality, and an appreciation of the organizational attempts at such assessment is presented. Whilst most questionnaire respondents considered that a comprehensive definition was impossible, one definition was proffered—'freshwater quality is the totality of features and characteristics of the water that bear upon its ability to support an appropriate natural flora and fauna, and to sustain legitimate uses'.

2.1 Introduction

All life on earth relies on water. There is plenty of it—'water, water, everywhere!'— but only about 0.5% is liquid fresh water and of that less than a quarter is at the surface; the remainder is underground (Royal Commission on Environmental Pollution, 1992). Species differ in the amount and type of water that they need, whether at the ecosystem, community, population, individual or cellular level. As humans, we have more power than any other species to influence the character and extent of the water resources which we and all other species need. With that power comes a responsibility to maintain the available water resource, and the organizations we use to carry out that responsibility for fresh waters are the subject of this chapter.

A dictionary (Chambers, 1983) definition of 'fresh' includes 'in a state of activity and health, not stale, faded or soiled, new, recently added, without salt'. Perhaps then, fresh water is that non-saline naturally amended fluid which gently seeps into the earth's surface and collects as groundwater; or lies in various states of laziness in ponds, pools, lochs or lakes; or trickles across the land surface, scouring and eroding its course down the gradient, finally wending its way across the valley floor to its ocean sink.

Fresh water is not just that pure chemical which is the combination of two atoms of hydrogen and one of oxygen, but that subtle concoction with additional materials—chemical and biological—dissolved or suspended in it, which fortify and flavour it, giving it its 'freshness'. The amendment is crucial. Those subtle additional materials—naturally occurring or of man's devising—make all the difference and give each aliquot of water its unique quality.

The same dictionary suggests that 'quality' is 'that which makes a thing what it is, property, attribute, grade of goodness and excellence'. The quality of fresh water is what it is—all its constituent parts. Given that there are scores of elements associated with fresh water and many thousands of chemical compounds, let alone a myriad of biological species, the absolute description of water quality is cumbersome to say the least, and some abbreviated label is desirable. A thesaurus leads thinking about quality to 'merit' and 'value' and thus to the notion of fitness for purpose. It also leads beyond excellence to 'distinction' and 'superiority' which suggests comparison, and to facilitate comparison, classification, which at its simplest may be just 'good' or 'bad'.

Given the potential complexity of definition, it is little wonder that when more than 80 British organizations with an interest in freshwater quality were asked how they defined, described and presented information about it, most respondents acknowledged the difficulty of giving a succinct definition and wrote in terms of freshwater use and fitness for use, of legislative standards and controls, or of classification schemes. This chapter summarizes the responses received in this exercise. Initially, it considers a short list of specific freshwater uses and associated quality descriptors, and, since many of these quality descriptors and their numerical standards have been subsumed into statutory instruments, the relevant pieces of specific legislation concerning fresh water are discussed. Yet concern over the maintenance of the available water resource requires a more holistic assessment of the generality of water quality, as opposed to a view limited to one or two characteristics, and an appreciation of the attempts at such assessment is presented. Throughout, an indication is given of which organization pursues which particular water quality consideration, ranging from that of the specific user group with relatively narrow interests, through the general public with its variable breadth of view and interest (see Tunstall *et al.*, this volume), to the highly environmentally-aware custodians and regulators of the aquatic environment who must maintain a very broad overview.

2.2 Use-Related Definitions of Freshwater Quality

2.2.1 *Abstraction for domestic water supply*

The Water Companies in England and Wales and the three Scottish Water Authorities, which are responsible for the public supply of 'wholesome' domestic water (for drinking, washing, cooking and food production purposes), have only an indirect interest in freshwater quality. They more frequently refer to 'raw water intended for drinking water'—their source water, and 'potable water'—their product. They generally apply the term 'raw water' to those springs, streams, rivers, reservoirs or groundwaters which are not significantly polluted and can be treated economically to produce potable water. Whilst seeking water which contains little ammonia, nitrate, iron, manganese, pesticides and bacteria, a major concern is the absence of taste, odour and colour. For the public water abstractor, quality involves fitness for use of the end product and is measured in relation to characteristics which are now defined and quantified in relevant legislation (see Section 2.3.2).

Likewise, those members of the public and industry who abstract privately are controlled and consider quality in similar terms (see Section 2.3.2). Those who bottle natural mineral waters and sell it as spring water, spa water or table water have their own legislative controls, but similar standards and thus a similar consideration of freshwater quality (see Section 2.3.2).

2.2.2 *Industrial uses*

British Water, an amalgam of the former British Effluent and Water Association and the British Water Industries Group, produces a data sheet (British Water, 1986) which recognizes nine grades of water from natural, through potable, softened, dealkalized, deionized, purified, apyrogenic and high purity, to ultra-pure and gives typical applications and, for all but natural water, typical characteristics. For natural water the applications listed are: once-through cooling systems, outside wash-down, irrigation, fisheries, fire-fighting, recreational, and natural mineral waters. Uses listed for potable water are drinking, domestic use, food and soft drinks, cooling systems, irrigation and fire-fighting. For both types of water, typical characteristics (quality) are the chemical and, where appropriate, microbiological limit values from the relevant statutory instruments (see Sections 2.3.1 to 2.3.4). For each of the remaining processed waters several typical uses are listed, and the corresponding quality reference is to a British Standard or a Trade Association guideline, again specifically, usually chemically, defined.

2.2.3 *Recreational uses*

Fresh waters have a range of recreational uses from a general amenity purpose, e.g. landscape beauty of value to tourists as well as the local population (a particular concern of bodies such as the Countryside Commission, the Countryside Council for Wales and Scottish Natural Heritage), through a variety of water sports during which there is increasing body contact with the water, e.g. boating, fishing, paddling, water-skiing, swimming. There is currently no statutory duty on local authorities to monitor recreational waters, nor are there any statutory standards or guidelines set by the UK Government or the European Community, unless the water is an identified bathing water for the purposes of the 1976 EC Bathing Waters Directive (see Section 2.3.4). However, the Institution of Environmental Health Officers has made an assessment of recreational water quality and issued a guide (Institution of Environmental Health Officers, 1993) for decision-makers in environmental health. They suggest that quality can be monitored in relation to any of 19 groups of bacteria, four groups of protozoa, seven groups of viruses, four groups of fungi, four groups of parasites, coliphages, four physical characteristics and 11 groups of chemicals. It may also be appropriate to take samples of shellfish, live and dead fish, birds and animals for microbial analysis. The Institution indicates that aesthetic indicators of quality are being developed and used and therefore that an assessment of water quality may also take account of 'visible materials that will settle to form objectionable deposits; floating debris, oil, scum and other matter; substances producing objectionable colour, odour, taste or turbidity and substances and conditions or combinations thereof in concentrations which produce undesirable aquatic life'.

British Waterways, which manages and cares for over 2,000 miles of Britain's canals and rivers, aims to achieve a minimum of Class 2 quality in the National Water Council system of classification (see Section 2.4.1) (and a separate system in Scotland, see Section 2.4.2) to support their principal businesses of amenity (enabling public access for boating, walking, cycling, and other leisure activities), coarse fisheries, water sales and wildlife conservation.

2.2.4   Effluent disposal (sewage and industrial)

Watercourses have ever been a means of disposal of unwanted materials. When the Scottish River Purification Authorities were established under the Rivers (Prevention of Pollution) (Scotland) Act, 1951 there was a specific duty imposed upon them by Section 17 of the Act 'to promote the cleanliness of the rivers and inland waters and the tidal waters in their areas, ...'. In the same and later legislation, provisions were made for the licensing of discharges in order to prevent pollution. The Environment Agency in England and Wales and the Department of the Environment (Northern Ireland) have similar obligations under their own legislation.

There has been a long history of the development of standards for acceptable quantities of materials in fresh water, from the Royal Commissions around the turn of the century which devised the now traditional 20 : 30 standard for Biochemical Oxygen Demand (BOD) and suspended solids (Hammerton, 1994), to those now covered by the various EC Directives on water quality (see Sections 2.3.1–2.3.6). A useful reference list of water quality standards can be found in the 'EQualS' computer database developed by the Water Research Centre with funding from the UK water industry. Traditionally, the regulators (National Rivers Authority (NRA) and River Purification Authorities) have set discharge consent conditions containing numerical chemical water quality standards only, but have fallen back on the qualitative catch-all biological statement that 'the discharge shall not contain any substances in sufficient concentration either separately or in combination to be harmful to flora and/or fauna downstream of the point of discharge'. More recently, where appropriate, a consent may have a toxicological standard incorporated; this will usually involve an oyster embryo bioassay or a 'Microtox' assessment.

2.2.5   *Fisheries*

For many years the guidance issued in the reports of the European Inland Fisheries Advisory Commission was accepted by those with a relevant interest (e.g. District Salmon Fishery Boards, the Atlantic Salmon Trust, and the pollution control authorities) (Solbé, 1988). This guidance formed the basis of the 1978 EC Freshwater Fisheries Directive (see Section 2.3.1) which now provides the primary use-related quality standards for salmonid and cyprinid fisheries. In many ways these standards form a benchmark for water quality on the basis that if the water is of sufficient quality to support a healthy salmon stock it is good enough to support most other activities.

2.2.6   *Wildlife and nature conservation*

Whilst many wild animals and plants are dependent upon fresh water whose very quality in turn has an impact on their life, a systematic set of standards has not been adopted (but see Howell and Mackay, this volume). In the absence of anything better, some of the other foregoing use-related standards have been applied somewhat arbitrarily. However, in the past decade or so, following the burgeoning interest in environment and nature conservation, many organizations have been calling for a broader definition of water quality beyond the chemical characteristics which have dominated many use-related standards. Thus, organizations such as English Nature, World-Wide Fund for Nature, the Royal Society for the Protection of Birds, and Scottish Wildlife Trust are wrestling with a more holistic approach and moving towards a new set of criteria which places water in a wider ecological framework (see Section 2.4.6).

A useful summary of the foregoing, and of the requirements for various uses of water and watercourses, is provided by the Forestry Commission (1993) and this is reproduced as Table 2.1.

2.3   Aspects and Definitions of Freshwater Quality in the Legislation

A number of pieces of national legislation contain definitions of specific aspects of freshwater quality mostly taken from EC Directives. Many have been referred to already, but the following notes provide a synopsis of the relevant content of the Directives from a British perspective. In all cases there is a simple compliance/non-compliance assessment of water quality and, apart from a possible difference between imperative and guideline values, no mechanism for ranking.

Table 2.1 Requirements for various uses of water and watercourses (from *Forests and Water Guidelines*, Forestry Commission, 1993).

Factor	Requirements for various uses of water and watercourses								
	Wildlife including fisheries	Drinking water supply	Hydro-electricity	Fish farming	Irrigation	Land drainage/flood control	Disposal and self-purification of waste[a]	Industrial supply[b]	Recreation
Water quantity									
High yield		✓	✓	✓	✓			✓	✓
Steady supply		✓	✓	✓	✓		✓	✓	✓
Peak flows controlled		✓	✓			✓			✓
Appropriate seasonal flows	✓	✓			✓		✓		✓
Water quality									
Water clarity	✓	✓		✓				✓	
Sediment free	✓	✓	✓	✓		✓		✓	
Uncoloured		✓						✓	
Untainted	✓	✓		✓				✓	
Low nutrient		✓						✓	
Free of toxic chemicals	✓	✓		✓	✓			✓	✓
Non-pathogenic	✓	✓		✓	✓			✓	✓
Moderate pH	✓	✓	✓	✓	✓		✓	✓	✓
Low algal production		✓	✓	✓	✓			✓	✓
Other requirements									
Adequate watercourse channels	✓					✓	✓		✓
Appropriate water temperature range	✓	✓		✓			✓		✓
Adequate oxygen level	✓	✓		✓			✓		✓
Adequate insect and algal production	✓								✓

[a] Poor upstream water quality could reduce the assimilatory capacity of the river downstream for legitimately discharged effluents.

[b] Requirements of industrial supplies vary, depending on whether water is used for processing or cooling.

2.3.1   The Freshwater Fisheries Directive (78/659/EEC)

The Freshwater Fisheries Directive—on the quality of fresh waters needing protection or improvement in order to support fish life—falls to the Environment Agencies to implement, but is of obvious concern to the various individual and corporate fishery interests. The Directive considers two categories of water: those suitable for salmonid or cyprinid fisheries, and sets guideline and/or imperative standards for temperature, dissolved oxygen, pH, suspended solids, BOD, total phosphorus, nitrites, phenolic compounds, petroleum hydrocarbons, non-ionized ammonia, total ammonium, total residual chlorine, total zinc and dissolved copper.

2.3.2   The drinking water Directives and associated legislation

These fall to the water supply authorities (see Section 2.2.1) to implement for public potable supply, and to the Local Authorities for private supply. Two EC Directives are relevant. Directive 75/440/EEC, concerning the quality required of surface water intended for the abstraction of drinking water, sets limit values for 46 physical, chemical and microbiological descriptors which water must meet after the application of one of three standard methods of treatment. Directive 80/778/EEC, relating to the quality of water intended for human consumption, defines the quality of drinking water supplies in terms of 65 parameters—4 organoleptic, 15 physico-chemical, 24 substances undesirable in excessive amounts, 13 toxic substances, 5 microbiological parameters and 4 parameters concerning minimum concentrations for softened water. Maximum admission concentrations are laid down for most of these parameters; guidance and comments are provided for the remainder.

2.3.3   The dangerous substances Directives

These are implemented by the Environment Agencies who consider their requirements of water quality when setting consent conditions to control discharges from industry and the sewerage authorities. The main Directive (76/464/EEC), on pollution caused by certain dangerous substances discharged into the aquatic environment of the Community, defines two lists of families and groups of substances, the first containing those substances selected on the basis of their toxicity, persistence and bioaccumulation which should be eliminated; the second containing materials whose concentration should be reduced. This Directive has spawned a number of so-called 'daughter' Directives which set quality standards for inland surface waters for specific organochlorines.

2.3.4   The Bathing Waters Directive (76/160/EEC)

This is implemented by the Environment Agencies, but affects the authorities responsible for the discharge of sewage effluents. It also involves the general public, and the Local Authorities dealing with matters of leisure and recreation, since the latter are required to inform the former about the quality of identified Bathing Waters. This Directive (amended by 91/692/EEC and with another proposal in prospect), affected by the Urban Wastewater Treatment Directive (Section 2.3.5), sets guideline and/or imperative limit values for *Escherichia coli*, faecal streptococci, enteroviruses, bacteriophages, pH, surface-active substances reacting with methylene blue, transparency, and dissolved oxygen, and qualitative standards for colour, mineral oils, phenols and 'tarry residues and floating materials such as wood, plastic articles, bottles, containers of glass, plastic, rubber or any other substance, waste or splinters'. Strictly the Directive applies only to 'identified' Bathing Waters, which in the UK are usually coastal (marine) sites, but the values have been applied as guides in the freshwater context, especially to standing waters which support recreational activities.

2.3.5 *The Urban Wastewater Treatment Directive (91/271/EEC)*

This Directive, concerning urban waste water treatment, is of direct relevance to the sewerage authorities and their regulators, and whilst confined to the provision of effluent treatment facilities in prescribed circumstances relating to the size of the population served and the 'sensitivity' of the receiving water, it nonetheless has a major environmental impact. Quantitative and qualitative freshwater standards are implicit in the Directive since it defines 'sensitive' areas as (a) freshwater lakes, or other freshwater bodies which are found to be eutrophic or which in the near future may become eutrophic if protective action is not taken; or (b) surface fresh waters intended for the abstraction of drinking water which could contain more than the concentration of nitrate (50mg L^{-1}) laid down under the relevant provisions of Council Directive 75/440/EEC (see Section 2.3.2). Under the terms of this Directive, eutrophication means the enrichment of water by nutrients, especially compounds of nitrogen and/or phosphorus, causing an accelerated growth of algae and higher forms of plant life to produce an undesirable disturbance to the balance of organisms present in the water and to the quality of the water concerned.

2.3.6 *The Nitrates Directive (91/676/EEC)*

This Directive concerns the protection of waters against pollution caused by nitrates from agricultural sources. It requires Member States to identify 'polluted waters', designate those areas of land which drain into them as 'vulnerable zones', and thereafter establish and implement programmes of remedial action. Polluted waters are defined first as surface fresh waters, in particular those used or intended for the abstraction of drinking water, which contain or could contain, if the required remedial action is not taken, more than the concentration of nitrates (50mg L^{-1}) laid down in accordance with Directive 75/440/EEC. Second, they may be groundwaters which contain more than 50mg L^{-1} nitrates or could contain more than 50mg L^{-1} nitrates if the required remedial action is not taken. Third, they may also be natural fresh waters which are found to be eutrophic or in the near future may become eutrophic if the required remedial action is not taken. Under the terms of this Directive, eutrophication has a definition similar to that of the Urban Wastewater Treatment Directive, except that the qualified reference to nutrients is replaced by a reference to nitrogen compounds alone.

Whilst it falls to the Environment Agencies to identify polluted waters, and Government Agriculture Departments to establish and implement remedial measures, the farming community and its representative associations (e.g. National Farmers' Union) have a strong interest in this aspect of water quality. Since the impact of eutrophication extends beyond chemical water quality *per se*, its repercussions are of interest to many of the nature conservation interests approached.

2.3.7   *The Habitats Directive (92/43/EEC)*

This Directive, on the conservation of natural habitats and of wild flora and fauna, imposes a number of new duties on the Government and public agencies, and these may then have an influence on the way freshwater quality is perceived. However, this Directive did not have a major focus in freshwater quality definition for most of the organizations approached during the questionnaire exercise.

2.4   General Assessment of Freshwater Quality

The regulatory authorities for the aquatic environment in the UK are required to collect, collate and report on water quality issues. To present the bulk of these data in a form which is both manageable and understandable for the general user, a number of presentational devices have been developed over the years, and aspects of these are considered below.

2.4.1   *National Water Council river classification scheme*

In 1978 the National Water Council (NWC) devised a river-quality classification scheme based mainly on physical and chemical determinands. The intention was 'to provide a common basis for both a general description of use and a scientific description of the corresponding limits on quality' (Royal Commission on Environmental Pollution, 1992). Four classes of water, the first subdivided, are defined in this scheme. Class 1A water, described as 'good quality', is considered to be water of high quality suitable for potable supply abstractions and for all other abstractions, game or other high class fisheries, and of high amenity value. Class 1B water, also described as 'good quality', is water of less high quality than Class 1A but usable for substantially the same purposes. Class 2, described as of 'fair quality', is water suitable for potable supply after advanced treatment, supporting reasonably good coarse fisheries and with moderate amenity value. Class 3 water is of 'poor quality' and polluted to an extent that fish are absent or only sporadically present; it may be used for low-grade industrial abstraction purposes, but would have considerable potential for further use if cleaned up. 'Bad quality', Class 4 water, is grossly polluted and likely to cause nuisance. Boundaries between classes are defined quantitatively in relation to dissolved oxygen, BOD, ammonia and toxicity to fish. An important note to the scheme states that where the presence of a chemical substance other than those used in the classification markedly reduces the quality of the water, the quality classification should be down-graded on the basis of biota present, and the reasons stated.

Since 1980 this NWC scheme has been applied in England, Wales and Northern Ireland. Whilst there has been a drive to find a better means of classification of water quality, it has remained something of a benchmark and provided a reference for subsequent water quality surveys.

2.4.2 Scottish water quality survey scheme

In Scotland the NWC scheme was not adopted because the emphasis placed on the criteria for drinking water was thought to be inappropriate with relatively little of the total water resource used for potable supply. Here an apparently simpler scheme (Scottish Development Department, 1987) was drafted and came into use, though it was no less subjective to apply and interpret. Based on BOD, dissolved oxygen and toxicity to fish, and therefore arguably a chemical classification scheme albeit with a biological override, four classes are defined: (1) Rivers unpolluted or recovered from pollution; (2) Rivers of fairly good quality; (3) Rivers of poor quality; and (4) Grossly polluted waters.

Inevitably the NWC and Scottish schemes fuelled ardent debate and discussion, especially amongst the regulators, out of which sprang a number of developments in the quest to define and classify water quality. Prime inter-related topics included in the debate were the degree of subjectivity and the lack of consistency associated with the application of the schemes, not least the statistical implications; the definition of boundaries along a continuum (i.e. when does water quality become water pollution? see Moss *et al.*, this volume); and the role and contribution of biological information in water quality definition and classification.

2.4.3 Chemical water quality indices

In an effort to combat some of the subjectivity and inconsistency the NRA adopted a clear set of chemical criteria, essentially those of the NWC scheme,

Table 2.2   Chemical criteria used in the NRA 'General Quality Assessment' river classification scheme.

Class	Dissolved Oxygen % saturation 5%-ile	BOD (ATU) $mg\,L^{-1}$ 95%-ile	Ammonia $mg\,L^{-1}$ 95%-ile
A	80	2.5	0.25
B	70	4	0.6
C	60	6	1.3
D	50	8	2.5
E	20	15	9.0
F	<20	—	—

Table 2.3   Chemical criteria used in the Scottish river classification scheme.

Class	Dissolved Oxygen % saturation 10%-ile	BOD (ATU) mg L^{-1} 90%-ile	Ammonia mg L^{-1} 90%-ile
1A	90	2	0.2
1B	80	4	0.5
2	60	6	1.0
3	25	10	5.0
4	<25	>10	>5.0

for five water classes (Table 2.2). More recently a similar approach has been recommended in Scotland when the opportunity was also taken to suggest the subdivision of the Scottish Class 1 to take account of the greater proportion of what may be called 'super quality waters' which fall into that class (Table 2.3).

These, with suspended solids, may be the determinands routinely monitored to assess sewage works discharge consent compliance and environmental impact, but in reality many water uses and habitat health are affected by the presence of other substances including nutrients, pesticides and metals. With this in mind some River Purification Boards (RPBs) used a chemical Water Quality Index (WQI) to describe their running waters. Based on some earlier American work, this device was developed at the Solway RPB (Scottish Development Department, 1976), and takes account of eight chemical, one physical and one bacteriological water characteristic. Data for each of the determinands are ranked, the determinands are weighted and a cumulative score ascribed to generate a scale from 0 to 100 where 100 represents the highest quality water and 0 the worst.

Traditionally, the quality of standing waters has been described and classified in relation to a qualitative description of biological factors, e.g. diversity and biomass of biota, phytoplankton, macrophytes and benthos. Quantified limits have also been provided for some chemical and physical factors, such as total phosphorus, chlorophyll, dissolved oxygen and Secchi transparency. As a result, standing waters have been classified as oligotrophic, mesotrophic, eutrophic or hypertrophic, though there is currently a move to classify such waters according to the extent of their departure from a natural, undisturbed condition (Moss *et al.*, this volume).

A new classification scheme has been developed for Scottish freshwater lochs (Fozzard *et al.*, this volume) based upon the extent to which human activity has altered or downgraded water quality and aquatic ecology.

2.4.4   Biological assessments

The biota occupying any particular water body is determined by a number of factors which have combined to make the specific environment what it is in that locality, i.e. to give it its own particular quality. Many of the factors are physical

Table 2.4   Criteria for the Ecological Quality Index (EQI).

Description	EQI (ASPT)	EQI (taxa nos)	EQI (BMWP)	Biological class
Good	>0.88	>0.78	>0.74	A
Moderate	0.77–0.88	0.58–0.78	0.50–0.74	B
Poor	0.66–0.76	0.37–0.57	0.25–0.49	C
Very poor	<0.66	<0.37	<0.25	D

(temperature, light regime, altitude, aspect, gradient, velocity, nature of substrate), whereas others are chemical, (substrate mineralogy, water composition). Whilst there are many components of the aquatic biota, attention has been focused on macro-invertebrates since they are present in all but the most polluted situations and are relatively easy to sample (see Hellawell, this volume).

As patterns of abundance, diversity and pollution tolerance emerged, scoring systems were developed which allowed biological indices to be assigned. The Trent Biotic Index (Woodiwiss, 1964) and the Chandler Score (Chandler, 1970) systems used in the 1970s and 1980s have given way to the Biological Monitoring Working Party (BMWP) score which is the summation of the scores assigned to the presence of particular families or species of macroinvertebrates.

A major criticism of using biological indices to monitor pollution is that they may reflect the physical as well as the chemical quality attributes of the environment. They are thus best fitted to those water bodies for which they were initially developed and their application to other situations may be inappropriate and misleading. A computerized River InVertebrate Prediction And Classification System (RIVPACS) (Wright *et al.*, 1989, this volume) has been developed by the Institute of Freshwater Ecology in collaboration with the water industry in an attempt to overcome this criticism. Using species lists recorded from a number of baseline sites of similar physical and chemical features across the UK, a computer prediction can be made of the benthic community expected at any given site assuming unpolluted water quality. The predicted community is allocated a score which is then compared with the observed BMWP score (or its derivatives) for that site and the ratio of the scores (called the Ecological Quality Index) is used to classify the water quality (Table 2.4).

2.4.5   *Water quality management*

The regulators' interest in water quality has two main focuses. The first is the task of general quality assessment to provide statements about the characteristics and status of the resource. As already indicated, traditionally this has been done through the medium of the chemical and biological classification schemes which have sought to provide a common scale. There are different schools of thought about the desirability of a scheme which combines a chemical and biological view. The Environment Agency has developed a General Quality Assessment (GQA) classification scheme. This will have four 'windows', each providing a discrete yet complementary view of the overall quality of river stretches. The first window is the chemical one; the classes A to F of this were described above. The remaining three windows (biological quality, nutrient status and aesthetic quality) are still under development. In Scotland it has been suggested that there should be a combined (chemical with biological) assessment, but hitherto there is no such scheme in place.

The second main interest of the regulators lies in water quality planning. The Water Resources Act 1991 provides for the setting of statutory Water Quality Objectives (WQOs) and the Environment Agency is continuing the work carried out by the NRA on the development of these. The intention of sWQOs is to establish clear quality targets in controlled waters, on a statutory basis, to provide a commonly-agreed planning framework for regulatory bodies and dischargers alike. Whilst the Environment Agency is responsible for the development of proposals for WQOs, it is ultimately for the Government to set them as statutory targets. This scheme is use-related, based on a suite of classification schemes defined by water quality standards appropriate to the requirements of the various identified river uses. Five uses are envisaged: River Ecosystems (formerly known as 'Fisheries Ecosystems'); Special Ecosystem; Abstraction for Potable Supply; Agricultural/Industrial Abstraction; and Watersports. The River Ecosystems approach—an extension of the GQA chemical 'window' which incorporates the additional determinands specified by the Freshwater Fisheries Directive—is well advanced and being tested in England. Whilst there are provisions in the Scottish legislation, to date there has been no requirement for the regulators to develop statutory WQOs for Scotland (see Howell and Mackay, this volume).

Many organizations—users, regulators and conservators—are expressing an interest in water quality issues. Sustainable development, permitting today's use of the water resource whilst leaving it in a fit state for future generations, requires an integrated approach to catchment management and the development of catchment management plans. The philosophy and application of Integrated Catchment Management is in a period of gestation (see Werritty, this volume), but it is becoming apparent to all concerned that water quality lies at the heart of the approach. Water quality is therefore gaining increasing multi-faceted attention (e.g. River Habitat Surveys: Raven *et al.*, this volume; SERCON: Boon *et al.*, this volume) and is therefore being described and classified in relation to an ever increasing array of variables.

2.4.6 *Proposals for the assessment of ecological water quality*

A recent proposal concerning the quality of fresh water was contained in the draft Directive on the Ecological Quality of Water, which has been considered by the Member States of the European Union (see Preface). In this proposal water was considered as just a part, albeit a major one, of a larger environmental entity, and whilst emphasis was placed on guarding against a departure or downgrading from a natural, anthropically undisturbed, condition, there was reference to the fact that water bodies have normal uses and cannot remain unused. The coverage proposed by the Directive is broad. Annex II, for example, on 'Good ecological water quality' contains a wide range of elements: dissolved oxygen, toxic or other harmful substances, levels of disease, diversity of invertebrate communities, diversity of aquatic plant communities, diversity of the fish population, higher vertebrate life, sediment structure and quality, and an absence of any significant influence by human activity. The application and implementation of such a classification scheme will require an analogous approach to that adopted for the latest standing water classification schemes since, where there has been a human impact, only 'control' sites or hindcasting will establish what the undisturbed condition may have been. However, more recent proposals recommend incorporating the draft Ecological Quality of Water Directive into a broader framework Directive on water policy.

2.5   Conclusions

There are scores of elements associated with fresh water, many thousands of chemical compounds, and a myriad of biological species. Furthermore, physical and other environmental aspects of the associated habitat have a bearing on water quality. Given its many aspects, the absolute description of water quality is cumbersome to say the least, and some abbreviated label is desirable. Water quality in each of its facets is perhaps definable, but communicating the complexity and interaction of all of the facets to achieve a total definition—if and when that is necessary—is most challenging.

Two respondents to the initial questionnaire regarding the organizational use of the term 'freshwater quality' provide a summary and concluding comment:

> There is no one definition of 'freshwater quality' ... This is because on the one hand the parameters which will define quality with regard to fresh water are still being developed. On the other hand the 'quality' of fresh water is to some extent contextual... The use of quality objectives is a good example of the contextual nature of good or acceptable freshwater quality as the catchments under consideration range from world-class fly fishing rivers to rivers running through heavily industrialized areas. What is considered good or acceptable in one case would not be acceptable in the other ... We tend to characterize this approach as pragmatic in that it accepts that there is a natural variety in the quality of fresh water, that man has historically impacted on the quality of water and that perceptions of the quality of water depend to some extent on the uses it is intended for. (M. D. Murray, personal communication)

Yet despite the variability and complexity, another respondent ventured a definition as follows:

> Freshwater quality is the totality of features and characteristics of the water that bear upon its ability to support an appropriate natural flora and fauna, and to sustain legitimate uses. (T. M. Leatherland, personal communication)

This latter definition concurs with the author's view that the quality of fresh water is what it is—all its constituent parts. In its totality it is too big for the human mind and it is doubtful if a full definition will ever be required for practical purposes. The best we can hope for in striving for a manageable, and therefore useful, definition is a more limited statement relevant to each practical working context—we must lay to one side that detail which for any moment in time is of lesser importance and relevance.

Acknowledgements

The author thanks all those who responded to his letter of enquiry about their use of the term freshwater quality. He apologizes to any who feel that their views have been omitted or misrepresented. Any opinions expressed are those of the author and not necessarily those of the Scottish Environment Protection Agency, whose permission to contribute this chapter is greatly appreciated.

References

Boon, P. J., Holmes, N. T. H., Maitland, P. S., Rowell, T. A. and Davies J. (This volume). A system for evaluating rivers for conservation (SERCON): development, structure and function.

British Water (1986). *Water Quality Classification. A Guide to the Quality of Water Required for the Various Uses for Engineers and Chemists in Industry.* London.

Chambers (1983). *Chambers 20th Century Dictionary.* W & R Chambers Ltd, Edinburgh.

Chandler, J. R. (1970). A biological approach to water quality management. *Water Pollution Control,* **69,** 415–421.

Forestry Commission (1993). *Forests and Water Guidelines,* Third Edition. HMSO, London.

Fozzard, I. R., Doughty, C. R. and Leatherland, T. M. (This volume). Defining the quality of Scottish freshwater lochs.

Hammerton, D. (1994). Domestic and industrial pollution. In: Maitland, P. S., Boon, P. J. and McLusky, D. S. (Eds), *The Fresh Waters of Scotland: a National Resource of International Significance.* John Wiley, Chichester, 347–364.

Hellawell, J. M. (This volume). The contribution of biological and chemical techniques to the assessment of water quality.

Howell, D. L. and Mackay, D. W. (This volume). Protecting freshwater quality through legislation: enforcement, inducement or agreement?

Institution of Environmental Health Officers (1993). *The Assessment of Recreational Water Quality (Fresh and Sea Water). A Guide for Decision Makers in Environmental Health.* London.

Moss, B., Johnes, P. and Phillips, G. (This volume). New approaches to monitoring and classifying standing waters.

Raven, P. J., Fox, P., Everard, M., Holmes, N. T. H. and Dawson, F. H. (This volume). River Habitat Survey: a new system for classifying rivers according to their habitat quality.

Royal Commission on Environmental Pollution (1992). *Freshwater Quality.* HMSO, London.

Scottish Development Department (1976). *The Development of a Water Quality Index. Applied Research and Development Report ARD 3.* Edinburgh.

Scottish Development Department (1987). *Water Quality Survey of Scotland 1985.* HMSO, Edinburgh.

Solbé, J. (1988). *Water Quality for Salmon and Trout.* The Atlantic Salmon Trust, Pitlochry.

Tunstall, S., Fordham, M., Green, C. and House, M. (This volume). Public perception of freshwater quality with particular reference to rivers in England and Wales.

Werritty, A. (This volume). Enhancing the quality of freshwater resources: the role of Integrated Catchment Management.

Woodiwiss, F. S. (1964). The biological system of stream classification used by the Trent River Board. *Chemistry and Industry,* **11,** 443–447.

Wright, J. F., Armitage, P. D., Furse, M. T. and Moss, D. (1989). Predictions of invertebrate communities using stream measurements. *Regulated Rivers: Research and Management,* **4,** 147–155.

Wright, J. F., Moss, D., Clarke, R. T. and Furse, M. T. (This volume). Biological assessment of river quality using the new version of RIVPACS (RIVPACS III).

3 'FRESHWATER QUALITY': THE USE OF THE TERM IN SCIENTIFIC LITERATURE

P. S. Maitland

Summary

1. Most publications do not define what is meant by 'freshwater' (or 'fresh water') or 'quality' in relation to their topic.

2. To distinguish it from (a) pure water (H_2O) and (b) inland water (any water not directly influenced by the sea), fresh water can be defined as 'water with a maximum defined (usually as 3–5‰) salt content'.

3. 'Quality', in the present context, usually has one of two meanings: (a) an objective attribute (for classification), and (b) a subjective standard (for human usage).

4. Emphasis in the literature has changed from little use of the concept of 'freshwater quality', through much usage of the term, to (in recent years) a trend towards the use of 'habitat quality', 'ecosystem quality', and similar terms.

3.1 Introduction

Water is one of the very few inorganic substances that occur in a liquid state over much of the earth, where it was present long before life existed. It is essential to all forms of life and its main properties have greatly influenced the ways in which life on earth have developed (e.g. its capacity to conduct heat, its transparency to light, its ability to dissolve many organic and inorganic compounds, its high surface tension and the anomalous expansion which takes place at $4\,°C$).

Yet most studies of water do not examine these properties, nor indeed any of the physical or chemical aspects of water itself, but concentrate on substances and organisms which occur within the medium of water, prompting Schroevers (1967) to ask 'Is water H_2O?'. Most of the relevant scientific publications fail to define what is meant by the use of the terms 'freshwater' and 'fresh water' and frequently these are equated to the medium occurring within 'inland waters'—as opposed to the sea.

3.1.1 What is fresh water?

There are many definitions of 'freshwater' or 'fresh water' in general and scientific literature. Macdonald (1977) defines it as 'of or pertaining to water not salt' and most scientific classifications are based on the salt content.

It is generally believed that the dominant feature of inland waters around the world is that they are fresh and it comes as a surprise to many people, not least to limnologists, that the total volume of inland water which is saline ($1.04 \times 10^5 \mathrm{km}^3$) (Vallentyne, 1972) is not much less than that of fresh water ($1.25 \times 10^5 \mathrm{km}^3$). Williams (1981) points out that this misconception is because, for most limnologists, fresh water is the only sort of inland water nearby. Macan (1963), referring to saline waters, had previously noted that 'whoever wishes to study them must often devote more effort to getting there and back than to scientific work' and that, in terms of human need, fresh water is more important than saline water.

As a definition of saline waters (and thus, by reversal, of fresh waters) Williams (1981) offered the rather facetious suggestion (but actually close to the dictionary interpretations) that they are 'those of higher salinity than fresh waters'. Beadle (1969) suggested that 'setting a salinity limit to fresh water is thus a very arbitrary proceeding' but later himself proposed 5‰ (Beadle, 1974). Williams (1964) had previously defined the limit as 3‰ and though he later agreed (Williams, 1981) that this had rightly been criticized as a very arbitrary value, he maintained that it is 'a useful notional figure'. There have been many other attempts to define 'fresh' and 'saline' waters but all are rather arbitrary. Thus, for example, Stewart and Kantrud (1972) regard any water with a conductivity of less than $800 \,\mu\mathrm{S}\,\mathrm{cm}^{-1}$ as fresh (any water over this value is saline), whereas Cowardin *et al.* (1979) place the upper conductivity of fresh water at $500 \,\mu\mathrm{S}\,\mathrm{cm}^{-1}$.

3.1.2 The interpretations of quality

The alternatives given to 'quality' in any dictionary or thesaurus are numerous but (in relation to water) actually fall into two main classes:

(a) Those which relate to the nature and concentration of substances dissolved or suspended in the water (e.g. attribute, condition, feature, mark, property, trait).

(b) Those which place the water in some kind of predetermined hierarchy, usually related to human use, depending on the nature and concentrations of dissolved or suspended substances (e.g. calibre, distinction, excellence, grade, merit, position, rank, standing, status, superiority, value, worth).

Both meanings are widely, but usually separately, used in the scientific literature.

Both interpretations of the word 'quality' have led to various systems of classification, but whereas in (a) the classifications are objective and no waters are (initially at any rate) described as 'good' (=high quality) or bad (= low quality), in (b) the reverse is true and the waters are placed in a hierarchical order from 'good' to 'bad'. Sometimes the two systems are brought together (e.g. in nature conservation assessments) where, within the classes defined under (a), waters are categorized ranging from 'good' (= an unmodified natural system of the class) to 'bad' (= a highly modified system).

The Royal Commission on Environmental Pollution (RCEP, 1992) considered how water quality is assessed, and noted that there is no single concept of 'water quality' which is universally accepted. In fact, whether water is of high or low quality depends entirely on the criteria against which it is judged. Traditionally this has been use related (e.g. water supply or fisheries) but in the field of limnology as a whole the concept has been much wider.

Secondly, the RCEP (1992) pointed out that the properties of pure water as a chemical compound are clearly defined (e.g. 'in a state of purity, at ordinary temperatures, a clear transparent liquid, perfectly natural in its reaction and devoid of taste or smell' (Macdonald, 1977)) but most importance is attached to substances in it and other aspects such as its temperature.

However, in spite of making these two points clear, the RCEP then fails to define what the Commission itself means by 'freshwater quality' either in the text or in its glossary.

3.2 This Review

The scientific literature on the topic of freshwater quality and associated subjects is an enormous one, with many thousands of references worldwide. Thus, the literature search on which this chapter is based does not claim to be in any way comprehensive because of the magnitude of the task. Instead, relevant topic fields have been reviewed and selected examples chosen from different areas. Attention was centred on 'limnological' journals, as opposed to those specializing in pollution control or fisheries.

3.3 The Literature

3.3.1 *Physics*

When water in a lake stratifies due to temperature and density differences between upper and lower layers (Smith, 1992), deoxygenation of the water may occur in the lower hypolimnion. Because of the potential damaging effect of such water if released into rivers, water engineers frequently wish 'to enhance the water quality of releases from reservoirs by employing outlet works that aerate the flow' (Smith and Wilhelms, 1980). In order to design hydraulic structures that re-aerate releases, techniques are needed to predict the magnitude of gas transfer that occurs during flow through any outlet structure. The approach adopted by Gunnison (1980) has been 'to convert conceptual descriptions for aerobic and anaerobic reservoir chemical processes into practical techniques for application to water-quality management problems'. Although the end objective is a change in the chemistry of the water concerned, the methodology involved is essentially physical.

The optical properties of water are also of importance to engineers in relation to public water supplies. Though the materials which colour water are rarely harmful, the public perception is that coloured water is not 'pure' and part of the expense in treating water for public consumption is the removal of any colour which may be present.

Water engineers have a specialized conception of water quality, and volume as well as quality is important to them. Glasgow has long been well known for the large volumes of excellent water available to it, which comes from Loch Katrine. When the scheme was first developed in 1859 and local wells in Glasgow—the source of various previous outbreaks of cholera and typhoid—were closed, local residents complained about the new water, saying that 'it has nae taste and nae smell' (both prime attributes of pure water). Today, 'Due to the high quality of the water, full chemical treatment is not required. Water flows from the reservoirs through the draw-off towers where chlorine and orthophosphoric acid are added, then into the straining wells where it passes through polyester mesh screens. Lime is also added to the water downstream of the straining wells' (Chambers, 1983).

Temperature is frequently regarded as an important aspect of water quality, both in relation to the stress which may be imposed on freshwater organisms by high (or low) temperatures and by its inverse relationship to the amount of dissolved oxygen at saturation which water can contain. In their water-quality simulations for the proposed Helms Pumped Storage Project in California, Chen *et al.* (1976) concluded that 'the most significant impact of pumped storage operation will be the increase in water temperature of the hypolimnion' of the reservoirs involved.

3.3.2   Chemistry

Many of the studies concerned with freshwater quality relate to chemistry, and some limnologists would argue that good chemical data are adequate to categorize the quality of any water both for human needs and ecological purposes. Common parameters which are measured for the purpose of determining the quality of a water include its content of oxygen, total dissolved salts, calcium, bicarbonate and other important ions. Where pollution is involved this range is widened to include, for example, various heavy metals, phosphate and nitrate.

As an example of the range in water chemistry which can occur in Scotland, the levels of calcium and sodium in a selection of lochs and rivers can be considered (Figure 3.1). The 'quality' of the water in these systems would be viewed differently by different people. For example, since there is no pollution involved, all the waters would be classified as high quality in pollution control terms. For water supply purposes, on the other hand, some of the waters would be too saline and others too hard to be classed as high quality. To a limnologist, the 'quality' of the waters shows a considerable range of relevance to ecology—but none of them could be conceived as of 'higher' or 'lower' quality relative to the others.

In studying the literature relevant to water quality, it is evident that the general use of the term is relatively new. For example, most of the older papers which are entirely relevant to this topic do not mention quality (e.g. Holden, 1966). Similarly, in an annotated bibliography of 349 papers on the Great Lakes published from

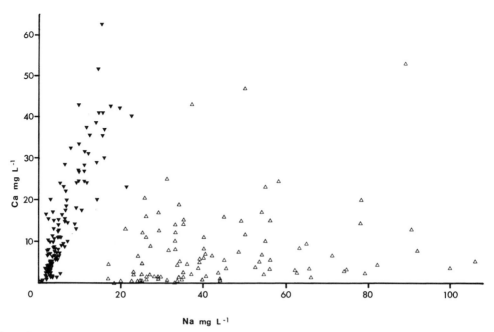

Figure 3.1   A comparison of sodium and calcium levels in a range of Scottish fresh waters in Tayside (closed triangles) and Shetland (open triangles).

1957–1964 (Hile, 1966), the word quality does not appear in any of the titles, although 73 of the papers deal with the topic as it is conceived at present. More recently, in another annotated bibliography reviewing 123 papers concerned with acid precipitation (Tollan, 1981), none of the titles included the word quality, yet more than half were directly concerned with the topic. However, it can be argued that within such specialized recent reviews the authors automatically assume that they are working within the field of freshwater quality research.

3.3.3   Biology

One of the problems in dealing with physical and chemical data concerning water quality is that each measurement is just a snapshot of the situation at the time of sampling, and there is often little indication from the data of the position before or after sampling. The use of living organisms as indicators can often overcome this, as to a varying extent (Hellawell, 1989, this volume), individually as species or collectively as communities, they provide an integrating picture of habitat conditions for hours, days, weeks, months or even years prior to sampling.

3.3.3.1   Bacteria and protozoa

One of the earliest uses of living organisms and their communities as biological indicators of water quality was the 'Saprobiensystem' developed by Kolkwitz and Marsson (1909). This was based on the fact that some species are exclusive to unpolluted waters, whereas others are more tolerant, indeed able to prosper, in highly polluted waters. Four zones of differing biology, reflecting major differences in water quality, are recognized in the system and the most polluted of these ('Polysaprobic') is characterized by a complete domination by micro-organisms.

3.3.3.2 Algae

Samples of algae collected as phytoplankton or periphyton can be used to characterize water quality (Rawson, 1956; Horner and Welch, 1981). Algal species composition and community structure provide evidence of physical and chemical conditions present in a water body over timescales ranging from weeks to months (Porter *et al.*, 1993).

3.3.3.3 Macrophytes

Aquatic macrophyte species and their communities occupy a wide range of habitats and water quality conditions and have often been used to characterize and classify the quality of water bodies both for human needs and ecological purposes (Holmes, 1989).

3.3.3.4 Invertebrates

Benthic invertebrates have been used for many years as a means of determining water quality both in rivers (Hynes, 1970) and lakes (Wiederholm, 1980). They are important in this respect in that they (a) live in, on, or near substrates, (b) have life cycles (usually many months) that are between those of algae (weeks) and fish (years), and (c) are relatively sessile compared with fish. These factors make benthic invertebrates well suited for use in assessing site-specific water quality, for comparing spatial patterns of water quality at multiple sites, and for integrating effects that represent 6–12 months of exposure at a site (Cuffney *et al.*, 1993). Benthic invertebrates are also particularly useful for monitoring cumulative effects at a site due to conditions in the entire catchment upstream, and consequently are used by many agencies as a cost-effective method of assessing water quality conditions in a regulatory context.

For example, aquatic invertebrates (insects, crustaceans, snails and worms) in the South Platte River basin (Colorado, Wyoming and Nebraska) indicated differences in water quality associated with different land-use practices (Tate, 1993). Samples of aquatic invertebrates were collected throughout the basin at sites located in rangeland, forests, agricultural land, urban, and a mixture of urban and agricultural land-use areas. Diversity of invertebrates, as measured by the number of different species collected at a site, was related to the land use in which the stream was located and provided a useful indicator of water quality in the South Platte River basin. Typically, sites with minimal human influence, such as rangeland and forest, had higher diversity than sites draining agricultural and urban land uses. Lowest diversity occurred at sites influenced by a mixture of urban and agricultural land use. Data collected in this study were useful in developing biological criteria for assessing water quality in arid-climate streams in the western USA.

3.3.3.5 Fish

The study of fish communities is an essential component of many water quality assessment programmes (Meador *et al.*, 1993a) as many species of fish are particularly sensitive indicators of water-quality conditions. This is true not only within the range of conditions found in nature, but also because human influences, such as changes in water chemistry or physical habitat modifications, can alter fish communities by disrupting their structures. Changes in fish community structure can be detected through changes in size components of the community, functional groups, species diversity and relative abundance (Wootton, 1990).

An example is found in the San Joaquin-Tulare basins which drain a large part of central California. Surface water quality in this area is primarily affected by agricultural land use and hydrological management such as flow diversions (Brown, 1993). As part of an assessment of water quality at fixed sites, fish community samples were collected using a range of standard methods at 13 sites in the San Joaquin River system. Native fish species accounted for only 10 out of 31 total fish species recorded and were found mainly at sites with good water quality, as indicated by low conductivity (or dissolved solids content). Sites with high conductivity had few or no native fish and relatively high numbers of introduced (non-native) species. Although other factors were likely to be involved, the replacement of native fish species by introduced fish species appeared to be related to declining water quality, as indicated by increased conductivity. Thus in this case, conductivity was used as a surrogate for the combined effect of several human impacts (intensive agriculture and the release of alien fish species).

3.3.4 Tissue analysis and toxicity testing

The determination of contaminant concentrations in biological tissues is now widely used as an approach in assessing one aspect of water quality and as a method of monitoring the distribution and concentrations of contaminants in space and time (Crawford and Luoma, 1994). Tissue analysis has three main benefits in relation to assessing this aspect of water quality (Phillips, 1980). First, concentrations of contaminants may be greater in tissues than in water because of bioaccumulation; therefore tissue analysis increases the probability of detecting substances only present in the water in trace amounts. Second, contaminant concentrations in organisms provide a time-averaged assessment. Third, concentrations of contaminants in tissues provide a direct measurement of their bioavailability.

A related topic is that of acute toxicity tests for assessing the potential hazard of chemical contaminants to aquatic organisms (Johnson and Finley, 1980). Static acute toxicity tests provide rapid and reproducible concentration-response curves for estimating the toxic effects of chemicals on aquatic organisms and thus provide a mechanism for setting standards for permissible levels of contaminants in natural waters (American Institute of Biological Sciences, 1978).

3.4 Holistic Approaches

In recent years it has become increasingly recognized that individual systems for assessing water quality are inadequate and indeed that the quality of the water itself is only one part of the habitat of aquatic organisms. Thus attention is increasingly being given to systems which adopt a wider perspective than simply describing and assessing water quality through one or more groups of organisms. Such approaches also consider the roles (in terms of reducing or improving water quality) of aquatic-terrestrial ecotones (Naiman and Décamps, 1990) and of the entire catchments on which much of the character of downstream waters depends (Werritty, this volume). Similar changes in attitude are taking place in relation to terrestrial ecosystems (Pimentel *et al.*, 1980).

Norton (1980) has pointed out that 'predictive capabilities of reservoir water quality models depend primarily on the degree of understanding of the many physical, chemical and biological processes that influence water quality'. Trophic classification should be used with care, for the limitations inherent in forcing fresh waters into categories with ill-defined limits must be recognized (Moss *et al.*, this volume). A more practical approach would be to place paramount consideration on the potential beneficial uses of various fresh waters and, possibly, the regional water quality characteristics required to meet those uses. From such analyses it would be readily apparent whether a water can support such uses or whether it can be managed to bring important water quality parameters within acceptable ranges (Howell and Mackay, this volume; Moss *et al.*, this volume).

The US Geological Survey's National Water Quality Assessment Program uses a multi-disciplinary approach that integrates physical, chemical and biological data to assess water quality in the nation's streams and rivers. Nationally consistent biological sampling methods have been developed so that results are comparable across river basins and geographic regions. Biological sampling methods are described in a series of published protocols that build on scientific understanding from multiple disciplines including aquatic community ecology, geomorphology, botany and ecotoxicology. These protocols provide consistent methods for (a) sampling and processing aquatic organisms whose tissues are analysed for organic compounds and major metals and trace elements; (b) collecting samples of algal, benthic invertebrate and fish communities; and (c) characterizing instream and riparian habitat (Meador *et al.*, 1993b)

In the UK too, the importance of assessing the whole habitat has come to the fore recently. This trend is illustrated by the development of various new systems of assessing aquatic systems—for example, SERCON (Boon *et al.*, this volume) and River Habitat Survey (Raven *et al.*, this volume).

Although the wider role of catchments has been known for a long time, it is only in recent years that the importance of catchment management in controlling both water quality and quantity has been properly recognized. The management of the catchment of Loch Katrine (Chambers, 1983) is a little known, but long established and successful example of sustainable catchment management in Scotland. Since the inception of the Loch Katrine water supply scheme for the City of Glasgow well over 100 years ago, the local water supply authority has owned and managed the catchment of this loch. The ground has been given over almost entirely to low intensity sheep farming and forestry—both of which are run at a profit. In addition to these activities there is a small sawmill, a sport fishery with several boats, a pleasure steamer and visitor centre. This careful, integrated management, which is apparently sustainable, has meant that the catchment has remained largely in a semi-natural condition over a very long period. There has been little change in the high quality of the water in the loch and its tributaries, so water treatment costs are relatively low. Most other systems of catchment management, other than complete wilderness, are likely to increase productivity in Loch Katrine. This would lower water quality (in terms of public supply) and necessitate conventional treatment—at present estimated at a capital cost of £100 million.

Winger (1986) pointed out that forested wetlands occupying floodplains of rivers are highly diverse and productive ecological systems. The wetlands are produced and maintained by fluvial processes and hydraulic regimes consisting of periodic flooding and subsequent drying out of the land. The resulting fluctuations in soil chemistry and biology provide a broad range of environmental conditions that are important in determining the role of forested wetlands in maintaining and improving water quality. The periodic shift between aerobic and anaerobic conditions in floodplain soils in response to flooding facilitates the assimilation of nutrients and organic matter, hastens the degradation of persistent pesticides, and decreases the bioavailability of heavy metals.

3.5   Indices

Because of the complexity of the data which result from extensive surveys, there have been many attempts in the past to present results in an abbreviated and convincing manner by the use of index numbers. The index number is a form of average derived by relating a group of variables to a common scale and then combining them into a single number (Scottish Development Department, 1976). The group should contain the most significant parameters of the data set, so that the index can describe the overall position and reflect change in a representative manner.

The concept of a general water quality index is not a new one but several of those which have been proposed in the past have met with criticism. This is largely because they can obscure the real data or provide values which are difficult to understand and therefore to interpret. One of the first proposals was that of Brown *et al.* (1970) and the concepts have been subsequently taken up in Scotland by the former Scottish Development Department (1976) and others elsewhere (Pugh, this volume). Some of the more recent indices in the UK, though complex, are being widely accepted after testing and experience. They include BMWP and ASPT (Hellawell, 1989, this volume), RIVPACS (Wright *et al.*, 1989, this volume), SERCON (Boon *et al.*, this volume) and RHS (Raven *et al.*, this volume).

3.6   Rivers vs. Lakes

For many years, relatively less attention was paid to the 'water quality' of lakes, other than for their relative importance as potable water supplies. There are therefore fewer schemes aimed at defining lake water quality in relation to human impact than there are for rivers. This is largely because rivers are subject to much more direct pollution than lakes. This attitude has changed over the last three decades, initially in relation to eutrophication and then concerning acidification.

In Europe, a recent review (Premazzi and Chiaudani, 1992) has examined the various techniques which have been used in the past for the assessment of lake water quality and the more significant schemes proposed for lake classification. General guidelines for lake assessment are proposed for the European Union. The primary objectives of a surface water quality monitoring programme are the characterization of the quality of water resources, the identification of problem waters and the evaluation of the effectiveness of pollution control actions. Suggestions are made for the design of survey networks (i.e. the number of lakes to be included within a programme), sampling procedure, sampling frequency, parameters for water quality assessment (physical, chemical and biological) and for habitat assessment (bottom substrates, flushing rates, morphology, stratification).

A simplified classification scheme is proposed for assessing the ecological state of freshwater lakes, to be used throughout the European Union. It is based on generally accepted physical, chemical and biological features such as sediments, transparency, dissolved oxygen, chlorophyll and phosphorus concentrations, acid neutralizing capacity, algae and macrophytes, macroinvertebrate and fish indices. Since the ultimate aim of a future EC Directive emanating from this work 'should be to reach a high ecological quality in all surface waters', a matrix of classes has been constructed which takes into account, among other things, the morpho-edaphic index. This now allows the division of lacustrine systems 'into complying (two classes: excellent, good) and uncomplying waters (three classes: fair, poor, bad)'.

Premazzi and Chiaudani (1992) base this new classification on 'five hierarchical classes of quality for freshwater lakes, in relation to their different natural states and with reference to the variation in their quality as a consequence of a more or less direct anthropogenic influence'. They regard the classification as providing a good basis for drawing maps of the present situation within the countries of the European Union and for measuring any changes in water quality. A parallel scheme, presently proposed by Moss *et al.* (1994, this volume), is effectively based on the earlier synoptic proposals of Maitland (1979), has a more useful ecological basis, and is more feasible logistically.

New and improved schemes of assessing the 'quality' of rivers are also being produced. SERCON is a broad-based technique for river conservation evaluation, designed to be more rigorous than present methods and to provide a simple way of communicating technical information concerning the 'quality' of rivers to decision makers (Boon *et al.*, this volume). It is likely that an equally useful system for lakes could be developed on the same principles.

3.7 Discussion

As an example of the contrasting approach to the use of the term 'freshwater quality' in the scientific literature, the habitats occupied by two widely different organisms may be cited. Both occur in fresh water (water with a conductivity of less than 3‰). The young of the Atlantic salmon *Salmo salar* live in running water with a high oxygen content, low temperature, and with little decaying organic matter. In contrast, the larvae of the drone fly *Eristalis tenax* (known as 'rat-tailed maggots') occur in small pools of standing water, often devoid of oxygen due to high temperatures, and with large amounts of decaying organic matter. Neither animal can survive in the habitat favoured by the other (Figure 3.2). Fishery managers would place the water quality requirements of *Salmo salar* as 'very high' (Solbé, 1988) and that of *Eristalis tenax* as 'very low' whereas a wider ecological view might regard both types of water as equally 'acceptable', though at either ends of an environmental spectrum (Maitland, 1979, 1980).

The 1972 Great Lakes Water Quality Agreement between Canada and the USA affirmed the commitment of the two countries 'to restore and enhance the water quality of the Great Lakes'. Among its provisions, this agreement included specific objectives for various properties of Great Lakes' water quality and called for the development of objectives for significant additional properties. These objectives are defined as '... the concentration or quantity of a substance or level of effect that the Parties agree, after investigation, to recognize as a maximum or minimum desired limit for a defined body of water or portion thereof, taking into account the beneficial uses or level of environmental quality which the Parties desire to secure and protect...'. Many of these objectives have been based on information obtained by toxicity testing.

A revised and strengthened Great Lakes Water Quality Agreement was signed

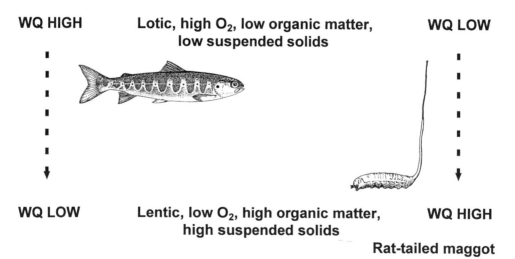

Atlantic salmon

WQ HIGH   **Lotic, high O$_2$, low organic matter,**   **WQ LOW**
low suspended solids

WQ LOW   **Lentic, low O$_2$, high organic matter,**   **WQ HIGH**
high suspended solids

Rat-tailed maggot

Figure 3.2   Differing water quality (WQ) needs of Atlantic salmon *Salmo salar* and rat-tailed maggot *Eristalis tenax*. Whilst the two species have very different water quality preferences, pollution biologists tend to regard the preferences of the salmon as 'high' water quality, even though rat-tailed maggots are not confined to polluted waters. (Drawings: R. Ade and D. Howell).

in 1978 (see also Zarull and Hartig, this volume). Subsequently, the following general objective was put forward to be added to the Agreement (Ryder and Edwards, 1985): that the waters of the Great Lakes system should be '... maintained and, as necessary, restored to a condition where a balanced and stable community of organisms is present which resembles as much as is feasible and practical the community that existed before the advent of anthropogenic intervention.' This is a similar concept to that proposed by RCEP (1992) in relation to eutrophication, where the desired aim should be to restore the water to the state that existed prior to anthropogenic disturbance.

Many studies which have examined water quality in relation to one or more aspects of the biota have failed to appreciate the importance of other aspects of the ecosystem (Pinay *et al.*, 1990). As part of the work of the Great Lakes Science Advisory Board, a conceptual approach was developed for the application of biological indicators of ecological quality in the Great Lakes basin (Ryder and Edwards, 1985). This approach to the concept of quality was regarded by the authors as a 'prerequisite to any level of practical application in the future by the ecosystem manager'. A general set of criteria was devised for biological indicators of ecosystem quality and various organisms were classified against the standard of 'an ideal indicator organism'. Candidate indicator organisms were divided into two categories—those intolerant of most cultural stresses and those tolerant of the same suite of stresses. The intolerant species were exemplified by lake charr *Salvelinus namaycush* and the crustacean *Pontoporeia hoyi* for oligotrophic systems, and walleye *Stizostedion* and the burrowing mayfly *Hexagenia* filled this role for mesotrophic systems. Carp *Cyprinus carpio* and sludgeworms (Tubificidae) were designated as tolerant organisms for both oligo- and meso-systems.

Generally, criteria for a useful indicator required that the organism 'have a broad distribution, be indigenous and integrative in nature; have well-documented and quantified niche dimensions; will exhibit a graded response to human intervention; will serve as a diagnostic tool for specific stresses; will not overlap other indicators markedly with regard to their indicative capabilities; will have historic, preferably quantified information pertaining to their abundance and other critical factors; may be easily collected; will maintain itself through natural reproduction; may be useful in laboratory experiments; responds to stress in a manner that will be both identifiable and quantifiable; will be important to humans and readily recognized by them'. The lake charr, of all the organisms considered, came closest to satisfying these criteria and was therefore designated a primary indicator/integrator organism for oligotrophic environments.

A simple, but very important, new concept which is being considered in various countries in one form or another—and has already been accepted by Canada (Department of Fisheries and Oceans, 1986) in relation to fish habitat—is that of 'no net habitat loss'. This looks to the future in relation to developments of any kind which may threaten fish habitats (including water quality) and makes it clear that approval will be given only if (a) there is no loss of fish habitat involved, or (b) the development is modified in such a way that there is no loss of fish habitat, or (c) any fish habitat which must be lost because of the development is compensated for by the restoration or creation of equivalent fish habitat elsewhere in the same system, so that there is no net loss of habitat.

The great advantage of this concept, in theory at least, is that it allows some flexibility in the commonly antagonistic relationship between conservation and human development. Effectively it is saying (a) do not destroy habitat unless you have to, but (b) if you have to (or do) then you must somehow compensate for the loss by creating equivalent habitat somewhere else (locally). To an extent at least, this must imply restoration of some degraded area, for it would be ecologically unacceptable to produce new (and initially artificial) aquatic habitat at the expense of, say, a local peatland of high conservation value.

3.8   Conclusions

The main conclusion from this review of the use of the term 'freshwater quality' by scientists is that most authors are not critical enough in defining their use of the term. Thus, it is suggested that the following terminologies will be helpful in making things clearer—especially where terms are used in the titles of papers.

'Freshwater' or 'fresh water'
Pure water $=$ H_2O
Fresh water $=$ Water with a maximum defined salt content
Inland water $=$ Any water not influenced directly by the sea

Quality
(a) Quality $=$ an objective attribute (for classification)
(b) Quality $=$ a subjective standard (for human usage)

In addition to this need to clarify the content and objectives of papers in the field of water quality, the role of wider aspects of 'quality' must be, and in many cases is being, recognized—for example the role of aquatic biota, of the aquatic habitat as a whole, of aquatic-terrestrial ecotones, and of the whole catchment.

Acknowledgements

I am very grateful to Nikki Wood for help with the literature search for this paper. I am grateful also to David Howell and a reviewer for helpful comments on an early manuscript.

References

American Institute of Biological Sciences (1978). Aquatic hazard evaluation of chemical pesticides. *Bioscience,* **28,** 600.

Beadle, L. C. (1969). Osmotic regulation and the adaptation of freshwater animals to inland saline waters. *Verhandlungen der Internationalen Vereinigung für theoretische und angewandte Limnologie,* **17,** 421–429.

Beadle, L. C. (1974). *The Inland Waters of Tropical Africa.* Longman, London.

Boon, P. J., Holmes, N. T. H., Maitland, P. S., Rowell, T. A. and Davies, J. (This volume). A system for evaluating rivers for conservation (SERCON): development, structure and function.

Brown, L. (1993). *Replacement of Native Fish Species by Introduced Fish Species in the San Joaquin-Tulare Basins is Related to Water Quality.* US Geological Survey, Sacramento.

Brown, R. M., McLelland, N. I., Deininger, R. A. and Tozer, R. Z. (1970). A water Quality Index—do we dare? *Water and Sewage Works,* **1,** 1–13.

Chambers, E. G. W. (1983). *Water Supply from Loch Katrine to Glasgow and Environs.* Strathclyde Regional Council, Glasgow.

Chen, C. W., Smith, D. J., Lee, S. S., Lambert, T. R. and Kilroy, T. (1976). *Water Quality Simulations for the Helms Pumped Storage Project.* Tetra Tech, Lafayette.

Cowardin, L. M., Carter, V., Golet, F. C. and LaRoe, E. T. (1979). *Classification of Wetlands and Deepwater Habitats of the United States.* US Fish and Wildlife Service, Washington.

Crawford, J. K. and Luoma, S. N. (1994). *Guidelines for Studies of Contaminants in Biological Tissues for the National Water-Quality Assessment Program.* US Geological Survey, Lemoyne.

Cuffney, T. F., Gurtz, M. E. and Meador, M. R. (1993). *Methods for Collecting Benthic Invertebrate Samples as part of the National Water-Quality Assessment Program.* US Geological Survey, Raleigh.

Department of Fisheries and Oceans (1986). *Policy for the Management of Fish Habitat.* Ottawa.

Gunnison, D. (1980). Description of reservoir chemical processes. *Environmental and Water Quality Operational Studies,* **E-80-4,** 5–7.

Hellawell, J. M. (1989). *Biological Indicators of Freshwater Pollution and Environmental Management.* Elsevier, London.

Hellawell, J. M. (This volume). The contribution of biological and chemical techniques to the assessment of water quality.

Hile, R. (1966). *US Federal Research on Fisheries and Limnology in the Great Lakes through 1964: an Annotated Bibliography.* US Fish and Wildlife Service, Washington.

Holden, A. V. (1966). A chemical study of rain and stream waters in the Scottish Highlands. *Freshwater and Salmon Fisheries Research,* **37,** 1–17.

Holmes, N. T. H. (1989). Typing British rivers—a working classification. *British Wildlife,* **1,** 20–36.

Horner, R. R. and Welch, E. B. (1981). Stream periphyton development in relation to current velocity and nutrients. *Canadian Journal of Fisheries and Aquatic Sciences,* **38,** 449–457.

Howell, D. L. and Mackay, D. W. (This volume). Protecting water quality through legislation: enforcement, inducement or agreement?

Hynes, H. B. N. (1970). *The Ecology of Running Waters.* University of Liverpool Press, Liverpool.

Johnson, W. W. and Finley, M. T. (1980). *Handbook of Acute Toxicity of Chemicals to Fish and Aquatic Invertebrates.* US Fish and Wildlife Service, Washington.

Kolkwitz, R. and Marsson, M. (1909). Ökologie der tierischen Saprobien. *Internationale Revue der gesamten Hydrobiologie u Hydrographie,* **2,** 126–152.

Macan, T. T. (1963). *Freshwater Ecology.* Longman, London.

Macdonald, A. M. (Ed.) (1977). *Chambers Twentieth Century Dictionary.* Chambers, Edinburgh.

Maitland, P. S. (1979). *Synoptic Limnology: the Analysis of British Freshwater Ecosystems.* Institute of Terrestrial Ecology, Cambridge.

Maitland, P. S. (1980). The habitats of British Ephemeroptera. *Proceedings of the International Symposium on Ephemeroptera, Winnipeg.* **3,** 123–129.

Meador, M. R., Cuffney, T. F. and Gurtz, M. E. (1993a). *Methods for Sampling Fish Communities as Part of the National Water-Quality Assessment Program.* US Geological Survey, Raleigh.

Meador, M. R., Hupp, C. R., Cuffney, T. F. and Gurtz, M. E. (1993b). *Methods for Characterizing Stream Habitat as part of the National Water-Quality Assessment Program.* US Geological Survey, Raleigh.

Moss, B., Johnes, P. and Phillips, G. (1994). August Thiennemann and Loch Lomond—an approach to the design of a system for monitoring the state of north-temperate standing waters. *Hydrobiologia,* **290,** 1–12.

Moss, B., Johnes, P. and Phillips, G. (This volume). New approaches to monitoring and classifying standing waters.

Naiman, R. J. and Décamps H. (Eds) (1990). *The Ecology and Management of Aquatic-Terrestrial Ecotones.* UNESCO, Paris.

Norton, J. L. (1980). Biological aspects of reservoir water quality modelling. *Environmental and Water Quality Operational Studies,* **E-80-4,** 4–5.

Phillips, D. J. H. (1980). *Quantitative Aquatic Biological Indicators.* Applied Science Publishers, London.

Pimentel, D. Garnick, E., Berkowitz, A., Jacobson, S., Napolitano, S., Black, P., Valdes-Cogliano, S., Vinzant, B., Hudes, E. and Littman, S. (1980). Environmental quality and natural biota. *Bioscience,* **30,** 750–755.

Pinay, G., Décamps, H., Chauvet, E. and Fustec, E. (1990). Functions of ecotones in fluvial systems. In: Naiman, R. J. and Décamps, H. (Eds), *The Ecology and Management of Aquatic-Terrestrial Ecotones.* UNESCO, Paris, 141–171.

Porter, S. D., Cuffney, T. F., Gurtz, M. E. and Meador, M. R. (1993). *Methods for Collecting Algal Samples as Part of the National Water-Quality Assessment Program.* US Geological Survey, Raleigh.

Premazzi, G. and Chiaudani, G. (1992). *Ecological Quality of Surface Waters. Quality Assessment Schemes for European Community Lakes.* European Commission, Brussels.

Pugh, K. B. (This volume). Organizational use of the term 'freshwater quality' in Britain.

Raven, P. J., Fox, P., Everard, M., Holmes, N. T. H. and Dawson, F. H. (This volume). River Habitat Survey: a new system for classifying rivers according to their habitat quality.

Rawson, D. S. (1956). Algal indicators of trophic lake types. *Limnology and Oceanography,* **1,** 18–25.

Royal Commission on Environmental Pollution (1992). *Freshwater Quality.* HMSO, London.

Ryder, R. A. and Edwards, C. J. (1985). *A Conceptual Approach for the Application of Biological Indicators of Ecosystem Quality in the Great Lakes Basin.* Great Lakes Fishery Commission, Windsor.

Schroevers, P. J. (1967). Is water H$_2$O? *Overdruk uit De Levende Natuur,* **70,** 273–284.

Scottish Development Department (1976). *Development of a Water Quality Index.* Edinburgh.

Smith, D. R. and Wilhelms, S. C. (1980). Water quality enhancement by aeration of the release. *Environmental and Water Quality Operational Studies,* **E-80-4,** 1–4.

Smith, I. R. (1992). *Hydroclimate: the Influence of Water Movement on Freshwater Ecology.* Elsevier, London.

Solbé, J. (1988). *Water Quality for Salmon and Trout.* Atlantic Salmon Trust, Pitlochry.

Stewart, R. E. and Kantrud, H. A. (1972). Vegetation of prairie potholes, North Dakota, in relation to quality of water and other environmental factors. *Geological Survey Professional Papers,* **585D,** 1–36.

Tate, C. (1993). *Invertebrate Biodiversity in the South Platte River Basin Reflects Differences in Land Use.* US Geological Survey, Lakewood.

Tollan, A. (1981). *SNSF Project. Acid Precipitation—Effects on Forest and Fish. Annotated Bibliography 1974–1980.* Norwegian Institute for Water Research, Oslo.

Vallentyne, J. R. (1972). Freshwater supplies and pollution: effects of the demophoric explosion on water and man. In: Polunin, N. (Ed.) *The Environmental Future.* Macmillan, London, 181–199.

Werritty, A. (This volume). Enhancing the quality of freshwater resources: the role of Integrated Catchment Management.

Wiederholm, T. (1980). Use of benthos in lake monitoring. *Journal of the Water Pollution Control Federation,* **52,** 537–547.

Williams, W. D. (1964). A contribution to lake typology in Victoria, Australia. *Verhandlungen der Internationalen Vereinigung für theoretische und angewandte Limnologie,* **15,** 158–168.

Williams, W. D. (1981). Inland salt lakes: an introduction. *Hydrobiologia,* **81,** 1–14.

Winger, P. V. (1986). *Forested Wetlands of the Southeast: Review of Major Characteristics and Role in Maintaining Water Quality.* US Fish and Wildlife Service, Washington.

Wootton, R. J. (1990). *Ecology of Teleost Fishes.* Chapman and Hall, London.

Wright, J. F., Armitage, P. D., Furse, M. T. and Moss, D. (1989). Prediction of invertebrate communities using stream measurements. *Regulated Rivers: Research and Management,* **4,** 147–155.

Wright, J. F., Moss, D., Clarke, R. T. and Furse, M. T. (This volume). Biological assessment of river quality using the new version of RIVPACS (RIVPACS III).

Zarull, M. A. and Hartig, J. H. (This volume). Water quality assessment based on beneficial use impairment.

4 PUBLIC PERCEPTION OF FRESHWATER QUALITY WITH PARTICULAR REFERENCE TO RIVERS IN ENGLAND AND WALES

S. Tunstall, M. Fordham, C. Green and M. House

Summary

1. The Rio Declaration on Environment and Development, and Agenda 21, have stressed that public participation in environment decision making is fundamental for sustainable development. It is important, therefore, to understand how members of the public view environmental resources such as fresh waters.

2. Surveys and qualitative research with various 'publics' show that fresh waters, particularly lakes and rivers, are highly valued as recreational and amenity resources and for nature conservation.

3. Members of the public regard rivers in England and Wales as affected by serious problems; they are particularly concerned about pollution and littering, but also about the impacts on rivers of engineering works and low flow conditions.

4. The research suggests that the public perceives the 'quality' of freshwater environments in a broad and holistic way, and there is evidence of strong support from local publics for integrated river restoration initiatives such as The River Restoration Project's demonstration project on the River Skerne in Darlington.

4.1 Introduction

I always feel quite tranquil, I used to take my little dog until he had to be put down. I always thought walking along a canal or river was nice and quiet, you could hear the birds, very tranquil and relaxing. (Secretary in Further Education College, female, Stockport).

It's just the solitude. I mean I go up Swaledale, Cundal, it's beautiful, no traffic, nothing. Kingfishers flying down the river, beautiful, it's a way of escapism really, getting away from work, getting away from the kids, getting away from everything, beautiful. (Skilled engineering worker and fisherman, York)

The Rio Declaration on Environment and Development has as one of its guiding principles that environmental issues are best handled with the participation of all concerned citizens. The UN's Agenda 21 Programme for Action for Sustainable Development also stresses that such public participation is fundamental for sustainable development (United Nations Conference on Environment and Development, 1992). Local Agenda 21 initiatives by local authorities in the UK are generating new interest in ways of involving local people in environmental decision making. In the light of these developments, it is vital to understand how the public view environmental resources such as fresh waters, the extent to which the public shares the concerns of environmental specialists and is supportive of action or can be mobilized to protect and enhance these resources.

While it is necessary to generalize about 'the public', it is important to bear in mind the diversity, complexity and, probably, conflict of views among different groups or 'publics' (Rayner, 1986). The term 'the public' tends to suggest a homogeneity and uniformity that may not exist. People have been found to differ in their perceptions: according to their experience of fresh waters, gender, age, stage in the life cycle, different types of user, residents in riverside properties from those at a distance, and people in one locality from those in another. Much of this chapter will address the perceptions of freshwater quality of the public in general: the general population or residents in particular areas rather than sub-groups within populations, and recreational users of water environments in general rather than specific categories of recreational user. Spray (this volume) examines the recreational use of fresh waters and different types of recreational user.

The term 'the public' is usually used in contrast with 'expert' or 'decision makers' to refer to 'lay members' or 'ordinary people'. Yet it is a truism that all of us spend more time being members of the public than experts, and members of the public may have a significant level of expertise and experience in relevant areas. Many people, 'lay members' and 'experts' alike, would share the enthusiasm for the special qualities and sensuous pleasures of freshwater environments expressed in the above quotations from focus group participants (Tunstall, 1995).

Perception can be narrowly defined to include only the immediate direct evidence of the senses, but it is common and useful to attach a broader meaning to the term and to allow it to embrace awareness, beliefs, attitudes and preferences. To examine perceptions and not preferences, what people experience and not what they like, might be to assume a passive rather than a participatory role for the public in relation to freshwater quality. Much of the research on public perception has addressed particular types of fresh water or aspects of freshwater quality, rather than the concept of freshwater quality as a whole. Much of our understanding of public perception of fresh waters has been derived from studies assessing the economic value of changes to particular aspects of freshwater environments (Hanley, this volume). This probably reflects the functional and divided responsibilities of the water management institutions which sponsor research and the specialisms of experts, rather than the way members of the public think about fresh waters. Indeed, the research suggests that the public perceives the 'quality' of freshwater environments in a broad and holistic way encompassing a range of aspects such as landscape and aesthetic qualities, wildlife and recreational value.

4.2 Research Methodology

At least three approaches, reflecting different theoretical perspectives, have been adopted by researchers attempting to assess public perceptions of environments: quantitative, qualitative and cultural approaches. Much of the research into the public perception of freshwater quality has employed quantitative methods—in particular, social survey methods. Quantitative studies set out to measure public perception through the use of standardized and structured sets of interview questions, stimulus materials such as photographs and drawings, and response categories, such as verbal and numerical scales. A strength of quantitative studies appreciated by decision makers is that the data are susceptible to statistical summary, analysis, and hypotheses and validity testing. Furthermore, with studies based on representative samples, findings can be generalized to the population from which they are drawn.

Concerns with such studies of public perceptions are that the conceptual framework that investigators bring to the studies—the ways in which they have chosen to tap behaviour, beliefs and attitudes, the wording, order and context in which topics are presented and questions asked, may affect the results (Schuman and Presser, 1981; De Vaus, 1991). A further consideration is the extent to which perceptions are stable over time, since most studies have involved one-off cross-sectional surveys at a particular time rather than repeated surveys or longitudinal surveys.

Secondly, social researchers have used qualitative methods to explore the meanings that individuals attach to environmental issues, such as the value of urban open spaces (Burgess *et al.*, 1988a), nature conservation (Harrison and Burgess, 1994), sustainability (Macnaghten *et al.*, 1995), river environments and flood defence (Tapsell, 1992) and river quality (Tunstall, 1995). Researchers have used the techniques of in-depth interviews, once-only focus groups (Krueger, 1994) and in-depth group discussions reconvened for as many as six sessions (Burgess *et al.*, 1988b,c). Participants, individually or in groups, are encouraged, by open non-directive questioning by an interviewer or moderator, to express their views in their own words and at length in an unstructured way. Some qualitative researchers argue that a quantitative methodology is not a suitable way to discover feelings and meanings for the environment, while a qualitative approach will provide deep and detailed insight into the way people in a social or community context think and talk about a topic, unconstrained by the conceptual framework and measurement techniques of the researcher (Burgess *et al.*, 1988b). It enables the researcher to uncover the issues of importance to the participants and to see through the participants' eyes (Bryman, 1988). In qualitative research, the data analysis focuses on description and the interpretation of the meanings of linguistic data from tape-recorded and transcribed interviews and discussions using systematic and computer-based procedures. The small, non-random samples used in qualitative studies mean that statistical analysis techniques are inappropriate and that it is difficult to generalize the findings of such studies.

A concern with qualitative studies and, to an extent, with quantitative surveys is the degree to which the social interaction between participants and interviewer or moderator may affect what people say. Furthermore, analyses of recent British Social Attitude Surveys have shown high levels of concern about environmental issues, particularly pollution, and that such concern is now widespread in British society and not confined to educated or middle-class social groups (Witherspoon and Martin, 1992; Witherspoon, 1994). This may lead to 'social desirability' effects, in which respondents in surveys are reluctant to admit that they do not attach importance to environmental issues. Those who have no interest at all in environmental issues may refuse to take part in studies.

In a third, cultural approach, public perceptions on environments, including rivers, have been accessed through the analysis of their representations in contemporary and past literature, paintings, the media and popular culture (Paton, 1993; Sadrin, 1993; Burgess, 1994). Such cultural products are usually made for a particular audience, often an elite, by special groups in society and they may reveal little of how the 'public' or ordinary people perceive the subject or perceived it in the past.

The three approaches may be seen as complementary. In particular, qualitative investigations are commonly used as exploratory or confirmatory methods in conjunction with quantitative studies but also as stand-alone techniques. This chapter draws on the findings from both quantitative and qualitative studies of public perception of fresh waters, mainly with reference to rivers rather than still waters. It focuses on research within England and Wales, and cites the results of recent studies carried out at Middlesex University, in particular: (a) results from a survey of the general population in four water company areas (Yorkshire, Anglian, North West and Welsh) carried out for the Foundation for Water Research (FWR) Benefit Assessment Project. This project published during 1996 a final version of its Interim Manual setting out methods and standard data to be used in evaluating the benefits of water quality improvements (Foundation for Water Research, 1994, 1996); (b) a small focus group study of the general population funded by the Polytechnics and Colleges Funding Council (PCFC) (Tunstall, 1995); (c) a series of public perception studies of floodplain residents and river corridor visitors carried out for the National Rivers Authority (NRA) Thames Region and nationally (House *et al.*, 1994a, b; Tunstall *et al.*, 1994).

4.3 Freshwater Sites as Places to Visit

The term 'fresh water' is not one that is commonly used by members of the public except, perhaps, in relation to fish and fishing by anglers. Members of the public are more likely to think and talk about different types of fresh water: rivers, streams, canals, ponds, reservoirs and lakes. The public may have different perceptions, expectations and preferences for these different types of waters. This appears to be the case with regard to freshwater sites as places to visit.

In the FWR general population survey, householders were asked to rate how enjoyable they thought a visit to some 13 places would be for them on a scale from 0 = would not enjoy at all, to 6 = very enjoyable. People did make distinctions between different types of freshwater site (Table 4.1) Two types, a lake and a river, were highly regarded as potential places to visit. A third type, canals, not natural fresh waters, and frequently in urban industrial or former industrial areas, was not as highly rated as rivers or lakes. Rivers and lakes were rated as more enjoyable places to visit than a local park, museum, leisure/sports centre, zoo or theme park. Overall, the 'naturalness' of places appears to be a key factor in their attractiveness for the householders as places to visit.

In the FWR general population survey, householders were asked a wide question: 'How often have you been near or walked across a river in the last 12 months?' in order to capture *any* contact with watercourses and not just intentional recreation visits. Three-quarters of those questioned had visited or been near a river in the last 12 months (shown as river corridor visitors in Table 4.1) and more than a third had made at least weekly visits. Thus most members of the public had some recent personal experience of rivers as a basis for their perceptions and attitudes. Not surprisingly, river corridor visitors anticipated greater enjoyment than non-visitors from visits to all the freshwater sites and to some other natural and man-made locations (Table 4.1).

Table 4.1   Anticipated enjoyment from visits to different sites: householders in four water company areas in England and Wales.

Site	River corridor non-visitors (mean score)	River corridor visitors (mean score)	All (mean score)
Beach	4.5	4.4	4.5
National park	4.0	4.5*	4.4
Country park	4.5	4.4	4.4
Lake	4.0	4.4*	4.3
Wood/forest	3.9	4.5**	4.3
Nature reserve	3.9	4.1	4.1
River	3.6	4.3**	4.1
Local park	3.5	3.8	3.7
Museum	3.3	3.7	3.6
Canal	2.8	3.5**	3.3
Zoo	2.8	2.8	2.8
Leisure/sports centre	2.4	3.0*	2.8
Theme park	2.6	2.6	2.6

Source: Foundation for Water Research, 1996

Scale: 0 = Would not enjoy at all, to 6 = Very enjoyable.

*t test significant at 0.05 level.

**t test significant at 0.01 level.

Number of cases: 542.

In the NRA public perception surveys of floodplain residents, reported frequency of visits to the rivers was high with more than 50% of respondents in the majority of studies visiting on at least a weekly basis. In the case studies of York and of the River Mole, there were high percentages visiting daily. In most studies the proportion of local residents who rarely or never visited their local rivers was very small: under 10% of those interviewed. Even allowing for some exaggeration, the studies indicate high usage of local rivers by floodplain residents (Green *et al.*, 1994; Tunstall *et al.*, 1994). People who choose to live near rivers and other fresh waters may be a self-selected group who value and use river corridor open spaces more than the population generally. It is common to find an association between visiting and proximity to rivers (Green *et al.*, 1994). There is evidence, too, that for people living near a river, the perceived quality of that river quite strongly affects residents' assessments of the desirability of their neighbourhood as a place to live (Green and Tunstall, 1992).

The FWR survey confirmed for the general population in the four water company areas what has been found in surveys of floodplain residents and river corridor visitors: that the activities engaged in most often when visiting rivers were informal and riverside ones—strolling, sitting, and walking the dog, rather than in-stream and specialized activities involving closer contact with the water such as fishing and boating. Experiences of rivers are also often incidental, occurring as part of people's everyday and working lives as well as being consciously sought during leisure and holiday times. However, the importance of certain fresh waters as a focus for recreation is indicated by the estimate of 41 million recreational visits made to canals and navigable rivers in Britain in the year based on the 1993 UK Day Visits Survey (Countryside Recreation Network, 1994).

The PCFC focus group discussions also indicated that people's awareness of, and the value that they attach to, rivers was not bounded by their current place of residence or experiences. In talking about rivers and river water quality, they drew on knowledge and experiences acquired over a lifetime and often in different parts of the country and indeed abroad. People's activities and involvement with rivers changed with the changing stages and vicissitudes of their lives. Survey data tend to obscure this detail and the rich variety of individual life experiences and perceptions.

Burgess (1994) has noted the importance of contact with water in childhood. Childhood and family memories of rivers were sometimes recalled spontaneously in the PCFC discussion groups. Some participants expressed a sense of loss because they believed that the experiences of their childhood, or of parents and relatives, were no longer available to present day children because of changes to water environments. They recalled swimming in rivers, feeding swans, playing on stepping stones and looking for frog spawn in streams and ponds. While some had the impression that river environments had changed for the worse, others were more sceptical of memories and thought that public perceptions and environmental awareness had changed as much as rivers.

We are more aware of what is going into the rivers than in the past because of television and the newspapers. I used to go swimming in the Orwell when I was small. I wouldn't dream of it now. But that has always had sewage pumping into it. (Manager, male, Ipswich)

The PCFC focus groups highlighted the importance of media coverage for public perceptions of freshwater and other environments, a point which has been emphasized by Burgess (1990, 1992). National, regional and local press coverage and radio and television programmes were frequently mentioned in the discussion groups as a source of information about fresh waters and water pollution in particular. The discussions suggest that apart from personal experience, these sources were the main influence on public awareness of, and attitudes towards, the water environment, rivers and water quality. Of course, journalists and programme makers can be expected to be influenced by, and to reflect, information from other sources, statutory and voluntary bodies, and the attitudes of the public; the media should be viewed as part of a process of influence and interpretation. Information from the media might be expected to be of particular importance in shaping attitudes towards those aspects of the freshwater environment of which individuals do not have experience. Furthermore, public awareness and concern about particular freshwater issues might be expected to develop as media coverage brings new issues to prominence on the public agenda and coverage of other issues is allowed to lapse.

4.4   Public Perception of Problems affecting River Environments

Some insight into the way the members of the public view the quality of riverine fresh waters may be gained by asking them about problems affecting rivers. In the FWR general population survey, respondents were asked to say how serious a problem each of a list of 11 items was for rivers in England and Wales, rating the items from 0 = not a problem, to 6 = major problem. These ratings may reflect beliefs as to how many, and how seriously, rivers are affected as well as respondents' subjective assessment of the importance of the impacts. The high scores given indicate that members of the public viewed rivers as affected by major problems (Table 4.2).

Pollution of river water and littering and fly dumping were rated as the most severe problems for rivers by both visitors and non-visitors (mean scores 5.2); litter and dumping which might be thought of as superficial or cosmetic problems were regarded by the public as of comparable importance to water pollution. The unnatural appearance of rivers due to river engineering (mean score 4.2), rivers running dry due to abstraction (mean score 4.1) and danger to children (mean score 4.1) were seen as the next most important problems. Visitors perceived some problems as less severe than non-visitors: the danger to children posed by rivers, rivers running dry, lack of wildlife, and of trees and plants. Rather than experience leading to greater identification of problems with rivers, it appears that those who in the past have had particularly bad experiences of rivers, or who on

Table 4.2   Perceived problems with rivers: householders in four water company areas in England and Wales.

Problem	River corridor non-visitors (mean score)	River corridor visitors (mean score)	All (mean score)
Litter and fly dumping	5.2	5.2	5.2
Pollution	5.1	5.2	5.2
Unnatural appearance due to engineering works	4.3	4.1	4.2
Rivers running dry	4.3	4.0	4.1
Danger to children	4.5	3.9**	4.1
Lack of wildlife	4.0	3.6	3.7
Lack of access and footpaths	3.8	3.6	3.6
Lack of recreational facilities	3.6	3.3	3.4
Lack of trees and plants	3.7	3.2*	3.3
How good is river water quality?	2.8	2.7	2.7

Source: Foundation for Water Research, 1996.
Scale problems: 0 = Not a problem, to 6 = Major problem.
Scale river water quality: 0 = Very polluted, to 6 = Very clean.
*t test significant at 0.05 level.
**t test significant at 0.01 level.
Number of cases: 542.

the basis of information from media or friends believed rivers to be in a bad state, chose not to visit.

4.4.1   Freshwater pollution and litter

Members of the public are very aware of and concerned about the pollution of fresh waters. In the British Social Attitudes Survey of 1993, pollution of Britain's rivers, lakes and streams was thought to be a more serious threat to the environment and to the respondents and their families than air pollution by industry or cars, nuclear power stations, the greenhouse effect, or pesticides and chemicals used in farming. Freshwater pollution was regarded as an 'extremely' or 'very' dangerous threat to the environment by 61%, and to the respondents and their families by 47% (Witherspoon, 1994). Public concern about water pollution is linked to public health concerns. The desire to eliminate a potential threat to health is an important motivation for wishing to improve waters, particularly grossly polluted waters (Green *et al.*, 1989; Tunstall, 1995). People in the PCFC focus groups still talked about the time when someone who fell into the Mersey or the Tyne had to be rushed to hospital to have their stomach pumped.

In the FWR general population survey, a majority of respondents in the four areas, when asked how good they thought the quality of water in the rivers in England and Wales was, generally gave rivers a middle rating (2, 3 or 4, mean score 2.7 on a scale of 0 = very polluted to 6 = very clean). National Rivers Authority statistics for 1992–4 showed that of the total length of rivers and canals in England and Wales, more than half (59%) were classed as of good water quality, a third (32%) as of fair quality and only 9% as of poor or bad quality according to the GQA Chemical Water Quality Classification. This suggests that the public believes the quality of water in rivers to be in a worse state than it actually is or that they have a different view of relative values to that of the classification system.

Furthermore, in the FWR general population survey, while over a third (36%) thought that overall the quality of the water in the rivers in England and Wales had been improving, a substantial minority (28%) believed that it had been getting worse and over a third (35%) that there had been no change during the last five years. NRA data indicate that while some stretches of river have deteriorated in recent years, more have improved and that, in the period 1990–1994, there has been an upgrading in overall water quality of 26% of the length of rivers and canals surveyed. These data again suggest that the public takes a more pessimistic view of the changing state of river water quality than is justified.

The substantial research literature on the public's perception of water quality in the USA and UK—what clues people use to decide whether a river or other fresh water is clean or dirty—has been reviewed by House (1986) and more recently by House and Herring (1994). In questionnaire surveys of river users and of those resident near rivers or other fresh waters, respondents have been asked to rate certain indicators as to whether or not they were perceived to be indicative of 'good' or 'bad' water quality or were present or absent in relation to the perceived water quality. House and Herring (1994) in their recent review concluded that those most commonly cited as being indicative of 'bad' water quality were algal growth, muddy waters, strange odours and dead fish, films of oil, rubbish in the water and strange colour.

Davies and Parker (1982) and House and Sangster (1991) showed that anglers and other river users were able to differentiate between good water quality (NWC class 1) and bad water quality (NWC class 4). The public's perception at these extremes appeared to be quite well related to the primarily chemical water quality classification used by the experts. However, the results of studies by House and Sangster (1991) and Green and Tunstall (1992) suggest that the public has a clearer idea of what it considers to be a polluted river than of what constitutes clean water. House and Herring (1994) argue that people may perceive urban rivers as being polluted, even those of technically very good chemical and biological quality, due to the presence of 'rubbish' and some form of discolouration or smell. The quality of the river corridor may also affect the public's perception of the quality of the water. In the PCFC focus groups, discussion of water quality often moved quickly to discussions of litter and dumping in rivers and their corridors, indicating that the two issues were closely linked, and perhaps confused, in people's minds. Different authorities have responsibility for these problems and, in the case of litter and dumping, it is mainly members of the public who have responsibility as some participants recognized. Some people felt very strongly and were quite angry about what they saw as the degraded condition of local rivers through water pollution and litter and the failure of the responsible authorities to take action (Tunstall, 1995).

In recognition of the importance of the public's perception of water and environmental quality, the NRA developed a new General Quality Assessment Scheme (GQA) which is to include consideration of the aesthetic impact of pollution parameters for the first time. NRA Research and Development projects were undertaken between 1992 and 1994 to evaluate the importance of many of the individual water quality impairment parameters—for example, foaming (Baker *et al.*, 1991); litter (NRA, 1992), coloured effluents (NRA, 1992) and sewage-derived waste (House *et al.*, 1994a)—to perceived water quality and the use of rivers and beaches for recreation and amenity. These research projects have resulted in the development of two aesthetic classifications, one for rivers and one for estuaries and coastal waters.

A field assessment procedure is being developed by the Water Research Centre (WRc) for the collection of data on the parameters to be included within the classification (WRc, 1994). A classification based on four classes of water quality has been proposed by the WRc. These classes are based on the degree to which each parameter is deemed to be present. Additional research is being undertaken to test the ability of members of the public to perceive changes in water quality. The results to date suggest that the public are indeed able to identify a deterioration in water quality associated with the gradual increase in the number or intensity of various parameters.

House and Herring (1994) examined aspects of aesthetic pollution—the subjective perception of solid, semi-solid and liquid waste matter in rivers and on beaches. In particular, they considered the public's perception of sewage-derived contaminants and the impact of litter from this source on the public's perception of river water quality and corridor quality, and the effect of this on their use of rivers for recreation and amenity. They found that, in principle, the presence of sewage-derived contaminants would have a greater impact on the public's enjoyment of a visit than any other form of aesthetic pollution. However, they also concluded that sewage-derived products are not regularly seen by the public; in part, this is the result of a failure to recognize the presence of sewage-derived solids when present either on site or in photographs or slides. Conversely, this may be due to a general unwillingness or inhibition about mentioning specific products. When such items were identified they were found to have a negative effect on perceived water quality (House and Herring, 1994).

Although two-thirds of respondents in the British Social Attitudes Survey have been found to be very concerned about the disposal of sewage (Young, 1991), comments made in focus groups (Tunstall, 1995) suggest that members of the public were less aware of sewage treatment works and discharges from combined storm overflows as a source of river water pollution than they were of industrial (and even possibly agricultural) pollution, perhaps because of the publicity given to legal cases on pollution incidents of these kinds. However, there appeared to be a much higher awareness of contamination of bathing waters and beaches by sewage effluent. In one group, shocked disbelief greeted a fisherman's description of sewage being discharged untreated into a local river: group members did not believe that such discharges were legal or something that happened in this day and age.

Fewer people questioned in the British Social Attitudes Surveys regarded acid rain as a very serious hazard than took this view of industrial pollution of rivers and seas (Young, 1990; Witherspoon and Martin, 1992). Public awareness of acid rain as a cause of damage to fresh waters in upland areas in Britain appears to be limited. In surveys of visitors, including fishermen interviewed beside lakes, rivers and streams in four upland areas, and the public interviewed at other locations throughout Britain, respondents were shown evidence in photographs and drawings of damage to freshwater ecosystems in the uplands. Only 33% spontaneously suggested acid rain or atmospheric pollution as a possible cause of the changes that had been described to them. The pollution of fresh waters in Britain was rated as of most concern out of a list of different environmental issues, and a large majority of those interviewed agreed that more public money should be spent on improving upland streams, rivers and lakes (Ecotec Research and Consulting Ltd, 1993).

Public understanding of the nature, sources and indicators of pollution may be deficient to some degree. However, all the studies show high levels of public concern about river water pollution and some studies indicate a willingness to pay for improvements (Green and Tunstall, 1992; Tunstall, 1995; Foundation for Water Research, 1996).

4.4.2 *River engineering*

Although not regarded as of comparable importance to water pollution, litter and dumping in the FWR survey, the public rated the unnatural appearance of rivers, because of engineering works, as the next most important problem for rivers in England and Wales. A questionnaire survey to NRA personnel found that physical habitat loss, principally through river engineering, was perceived to be the most important form of riverine degradation in England and Wales. Of the specific reasons for river engineering, the requirement to defend land and property from the risk of flooding was perceived to be the most important, although land drainage and the relocation of rivers for transport links were widespread reasons for river engineering (River Restoration Project, 1993). It is possible that the public is not as fully aware of the extent to which rivers have been modified or channelized as are the professionals concerned with river management.

Floodplain residents may perceive flood risk and flood alleviation proposals differently from river managers and flood defence engineers (Green *et al.*, 1991; Fordham, 1993). Surveys of floodplain residents have shown that the perceived effects of proposed works on the river environment were very important factors in public response to flood alleviation proposals (Tunstall *et al.*, 1994). For those living close to a river, their environment represented both asset and hazard. They had more to gain from flood defence schemes but also more potentially to lose if they perceived the scheme to have a detrimental environmental impact. Even in Maidenhead, Berkshire, where a survey was carried out with flooded and flood-affected householders in the aftermath of the 1990 flood, only a quarter of those questioned agreed that a flood alleviation scheme should be carried out regardless of the environmental impact (Sangster *et al.*, 1990; Tunstall *et al.*, 1994).

One study carried out for the NRA aimed to address the issue of how the public perceived the channelization of rivers and the 'hard' engineering approach to flood defence employed in the 1960s and 1970s. A survey was conducted with residents living near the River Mole and River Ember flood alleviation scheme in Surrey, which included a concrete-lined and classic trapezoidal channel as well as more natural sections of river. Local residents, many of whom had experienced serious flooding in the area, appreciated the level of flood protection that the scheme afforded, and the positive impact they considered the scheme to have had on property values. Generally, they had accepted the scheme, visited the rivers frequently and still valued them as a recreational resource and for their wildlife. However, residents viewed the concrete channel, the regimented appearance of the rivers and lack of vegetation along some sections as very negative aspects of the scheme. Although two-thirds of those questioned believed that the rivers still provided a good habitat for wildlife, many also felt that there had been a loss of wildlife habitats as a consequence of the scheme.

Had a softer approach to river engineering been available at the time the scheme was designed, there were strong indications in the survey that the public would have preferred this (Tapsell and Tunstall, 1993). Certainly, other surveys in the Thames region confirmed that floodplain residents had a strong preference for 'natural' and low impact flood alleviation structures with 'natural' rather than concrete channels and banks for both urban and rural areas (Tunstall *et al.*, 1989; Tunstall and Fordham, 1990; Wigg and Tunstall, 1991).

Another study examined the public perception of a section of a small Thames tributary, the Ravensbourne River, where it passed through Queen's Mead rec-reation ground near the centre of Bromley in Kent. Following extensive flooding in the area in 1968, the river in the park was channelized, resulting in a vertical-sided concrete-lined channel cutting across the park in a straight line behind high railings (see Plate 1c). The form of the river was one of the main aspects of the park disliked by respondents, and almost half spontaneously commented on the ugliness of the channel. Although the concrete was seen by most as being unat-tractive, many respondents felt that it was necessary because of the flooding and was, therefore, functional. Respondents were also extremely critical of the river as a habitat for wildlife considering it both too harsh and also too polluted an environment to support wildlife. Typical comments were:

> Looks horrible and river bed is slimy and smelly.
> Ugly, like a sewer.
> It's filthy. A diabolical place.
> (On wildlife) You're joking. Very occasional mallard but they quickly move on. No fish.

There was strong support from those interviewed for hypothetical proposals (there were no plans at the time to implement a scheme) to restore the river in the park to a more natural condition, in particular for the more radical restoration scheme involving a new meandering channel on a new course with earth banks and two small wetland areas. Respondents also favoured increased public expenditure on river restoration initiatives (Tapsell *et al.*, 1992).

In the study, 8-year-old children in a class at the nearby primary school were asked to draw a picture of how they would like the river in the park to be. Their drawings show a meandering flowing river with water-birds and fish, and on the banks flowers, trees, butterflies and picnicking and sunbathing families (see Plate 1a) (Tapsell *et al.*, 1992). There has been little detailed research on the perceptions and preferences of children and young people for fresh waters although they are probably important users of pond, river and lake environments. Their way of looking at these resources and their preferences may be different from those of older people.

4.4.3 Low flows in rivers

The NRA produced a list of 40 river stretches in England and Wales identified as needing priority action because of unacceptably low flow levels, usually the result of excessive abstraction commonly from groundwater, but also from surface water (NRA, 1993). Some low-flow alleviation schemes have now been fully implemented and others are under way or planned (NRA, 1995). In the FWR general population survey, rivers running dry through over-abstraction was rated as an important problem but less so than pollution and littering. Respondents have been asked in several surveys to give their priorities for water services. 'Ensuring, by reducing the amount of water taken for public supply that no rivers run dry' was given a high rating in most surveys (Tunstall *et al.*, 1994). In a survey for the Office of Water Services in four water company areas, a majority of householders (54%) believed that building more reservoirs and taking more water from the rivers would damage the environment. However, nearly half (48%) nonetheless favoured these measures as a way of avoiding supply restrictions. In all the areas, almost 90% of people were most in favour of speeding up existing programmes to reduce leakages from water mains, as well as voluntary reductions in water consumption as a means of reducing the risk of a hose pipe ban (Green *et al.*, 1993).

Although concern about rivers running dry appears high, the evidence on public awareness of low flows in particular rivers is limited and mixed. In a study of the alleviation of low flows in the River Darent in Kent, awareness was highest (not surprisingly) among local residents (97%) but only 71% of visitors were aware that the river was subject to low flows. Respondents in the survey may have been reluctant to admit that they did not know (Environmental Resources Management, 1993). In another study, anglers were interviewed at sites within 32 km of two of the NRA's low flow rivers, the River Misbourne and the River Ver. Both rivers had hardly been fished within the previous year but had potential as trout streams. Many anglers had not heard of these rivers or their low flow condition (House *et al.*, 1994b).

Other surveys of those visiting or living near to rivers affected by low flows showed that members of the public recognized and were concerned about flow levels in the rivers (House *et al.*, 1994b). For example, residents who had visited badly affected or dry sites on the River Misbourne, Buckinghamshire and the Town Branch of the River Wey, in Hampshire, considered the amount of water in the river there as the worst feature of the sites and that more water in the river along with more birds, dragonflies and insects would make most difference to their enjoyment of the river. Furthermore, in the surveys of residents and visitors at the River Misbourne, 'the amount of water' was found to be the most important characteristic in determining the respondents' overall rating of the river as a place to visit. There was strong public preference for, and some willingness to pay for, some action to alleviate low flows in these studies (Environmental Resource Management, 1993; House *et al.*, 1994b).

The River Kennet was not one of the 40 low flow rivers originally identified by the NRA as a priority for action. A survey and qualitative studies of those living near the Upper Kennet indicated that the majority of respondents felt that the river had changed adversely in the last 10 years. Water levels were found to be of greatest concern to the local population and the survey showed that an increase in the level of the Kennet would make the most difference to respondents' enjoyment of the river. There were distinct differences between the public and the NRA in their perceptions of low flows on the Upper Kennet. Whilst there was acceptance by the public that changes in management and drought were contributory factors to recent low river levels, there was an overwhelming perception that abstraction was the main cause of low flows in the River Kennet. The NRA had not convinced the local population that abstraction was not a significant factor (Sawyer and Fordham, 1993).

4.4.4 Safety issues

In the FWS general population survey, the danger to children was rated as an important problem for rivers. At freshwater sites, the very element that is a particular attractor—the water itself— presents an additional danger, particularly to children. FHRC studies indicate that safety concerns are an important consideration for the public when assessing flood alleviation proposals and schemes (Tunstall *et al.*, 1994). For example, proposals to take down the riverside railings and create a more natural channel in a park raised questions concerning public safety, particularly of children, and the children themselves expressed some fears for the safety of small children (Tapsell *et al.*, 1992). Wider safety issues may enter into public perceptions of freshwater sites and their qualities. Certainly, Burgess *et al.* (1988a) found that fears about safety were major considerations for women and children in discussions about urban open spaces.

4.5 Ideal River Settings: Landscape Features and Wildlife Habitats

Another way of exploring the issue of the public perception of freshwater quality is to consider how the public would like freshwater sites to be. A number of studies have examined public preferences for rivers in terms of ideal river settings for residents and users (Burrows and House, 1989; House and Sangster, 1991; Green and Tunstall, 1992; Sawyer and Fordham, 1993) and ideal freshwater fishing sites for anglers (House *et al.*, 1994b). House and Sangster (1991), through surveys of in-stream and bankside users interviewed at different river locations, focused on detailed preferences for different types of vegetation in the river corridor, and river features such as depth, flow, width, channel form and plants in the river. The authors concluded that members of the public had some very definite ideas of what they perceived to be their ideal river setting. Far from preferring manicured and highly managed settings, as has sometimes been assumed, the public showed a strong preference for a 'natural' environment: natural river banks and winding channels, and naturally worn paths, a marked desire for trees, and a strong preference for a diversity of vegetation in terms of trees, plants and grasses. These preferences indicate a greater compatibility of the public's views with nature conservation than was previously recognized.

Green *et al.* (1989) asked residents living at least 2km from a river in various locations in England to consider which of a wider range of developed and natural features would most add to their enjoyment of a river corridor. Natural features were highly rated indicating that the respondents would prefer to visit a river corridor in a mature landscape with many well grown trees and plants and which supports a diverse population of birds, insects and plants in and near the water, but which was easily accessible and had certain facilities: toilets and adequate car parking. Recreational facilities and places to visit were given lower average ratings and were not wanted by significant minorities. Principal components analysis of the preferences for river corridor features showed that different underlying preferences were held by different groups: those with children and those without, and those who had and had not visited a river in the last six months. For example, current visitors who formed the greater proportion of the sample wanted a relatively unspoilt, natural river corridor: they rated a 'rich environment' with natural features more highly and other components comprising 'places to visit' and 'facilities' lower than non-visitors (Green and Tunstall, 1992). Public perceptions of what constitutes a rich environment may not be, and in some instances has been found not to be, the same as those of ecologists (Harrison and Burgess, 1994).

River corridors are visited and valued by the public for the rich natural environment they offer, including their wildlife. Looking at wildlife was commonly cited as one of the reasons for visiting river corridors in studies of visitors and residents (Environmental Resource Management, 1993; Sawyer and Fordham, 1993; Tapsell and Tunstall, 1993; Tapsell *et al.*, 1993). The PCFC focus groups showed how local rivers were appreciated for the opportunities they offered for everyday encounters with nature. Parents valued the chance to introduce their children to the living world at the riverside (Tunstall, 1995). Lack of wildlife habitats was perceived to be a significant problem with rivers in England and Wales in the FWS general population survey. The perceived effects on wildlife and wildlife habitats were important factors in public attitudes towards other aspects of river environments such as river engineering schemes and proposals (Tapsell and Tunstall, 1993; Tunstall *et al.*, 1994), river pollution (Green *et al.*, 1989) and low flows in rivers (House *et al.*, 1994b).

4.6 Integrated River Management, River Restoration and Public Participation

The PCFC focus groups and the survey research cited above indicate that members of the public are interested in the quality of river environments as a whole rather than in particular aspects. In the discussions, they showed impatience with the divided institutional responsibilities that lead to, for example, river engineering being seen as a separate issue from water pollution or littering and dumping in river corridors, and that may act as barriers to tackling problems in a holistic way.

The River Restoration Project is an independent body, working in partnership with other organizations with the aim of furthering integrated river restoration initiatives in the UK. It is mounting two initial demonstration projects which aim to put into practice state-of-the-art river restoration techniques with funding from the European Commission LIFE programme (Nielsen, in press). The River Skerne in Darlington, County Durham, was selected as one site for a demonstration project. The River Restoration Project with funding from the NRA, Darlington Borough Council and Northumbrian Water, commissioned a survey to monitor public perceptions of the river and the associated park, river pollution and river habitats. It also studied public preferences for restoration proposals, including the provision of a footbridge and pathways, before finalizing the design and beginning restoration work. The main attractions of this urban river site were found to be the green open space and the 'natural' environment of the river, trees and other vegetation. The area was valued as a quiet place to visit and to enjoy the wildlife. The main negative aspects of the site included problems not directly related to the river: dog fouling, rubbish and litter, and vandalism, as well as the perceived poor quality of the river water. The proposed integrated approach to river restoration—the provision of additional planting and landscaping, the creation of meanders and new wetland and pond areas—was well received by the majority of those interviewed and was perceived as a chance to improve the area generally. Restoration was seen as offering increased scope for recreation and for wildlife and educational opportunities for local school children. It is intended that public perceptions should be monitored at intervals as the restoration scheme is implemented and matures (River Restoration Project, 1995).

The Skerne study, like other studies of floodplain residents (Tunstall *et al.*, 1994) showed that local people attached high importance to being consulted so that they could make their views known over plans affecting their local watercourses and associated land. Expressions of interest and concern for freshwater environments are without cost and a further issue is the extent to which members of the public are prepared to modify their behaviour, become involved in decision making and community action and to pay to improve river and other freshwater environments. In the Skerne study, as many as one-third of the respondents expressed an interest in taking an active part in decision making and management of the site (River Restoration Project, 1995). The PCFC focus groups' studies indicated that some members of the public, echoing Agenda 21, considered it important that local communities, school children, youth groups and local residents should be actively involved in initiatives to improve local rivers in order to engender a feeling of 'local ownership' of such schemes. Such participation was thought to be desirable in order to raise awareness and understanding of river environments and to encourage responsible behaviour towards them—for example, in relation to litter, vandalism and the use and disposal of products.

The Medway River Project in Kent is an example of a Countryside Management Project focused on a river which has sought to maximize local community involvement in river enhancement schemes (Medway River Project, 1994). This project has attracted local sponsorship and community support in the form of over 10,000 volunteer days of action since 1988. Youth groups, schools, people on probation, prisoners at Rochester prison and others have undertaken tasks such as litter clearance, building stiles, bank restoration and the creation of habitats and of an Educational Nature Reserve. The extent to which this and other comparable projects have raised public awareness, understanding and support for improvements to river environments through active involvement has not been systematically evaluated. However, the growth in the number of groups and days of voluntary action has been seen as one measure of the success of the Medway River Project and the approach. Another is the way other organizations across the country have become active in similar schemes and partnerships involving public participation (Brown and Howell, 1992; Smith, 1994).

4.7 Conclusions

It's a fundamental resource really, I mean, it's useful and necessary in the sense of being recreational and also for industry but, I mean it is something that really needs to be protected and for the moment it is just sort of, used as a profit thing, instead of . . . it's the essence of life . . . without water we are all dead. Not just us but all the flora and fauna and everything. (Print worker, male, Aberystwyth).

I was brought up in a rural area where there was no pollution. Of course this was a long time ago and it was wonderful. And I would like to think that it would be the same for everyone today and, as you say, in the future. Plus it's a health hazard, pollution and all the badness that comes out if you go near or touch the water. It's also bad for the wildlife and the flora and fauna. So I would just like to think that it would eventually come back to the standard it used to be years ago. (Seaman's widow, Stockport).

The quotations from members of the public in focus groups capture something of what freshwater quality means to people: the value they attach to fresh waters as places to visit and their intrinsic value. In summary, it appears from the research that the public's view of what constitutes high quality in fresh waters is a holistic one—of rivers, and probably also lakes and ponds, that have unpolluted and plentiful waters, in surroundings that are safe and free from litter, that provide what the public considers to be a rich natural environment with abundant trees, plants and wildlife. The comments also illustrate the moral or spiritual values underlying concern for the freshwater and other environments which have been identified in survey research (Green and Tunstall, 1992; Witherspoon, 1994). For some people, fresh waters have a symbolic significance: symbols of purity and continuity; they are recognized as basic to life and are seen as important indicators of our will to take care of the environment in general.

Research shows that while the public may not share the experts' detailed awareness of the factors affecting fresh waters, many members of the public feel strongly about the issue of freshwater quality and support proposals to protect and enhance these resources. There is, therefore, considerable scope to involve local people in planning and action to improve fresh waters—to pursue the participatory approach recommended in Agenda 21.

Acknowledgements

The authors wish to acknowledge receipt of funding for the research described in this chapter from the following bodies and to thank these organizations for their support: Foundation for Water Research; Water Research Centre; NRA Thames Region and NRA nationally; Polytechnics and Colleges Funding Council. Permission to publish data in Tables 4.1 and 4.2 from the Foundation for Water Research (1996) is also gratefully acknowledged.

References

Baker, M. C. G., Bealing, D., James, H., Lewis, S., Taylor, L. and Jones, S. (1991). *Foaming in Rivers: An Initial Assessment of the Problem in UK.* WRc Report NR 2778 (NRA ref No A4.10), Water Research Centre, Medmenham.

Brown, A. E. and Howell, D. L. (1992). Conservation of rivers in Scotland: legislative and organisational limitations. In: Boon, P. J., Calow, P. and Petts, G. E. (Eds), *River Conservation and Management.* John Wiley, Chichester, 407–424.

Bryman, A. (1988). *Quantity and Quality in Social Research.* Unwin Hyman, London.

Burgess, J. (1990). The production and consumption of environmental meanings in the mass media: a research agenda for the 1990s. *Transactions, British Institute of Geographers,* **15,** 139–161.

Burgess, J. (1992). The cultural politics of economic development and nature conservation. In: Anderson, K. and Gale, F. (Eds), *Inventing Places: Studies in Cultural Geography.* Longman, Cheshire, Melbourne, 235–251.

Burgess, J. (1994). Rivers in the Landscape: A Cultural Perspective. Background paper for presentation 'How do we know what people value?' Conference on Water Quality: Understanding the Benefits and Meeting the Demands, London, 9 March 1994.

Burgess, J., Harrison, C. M. and Limb, M. (1988a). People, parks and the urban green: a study of popular meanings and values for open space in the city. *Urban Studies,* **25,** 455–473.

Burgess, J., Limb, M. and Harrison, C. M. (1988b). Exploring environmental values through the medium of small groups: 1. Theory and practice. *Environment and Planning,* **20,** 309–326.

Burgess, J., Limb, M. and Harrison, C. M. (1988c). Exploring environmental values through the medium of small groups: 2. Illustrations of a group at work. *Environment and Planning,* **20,** 457–476.

Burrows, A. M. and House, M. A. (1989). Public's perception of water quality and the use of water for recreation. In: Laikari, H. (Ed.), *River Basin Management— V.* Pergamon Press, Oxford, 371–379.

Countryside Recreation Network (1994). 1993 UK Day Visits Survey. *Countryside Network News,* **2,** (1).

Davies, I. and Parker, D. J. (1982). 'Water quality control and urban angling interests'. Paper presented at the Institute of British Geographers annual conference, Southampton, January 1982.

De Vaus, D. A. (1991). *Surveys in Social Research*. Third Edition. Allen and Unwin, London.

Ecotec Research and Consulting Ltd (1993). *Evaluation of a Cost Benefit Analysis of Reduced Acid Rain Deposition: a Contingent Valuation Study of Aquatic Ecosystems*. Working Paper Five. Ecotec Research and Consulting Ltd, Birmingham.

Environmental Resources Management (1993). *River Darent Low Flow Alleviation Annex IV: An Economic Analysis of the Benefits Derived from the Alleviation of Low Flows in the River Darent*. National Rivers Authority Southern Region, Worthing.

Fordham, M. (1993). 'Valuing the environment: the attitudes of floodplain residents and flood defence engineers'. Paper presented at the Conference, Values and the Environment, University of Surrey, 23–24 September. Flood Hazard Research Centre, Enfield.

Foundation for Water Research (1994). *Assessing the Benefits of River Water Quality Improvements: Interim Manual*. Marlow.

Foundation for Water Research (1996). *Assessing the Benefits of Water Quality Improvements in Rivers, Estuaries and Coastal Waters*. Foundation for Water Research Publication No. 151, Marlow.

Green, C. H. and Tunstall, S. M. (1992). The amenity and environmental value of river corridors in Britain. In: Boon, P. J., Calow, P. and Petts, G. E. (Eds), *River Conservation and Management*. John Wiley, Chichester, 425–441.

Green, C. H., Tunstall, S. M. and House, M. A. (1989). Evaluating the benefits of river water quality improvement. In: Van der Staal, P. M. and Vught, F. A. (Eds), *Impact Forecasting and Assessment: Methods, Results and Experiences*. Delft University Press, Delft, The Netherlands, 171–180.

Green, C. H., Tunstall, S. M. and Fordham, M. (1991). The risks from flooding: which risk and whose perception? *Disasters*, **15**, 227–236.

Green, C. H., Tunstall, S. M., Herring, M. C. and Sawyer, J. (1993). *Customer Preferences and Willingness to Pay for Selected Water and Sewerage Services: Technical Report*. Office of Water Services, Birmingham.

Green, C. H., Tunstall, S. M., Garner, J. and Ketteridge, A.-M. (1994). 'Benefit transfer: rivers and coasts'. Paper prepared for the CEGB meeting on benefit transfer. HM Treasury. Flood Hazard Research Centre, Enfield.

Hanley, N. (This volume). Assessing the economic value of fresh waters.

Harrison, C. M. and Burgess, J. (1994). Social constructions of nature: a case study of conflicts over the development of Rainham Marshes. *Transactions, the Institute of British Geographers*, **19**, 291–310.

House, M. A. (1986). 'Water quality perception and recreation'. Background paper to the Social Costs of Sewerage Project for the Department of the Environment. Flood Hazard Research Centre, Enfield.

House, M. A. and Sangster, E. K. (1991). Public perception of river corridor management. *Journal of the Institution of Water and Environmental Management*, **5**, 312–317.

House, M. A. and Herring, M. (1994). *Aesthetic Pollution Public Perception Survey*. Report to the Water Research Centre, Enfield.

House, M. A., Herring, M., Green, M. J. and Palfrey, A. E. (1994a). *Public Perception of Aesthetic Pollution*. Foundation for Water Research Report, FR 0439. Foundation for Water Research, Marlow.

House, M. A., Tunstall, S. M., Green, C., Portou, J. and Clarke, L. (1994b). *Evaluation of Use Values from Alleviating Low Flows*. R&D Note 258, National Rivers Authority, Bristol.

Krueger, R. A. (1994). *Focus Groups: A Practical Guide for Applied Research*. Sage, London.

Macnaghten, P., Grove-White, R., Jacobs, M. and Wynne, B. (1995). *Public Perceptions and Sustainability in Lancashire*. Report to Lancashire County Council. Centre for the Study of Environmental Change, Lancaster University, Lancaster.

Medway River Project (1994). *Six Year Review 1988–94. Annual Report 1993–4*. Maidstone.

Nielsen, M. B. (in press). River restoration: report of a major EU Life demonstration project. *Aquatic Conservation: Marine and Freshwater Ecosystems*.

NRA (1992). *Sources, Pathways and Sinks of Litter in Rivers and Marine Waters*. Research and Development Project 321. Bristol.

NRA (1993). *Low Flows and Water Resources: Facts on the Top 40 Low Flow Rivers in England and Wales*. Bristol.

NRA (1995). *Annual Report and Accounts 1994/95*. Bristol.

Paton, M. G. (1993). Cruising down the river: Jerome K. Jerome's *Three Men in a Boat* and the Victorian comic novel. In: Piquet, F. (Ed.), *Le Fleuve et ses Metamorphoses*. Didier Erudition, Paris, 459–466.

Rayner, S. (1986). Management of radiation hazards in hospitals. *Social Studies of Science*, **16,** 573–591.

River Restoration Project (1993). *The River Restoration Project Phase 1: The Feasibility Study*. Huntingdon.

River Restoration Project (1995). *River Skerne Public Perception Survey: Stage Two*. Huntingdon.

Sadrin, A. 1993. La Tamise chez Dickens. In: Piquet, F. (Ed.), *Le Fleuve et ses Metamorphoses*. Didier Erudition, Paris, 449–453.

Sangster, E., Doizy, A. and Tunstall, S. M. (1990). *Flooding in the Maidenhead Area in February 1990 and its Effects*. Draft report to the National Rivers Authority Thames Region. Flood Hazard Research Centre, Enfield.

Sawyer, J. A. and Fordham, M. H. (1993). *Upper Kennet Public Perception Study*. Final Report to the National Rivers Authority. Flood Hazard Research Centre, Enfield.

Schuman, H. and Presser, S. (1981). *Questions and Answers in Attitude Surveys: Experiments on Question Form, Wording and Context*. Academic Press, New York.

Smith, B. (1994). 'The Medway River Project: an example of community participation in integrated river management'. Paper presented to the International Conference on Integrated River Basin Development, Institute of Hydrology, Wallingford.

Spray, C. J. (This volume). Assessing the recreation value of fresh waters: the UK experience.

Tapsell, S. M., Tunstall, S. M., Costa, P. and Fordham, M. (1992). *Ravensbourne River Queen's Mead Recreation Ground Survey*. Report to the National Rivers Authority Thames Region. Flood Hazard Research Centre, Enfield.

Tapsell, S. M. (1992). *Public Perception of Flooding and Flood Defences in York*. Interim Report to National Rivers Authority. Flood Hazard Research Centre, Enfield.

Tapsell, S. M. and Tunstall, S. M. (1993). *River Mole Flood Alleviation Scheme Survey*. Report to the National Rivers Authority Thames Region. Revised (1994). Flood Hazard Research Centre, Enfield.

Tapsell, S. M., Tunstall, S. M. and Fordham, M. (1993). *Public Perception of Flooding and Flood Defences in York*. R&D Note 213. National Rivers Authority Thames Region. Flood Hazard Research Centre, Enfield.

Tunstall, S. M. (1995). *Public Perceptions of Rivers and River Water Quality: Results from a Focus Group Study*. Report to the Foundation for Water Research Benefit Assessment Project. Flood Hazard Research Centre, Enfield.

Tunstall, S. M., Fordham, M. and Glen, C. (1989). *Eton Wick: A Survey of Residents' Perceptions of Flood Risk and Flood Alleviation Schemes*. Report to the National Rivers Authority Thames Region. Revised (1994). Flood Hazard Research Centre, Enfield.

Tunstall, S. M. and Fordham, M. (1990). *Thames Perception and Attitude Survey—Datchet to Walton Bridge*. Report to the National Rivers Authority Thames Region. Revised (1994). Flood Hazard Research Centre, Enfield.

Tunstall, S. M., Tapsell, S. M. and Fordham, M. (1994). *Public Perception of Rivers and Flood Defence: Summary of Regional and National R&D*. National Rivers Authority, Bristol.

United Nations Conference on Environment and Development (1992). Agenda 21. Switzerland: Conches.

WRc (1994). *Development and Testing of General Quality Assessment Scheme—Project 469*. Progress Report 3 (PR3). Medmenham.

Wigg, A. H. and Tunstall, S. M. (1991). *Customer Perception in the Lower Colne Valley*. Report to the National Rivers Authority Thames Region. Flood Hazard Research Centre, Enfield.

Witherspoon, S. (1994). The greening of Britain: romance and rationality. In: Jowell, R., Curtice, J., Brook, L. and Ahrendt, D. (Eds), *British Social Attitudes Survey: The 11th Report*. Dartmouth, Aldershot, 107–139.

Witherspoon, S. and Martin, J. (1992). What do we mean by green? In: Jowell, R., Brook, L., Prior, G. and Taylor, B. (Eds). *British Social Attitudes Survey: The 9th Report*. Dartmouth, Aldershot, 1–23.

Young, K. (1990). Living under threat. In: Jowell, R., Witherspoon, S. and Brook, L. (Eds), *British Social Attitudes: The 7th Report*. Gower, Dartmouth, 77–108.

Young, K. (1991). Shades of green. In: Jowell, R., Brook, L. and Taylor, B. (Eds), *British Social Attitudes: The 8th Report*. Dartmouth, Aldershot, 107–129.

5 FRESHWATER QUALITY IN EUROPE: TALES FROM THE CONTINENT

L. W. G. Higler and L. van Liere

Summary

1. Water quality should be defined on the basis of the total biotic and abiotic characteristics of surface waters as a point on a yardstick between water unacceptable for consumption and habitation, and a reference point (where anthropic influence is nil) or a chosen target point, under the current hydrological, chemical and biogeographical conditions.

2. Water quality demands both in the Netherlands and for the international border river, the Rhine, have been incorporated in a series of laws and agreements. These started with measures to combat organic pollution, followed in later phases by emphasis on inorganic nutrients and toxic substances, and finally by the setting up of ecological quality objectives including the relationship of the water bodies themselves with their physical surroundings.

3. Water quality in Europe, as determined by the presence of organic pollution and inorganic nutrients, has improved during the last 10 years in the industrialized parts of Europe, but has deteriorated in the eastern parts in the same period.

4. Europe as a whole is still occupied with the phase of inorganic nutrients and toxic substances, although ways of defining water quality which incorporate biota and their physical surroundings are at hand. Indeed, the proposed EC framework Directive on water policy is likely to require much broader assessments of 'quality' to be made.

5.1 Introduction

Quality, a relative concept, is the perception or assessment of a certain state. This can also be applied to the quality of water. One of the few definitions provided for assessing 'water quality' is the 'description of the result of an assessment of a water body' (Murk, 1990). The quality is defined here as a point on a yardstick located between 'excellent' and 'very bad', although both extremes occur against a background of human impacts. Water quality can be defined only by objective, measurable parameters in relation to a reference (or chosen) state of a river or lake system. Parameters used are often still exclusively chemical, although the uses for which water quality is assessed may include drinking water, recreation and ecology. In the countries with a longer history of water quality management (in general, industrialized countries with many degraded waters), but with enough funds to be able to set something aside for 'luxury goals' like recreation and nature conservation, there has been a gradual change from a purely chemical approach to one in which ecological descriptions are included.

In this chapter, the history of such changes will be demonstrated using examples from the Netherlands and the River Rhine. The 'chemical' state of European waters and the European Union's plans to define ecological quality objectives will also be discussed.

5.2   Case Study: The Netherlands

5.2.1   *The development of water quality objectives*

The Netherlands is a densely populated, partly industrialized country, with various agricultural practices and a long history of fighting back the sea and coping with floods, the discharge of superfluous rain water, and retaining or distributing fresh water for agricultural purposes. From the Middle Ages onwards, dikes have been constructed as a means of flood protection, and land has been reclaimed (polders), to control the water level precisely. From the beginning to the middle of the twentieth century there was a slight growth in awareness of water pollution, primarily because of smell and fish kills caused by oxygen depletion resulting from high loads of organic material. After World War II the fight against pollution received increasingly more attention in society and by policy-makers. This reached a peak in the concept of an integrated ecosystem approach, in which the focus was not only the water body itself, but all influences from surrounding areas with it (V and W, 1989).

Since 1968, statutory measures have been introduced nationally for regulating quantitative and qualitative water management. At first, legislation emphasized the need for adequate quantities of fresh water and expressed water quality in terms of a few chemical parameters. A programme to establish water purification plants resulted in the treatment of nearly 100% of all point sources of water pollution. In later memoranda ecological quality objectives were defined, but standards were still set in chemical terms. Aquatic ecologists raised their voices with a plea for ecological water quality assessment, and national adaptations of existing saprobity systems and regional classifications were established. In 1985, an important memorandum was published, in which the integration of qualitative and quantitative water management was proposed (V and W, 1985). Further developments occurred in 1988 when ecological quality objectives were formulated for 16 water types, described using lists of characteristic species (CUWVO, 1988). An overview of the legislation and agreements is given in Table 5.1; the definitions used and the ways in which they have changed are presented in Table 5.2.

At present, Water Authorities are obliged to manage surface waters, including their shores and aquatic sediments, to ensure that ecosystems retain a certain minimum quality. They are also required to study the structure and functions of these ccosystems, to define the optimum ecological quality objective under present circumstances (i.e. current hydrology and the impact of surrounding areas), and to determine the measures by which such objectives can be met. This is an important task for ecologists, who, 20 years ago, merely described problems in rather qualitative terms: they often emphasized, for instance, the decrease in species numbers or even the extinction of certain species. However important this might have been, ecologists now need to explain their meaning more precisely in terms of ecological quality objectives. Water managers and politicians now demand to know what the water quality objective is for any particular body of water, and how they can accomplish the task of improving the ecological quality so that the target is met. This task has not been easy, and has involved establishing a network of so-called 'cenotypes' (Verdonschot, 1992). Cenotypes are descriptions of surface waters possessing certain biotic (macroinvertebrate) and abiotic characteristics, and are connected by arrows, indicating changes in abiotic conditions. In theory, any given situation can be placed in the network and connected to desired situations by management measures. A further step of translating the cenotype network into an expert system is now under way.

5.2.2   *Organization*

The so-called 'national waters' (the continental part of the North Sea, large rivers and Lake IJssel) fall under two governmental institutions directly responsible to the Ministry of Transport, Public Works and Water Management. All other surface waters fall under Regional Water Authorities and Provincial Water Boards. The Water Authorities, dating from the early Middle Ages, have functioned as autonomous institutions on a cooperative basis (an early stage of democracy). Gradually, these are being merged into larger entities and have been brought under the supervision of Provinces. The national government defines the standards to be set for water quality in a wider perspective so that lower authorities can define their own standards, at least within certain limits.

5.3   Case Study: River Rhine

International rivers represent a special challenge. The River Rhine is a good example, since negotiations between riparian countries have been going on for many years. However, national interest has prevailed. The 1320 km long river flows through the most densely populated and industrialized parts of Europe and provides, among other things, drinking water for millions of people. The treatment of drinking water, especially in the downstream sections of the river, has become more difficult; this was one of the main reasons to start international cooperation in the control of water pollution. Pollution was caused not only by domestic and

Table 5.1   Laws and Acts relating to water management.

Water quality	*Water quantity*
	First Memorandum on Water Management (V and W, 1968) Mainly water quantity regulations
Water Pollution Act (V and W, 1970) A system for the licensing of wastewater emissions	

Indicative Long-term Programme Water
   1975–1979 (VROM, 1975)
Definitions of ecological functions, development
   of sewage treatment plants	

Indicative Long-term Programme Water 1980–1984 (VROM, 1981)	
Waters are ecosystems/definition of ecological quality objectives	
Objectives divided into: basic, middle and highest level	
Addition to the Water Pollution Act (V and W, 1981b)	

Directives for surface waters used for drinking water,
   bathing water, water for salmonids, carps and shell-
   fish.	

	Second Memorandum on Water Management (V and W, 1984)
	   Mainly water quantity regulations, but with the addition of an addendum on the Indicative
	      Long-term Programme (VROM, 1986).

	To Cope with Water (V and W, 1985)
	   Definition of 15 water types with ecological quality objectives for the lowest, middle and highest
	      levels

Indicative Long-term Programme Water 1985–1989 (VROM, 1986)	
The water quality of the Netherlands, further defi- nitions of ecological quality	

Ecological references for Dutch surface waters
   (CUWVO, 1988)
Classification of 16 water types, and five 'main types':
   lakes (shallow and deep), ditches, brooks, canals	

	Third Memorandum on Water Management (V and W, 1989)
	   Integrated quality and quantity of surface waters, groundwater and aquatic sediment. Chemical
	      and ecological quality objectives.
	   Attention for the surrounding environment (catchment approach).

Table 5.2 Water quality as described in successive Acts in the Netherlands.

'Basic quality' (VROM, 1975) defines the acceptable environment for aerobic biocoenosis, including larger fish species (pike, pike-perch, perch, roach and bream), and instances in which fish-eating predators do not die by toxic, non-fractionable and accumulating agents. A shortlist of standard values of chemical parameters is added.

'Basic quality' (VROM, 1981) is here defined analogous to the above description, but now has a list of 39 parameters with their standard concentrations added. The implementation of these quality objectives is a minimum demand for *all* Dutch freshwater bodies and should be realized within five years. Ecological water quality goals describe better quality; six types of freshwater ecosystem are defined.

'Basic quality' (VROM, 1986) now defines the quality of water, aquatic sediments and the shore. There should be no inconveniences (especially smell) for the surrounding area; the water looks clean. The system must have the potential for sustaining aquatic biocoenoses, including higher aquatic organisms (e.g. certain fish species), as well as terrestrial species (birds and mammals) that are consuming aquatic organisms; it should offer possibilities for human use (recreation, drinking water and irrigation).
CUWVO (1988) defines three 'ecological quality levels':
- 'Ecological quality of the highest level' is defined as: the natural situation.
- 'Ecological quality of the lowest level'; the same as basic quality (VROM, 1986) with the addition: a certain diversity of producers, consumers, decomposers. Influences from outside the system may not cause death or hamper reproduction and growth of organisms of different trophic levels. If necessary for the maintenance of populations, migration should be possible. Standing waters should have a clarity sufficient for plant growth; dominance of blue-greens is undesirable.
- 'Ecological quality of the middle level' is the level somewhere between the natural situation and the 'lowest level'; this level is to be determined by regional Water Authorities.

AMK ('General Environmental Quality'). AMK is a set of over 100 parameters (both abiotic and biotic) for which standard values have been set. These standards should be met by the year 2000.

industrial sewage, but also by oil spills, non-point agricultural discharges and salt (millions of tonnes per year) from the French potassium mines. Increasing amounts of known and unknown toxic compounds, heavy metals, and viruses have forced drinking-water companies into making massive investments. The history of this laborious battle against pollution reads like a thriller, with its themes of death, political incompetence, heroes, failures and successes.

The first international commission's goal was to protect salmon. This Dutch-German commission started its meetings in 1921. Members of the Commission observed a reduction of 50% in the number of salmon by 1935, as compared with 1921. When salmon became extinct in the region in 1950, the committee still existed (Schalekamp, 1993)! Prompted by the rapid increase in pollution of the Rhine after World War II, the governments of Switzerland, France, Luxembourg, Germany and the Netherlands established the 'International Committee for Protection of the Rhine against Pollution'. Only in 1963 was a treaty under international law signed. However, despite many conferences, the results were not impressive. In 1969, a coordinating organization of 114 drinking-water companies, the 'International working party of waterworks along the Rhine' (IAWR) was set up (Schalekamp, 1993). In 1982, a cross-border warning and alarm system was set up and since 1984 eight international main warning stations have been involved. Toxicity is shown automatically with biotests; eutrophying and toxic compounds are measured continuously. The warning and 'all clear' signs flow like a wave downstream from station to station to enable the drinking-water companies to stop their intake (Malle, 1994).

A fire at the Sandoz warehouse in 1986 (when a mixture of some 30 pesticides was spilled into the river and did what pesticides were made for: to kill) caused the death of the river biota downstream from Basel. This formed the prelude to the establishment of the Rhine Action Programme in 1987. The programme, agreed by all riparian countries and the European Community, has four objectives (International Commission of the Protection of the Rhine, 1987).

- The ecosystem of the Rhine should be improved to the extent that fish species such as the salmon may again become indigenous.
- Safe production of drinking water from the Rhine should be unequivocally guaranteed in further years.
- Sediments should be clean enough to be used on land or dumped into the sea without causing harm to the environment.
- The pollution of the Rhine should be reduced to such an extent as to allow the requirements of the North Sea Action Programme to be met.

Gradually, progress has been made. Cities and industries have established water-purification plants; the concentration of heavy metals, ammonium, DOC (Dissolved Organic Carbon) and organic halogen compounds have diminished substantially and the oxygen concentrations are good. Nevertheless, not all goals have been reached.

- Production of drinking water is not continuously possible by means of simple mechanical and 'natural' methods (e.g. sand-filtration).
- Recovery of migratory fish populations is only partial.
- Reduction in the emission of several selected toxic substances and nutrients has only partially succeeded (50% reduction in 1995 compared with 1985).
- Diffuse discharge of nutrients and pesticides is, and will continue to be, a large problem in the future (Gast, 1995).

It is widely recognized that for ecological rehabilitation of the River Rhine not only should water quality improve, but habitat rehabilitation is required as well. Floodplains, most of which have disappeared, should be re-established. Fish migration is hampered because of locks, weirs and dams, and missing fish passes (Van Dijk *et al.*, 1995). The 'Ecological Master Plan for the River Rhine' (Schulte-Wülwer-Leidig, 1995) proposes the following targets:

- Restoration of the mainstem as the backbone of the Rhine ecosystem, including its main tributaries, providing habitats for migratory fish.

• Protection, improvement and preservation of ecologically important reaches of the Rhine catchment area to increase diversity of indigenous species.

Such habitat improvements depend heavily on local planning; an overview of construction improvements is given in Van Dijk *et al.* (1995).

The approach of the Rhine Action Programme, including recent restoration activities such as the installation of fish passes and the creation of floodplains, is an example for those coping with other European rivers. The River Danube waterworks have established a comparable coordination group. There are also plans for restoring the Danube (estimated total cost about US $ 200×10^9, excluding maintenance). The European Union plans to start the improvement of the ecological quality of surface waters in 1999; for this, the annual budget is anticipated to be US $ 43×10^9 (Statzner *et al.*, in press). It is tempting to speculate whether the profits made in the past, in which river ecosystems were polluted and destroyed, have been in the same order of magnitude.

5.4   Water Quality in Europe

The European Environment Agency (EEA) in Denmark has recently published a report on the status of water systems in Europe (Kristensen and Hansen, 1994). It contains maps with data on total nitrogen, total phosphorus and organic matter (as BOD or COD) in rivers, lakes and reservoirs. The legends on the maps refer to 'European Water Quality', thus indicating that water quality can be expressed in terms of chemical parameters. There are also written descriptions of ecological water quality defined on the basis of a mixture of chemical and ecological criteria. The following definitions are used for river quality classification.

'*Good quality*'. River reaches with nutrient-poor water and low levels of organic matter. They are saturated with dissolved oxygen, have rich invertebrate fauna and form a suitable spawning ground for salmonid fish.

'*Fair quality*'. River reaches with moderate organic pollution and nutrient content, and good oxygen conditions. They are rich in flora and fauna and have a large fish population.

'*Poor quality*'. River reaches with heavy organic pollution and usually a low oxygen concentration. The local sediment is anaerobic; there is an occasional mass occurrence of organisms insensitive to oxygen depletion; the fish population is either small or absent, with periodic fish kill.

'*Very poor quality*'. River reaches with excessive organic pollution, prolonged periods of very low oxygen concentration or total deoxygenation, anaerobic sediment, severe toxic input and devoid of fish.

It is clear from these definitions that 'good quality' is restricted mainly to nutrient-poor reaches with low levels of organic matter, thus confining this part of the classification to the upper reaches of mountain rivers and ignoring the natural processes in catchments. For example, the input of organic matter in forest headwaters is the main source of energy for this type of ecosystem and, inevitably, lower reaches become richer in nutrients and organic matter by accumulation of the products of metabolism in tributaries and floodplains.

Nevertheless, some general conclusions can be drawn at a European scale.

- Organic pollution has decreased over the last 15 years, with the exception of Eastern Europe, where an increase is still observed.
- Nutrient levels are lowest in Nordic rivers and lakes. High levels of phosphorus are correlated with a high population density, and high nitrogen levels with intense agricultural activity. In most European rivers and many lakes phosphorus concentrations have decreased during the past 15 years. Although ammonium concentrations in rivers have decreased as well, they have increased in several Eastern European rivers. Nitrate concentrations are still increasing in most rivers.
- Acidification is also dealt with in the EEA report (Kristensen and Hansen, 1994), with the southern part of Norway, Sweden and Finland being the most heavily affected, together with some other parts of Europe.
- Heavy metals, organic micropollutants and radioactivity affect surface waters in different ways. The effects on aquatic organisms are sometimes well known but often uncertain. They probably form a growing threat to many aquatic ecosystems.
- River regulation, widely interpreted (construction of reservoirs, channelization, land drainage and irrigation), has an enormous impact on processes and structural aspects of rivers; it therefore influences water quality in many ways.

Strictly speaking, definitions or descriptions of water quality do not apply to physical- or hydrological-state variables. This is reflected in the statement 'Deterioration of water quality, channelization, loss of wetlands, etc., have detrimentally affected many European freshwater habitats ...' (Kristensen and Hansen, 1994; page 14). Water quality is expressed in terms of eutrophying and toxic substances in the water: low concentrations are defined as good, high concentrations as very poor. Using appropriate concentration standards for these substances is a reasonably good way of classifying the problem of eutrophication and pollution, at least as a starting point. Many EC Directives on separate aspects of water management and water quality have been launched during the past 20 years. A proposal on the ecological quality of water has been submitted recently by the Commission of the European Economic Communities (1994) (see Preface) in which terms such as 'ecological water quality' and 'sustainable development' are cited, along with the principle of 'subsidiarity'. This means that the classification of the ecological state of different water bodies in the Member States may be different, and that the present quality must be maintained or improved. Member States will define their own ecological water quality standards according to the specific circumstances in their countries, and must also undertake measures (of their own choosing and within their capabilities) to improve water quality. This is a similar approach to that followed in the Netherlands, albeit on another scale.

Belgium (at least Flanders) also has an ecological typology for its watercourses based on a classification of water types linked with a physical and geographical division (Schneiders *et al.*, 1996, this volume). Other countries have regional or catchment-based typologies (see Schneiders *et al.*, 1996 for an overview). It will certainly take some time and effort before all Member States have met the requirement of the proposed Directive and put in place ecological water quality assessment as intended by the European Union.

5.5 Conclusions

Water quality has been defined mainly by abiotic parameters as the only way to manipulate the condition of surface waters. The resulting biocoenoses are not always those that are expected or predicted. This is because natural areas have been degraded in most industrialized countries to such an extent that recovery is impossible. Although the actual situation in Eastern European countries seems to be disastrous, there are still many surface waters that exist under more or less natural conditions. These can be considered as target situations, and could function as a nucleus for recolonizing restored waters in the formerly damaged landscape.

Acknowledgements

We are very much obliged to Ruth de Wijs (National Institute of Public Health and the Environment) for her efficient linguistic help.

References

Commission of the European Economic Communities (1994). Proposal for a Council Directive on the ecological quality of water. EEC 94/C 222/6-15.

CUWVO (1988). (Co-ordination Commission for the Execution of the Water Pollution Act). *Ecological Goals for Dutch Surface Waters*. SDU, The Hague (in Dutch).

Gast, M. K. H. (1995). Vorwort des Präsidenten (Preface by the President). In: Brauch, H.-J. and Jülich, W. (Eds), *IAWR Rheinbericht '91–'93*. IAWR, Amsterdam, 1–3 (in German).

International Commission for the Protection of the Rhine against Pollution (1987). *Rhine Action Programme*. Technisches Wissenschaftliches Sekretariat, Koblenz (in German and French).

Kristensen, P. and Hansen, H. O. (1994). *European Rivers and Lakes. Assessment of their Environmental State. EEA Environmental Monographs 1.* European Environment Agency, Copenhagen.

Malle, K.-G. (1994). Accidental spills—Frequency, importance, control, countermeasures. *Water Science and Technology,* **29,** 149–163.

Murk, A. J. (1990). *Ecological Standards for Water Management*. Health Council, The Hague. No A 90/1 (in Dutch).

Schalekamp, M. (1993). *Vater Rhein: die Sonne geht auf!* (Father Rhine, the sun is rising!). Schweizerischen Vereins des Gas- und Wasserfaches (SVGW), Zürich, 116.

Schneiders, A., Wils, C., Verheyen, R. F. and de Pauw, N. (1996). Ecological water quality objectives, a useful frame of reference for ecological impact assessment. *European Water Pollution Control,* **6,** 8–16.

Schneiders, A., Wils, C. and Verheyen, R. F. (This volume). The use of ecological information in the selection of priority zones for river conservation and restoration in Flanders.

Schulte-Wülwer-Leidig, A. (1995). Ecological Master Plan for the Rhine catchment. In: Harper, D. M. and Ferguson, A. J. D. (Eds), *The Ecological Basis for River Management*. John Wiley, Chichester, 505–514.

Statzner, B., Capra, H., Higler, L. W. G. and Roux, A. L. (in press). Focusing Management Budgets on nonlinear responses of economic and ecological systems: potentials for rapid environmental improvement. *Freshwater Biology.*

Van Dijk, G. M., Marteijn, E. C. L. and Schulte-Wülwer-Leidig, A. (1995). Ecological rehabilitation of the River Rhine: plans, progress and perspectives. *Regulated Rivers: Research and Management,* **11,** 377–388.

Verdonschot, P. F. M. (1992). Typifying macrofaunal communities of larger disturbed waters in The Netherlands. *Aquatic Conservation: Marine and Freshwater Ecosystems,* **2,** 223–242.

V and W (Ministry of Transport and Public Works) (1968). *First Memorandum on Water Management.* SDU, The Hague (in Dutch).

V and W (Ministry of Transport and Public Works) (1970). *Water Pollution Act.* SDU, The Hague (in Dutch).

V and W (Ministry of Transport and Public Works) (1981a). *Water Management in The Netherlands.* Second Memorandum on Water Management. SDU, The Hague (in Dutch).

V and W. (Ministry of Transport and Public Works) (1981b). *Additions in the Water Pollution Act.* Nederlandse Staatscourant (July 31, 1981). SDU, The Hague (in Dutch).

V and W (Ministry of Transport and Public Works) (1984). *Second Memorandum on Water Management.* SDU, The Hague (in Dutch).

V and W (Ministry of Transport, Public Works and Water Management) (1985). *Memorandum: To Cope with Water: Towards an Integrated Water Management.* SDU, The Hague (in Dutch).

V and W (Ministry of Transport, Public Works and Water Management) (1989). *Third Memorandum on Water Management. Water for Now and in the Future.* SDU, The Hague (in Dutch).

VROM (Ministry of Housing, Physical Planning and Environment) (1975). *First Indicative Long-Term Programme Water 1975–1979. Combat of Pollution of the Surface Water.* SDU, The Hague (in Dutch).

VROM (Ministry of Housing, Physical Planning and Environment) (1981). *Second Indicative Long-term Programme Water 1980–1984.* SDU, The Hague (in Dutch).

VROM (Ministry of Housing, Town and Country Planning and Environment) and Ministry of Transport and Waterworks (1986). *Third Indicative Long-term Programme Water 1985–1989.* SDU, The Hague (in Dutch).

6   WATER QUALITY IN THE USA: EVOLVING PERSPECTIVES AND PUBLIC PERCEPTION

J. A. Gore

Summary

1. Historically, people in North America have viewed 'water quality' in terms of the contaminant load which restricts human use of water rather than those qualities and quantities of water required to maintain the integrity of the water body itself. Since they are perceived to be rapidly self-renewing, running waters have taken the major burden of providing high quality water for growing populations.

2. In the mid-twentieth century, setting permissible limits for substances in the drinking water supply was the role of the US Public Health Service. The first dramatic redefinition of 'water quality' occurred after 1972 and the passage of the National Environmental Policy Act (NEPA). The Clean Water Act of 1972 forbade the release of any toxic substance by 1985 and required that individual states protect pristine aquatic ecosystems, but virtually all industries have been granted variances from this requirement.

3. That surface waters must have sufficient quality to maintain intrinsic biological communities is a relatively recent consideration within the regulatory structure of most states and is open to much debate. 'Biological integrity' is only loosely defined and each agency interprets that condition as appropriate and supported by individual legislatures.

4. A more comprehensive definition of the water quality needed to maintain the integrity of aquatic ecosystems would ensure that: (a) the physical characteristics of the water body are consistent with geomorphic characteristics of the catchment, (b) chemical and physical conditions of the water are adequate to support the growth, survival and reproduction of the community historically characteristic of the stream, (c) historical hydrologic characteristics and variability are maintained, and (d) the biological communities contain native flora and fauna at relative abundances and diversities known to have been observed historically.

6.1 Introduction

With the world's population expected to double within the next few decades yet the resource base remaining essentially constant, there is little doubt that the availability of water resources will be a premier environmental issue beyond the year 2000. In the USA, where population growth is reasonably slow, and despite government reports warning of demand problems for more than 20 years (Ridker, 1972), the general population has only recently become aware of potential problems in water resource availability and the quality of the water. Historically, people in North America have viewed water quality in terms of the contaminant load which restricts human use of water rather than those qualities and quantities of water required to maintain the integrity of the water body itself. For the most part, the American public perceives good water quality to be that potable supply which comes from the tap within their residences. Where the majority of the municipal water supply is primarily derived from aquifers, resource availability and deteriorating water quality are becoming a concern. Eight of the 50 states utilize over 60% of the groundwater supply. For example, in the predominantly semi-arid state of Texas, nearly all major cities were founded near springs, or along the banks of rivers which receive most of their flow from springs or groundwater. Of some 275 springs that provided fresh water to municipalities and lotic ecosystems, more than 30% no longer flow. Those that remain have severely reduced discharges (Brune, 1981).

In some regions of the USA, water withdrawal from underlying aquifers has far exceeded recharge rates. In southern Alabama, primary aquifers have declined over 60 m in the past 10 years. In south-western Florida, where sheetflows across the great wetlands of the Everglades once continuously recharged shallow and deep aquifers, fresh water is being withdrawn at such a rate that coastal areas, especially around the city of Naples, suffer from saltwater intrusions into freshwater aquifers. The natural ability of this vast nutrient processor has been further diminished by canalization to allow for human development. The bulk of the water for agriculture, industry, and residential use is returned to these canals. Chemical water quality in this canal system has declined continuously over the past 30 years to the point that some coastal riverine systems support less than one-half of their historical community diversity (Nordlie, 1990).

Since they are perceived to be rapidly self-renewing running water ecosystems, rivers and streams have taken the major burden of replacing depleted spring flows to provide quality water for growing populations. Not without considerable expense, rivers have been impounded or diverted and treated to provide clean, potable water. The presence of these reservoirs has a direct impact on physical and chemical conditions downstream. The scientific literature is replete with data on the impact from low flows, lower sediment levels, altered nutrient levels and thermal regimes (Ward and Stanford, 1979; Petts, 1984). In semi-arid zones, where impoundment is most needed and evaporation rates are the highest, the presence of a series of riverine impoundments can lead to concentrations of metal salts so high that they approach those of brackish estuaries (Gore and Bryant, 1986).

Despite some efforts to ameliorate changes in the physical and chemical composition of release waters (Cassidy, 1989), these changes are largely irreversible during the life of the impoundment.

Historically, then, in one of the countries boasting the highest per-capita consumption of water in the world (over 375 L d^{-1}), clean, fresh water has been viewed as inexpensive and unlimited in supply. As aquifers decline, surface water quality declines, and aquatic ecosystems deteriorate, this view is changing. Public and political perception is still focused on supply issues with chemical and physical alteration a secondary concern. In south Florida, for example, public officials are commissioning studies to determine the feasibility of surface reservoirs and aquifer recharge and storage (ARS) as alternatives to maintain a dwindling supply. The extremely high costs of treatment of such waters has received little attention. Meanwhile, a number of citizen action groups and non-profit conservation groups are calling for the restoration of wetland ecosystems as the natural and efficient method to restore aquifer recharge. Supported by a plethora of research on the impacts of altered flows, altered physical and chemical conditions, as well as dramatic changes in aquatic ecosystem structure, regulatory agencies are beginning to address the concept of water quality in terms of 'ecosystem health' rather than the previous issue of potability to humans.

This chapter is a review of public, regulatory, political, and scientific views of water quality in the USA and the potential for changing these perspectives and perceptions in the twenty-first century as the conflicts with the Property Owners' Rights movement gain momentum in North America.

6.2   The Evolution of 'Water Quality' and 'Pollution'

Humans seem to have been moulded in their evolution by the water they drink. If a list were made of the average concentration of chemicals in the average river and compared with those values most commonly listed as maximum concentrations allowable by regulatory agencies, it would not be surprising to find that toxic concentrations are listed as 'high' when they naturally occur at high levels in natural waters, and are 'low' if the amounts are low in natural bodies of water. That is, the quality of water has been generally regarded to be those conditions which are not injurious or threatening to human health. However, these views have changed over the past decades. In North America, and especially within the USA the first dramatic redefinition of 'water quality' occurred after 1972 and the passage of the National Environmental Policy Act (NEPA).

Because of the observed 'flexibility' of the human body to tolerate various levels of certain elements (especially the ability of humans who reside in arid and semi-arid zones to tolerate the laxative effects of high concentrations of magnesium and sulphate), it has always been difficult to determine which levels of specific elements are acceptable in water supplies. Prior to NEPA, the role of determining permissible amounts of these elements in the public drinking water supply was determined by the US Public Health Service. The differences and the relationships between what constituted good water quality and poor water quality or 'pollution' were vague and often relegated to the legal arena. Industrial organizations like the American Petroleum Institute, the American Iron and Steel Institute, and the Manufacturing Chemists Association, convinced key legislators that industrial waste posed no threat to the public waterways, that 'streams are nature's sewers' (Gottlieb, 1988).

The US Congress' first attempt to protect the waters of the nation was the passage of the Water Pollution Control Act of 1948 which established a rather limited federal role in regulating pollution of interstate waterways. It also provided for research into the ecology of aquatic ecosystems and directed the Surgeon General of the USA, the head of the Public Health Service, to implement pollution control programmes. In 1952, a report to Congress indicated that not one single enforcement action had been taken as a result of the Act. It was not until 1956, when amendments to the Act required the states to propose a water management plan in order to obtain federal support for water treatment facilities, that standards for allowable chemical contamination were first considered. Again, the problem lay in the vague definition of 'pollution' and, therefore, 'water quality'.

To humans, water pollution was (and probably still is) the occurrence of anything 'foreign' in natural waters. Recognizing that a considerable amount of allochthonous material is critical to supporting natural aquatic communities, North American aquatic ecologists, working in the 1950s and 1960s, proposed a definition of pollution which, for all intents and purposes, remains what most aquatic ecologists believe to be a working definition today. Patrick (1953) defined pollution as 'anything which brings about a reduction in the diversity of aquatic life and eventually destroys the balance of life in a stream,' (p. 33). Ide (1954) similarly reported that 'pollution is any influence on the stream brought about by the introduction of materials to it which adversely affects the organisms living in the stream.' (p. 87). Although these definitions are quite acceptable to most aquatic ecologists, these same definitions are vague from a regulatory standpoint because they do not imply a necessary decline in usefulness to humans. The generally accepted legal definition of pollution (therefore, poor water quality) was 'the addition of something to water which changes its natural qualities so that the riparian proprietor does not get the natural water of the stream transmitted to him' (Coulson and Forbes, 1952, p. 198). Doubtless the 'riparian proprietor' was human.

The intent of regulations, enacted at the federal and state level in the decades of the 1950s and 1960s, then, was to protect water users from the effects of pollution rather than to prevent water quality changes. As an example, the state of California defined three levels of water quality: *contaminated*, when discharges of industrial or domestic wastes to water supplies create an actual hazard to public health; *polluted*, when impairment does not create an immediate public health hazard but does adversely affect the waters of the state; and a *nuisance*, when odours are created or the waterway becomes unsightly (Gorlinski, 1957). The declared water-quality level determined which member of a sub-set of state, regional, or local government entities was required to respond. In the cases of 'polluted' or 'nuisance' conditions, the regulatory agencies were allowed to balance economic benefit and the cost of ameliorating conditions, in response.

With increasing awareness of the complex nature of aquatic communities and the physical and chemical conditions which maintain their integrity, and the publication of seminal works on the biology of polluted waters (Hynes, 1960), the Water Quality Act of 1965 was passed and led to the formation of the Federal Water Pollution Control Administration (FWPCA). At that time, some definition was given to the term 'water quality'. The FWPCA (1966) proposed guidelines which included the stipulation that no water quality standard would be approved which allowed any wastes amenable to treatment to be discharged into interstate waters regardless of water quality criteria or water use proposed. Thus, *water quality standards* were those limits to unnatural alteration of water quality that were permitted or accepted as being compatible with use of those waters, while *water quality criteria* were those limits of variation or alteration of water quality, as judged by scientific data, which do not have an adverse effect on the use of the water by humans or specified organisms inhabiting the water. Despite the mention of some sort of ecosystem integrity as a component of water quality, the enactment and enforcement of the Water Quality Act of 1965 was aimed at human consumption. Indeed, Federal guidelines (FWPCA, 1966) indicate, 'If it is possible to provide for prompt improvement in water quality at the time initial standards are set, the standards should be designed to prevent any increase in pollution ...' (p. 5) and that these standards be reviewed '... to take into account changing technology of waste production and waste removal ...' (p. 10). Thus, the effective definition of 'water quality' became a sliding scale of standards to accommodate human consumptive patterns and treatment abilities. A classification system was established, then, which was based upon social, economic and technological changes within the human population.

One of the first pieces of federal legislation to recognize the value of water bodies for recreation *and* habitat for instream residents was the Wild and Scenic Rivers Act (WSRA) of 1968. This Act prevents the construction of dams, water diversions, and other sorts of development along free-flowing rivers in the USA. In effect, this legislation recognizes that the integrity of the riverine ecosystem is not only dependent upon in-stream chemical and physical conditions but upon the integrity of riparian ecosystems and hydrological conditions of the catchment. This publicly supported and initiated legislation was based on citizen groups' recognition of the value of aquatic systems beyond their physical and chemical condition. Interestingly, in a survey of public attitudes towards several Indiana rivers and streams, the attitudes which describe wild and scenic qualities (clean running, unpolluted and unfettered) corresponded proportionately to the physical, biological, and water quality parameters used to protect those same water bodies under the WSRA (Melhorn *et al.*, 1975). Over 15,000 km of river have been designated as either wild rivers, scenic rivers, or recreational rivers under the jurisdiction of the WSRA. This is one of the few pre-NEPA enactments which has continued to be re-authorized to this day. However, other than the Endangered

Species Act, few things have sparked more controversy than wild and scenic river designation, since industrial, agricultural, recreational and ecological interests all vie for the benefits of the river. With economic slow-downs of the 1980s and 1990s, the WSRA has been seen as a hindrance to progress and has come under constant attack by conservative law-makers and is traditionally one of the first Acts to be considered by a conservative-dominated Congress for denial of re-authorization.

6.3 The Legal Regulatory Interpretation since 1972

In the USA, water-quality concerns are based upon public demand for disease-free, uncontaminated water at the tap. As previously stated, prior to 1972 water-quality regulations were governed by individual states and were based upon criteria aimed at eliminating microbiological contamination. Other than the chemical content of drinking water, little thought was given to the dynamic physical and chemical interactions within aquatic ecosystems and the mere presence of water in wetlands, lakes, ponds, and rivers was assumed to be sufficient to support those ecosystems. Since 1972, and until recent times, regulatory focus has been upon end-of-pipe controls of identifiable contaminants from municipal and industrial outfalls. The Federal Water Pollution Control Act of 1972 (passed when Congress overrode President Nixon's veto) was renamed the Clean Water Act (CWA) (33 USC 466 *et seq.*), when renewed in 1977. Combined with the Water Quality Act of 1987, the CWA (subject to re-authorization by Congress in 1996, having not been renewed in 1994) serves to control pollution of surface waters in the US. The primary goal of the CWA was to make all US surface waters safe for fishing and swimming by 1983 and to restore and maintain the chemical, physical, and biological integrity of the nation's waters. Progress has been made, but by 1990 37% of rivers and streams in the USA still did not meet fishing and swimming standards. This figure could be considerably higher since less than 40% of all river length has been assessed (Patrick, 1992).

The bane of the developer is the heart of the CWA—Section 404—which establishes national effluent standards and limits the amounts of conventional and toxic substances to be discharged into surface waters. '404-Permits', issued by the US Army Corps of Engineers, allow the discharger to release a specified amount of these materials into the water. So poorly enforced is this discharge permit in some states, that at least 20% of the nation's industries find it cheaper to pay repeated fines than to go to the expense of waste control technology (Gleick, 1993). The original CWA of 1972 forbade the release of any toxic substance by 1985, but virtually all industries have been granted variances from this requirement and current Congressional efforts are focused upon limitation of the CWA.

The CWA requires that individual states protect existing pristine aquatic ecosystems. States are allowed to create more restrictive standards but must meet federal standards (US Environmental Protection Agency, 1994). The Water Quality Act required all states to submit a list of standards by which they would classify all water bodies in their states. With decreasing budgets and facing the obligation

Table 6.1 A typical stream classification. Composite based upon several state standards but within Water Quality Act recommendations.

Stream class	Typical use	Dissolved Oxygen (mg L^{-1})	Coliforms (counts/100 mL)
A	Potable water	>5	<20
B	Primary contact (swimming, fishing)	>4	<500
C	Secondary contact (boating, fish and wildlife propagation)	>4	<5000
D	Agriculture/industrial	>3	No standard

to clean up and restore contaminated surface waters, most states have had difficulty implementing and meeting the federal standards. Only one state, Michigan, has taken on primacy of enforcing 404 requirements (Steiner *et al.*, 1994). Most states have adopted a classification based upon ambient water quality, the water bodies being classified by their maximum beneficial use to humans or with passing recognition of the quality of the water to sustain ecological integrity (Tables 6.1 and 6.2). In some cases, the suggestion of ecological stability within the classification is based upon the ability of the system to sustain a recreational fishery (Table 6.1) or a commercial fishery (Table 6.2). This allowed some states to classify some low-quality waterways as virgin trout streams (Vesiland and Pierce, 1983). With this sort of classification it is also not uncommon to justify the construction and operation of irrigation storage reservoirs and hydropower dams based upon the 'benefit' of supporting a trout fishery in the tailwater of a formerly warm-water river because of a hypolimnetic release (Petts, 1984). In fact, many of these trout fisheries are not reproducing but must be replenished from hatcheries at regular

Table 6.2 Water classification system for the State of Florida. As required by the Water Quality Act.

Stream class	Typical use	Dissolved Oxygen (mgL^{-1}) EPA	Florida	Coliforms (counts/100 mL) EPA	Florida	Nitrate (mgL^{-1}) EPA	Florida
I	Potable water	≥5.0	≥5.0	0	≤200	≤10.0	≤10.0
II	Shellfish propagation		≥5.0		≤70		
III—Fresh	Balanced ecosystem		≥5.0		≤200		
III—Marine	Balanced ecosystem		≥4.0		≤200		
IV	Agriculture		≥3.0				
V	Industrial		≥0.3				

intervals ('put-and-take' fisheries) since that same thermal regime will not support the secondary production of aquatic invertebrates to sustain the diet of the trout population (Gore, 1977; Stanford and Ward, 1979).

The Act also requires states to develop and implement plans to control diffuse pollution, largely neglected until recent years, and established a federal programme to protect wetlands (Section 401). This has been only partially successful because, as of 1995, the ability to delineate and define wetlands remains a critical problem.

Section 101 of the CWA reads, 'The objective of this Act is to restore and maintain the chemical, physical, and biological integrity of the Nation's waters'. That surface waters must have sufficient quality to maintain intrinsic biological communities is a relatively recent consideration within the legal and regulatory structure of most states and is open to much debate. 'Biological integrity' is only loosely defined and each state agency interprets that condition as appropriate and supported by individual legislatures. The basic problem has been the ability to measure and define biological integrity in aquatic ecosystems. The ability of aquatic ecosystems, especially rivers and streams, to recover from various levels of disturbance has yet to be fully defined (Gore *et al.*, 1990). As a result, providing a definable measure of integrity and sustained 'ecosystem health' is a subjective decision by regulatory agencies. Thus, state statutes often indicate that 'the water of the state shall be of sufficient quality to support aquatic species without detrimental changes in the resident biological community'. This linkage of water quality to biological and landscape processes is a recent concept and is based upon new scientific perspectives on what conditions maintain the integrity of aquatic ecosystems.

6.4   Ecosystem Research and Regulatory Change

Although limnology has a long-standing history of research into the structure and function of lake and pond ecosystems, the ecology of rivers and streams, and especially wetlands, received little attention until the past few decades. Inspired by the work of Hynes (1970), lotic ecologists in the USA have attempted to define water quality as the physical and chemical condition *along with* those ecosystem components and dynamics which promote lotic ecosystem integrity; that is, those conditions which promote ecosystem health. The research on ecosystem structural templates and functional dynamics is reflected in a ten-fold increase in scientific journals devoted to the ecology of running waters and wetlands, as well as numerous texts, continually updating the 'state-of-the-art' (see Minshall, 1988, for a review). Special symposia have been sponsored by the National Science Foundation to assess research needs in basic science (Stanford and Covich, 1988) and by the Environmental Protection Agency (EPA) to propose research needs for determining the ability of streams to recover from disturbance (Yount and Niemi, 1990). These symposia have influenced both regulatory agencies and the content of contemporary texts (Allan, 1994; Patrick, 1994, 1995) which reflect the more holistic approach to assessing water 'quality' and ecosystem health, as well as clarifying research directions in the restoration of aquatic ecosystems (National Research Council, 1992).

The history of incorporating some index of biological integrity into assessing water quality in North America can be traced to Patrick (1949) who proposed numbers and kinds of taxa to determine river and stream ecosystem health. However, the passage of the CWA and the desire to produce a defensible, yet rapid, bioassessment technique resulted in numerous proposals to monitor and define water quality in terms of biotic integrity (Cairns and Pratt, 1993). Current evaluation techniques are based primarily on the presence or absence of macroinvertebrate species combined with a numerical analysis of the tolerance of those species to certain forms of pollution, primarily organic loading. These techniques range from biotic indices (specific, generic, or familial levels with tolerance values assigned to each taxon) to various indices of community diversity (ranging from numerical calculations of richness and/or equitability to various ratios of intolerant Ephemeroptera, Plecoptera, and Trichoptera (EPTs) to less tolerant orders and percent gains or losses of critical taxa) (Resh and Jackson, 1993, review these techniques). Because of the ease of calculation, and despite criticism for inability to detect changes from communities dominated by clean water forms to those dominated by pollution-tolerant forms, a simple index of community diversity (most commonly, Shannon's diversity) has become the regulatory standard in most states as an additional criterion of water quality. Although some states (Wisconsin, for example), have adopted a diversity index combined with weighted pollution-tolerance values (Hilsenhoff, 1982, 1988), the majority of states have adopted a range of Shannon diversity values to classify existing surface water conditions. For example, the state of Florida statute states that the index for benthic macroinvertebrates cannot be reduced to less than 75% of background levels as measured by three samples from a Surber-type ($0.1\,m^2$) sampler or three artificial substrates (Hester-Dendy type) incubated for three weeks, or, in the case of standing waters, by three Ponar grabs. Although a Florida index (Ross and Jones, 1979) similar to that of Wisconsin is available, the State also accepts measurement of Shannon diversity. The Index of Biological Integrity (IBI) (Karr *et al.*, 1986) is based upon abundance and condition of fish communities in selected running waters but is not generally applicable to lentic or wetland situations. IBI combined with several metrics for macroinvertebrate community analysis (primarily diversity measures combined with relative abundances of functional feeding groups (Vannote *et al.*, 1989)) constitutes the EPA Rapid Bioassessment Procedure (RBP) (Plafkin *et al.*, 1989) and is the current outgrowth of evaluating biological integrity as a component of water quality. RBP is currently being evaluated by most state departments of environmental protection as the technique to replace simple evaluation by change in community diversity.

As research into the role of landscape processes has gained greater attention (Hunsaker and Levine, 1995), evaluation of *in situ* conditions may not prove adequate for a proper assessment of ecosystem health or water quality. That is, current monitoring and evaluation techniques still rely upon a 'snapshot' of physical, chemical, and biological condition at the instant of sampling. Although it can be argued that introducing elements of community composition indicates a *response* of target species to alteration in ecosystem condition, it is difficult to support the notion that changes in population dynamics, energetics, nutrient flow, and productivity are also being measured. Yet it is the predictability of these ecosystem conditions which promotes continued integrity (Resh *et al.*, 1988). The integrity of aquatic ecosystems is governed by a range of factors measured at many different levels of resolution (Minshall, 1988). At the catchment level, vegetation, land-use patterns, drainage density, geological history, and hydrography are important controlling factors (Naiman *et al.*, 1988). At a river or stream level, factors such as width, gradient, water chemistry, variation in discharge, temperature, and particulate organic matter have been shown to influence ecosystem stability (Meyer *et al.*, 1988). Finally, within a reach, individual habitat patches and their biotic structure are governed by incident light, temperature, current velocity, substrate composition and permeability, as well as the redox potential (Power *et al.*, 1988; Statzner *et al.*, 1988).

In addition to the landscape-influenced phenomena which govern the integrity of aquatic ecosystems, a recent concern has been the impact of introduced species on that stability. For example, introduced fish species have been shown to alter ecosystem structure and function (Maitland, 1995). Introduced exotic vegetation can also alter community structure, water quality and biological integrity. The recently introduced Australian cajeput (*Melaleuca quinquenervia*) readily invades the ecotone between flatwoods and cypress swamps in south Florida. Being fire-tolerant and flood-tolerant, *Melaleuca* stands have spread and resulted in altered wetland hydroperoid and changes in the organic component of wetland soils, thus changing the ability of these wetlands to process materials transported in sheetflow (Myers and Ewel, 1990). The introduction of water hyacinth (*Eichhornia crassipes*) has resulted in accelerated water losses and changes in energetics in rivers and streams in the southern USA (Gangstad and Ash, 1987).

Finally, it has become apparent that the simple existence of water within a stream channel is not sufficient to support the biota of the lotic ecosystem. Both fish and macroinvertebrates have been shown to have definable tolerances to hydraulic conditions (Statzner *et al.*, 1988; Heede and Rinne, 1990). Thus, these instream flow conditions must also be maintained in order to ensure biological integrity. Currently maintained by the US Fish and Wildlife Service, the Instream Flow Incremental Methodology (IFIM) has been developed to establish flow reservations to preserve lotic ecosystems. IFIM is a series of concepts, techniques and computer programs to combine channel morphology, characteristics of flow and biological preferences of target organisms to predict gains or losses in physical habitat under new or modified flow regimes (Bovee, 1982). IFIM is one of the primary negotiating tools in disputes over flows needed to maintain ecological integrity (Stalnaker, 1993). IFIM is based on the assumption that lotic biota have their distribution and certain phases of their life cycles controlled by the hydraulic conditions within the water column. The essence of IFIM is the computer simulation of the physical habitat, PHABSIM, which predicts changes in velocity, depth and channel resistance in each habitat element surveyed. These conditions are compared with the habitat preferences of target species, guilds or communities. The amount of usable habitat area (or volume) is predicted for each discharge of concern. Bovee (1982, 1986) has provided details of the IFIM procedures. Reviews of this technique and appropriate application have been provided by Gore and Nestler (1988) and Nestler *et al.* (1989). Traditionally, this technique has been used to predict minimum flow requirements to maintain biota in cases where reservoir manipulation or irrigation diversion and abstraction are potential disturbances. Although this technique is almost always required by Federal regulators for permitting structures which alter the hygrograph of the river, the individual states have not incorporated instream flow requirements into water quality standards, although several states are currently considering such action. Evaluation of wetlands in relation to hydrological conditions, especially links between hydroperiod and water quality, are only now being investigated and more research must be supported before similar flow/hydroperiod standards can be produced for wetland delineation and regulation (Steiner *et al.*, 1994).

It appears that the next regulatory step will be the incorporation of these landscape, catchment, and reach-length phenomena into a more comprehensive definition of aquatic ecosystem health and, therefore, water quality. These processes must be observed (and adequate measurement techniques developed) in order to ensure that the integrity of the aquatic ecosystem is being maintained:

(a) The physical characteristics of the water body are consistent with geomorphic characteristics of the catchment.
(b) Chemical and physical conditions of the water are adequate to support the growth, survival and reproduction of the community that is historically characteristic of the stream.
(c) Historical hydrologic characteristics and variability are maintained.
(d) The biological communities contain native flora and fauna at relative abundances and diversities known to have been historically observed.

The State of Texas is currently considering proposing such standards (Doyle Mosier, Lower Colorado River Authority: personal communication).

6.5 New Definitions and Private Property Rights

Superimposed upon a desire to improve the definition of conditions which are an integral part of water quality and to refine currently existing statutes, is the growing public sentiment that environmental regulations of any sort constitute an illegal 'taking' of private property for public use. This 'taking' is reflected most commonly when wetland ecosystems are being evaluated but can create problems for water quality regulation in other situations as well.

The US Army Corps of Engineers, under their Section 404 authority, have ultimate control over the delineation and protection of sensitive wetlands in the

USA. Jurisdictional wetlands may not be developed or, if they are permitted for development, must be mitigated and/or compensated for by a purchase or preservation of comparable areas of wetlands on a 2:1 to 3:1 trade of protected lands to developed lands. More than 50% of the wetlands in the USA have been lost to development since the 1780s (Dahl, 1990). Of the remaining wetlands, some 80% of those are privately owned (*Environmental Reporter*, 1990); hence, the concern over wetland protection. Private property owners argue that the inability to develop their own property due to wetland protection ordinances (or any others) constitutes a 'taking', while legal authorities argue that wetland protection under the CWA is a proper use of the police powers of government (Rapaport, 1986). In most cases, states make every opportunity to create fee-simple programmes (cash purchase without restriction on easements, tax-incentives, or transfer of ownership) to purchase those lands from the property owner. Florida's Conservation and Recreation Land (CARL) programme, funded by state document taxes, has been successful in purchasing properties from willing sellers to create an extensive system of preservation areas (Mann, 1995). Planned purchases of more than 200,000 ha of land in south-west Florida will allow the restoration of sheetflows in extensively canalized regions and will promote better water quality and groundwater recharge.

Regardless of such programmes, over the past decade private property rights groups have pressured both the US Congress and individual legislatures to create new laws which protect private property owners' rights to develop their land or, at the least, to compensate private property owners for loss in value and/or income if the property is declared to be jurisdictional. Although such pressure has not yet yielded US Congressional action, some states have passed, or are considering passage of, laws to protect private property owners' rights against takings by the enforcement of environmental regulations.

Florida's Hayes (Private Property Rights) Act of 1995 has established mandatory compensation to land owners if it can be demonstrated that an actual or perceived loss of income has been incurred through enforcement of environmental regulations which restrict the use of that person's property. Although this Act is untested in the legal system and is enforceable only for property rights disputes which occur after the date of enactment, the Hayes Act has had some unexpected impacts on other programmes including one which is aimed at protecting water quality. The Outstanding Florida Water (OWF) programme, administered by the Florida Department of Environmental Protection, has the goal of protecting water quality by protecting aquatic ecosystems (rivers, lakes, wetlands and sloughs) which have been determined to have outstanding recreational *or* ecological value. Aquatic ecosystems are nominated by public or private entities (conservation organizations, state agencies, clubs, and so on) to the state. These systems are evaluated for their ecological and recreational value and, if designated as OFWs by the State Environment Regulatory Commission, water quality (including hydrological conditions) cannot fall below those levels measured at the time of the ecological inventory. The state does not attempt to purchase the lands and OFW designation does not prevent development. However, discharge permits and development activity are more closely monitored for the 'no-net-loss' provision. Although it has never been demonstrated, private property rights groups argue that OFW designation creates a condition in which property values decline, since developers are reluctant to bear possible added expenses to maintain water quality, and, thus, under the new Act, OFW designation should also be considered a taking. The passage of this law has resulted in the Florida Department of Environmental Protection reconsidering any or all preservation and conservation programmes and to limit, further, their enforcement of existing water quality standards and regulations. With continued Congressional attempts to weaken the CWA, the experience of Florida in the first year of operation of a private property rights Act may be a model for the coming decade in the rest of the USA.

6.6   Science and Citizen Coalitions

With declining budgets, yet increased pressure by Congress for individual states to take over responsibility of environmental monitoring and management, many non-government conservation groups have begun the promotion and organization of citizen water quality monitoring groups. In fact, it was an environmental organization which first expressed any kind of interest in the quality of America's waters. In a report published and circulated in the late 1920s, the Izaak Walton League noted that 85% of the nation's waterways were polluted and that only 30% of the municipalities treated their wastes (Switzer, 1994).

The first national programme to have citizens monitor water quality was implemented by the Izaak Walton League of America in 1974 (Firehock and West, 1995). The Save Our Streams (SOS) programme allowed citizen groups to adopt a catchment or stream and, through training provided by the League, to monitor water quality through simple field-grade chemical tests. With the advent of the Rapid Bioassessment Procedure, the SOS programme incorporated training in the identification of benthic macroinvertebrates as part of its monitoring work. Initially such programmes were not well received by state regulatory agencies but, with continued decline in budgets and the need to expand monitoring programmes to determine the extent of diffuse sources of pollution (under Section 319 of the CWA), states are recognizing the value of work with the public and gaining support for the regulatory framework which governs water quality.

Volunteer monitoring has the effect of transferring ownership of water quality problems to the citizens most directly affected by the disturbance. Although the data are still used by regulatory agencies on a limited basis, many state agencies are establishing programmes, as co-sponsors of SOS, to enhance training opportunities and to investigate better use of volunteer monitoring data (Penrose and Call, 1995). States have used these data to identify new point sources of pollution, to establish long-term monitoring networks while using their own technical expertise to identify and respond to 'hot spots', and in the monitoring of restoration activities and the placement of best management practices (Thompson and Green,

1994). Where SOS programmes have not evolved, other conservation organizations have created similar programmes, often in concert with local regulatory agencies. In Collier County, Florida, The Conservancy, with support and sponsorship by county and City of Naples agencies, is providing training and low-cost laboratory analysis of water samples from rivers, bays and estuaries collected by citizen action groups. These data are used by City and County staff to supplement monitoring programmes which have been severely curtailed by budgetary cuts.

Scientific societies are also beginning to take an active role in supporting the activities of citizen conservation organizations, regulatory agencies and private consulting groups. For example, the North American Benthological Society (NABS), the single largest association of lotic ecologists, has established a Technical Information Committee which provides annual workshops to regulatory agencies and consulting groups on current theory and techniques in water quality assessment, and other environmental issues related to more effective protection and evaluation of aquatic ecosystems. The NABS Conservation and Environmental Issues Committee provides a volunteer corps of qualified professional and academic aquatic ecologists to citizens groups and state agencies when expertise on issues related to aquatic ecosystems is required.

There continues to be a great need to bring together scientists, resource managers, and the public in a forum to address common needs in water issues. This establishes a strong coalition at a regional and national level and, with the development of a monitoring network and good predictive tools, the ability to predict and anticipate needed changes in water resource management, as well as creating flexible programmes which can readily respond to new resource conflicts and disturbances. The first steps in creating such a coalition have been taken in the establishment of The Freshwater Imperative (FWI) (Naiman *et al.*, 1995). Through workshops sponsored by the Environmental Protection Agency (EPA), the National Aeronautics and Space Administration (NASA), the National Oceanic and Atmospheric Administration (NOAA), the National Science Foundation (NSF), and the Tennessee Valley Authority (TVA), the FWI has a goal of obtaining 'a predictive understanding of freshwater ecosystems and resources that can be used to improve detection, assessment, and forecasting of environmental effects and to develop management and mitigation alternatives for scenarios of potential environmental change' (Naiman *et al.*, 1995, p. xiii). With an understanding that freshwater ecosystems are the central component of regional and global sustainability and that cooperation between the public, research entities, and regulatory agencies is necessary to promote and maintain freshwater quality, the FWI workshops have identified research priorities which must be addressed in a joint effort. These are:

(a) Ecological restoration and rehabilitation.
(b) Maintenance of biodiversity.
(c) Addressing modified flow patterns.
(d) Ecosystem goods and services (that is, the commercial (fisheries) and ecological (waterfowl, riparian growth, etc.) productivity).

(e) Predictive rather than reactive management.

(f) Solving future problems (global warming, etc.).

These research needs are linked to and supportive of regulatory policy which must evaluate best management practices, apply ecological engineering techniques, and maintain and evaluate monitoring programmes. Implementation of the FWI is estimated to cost $200 million per year, less than 1% of the annual cost of procurement, regulation, and remedial protection of waters in the USA. As many state agencies move towards an ecosystem management approach to their regulatory activity, the objectives and goals of the FWI programme should be reviewed and integrated into catchment-level management of water resources.

References

Allan, J. D. (1994). *Stream Ecology.* Chapman and Hall, London.

Bovee, K. D. (1982). A guide to stream habitat analysis using the instream flow incremental methodology. *Instream Flow Information Paper No. 12,* US Fish and Wildlife Service, FWS/OBS-82/26.

Bovee, K. D. (1986). Development and evaluation of habitat suitability criteria for use in the instream flow incremental methodology. *Instream Flow Information Paper No. 21,* US Fish and Wildlife Service, Biological Report 86(7).

Brune, G. (1981). *Springs of Texas.* Vol. 1. Branch-Smith, Fort Worth, Texas.

Cairns, J. and Pratt J. R. (1993). A history of biological monitoring using benthic macroinvertebrates. In: Rosenberg, D. M. and Resh, V. H. (Eds), *Freshwater Biomonitoring and Benthic Macroinvertebrates.* Chapman and Hall, London, 10–27.

Cassidy, R. A. (1989). Water temperature, dissolved oxygen, and turbidity control in reservoir releases. In: Gore, J. A. and Petts, G. E. (Eds), *Alternatives in Regulated River Management,* CRC Press, Boca Raton, Florida, 27–62.

Coulson, H. J. W. and Forbes, U. A. (1952). *The Law of Waters, Sea, Tidal, and Inland, and of Land Drainage.* 6th Edition (Edited by S. R. Hobday), Sweet and Maxwell, London.

Dahl, T. E. (1990). *Wetlands Losses in the United States 1780s to 1980s.* US Fish and Wildlife Service, Washington, DC.

Environmental Reporter (1990). Federal wetland conservation policy may collide with constitutional rights. **21,** 377–378.

Firehock, K. and West, J. (1995). A brief history of volunteer biological water monitoring using macroinvertebrates. *Journal of the North American Benthological Society,* **14,** 197–202.

FWPCA (1966). *Guidelines for Establishing Water Quality Standards for Interstate Waters.* US Department of the Interior, Washington, DC.

Gangstad, E. O. and Ash, C. G. (1987). Environmental conditions for water resource projects. In: Gangstad, E. O. and Stanley, R. A. (Eds), *Environmental Management of Water Projects.* CRC Press, Boca Raton, Florida, 3–25.

Gleick, P. H. (1993). *Water in Crisis: A Guide to the World's Freshwater Resources.* Pacific Institute for Studies in Development, Environment and Security, Berkeley, California.

Gore, J. A. (1977). Reservoir manipulations and benthic macroinvertebrates in a prairie river. *Hydrobiologia,* **55,** 113–123.

Gore, J. A. and Bryant, R. M. (1986). Changes in fish and benthic macroinvertebrate assemblages along the impounded Arkansas River. *Journal of Freshwater Ecology,* **3,** 333–345.

Gore, J. A., Kelly, J. R. and Yount, J. D. (1990). Application of ecological theory to determining recovery potential of disturbed lotic ecosystems: research needs and priorities. *Environmental Management,* **14,** 755–762.

Gore, J. A. and Nestler, J. M. (1988). Instream flow studies in perspective. *Regulated Rivers: Research and Management,* **2,** 93–101.

Gorlinski, J. S. (1957). Legal basis for water pollution control in California. In: *Waste Treatment and Disposal Aspects to Development of California's Pulp and Paper Resources*, California State Water Pollution Control Board, Sacramento, 61–63.

Gottlieb, R. (1988). *A Life of Its Own: The Politics and Power of Water*. Harcourt, Brace, Jovanovich Publ., New York.

Heede, B. H. and Rinne, J. N. (1990). Hydrodynamic and fluvial geomorphological processes: implications for fisheries management and research. *North American Journal of Fisheries Management,* **10,** 249–268.

Hilsenhoff, W. L. (1982). *Using a Biotic Index to Evaluate Water Quality in Streams*. Technical Bulletin No. 100, Wisconsin Dept. of Natural Resources, Madison, Winsconsin.

Hilsenhoff, W. L. (1988). Seasonal correction factors for the Biotic Index. *Great Lakes Entomologist,* **21,** 9–13.

Hunsaker, C. T. and Levine, D. A. (1995). Hierarchical approaches to the study of water quality in rivers. *BioScience,* **45,** 193–203.

Hynes, H. B. N. (1960). *The Biology of Polluted Waters*. Liverpool University Press, Liverpool.

Hynes, H. B. N. (1970). *The Ecology of Running Waters*. University of Toronto Press, Toronto.

Ide, F. P. (1954). Pollution in relation to stream life. In: *First Ontario Industrial Waste Conference*. Pollution Control Board of Ontario, Toronto, 86–108.

Karr, J. R., Fausch, K. D., Angermeier, P. L., Yant, P. R. and Schlosser, I. J. (1986). *Assessing Biological Integrity in Running Waters. A Method and its Rationale*. Special Publication No. 5, Illinois Natural History Survey, Champaign, Illinois.

Maitland, P. S. (1995). The conservation of freshwater fish: past and present experience. *Biological Conservation,* **72,** 259–270.

Mann, C. C. (1995). Filling in Florida's gaps: species protection done right? *Science,* **269,** 318–320.

Melhorn, W. N., Keller, E. A. and McBane, R. A. (1975). *Landscape Aesthetics Numerically Defined (Land System): Application to Fluvial Environments*. Water Resources Research Center, Technical Report No. 37, Purdue University, West Lafayette, Indiana.

Meyer, J. L., McDowell, W. H., Bott, T. L., Elwood, J. W., Ishizaki, C., Melack, J. M., Peckarsky, B. L., Peterson, B. J. and Rublee, P. A. (1988). Elemental dynamics in streams. *Journal of the North American Benthological Society,* **7,** 410–432.

Myers, R. L. and Ewel, J. J. (1990). Problems, prospects, and strategies for conservation. In: Myers, R. L. and Ewel, J. J. (Eds), *Ecosystems of Florida*. University of Central Florida Press, Orlando, Florida, 619–632.

Minshall, G. W. (1988). Stream ecosystem theory: a global perspective. *Journal of the North American Benthological Society,* **7,** 263–288.

Naiman, R. J., Décamps, H., Pastor, J. and Johnston, C. A. (1988). The potential importance of boundaries to fluvial ecosystems. *Journal of the North American Benthological Society,* **7,** 289–306.

Naiman, R. J., Magnuson, J. J., McKnight, D. M. and Stanford, J. A. (1995). *The Freshwater Imperative. A Research Agenda*. Island Press, Washington, DC.

National Research Council (1992). *Restoration of Aquatic Ecosystems*. National Academy Press, Washington D.C.

Nestler, J. M., Milhous, R. T. and Layzer, J. B. (1989). Instream habitat modelling techniques. In: Gore, J. A. and Petts, G. E. (Eds), *Alternatives in Regulated River Management*. CRC Press, Boca Raton, Florida, 295–315.

Nordlie, F. G. (1990). Rivers and springs. In: Myers, R. L. and Ewel, J. J. (Eds), *Ecosystems of Florida*. University of Central Florida Press, Orlando, Florida, 395–425.

Patrick, R. E. (1949). A proposed biological measure of stream conditions, based on a survey of the Conestoga Basin, Lancaster County, Pennsylvania. *Proceedings of the Academy of National Sciences of Philadelphia,* **101,** 277–341.

Patrick, R. E. (1953). Biological phases of stream pollution. *Proceedings of the Pennsylvania Academy of Sciences,* **27,** 33–36.

Patrick, R. E. (1992). *Surface Water Quality: Have the Laws Been Successful?* Princeton University Press, Princeton, New Jersey.

Patrick, R. E. (1994). *Rivers of the United States. Vol. I—Estuaries*. John Wiley, New York.

Patrick, R. E. (1995). *Rivers of the United States. Vol. II—Chemical and Physical Characteristics*. John Wiley, New York.

Penrose, D. and Call, S. M. (1995). Volunteer monitoring of benthic macroinvertebrates: regulatory biologists' perspectives. *Journal of the North American Benthological Society,* **14,** 203–209.

Petts, G. E. (1984). *Impounded Rivers.* John Wiley, Chichester.

Plafkin, J. L., Barbour, M. T., Porter, K. D., Gross, S. K. and Hughes, R. M. (1989). *Rapid Bioassessment Protocols for Use in Streams and Rivers: Benthic Macroinvertebrates and Fish.* EPA 444/4-89-001. US Environmental Protection Agency, Washington, DC.

Power, M. E., Stout, R. J., Cushing, C. E., Harper, P. P., Hauer, F. R., Matthews, W. J., Moyle, P. B., Statzner, B. and Wais de Badgen, I. R. (1988). Biotic and abiotic controls in river stream communities. *Journal of the North American Benthological Society,* **7,** 456–479.

Rapaport, S. (1986). The taking of wetlands under Section 404 of the Clean Water Act. *Environmental Law,* **17,** 111–124.

Resh, V. H., Brown, A. V., Covich, A. P., Gurtz, M. E., Li, H. W., Minshall, G. W., Reice, S. R., Sheldon, A. L., Wallace, J. B. and Wissmar, R. C. (1988). The role of disturbance in stream ecology. *Journal of the North American Benthological Society,* **7,** 433–455.

Resh, V. H. and Jackson, J. K. (1993). Rapid bioassessment approaches to biomonitoring using benthic macroinvertebrates. In: Rosenberg, D. M. and Resh, V. H. (Eds), *Freshwater Biomonitoring and Benthic Macroinvertebrates.* Chapman and Hall, London, 195–233.

Ridker, R. G. (1972). Future water needs and supplies. Vol 3. In: Ridker, R. (Ed.) *Commission on Population Growth and the American Future.* Government Printing Office, Washington, DC.

Ross, L. T. and Jones, D. A. (Eds) (1979). *Biological Aspects of Water Quality in Florida.* Technical Series Vol. 4, No. 3. Department of Environmental Regulation, State of Florida, Tallahassee, Florida.

Stanford, J. A. and Covich, A. P. (1988). Community structure and function in temperate and tropical streams. Preface. *Journal of the North American Benthological Society,* **7,** 261–262.

Stanford, J. A. and Ward, J. V. (1979). Stream regulation in North America. In: Ward, J. V. and Stanford, J. A. (Eds), *The Ecology of Regulated Streams.* Plenum Press, New York, 215–236.

Stalnaker, C. B. (1993). Fish habitat models in environmental assessments. In: Hildebrand, S. G. and Cannon, J. B. (Eds), *Environmental Analysis: The NEPA-Experience.* CRC Press, Boca Raton, Florida, 150–162.

Statzner, B., Gore, J. A. and Resh, V. H. (1988). Hydraulic stream ecology: observed patterns and potential applications. *Journal of the North American Benthological Society,* **7,** 307–360.

Steiner, F., Pieart, S., Cook, E., Rich, J. and Oltman, V. (1994). State wetlands and riparian area protection programs. *Environmental Management,* **18,** 183–201.

Switzer, J. V. (1994). *Environmental Politics: Domestic and Global Dimensions.* St. Martin's Press, New York.

Thompson, J. N. and Green, D. L. (1994). *Riparian Restoration and Streamside Erosion Control Handbook.* Tennessee Department of Environment and Conservation, Nashville, Tennessee.

US Environmental Protection Agency (1994). *National Primary Drinking Water Standards.* EPA 810-F-94-001. US EPA, Office of Water, Washington, DC.

Vannote, R. L., Minshall, G. W., Cummins, K. W., Sedell, J. R. and Cushing C. E. (1980). The river continuum concept. *Canadian Journal of Fisheries and Aquatic Sciences* **37,** 130–137.

Vesiland, P. A. and Pierce, J. J. (1983). *Environmental Pollution and Control.* 2nd Edit. Butterworths, Boston.

Ward, J. V. and Stanford, J. A. (Eds) (1979). *The Ecology of Regulated Streams.* Plenum Press, New York.

Yount, J. D. and Niemi, G. J. (1990). Recovery of lotic communities and ecosystems following disturbance: theory and application. Preface. *Environmental Management,* **14,** 515–516.

PART TWO
CHEMICAL AND BIOLOGICAL METHODS FOR ASSESSING WATER QUALITY

7 THE CONTRIBUTION OF BIOLOGICAL AND CHEMICAL TECHNIQUES TO THE ASSESSMENT OF WATER QUALITY

J. M. Hellawell

Summary

1. Water quality can only be defined in terms of intended use; for example, potable supply, industrial cooling, effluent disposal, fisheries, recreation, wildlife and nature conservation. Generally, the aim is to set critical values for selected parameters or determinands which are considered to indicate a particular quality state.

2. Chemical and biological methods of analysis are complementary rather than competitive: each approach has strengths and weaknesses. Chemical methods tend to be mainly '*in vitro*' and enjoy advantages in terms of reliability, accuracy, precision and reproducibility. Results are obviously restricted to those determinands which are measured and their relevance depends on the extent to which their significance is understood in relation to the intended use of the water. Biological methods are largely '*in vivo*' in approach. Living systems from the sub-cellular, through organisms, to whole ecosystems may be utilized. At each level of increasing complexity the results tend to be more directly relevant to wider environmental protection and regulation. However, the behaviour of higher orders of biological organization in relation to environmental changes tends to be complex and is not readily measured and analysed.

3. Temporal variations in water quality effect an integrated response from biological systems and studying these may be a more effective means of assessing such variations than continuous monitoring of a necessarily restricted range of abiotic parameters.

4. The quest for the ideal single measure of biological water quality, often in the form of an 'index', has largely been driven by comparing the behaviour of each measure in relation to other parameters, such as chemical determinands, or to subjective preconceptions of the 'true' water quality based on detailed knowledge of a particular site. By iterative modification of indices, a solution which provides a good match with the perceived quality is obtained. The index can then be utilized elsewhere to assess the status of less well-known waters.

7.1 Introduction

'Quality' is a widely used word but a difficult concept, at least in absolute terms, to elucidate. It has been defined as 'the degree of excellence, the relative nature or kind or character; the class or grade of a thing as determined by this; general excellence'. There would appear to be no satisfactory, absolute measure of water quality other than the extent to which a sample deviates from pure 'dihydrogen oxide'. Even if, however, one had an accurate analysis of all the additional substances which were present, this would not necessarily be a helpful expression of the quality of that water.

In the field of quality management, 'quality' has a more specific application which may be defined as 'the degree to which a product is fitted to the purpose for which it was made'. Here quality is seen to be a relative rather than an absolute criterion, and it introduces the useful concept of 'fitness for purpose'. Thus a quality product is not necessarily one which is made from the most expensive materials nor machined to the highest precision possible, but one which exactly meets the specification drawn up for the particular need, neither more nor less. This pragmatic approach can be applied to the definition of water quality. For example, water which is suitable for human consumption may, because of its zinc content, be toxic to fish (Hellawell, 1988). Conversely, water in which fish thrive may be totally unacceptable for potable supply unless it is heavily treated. Which of these waters is higher or lower in quality? From the potable water-supply engineer's viewpoint one would say the former was higher quality. Yet a fish farmer would regard the latter to be better. Hence, any method of assessing water quality must itself be qualified in relation to the intended use of the water.

Once the concept of fitness for purpose is accepted, it may be applied to the development of Water Quality Standards or Objectives. These are invariably set in terms of chemical determinands but the standards are most often intended to secure biological ends, for example the protection of public health.

For many, if not most purposes it is neither practicable nor possible to include all the parameters or determinands which could be utilized. Instead, a limited range of measures is employed. Often these are the major components considered to be indicative of the overall water quality, or those which are known to be critical for a particular use. Experience suggests that if these indicators are selected with care, it is possible to provide an acceptable assessment of the general quality of the water from a restricted number of measurements.

There is a vast and increasing range of methods for the assessment of water quality and it is not possible to provide a comprehensive review here. Historically, chemical methods have tended to take priority since pollution control legislation, and the regulatory agencies established within this legal framework, have usually set standards in chemical terms. In this chapter, emphasis is placed on biological methods in relation to chemical methods. Biological methods have normally played only a supporting role in the formal regulatory system, but the increasing importance of conservation has led to increased support for a biological approach (Karr, 1993). This chapter can only provide a general, almost purely philosophical, overview: each approach being considered in the widest context of environmental monitoring of water quality.

7.2   Chemical and Biological Approaches

As will be seen below, to continue to maintain the conventional, simplistic contrast between the analytical chemist in the laboratory and the freshwater biologist in the field has become increasingly untenable. Tissue analyses of bioaccumulated substances and biochemical investigations of toxicological effects of pollutants have blurred the distinctions between these disciplines. However, differences remain with regard to the basic approaches and these have been reviewed elsewhere (Hellawell, 1978, 1986). They need only be considered briefly here.

7.2.1   *Chemical analysis*

Chemical analyses are undertaken on water samples in order to determine the quantities of specified substances. The range of substances for which proven analytical procedures are available is very wide and increasing. The threshold levels of detection are often minuscule and decreasing. Thus, a chemical analysis can provide definitive information on the contents of the sample. Automation of analytical procedures makes for high efficiency and allows frequent sampling to be undertaken economically. If reliable chemical quality criteria for a particular use can be established and if the sampling regime is robustly designed, then this approach is extremely efficient.

7.2.2   *Biological field sampling*

Field sampling of the biota utilizes the 'indicator species' concept in which the water quality is inferred from the presence and abundance of those organisms for which the environmental preferences are reasonably well known. For example, the presence of a species which requires high dissolved oxygen levels implies that the environmental levels are generally high, but the precision of the inference is limited by the knowledge of the responses of the indicator organism to varying oxygen concentrations. This is true of virtually all the fluctuating parameters to which organisms respond.

It is often stressed that *in situ* biological methods are superior in that biota exhibit an integrated response to a fluctuating environment, whereas chemical samples only reveal the quality state at the moment of sampling. This difference has been less marked since the development of probes suitable for continuous monitoring of a range, albeit limited, of chemical determinands. In reality, biological methods are valuable in estimating sustained thresholds of quality parameters because while the organisms may tolerate extreme conditions for a limited time, if these persist the susceptible species will disappear. However, even when conditions improve, recovery may be delayed. Hence, biological methods tend to provide a retrospective view of water quality and may provide a misleading impression of the actual condition at any given time.

Biological methods are particularly relevant for assessing 'environmental' water quality; that is, those aspects of water which have ecological consequences—such as seasonal variations in discharge and velocity—which cannot be assessed readily in the laboratory from a limited number of samples.

7.3   *In Vitro* and *In Vivo* Methods

While chemistry and biology are different disciplines, the distinctions between chemical and biological methods of assessing water quality are somewhat artificial. For example, the determination of chlorophyll-*a* concentration to estimate algal biomass is more akin to a conventional chemical analysis than to a traditional biological method. Similarly, biochemical oxygen demand (BOD) is often considered to lie within the domain of the chemist but the procedure depends on the presence of micro-organisms capable of degrading the substrates present in the sample. Analysis of tissue to determine the presence of pesticide residues or the accumulation of heavy metals is essentially a chemical method, but the interest in these determinands is a biological one and the results must be interpreted with care, having particular regard to the life-history and physiological characteristics of the organisms. Tests to determine the toxicity of pesticides or heavy metals are intrinsically biological yet the data may be needed to establish chemical water quality standards.

A more useful distinction might be to consider the philosophy behind the two main approaches. In general, chemical methods are essentially concerned with the composition of the water sample (or other material) as determined in the laboratory. This may, for the purposes of this review at least, be conveniently called the *in vitro* approach, since the sample is often confined within a bottle or similar container. Even when the methodology is modified to enable measurements to be made in the field, perhaps even continuously by means of a 'probe', the technology is still essentially an *in vitro* approach. Biological methods are generally intended either to measure the direct impact of the water on the biota or to provide an indirect assessment of the chemical composition of the water. This approach can, by analogy, be called the *in vivo* approach, again at least for the purposes of this review.

This terminology emphasizes the differences in the concepts which are being applied (Table 7.1). The sample in a bottle (*in vitro*), whether consisting of water, sediment, cells, tissues or organs, is a discrete entity and the analysis will utilize a predetermined suite of methods to measure selected determinands or other attributes. The advent of greater automation in chemical analysis has ensured standardization of procedures and control of variables. The analytical results will probably be obtained with a high degree of accuracy and precision and, if sub-sampled, will be highly repeatable. Where statistical analyses of the resulting data are required, these too are likely to be based on robust methods. All these factors contribute to a high level of confidence in the *in vitro* results. This confidence is, however, restricted to the sample and may not necessarily provide an adequate picture of *in situ* water quality, especially if this varies temporally or even spatially.

Table 7.1 Comparison of the main differences between chemical (*in vitro*) and biological (*in vivo*) methods. (For fuller explanation, see text.)

Chemical methods (in vitro)	Biological methods (in vivo)
Procedure closely defined Standard analytical methods have been developed for most determinands	Procedure often adapted Some biological procedures have been standardized but many field methods are modified by operators to meet local circumstances
Variables controlled Laboratory conditions enable considerable control to be effected	Variables uncontrolled The complexity of biological systems and natural variability together with the vagaries of field conditions limits control
Determination precise Chemical analyses are often able to determine minute quantities of substances with a known precision	Determination imprecise Biological methods may be imprecise; for example, it may be difficult to identify species with certainty
Results repeatable Replicate samples or sub-samples may be used to refine the determination	Results unrepeatable Intrinsic biological variability and the destructive nature of some sampling methods limits repeatability
Statistically robust Reduced variability and the applicability of standard statistical procedures assists in the assessment of results	Statistically tenuous Considerable variability and complexity and limited replication impair statistical confidence
Relevance extrapolated Results can only be applied to environmental assessments where considerable additional data on the likely or potential consequences for biota are known	Relevance immediate Direct involvement of biological systems facilitates the application of results to environmental management

A better perspective of the true situation can only be gained by an adequate sampling programme or by the use of continuous-monitoring probes.

However, the significance of the results of *in vitro* analyses for environmental protection purposes has to be derived by a process of extrapolation, based on existing knowledge of the likely consequences of exposure to the given levels of the determinands under the conditions prevailing at the time of sampling. This can usually be predicted with confidence only after considerable accumulation of other data. Finally, the presence of other substances for which analysis has not been undertaken may be significant and their effects cannot be evaluated. However comprehensive the suite of determinands which are analysed, there remains the possibility that an unknown or unsuspected substance may be present at concentrations which are of environmental significance.

Sometimes *in vitro* laboratory measures could engender misleading conclusions if extrapolated without regard for the actual environmental conditions. For example, a water sample from a highly turbulent stream polluted by organic waste may have high biochemical oxygen demand (BOD) when measured in the laboratory. However, this level of BOD may not cause significant ecological effects *in situ* simply because the high turbulence leads to rapid re-oxygenation and the oxygen demand is continually met.

In developing biological methods one seeks to eliminate these uncertainties by measuring the direct impact of substances on living systems. In order to do this quantitatively, it is important that the level of exposure—that is, concentration and duration—is known. Preferably, reliable physical and chemical analyses would also be undertaken but even without precise knowledge of what may be present, the direct impact of the water, of whatever quality, may be assessed.

In practice, biologists often modify so-called 'standard methods', either in the light of personal experience, or to meet particular circumstances. It is, therefore, sometimes difficult to compare results. This feature is exacerbated by the inherent variability in biological systems and may be further compounded by the well-known variability which becomes evident when several biologists attempt to assess water quality at the same field site using a standardized procedure. This problem has been evident for a considerable time. For example, Needham and Usinger (1956) investigated the variability in results using a standardized procedure by five operators, one of whom showed a consistent tendency to collect more organisms. Statistical analyses of biological field data are usually compromised by the inadequacy of sample replication. Studies conducted by Chutter (1972) in South Africa and by Chutter and Noble (1966) in California of the number of replicate samples which are required to obtain estimates of the population of benthic macro-invertebrates within a given error at a 95% confidence level, gave remarkably similar results. Apparently, 100 samples would be required to estimate the population with an error of 10%. Such findings have a significant bearing on those methods which rely on population estimates—for example, diversity measures (see Section 7.7.3). The number of samples required to be 95% certain that at least one representative of a given taxonomic group is present may also be much larger than might be supposed. Table 7.2 provides examples selected from the classic study by Needham and Usinger (1956) of a Californian stream, mentioned above. However, many biological water quality indices (see below) provide acceptable estimates with more manageable numbers of replicates.

7.4 *In Vitro* Biological Methods

The advantages of *in vitro* methods outlined above have been utilized in biological methods which are comparable with conventional chemical analytical procedures. For example, algal biomass may be estimated from *in vitro* measurement of chlorophyll-*a* (Marker, 1972). Other similar, biochemical determinations are used as substitutes for direct cell or organism counts, including ATP (Stadelmann, 1974), enzyme activity (Lenhard, 1965) or even carbon (Crisp, 1971).

Table 7.2 The number of samples required to be 95% certain that at least one representative of a group of organisms will be secured. Data selected from Needham and Usinger (1956).

Organism or taxonomic group	Number of samples
Plecoptera	2
Isoperla	12–17
Ephemeroptera	1–2
Baetis	2–3
Ephemerella	2
Rhithrogena	2
Trichoptera	1
Brachycentrus	4–5
Glossosoma	2–3
Hydropsyche	6–9
Lepidostoma	3–4
Rhyacophila	9–13
Diptera	1
Simuliidae	3
Chironomidae	2

The bioaccumulation of important pollutants such as pesticides or heavy metals (Phillips, 1980; Mance, 1987) can give indirect indications of environmental levels but is, in itself, valuable for assessing the direct impacts of such substances on the biota. Knowledge of the physiological significance of accumulated substances must be derived from toxicological studies which, in turn, form the link between *in vitro* and *in vivo* approaches.

7.5 Toxicity Testing—the *In Vitro/In Vivo* Link

Toxicity tests are a good example of the complementary relationship between chemical (*in vitro*) and biological (*in vivo*) approaches. An effective test must include accurate measurements of the concentrations of the substance to which the organisms are exposed. It is rarely adequate to assume that the test solution as initially made up will remain unchanged during a protracted exposure. Similarly, the population of test organisms must be understood biologically (genetic variability, life-history stage and so on) and maintained to eliminate stresses other than those imposed by the toxicant. Without such safeguards, the inferences drawn from the test results may be highly misleading.

7.5.1 *Determination of lethal toxicity*

Traditional aquatic toxicity tests (Alabaster and Lloyd, 1982) are usually whole-organism lethal tests. The test population is exposed to a range of environmental concentrations of the substance under investigation in order to determine how much kills a given fraction (usually 50%) in a given time, usually of the order of hours or days (e.g. 96h LC_{50}). These measures, when made under strictly controlled conditions, are useful guides to the relative acute toxicity of substances to a given test species but, in the environment at large, other factors come into play and extrapolations may be difficult to apply. For example, the substance may be volatile or become absorbed or bound onto various surfaces. Some substances may have synergistic or antagonistic toxic effects. Oxygen, pH and temperature variations can influence toxicity and different developmental stages of the organism may vary in their susceptibility. In addition, different species vary in their response to specific toxicants so it is not usually possible to provide more than a general indication of the significance of a particular pollutant (Hellawell, 1988).

Chronic tests, that is, tests conducted at lower concentrations than those used for acute tests, may be more relevant in that they more closely emulate the environmental conditions which are commonly encountered. However, long-term tests are expensive to conduct and may be less reproducible, but can prove invaluable in revealing behavioural or reproductive abnormalities which are not evident during acute tests. This factor is particularly important when acute tests indicate low toxicity and one may presume that the ecological impact of the substance may be low. However, if reproductive capacity is impaired or abnormal behaviour such as failure to avoid predators affects survival, then the ultimate effect on the population may be as severe as that caused by an acutely toxic material.

7.5.2 Sub-lethal/pathological effects

Many substances have chronic or sub-lethal pathological effects and studies of mutagenicity (often in cell culture (Ames *et al.*, 1975; Sharma, 1994)), tissue lesions, malformation, necrosis or organ malfunction, and other effects (Hughes *et al.*, 1979), are appropriately undertaken using *in vitro* techniques.

7.5.3 Physiological effects

Physiological changes, with or without evident pathology, also lend themselves to the *in vitro* approach. These commonly include respiratory function (Heath, 1972) and impairment of reproductive capacity (Macek, 1968; Mount, 1968).

7.5.4 Behavioural responses

Behavioural responses to toxicant exposure have been widely studied, since these can have significant consequences for the indefinite survival of populations of species. This is so even when other, acute or chronic pathological changes are not evident. For example, Ogilvie and Anderson (1965) studied the effects of DDT on temperature selection by young salmon while Silbergeld (1973) investigated the effects of chronic sub-lethal exposure to dieldrin on the adaptation of freshwater fish to thermal stress.

7.6 *In Vivo* Field Observations

The majority of biological methods are essentially derived from field observations of the identity and abundance of organisms. The underlying concept, as mentioned above, is that the presence of populations of certain plants and animals provides an indication of the prevailing chemical water quality (Hellawell, 1978, 1986). This concept may be extended even further by saying that the community of animals and plants present constitutes the 'biological' water quality and it need not be defined in any other terms. An early classification of highly organically polluted waters (the 'Saprobiensystem', see Section 7.7.2) was essentially an expression of environmental quality in terms of the community of organisms present. However, for most purposes the biological indicators are employed to express a more general measure of water quality which embraces general quality parameters such as dissolved oxygen levels and the presence of toxicants.

7.6.1 Field sampling methods

The removal of a sample of the habitat and the organisms which it contains is the basis of much biological monitoring of water quality. A variety of nets, grabs and corers has been developed for this purpose. Each method has particular characteristics, especially regarding selectivity, which have implications for data analysis and need to be understood in order to interpret the results correctly.

7.6.2 Artificial substrates—colonization samplers

Organisms do not simply respond to chemical water quality: other environmental variables, including the nature of the habitat or the substrate, are also important. This may mean that the absence of an indicator species is not caused by inadequate chemical water quality but by an unsuitable physical environment. In order to overcome the difficulties in interpretation which habitat variability can cause, some methods rely on the colonization of a standardized substrate, usually by algae or macroinvertebrates. However, this may itself introduce further complications for interpretation since the construction of the artificial substrate, the rate of colonization, the stability of the colony and even the extent to which there are existing proximate populations from which colonization can occur, all influence the type of community which may be present at any time (Hellawell, 1978).

7.7 Analysis of Biological Data

The complexity of biological community composition necessitates the development of analytical methods in order to convert field data into water quality information. This becomes particularly important when considerable data have been accumulated and unwieldy lists of the numbers of species present need to be codified in order to facilitate reporting and discussion. It needs to be recognized that the result obtained is inevitably a function, at least in part, of the analytical procedure adopted. For example, a pollution index developed from the known responses of macroinvertebrate communities to organic enrichment cannot sensibly be used to assess the impact of lowered pH.

Subsequent sections will consider the advantages and disadvantages of commonly used data analysis methods.

7.7.1   Basic data

Of the several measures in this category, the most commonly used in water quality assessment is species richness, which is currently equated, though incorrectly, with biodiversity. Often a simplistic approach is applied in which it is considered that the richer the community in terms of species, the better the environment and, therefore, the higher the water quality. This concept is fundamental to the derivation of some 'diversity measures', as explained below.

7.7.2   Pollution indices

Organisms exhibit a range of responses to pollutants, and these responses may be used in deriving pollution indices. The fullest development of this concept is with regard to organic enrichment and the consequent oxygen depletion. The classic description of these responses is to be found in the 'Saprobiensystem' (Kolkwitz and Marsson, 1909) which forms the basis of a whole series of further developments and refinements including the Trent Biotic Index (Woodiwiss, 1964) and the Biological Monitoring Working Party (BMWP) score (Chesters, 1980). The last is an excellent example of the procedure whereby the collective wisdom of practising biologists was used in order to adjust, iteratively, the procedure for calculating the score until the method provided the 'correct' or 'expected' result when applied to situations where sufficient other data were available to derive a preconception of the 'true' water quality.

When originally developed, it was intended that the total BMWP score should be used to measure the biological quality of the water, but there has been a tendency more recently to calculate the Average Score per Taxon (ASPT) by dividing the total score by the number of taxa present. This is likely to equate better with 'chemical' water quality since the original values assigned to each taxon were based on known pollution tolerances. Preference for ASPT has been expressed on the basis of its greater seasonal stability and better correlation with water quality (Armitage *et al.*, 1983; Pinder, 1989). However, these reductions obscure other perceptions of the 'biological' quality of the water and are, in effect, biological substitutes for chemical analyses. The issue of the selection of indices is discussed further below.

7.7.3   Diversity measures

The composition of natural communities with respect to the distribution of the numbers of individuals of each species can be described mathematically, for example as a log-normal distribution (May, 1974). When communities are subjected to stress, for example by pollutants or other environmental perturbations, their structure changes. Diversity indices (Simpson, 1949; McIntosh, 1967; Wilhm and Dorris, 1968) may be used to assess the extent to which a community changes under stress. Such indices have been criticized for appearing to fail to correlate directly with known chemical water quality states. For example, diversity may be low when water quality, as judged by chemical criteria, is high (Archibald, 1972).

Headwaters often exhibit low biological diversity when the water is unpolluted emphasizing that pristine water and harsh environmental factors (extreme velocity and temperature cycles, for example) contribute to a paucity of species. This feature has probably led to a recent decline in the use of diversity indices, although their value may not be fully appreciated. A major advantage of diversity indices is that their use is not strictly confined to assessing particular categories of pollutants. They are founded upon the single prior assumption, established by observation, that a reduction in community diversity is often associated with environmental perturbation. The identity of the cause of the perturbation may have to be sought by the application of other methods.

7.7.4   Comparative methods

These methods are helpful in assessing spatial or temporal changes, for example upstream and downstream of a point of effluent discharge, or before and after some incident has occurred. The upstream or 'before' community is compared with the downstream or 'after' community and the difference is attributed to the impact of the effluent or other change. The pollution and diversity indices mentioned above may be used in this way, as may many common ecological comparative indices (Jaccard, 1912; Czekanowski, 1913; Sokal, 1961; Mountford, 1962).

7.8   Conclusions

The range and variety of methods, both biological and chemical, for assessing water quality are themselves indicative of the intrinsic difficulty in deriving a fully satisfactory absolute measure of water quality. The targets for water pollution abatement and control have changed markedly over the last century. Gross contamination from organic domestic and toxic industrial wastes masked the chronic effects of other, more insidious pollutants. When the former were largely under control it became evident that pesticides and even agricultural fertilizers could inflict considerable ecological damage. The history of pollution control is reflected in the refinement of chemical and biological methods of assessing water quality. Now greater emphasis is placed on sub-lethal effects and the need for greater concern for the conservation of aquatic communities. This inevitably means that integration of chemical and biological techniques will continue to be required. While methods improve and develop, the underlying philosophies of laboratory and field approaches will remain. More refined analytical suites, better methods of field sampling, and more powerful software for data analysis should not be allowed to obscure the key issues of relevance, utility and even pragmatism.

Of necessity, it has been possible to provide only a very superficial overview of the range and use of chemical and biological methods, yet it must be evident that there is a wide array of possible methods from which to choose. Selection of an appropriate method must depend on clear objectives and experience, or at least some familiarity with the strengths and weaknesses of each approach (Hellawell, 1977). It is evident that often too much is expected from a method or it is applied indiscriminately. As an example, one might take the use of diversity indices. These have been criticized for failing to reveal changes in water quality when moving downstream from the headwaters to the lowland reaches. Typically, chemical water quality in the headwaters is high (clean) but deteriorates as one moves downstream, yet diversity is often lowest at the head of the stream, increases downstream to the mid-reaches, and then declines once more. Community diversity is low in the headwaters because the water is low in nutrients, the environment is harsh (high discharges and low temperatures in winter, low discharge and high temperatures in summer) and the range of available micro-habitats is restricted. In the middle reaches nutrient levels are higher, conditions more equable and habitats more varied, hence the community is more diverse. In the lowest reaches, habitats are once more restricted and conditions more difficult for many species resulting in lowered diversity. Failure to recognize that the community, and thus the index, is an expression of the whole environment and not simply the chemical water quality, could lead to false conclusions regarding the utility of diversity indices. Similarly, the greater use of ASPT rather than the full BMWP score means a loss of information. The same ASPT could be derived from highly dissimilar communities, one with many taxa and the other with very few. Again, preoccupation with chemical water quality means that the value of the full BMWP score in expressing the biological water quality is lost.

Finally, experience suggests that no single method or index is alone sufficient to measure water quality: a combination of two or more, preferably of different kinds, is essential for an adequate understanding (Hellawell, 1977). And always the purpose of assessment must not be lost sight of—which, of course, is where this chapter began.

References

Alabaster, J. S. and Lloyd, R. (1982). *Water Quality Criteria for Freshwater Fish.* 2nd Edition. Butterworth, London.

Ames, B. N., McCann, J. and Yamasaki, E. (1975). Method for detecting carcinogens and mutagens with *Salmonella*/mammalian microsome mutagenicity test. *Mutation Research,* **31,** 347–363.

Archibald, R. E. M. (1972). Diversity of some South African diatom associations and its relation to water quality. *Water Research,* **6,** 1229–1238.

Armitage, P. D., Moss, D., Wright, J. F. and Furse, M. T. (1983). The performance of a new biological quality score based on macroinvertebrates over a wide range of unpolluted running-water sites. *Water Research,* **17,** 333–347.

Chesters, R. K. (1980). Biological Monitoring Working Party. The 1978 national testing exercise. *Department of the Environment. Water Data Unit Technical Memorandum,* **19,** 1–37.

Chutter, F. M (1972). A reappraisal of Needham and Usinger's data on the variability of a stream fauna when sampled with a Surber sampler. *Limnology and Oceanography,* **17,** 139–141.

Chutter, F. M. and Noble, R. G. (1966). The reliability of a method of sampling stream invertebrates. *Archiv für Hydrobiologie,* **62,** 95–103.

Crisp, D. J. (1971). Energy flow measurements. In: Holme, N. A. and McIntyre A. D. (Eds), *Methods for the Study of Marine Benthos. IBP Handbook No. 16.* Blackwell Scientific Publications, Oxford, 197–279.

Czekanowski, J. (1913). *Zary metod statystycznych.* Warsaw.

Heath, A. G. (1972). A critical comparison of methods for measuring fish respiratory movements. *Water Research,* **6,** 1–7.

Hellawell, J. M. (1977). Change in natural and managed ecosystems: detection, measurement and assessment. *Proceedings of the Royal Society London, B,* **197,** 31–56.

Hellawell, J. M. (1978). *Biological Surveillance of Rivers.* Water Research Centre, Medmenham and Stevenage.

Hellawell, J. M. (1986). *Biological Indicators of Freshwater Pollution and Environmental Management.* Elsevier Applied Science Publishers, London and New York.

Hellawell, J. M. (1988). Toxic substances in rivers and streams. *Environmental Pollution,* **50,** 61–85.

Hughes, G. M., Perry, S. F. and Brown, V. M. (1979). A morphometric study of effects of nickel, chromium and cadmium on the secondary lamellae of rainbow trout gills. *Water Research,* **13,** 665–679.

Jaccard, P. (1912). The distribution of the flora in the alpine zone. *New Phytologist,* **11,** 37–50.

Karr, J. R. (1993). Defining and assessing ecological integrity: beyond water quality. *Environmental Toxicology and Chemistry,* **12,** 1521–1531.

Kolkwitz, R. and Marsson, M. (1909). Ökologie der tierischen Saprobien. *Internationale Revue der gesamten Hydrobiologie u Hydrographie,* **2,** 126–152.

Lenhard, G. (1965). The dehydrogenase activity as a criterion of toxic effects in biological purification systems. *Hydrobiologia,* **25,** 1–8.

Macek, K. J. (1968). Reproduction in brook trout (*Salvelinus fontinalis*) fed sublethal concentrations of DDT. *Journal of the Fisheries Research Board of Canada,* **24,** 1787–1796.

Mance, G. (1987). *Pollution Threat of Heavy Metals in Aquatic Environments.* Elsevier, London.

Marker, A. F. H. (1972). The use of acetone and methanol in the estimation of chlorophyll in the presence of phaeophytin, *Freshwater Biology,* **2,** 361–385 .

May, R. M. (1974). General introduction. In: Usher, M. B. and Williamson, M. H. (Eds), *Ecological Stability.* Chapman and Hall, London, 1–14.

McIntosh, R. P. (1967). An index of diversity and the relation of certain concepts to diversity. *Ecology,* **48,** 392–404.

Mount, D. I. (1968). Chronic toxicity of copper to fathead minnows (*Pimephales promelas,* Rafinesque). *Water Research,* **2,** 215–223.

Mountford, M. D. (1962). An index of similarity and its application to classificatory problems. In: Murphy, P. W. (Ed.), *Progress in Soil Zoology.* Butterworth, London, 43–50.

Needham, P. R. and Usinger, R. L. (1956). Variability in the macrofauna of a single riffle in Prosser Creek, California, as indicated by the Surber sampler. *Hilgardia,* **24,** 383–409.

Ogilvie, D. M. and Anderson, J. M. (1965). Effect of DDT on temperature selection by young Atlantic salmon, *Salmo salar. Journal of the Fisheries Research Board of Canada,* **22,** 503–512.

Phillips, D. J. H. (1980). *Quantitative Aquatic Biological Indicators. Their Use to Monitor Trace Metal and Organochlorine Pollution.* Applied Science Publishers, London.

Pinder, L. C. V. (1989). Biological surveillance of chalk streams. *Freshwater Biological Association Annual Report, 1989,* 81–92.

Sharma, A. K. (1994). Cell biology techniques for the detection of toxic and mutagenic substances. In: Salanki, J., Jeffrey, D. and Hughes, G. M. (Eds), *Biological Monitoring of the Environment. A Manual of Methods.* CAB International and IUBS, Oxford, 25–40.

Silbergeld, E. K. (1973). Dieldrin. Effects of chronic sublethal exposure on adaptation to thermal stress in freshwater fish. *Environmental Science and Technology,* **7,** 846–849.

Simpson, E. H. (1949). Measurement of diversity. *Nature, London,* **163,** 688.

Sokal, R. R. (1961). Distance as a measure of numerical similarity. *Systematic Zoology,* **10,** 71–79.

Stadelmann, P. (1974). Biomass estimation by measurement of adenosine triphosphate. In: Vollenweider, R. A. (Ed.), *A Manual on Methods for Measuring Primary Productivity in Aquatic Environments.* IBP Handbook No. 12. 2nd Edition. Blackwell, Oxford, 26–30.

Wilhm, J. L. and Dorris, T. C. (1968). Biological parameters for water quality criteria. *Bioscience,* **18,** 477–481.

Woodiwiss, F. S. (1964). The biological system of stream classification used by the Trent River Board. *Chemistry and Industry,* **11,** 443–447.

8 BIOLOGICAL ASSESSMENT OF RIVER QUALITY USING THE NEW VERSION OF RIVPACS (RIVPACS III)

J. F. Wright, D. Moss, R. T. Clarke and M. T. Furse

Summary

1. RIVPACS is a software package for assessing the biological quality of running water sites. It offers site-specific predictions of the macroinvertebrate fauna to be expected in the absence of environmental stress, for comparison with the observed fauna.

2. A new version of the system (RIVPACS III) has been developed from a comprehensive set of high quality reference sites throughout the UK.

3. RIVPACS III sets higher standards and has application to a wider range of running water sites than previous versions. The system was used throughout the UK for the biological component of the 1995 General Quality Assessment.

8.1 Introduction

RIVPACS (River InVertebrate Prediction And Classification System) is a microcomputer-based system developed by the Institute of Freshwater Ecology (IFE) for the biological assessment of river quality. In this context, river quality is the extent to which the watercourse supports those biotic assemblages which should be present in the absence of environmental stress. Hellawell (1986) defines three major categories of environmental stress (natural, imposed and environmental manipulation), the last two of which are the direct consequence of man's activities. All three categories of stress are capable of influencing river quality in the biological sense (see Wright *et al.*, 1994 for further discussion of environmental stress and the RIVPACS approach). Essentially, RIVPACS gives site-specific predictions of the macroinvertebrate fauna based on environmental features, and sets a 'target' of the fauna to be expected in the absence of major environmental stress. Comparison of this target with the fauna observed at a site is the basis of the biological assessment.

The biological classification of sites on which RIVPACS is based has been developed using macroinvertebrate data for a series of high-quality reference sites. An additional feature of the system is the facility to place new sites of high biological quality within the context of this national classification. However, it is the novel prediction system which has attracted the greatest interest in the UK and overseas. An account of the RIVPACS approach, including some examples of RIVPACS II predictions at different taxonomic levels may be found in Wright *et al.* (1994).

RIVPACS II, which was developed from a 438 site reference data set was used for the biological component of the 1990 River Quality Survey throughout Great Britain and, on a more experimental basis, in Northern Ireland. Almost 9000 sites were assessed, and whereas the RIVPACS approach was shown to be sound, it was also apparent that further development was required to ensure that the system performed satisfactorily across the full range of river sites in the UK.

For example, RIVPACS II had inadequate representation of some stream types and geographical areas, and there was a need to increase the number of small stream reference sites. Inadequacies were demonstrated in the prediction of the fauna of chalk streams. Also, some reference sites were shown to be subject to mild environmental stress and would therefore be unacceptable for incorporation in RIVPACS III.

With these considerations in mind, the sponsoring organizations funded the further development of the system in order to meet four major objectives. These were to make the system more robust, to enlarge the existing database of reference sites, to seek improved procedures for classification and prediction, and finally to develop an upgraded version of RIVPACS for use in the 1995 General Quality Assessment (GQA) survey. A number of these topics will be the subject of separate papers and the emphasis here will be on the main features of the new system.

8.2   The RIVPACS III Data Set

Two complementary routes were adopted for increasing the reference data set of high-quality sites from the 438 sites in RIVPACS II. First, RIVPACS-compatible site data from other projects undertaken by the IFE were examined for their suitability. They included more than 100 sites across Great Britain examined under contract to the Nature Conservancy Council (1987–1991) and 50 small stream sites in England and Wales from a project entitled the Faunal Richness of Head-water Streams, funded by the National Rivers Authority and the Natural Environment Research Council.

Secondly, the sponsoring organizations for RIVPACS III were invited to offer suggestions on the river types and geographical locations which they believed were still under-represented in the reference data set. As a result of this interactive process, a further 55 sites in England and Wales, and 36 sites in Scotland were selected. The scope of the system was also increased by the selection of 70 sites in Northern Ireland. All the new samples were subject to species level identification by staff at the IFE River Laboratory.

Once all the data for the new sites had been transferred to computer and verified, rigorous procedures were used to ensure that the reference sites for RIVPACS III were of the highest quality. Several classification and prediction exercises were carried out before the final reference site list was agreed. The severity of this exercise was such that 52 of the 438 sites in RIVPACS II were rejected. The final data set for RIVPACS III included 614 reference sites in Great Britain (GB) and a further 70 sites in Northern Ireland (NI).

The full data set of 684 sites holds information on 642 macroinvertebrate taxa (mainly species) from 117 different families. Within the GB reference sites, BMWP (Biological Monitoring Working Party) score varies from 101 to 293, number of BMWP taxa from 17 to 46 and ASPT from 4.46 to 7.27, all based on three seasons' samples (spring, summer and autumn) combined. The equivalent information for the NI reference sites is 104–238 (BMWP score), 21–40 (number of BMWP taxa) and 4.52–6.87 (ASPT).

8.3 Development of RIVPACS III

Many classification and prediction exercises were undertaken before RIVPACS III was finalized. In early exploratory analyses, an attempt was made to classify all UK sites within a single scheme. It was soon apparent that the much larger number of sites in Great Britain compared with Northern Ireland was likely to generate problems in optimizing classification group size for each of the two sections. In addition, not all sites for Northern Ireland fell into NI-only classification groups, despite the fact that Northern Ireland has a more restricted fauna than Great Britain. It was concluded that a classification with these features would be incapable of delivering an acceptable prediction system for Northern Ireland. Consequently, separate classification and prediction systems were developed for each of the two sections, to ensure more reliable systems in each case.

Following a comparison of many different classification and prediction procedures using 410 sites from the RIVPACS II data set, two procedures were selected for final appraisal once the RIVPACS III data set had been assembled. These were:

- TWINSPAN for site classification (Hill, 1979) coupled with multiple discriminant analysis (MDA) for prediction to group (that is, the technique used in RIVPACS II) and
- Semi-strong hybrid multidimensional scaling (SSH) using the PATN package (Belbin, 1992), followed by K-means clustering (Moss, 1985) and MDA for prediction to group.

This second approach had given encouraging results which marginally outperformed TWINSPAN/MDA when used on 410 sites from the RIVPACS II data set. On the enlarged data set of 614 GB sites, including a wider range of sites with more headwater streams, it failed to perform as well as TWINSPAN/MDA and had to be rejected.

It was now clear that RIVPACS III should be developed using TWINSPAN.

However, in the early analyses, based on standardized species data for site classification, this approach was only partially successful in creating coherent groups of chalk stream sites. These streams not only have high species richness, but also support high densities of macroinvertebrates due to their flow, temperature and chemical regimes, all of which encourage luxuriant growth of macrophytes which in turn favour high densities of invertebrates.

In addition to the species data for each site, family data (log.categories of abundance 1–9, 10–99, etc.) were also available for each season. By using both the species (presence/absence data) and families (log.abundance data) in the TWINSPAN classification, sites which shared a high abundance of a number of different families now had more in common than when the analysis was confined to species data only, as in RIVPACS II.

Once the details of the approach had been settled, both the 614 site GB and 70 site NI data sets were classified independently using TWINSPAN. Normal practice was to develop each classification to more levels than were eventually used. Thus, in the case of the GB data set the classification was developed to nine levels, giving 122 TWINSPAN groups. Careful appraisal of these groups, bearing in mind group size, geographical location and the BMWP index values of the sites within each group led to the recombination of many daughter groups with the constraint that the final groups had existed at a higher level in the division process.

This produced a classification of 44 groups (range of group size 5–31) which was further examined by the development of a group prediction system using MDA. ANOVA was performed on the environmental data and BMWP indices at the 44 group level and after appraisal further recombination reduced the number of groups to 35.

The 35 group classification, when subjected to the internal MDA test using the preferred set of environmental variables (Option 1 of RIVPACS II) predicted 51.6% of the 614 sites to the 'correct' group, defined as the group in which a site was placed in the original TWINSPAN classification. There were a further 111 sites (18.1%) in which the second highest probability of group membership based on MDA was for the correct group. Prediction to the correct group (out of a possible 35 groups) using environmental features is a very severe test and marginally incorrect predictions on this test are still of value in developing a general prediction system. Further internal checks involving comparison of the observed and expected taxa indicated a slightly better match for RIVPACS III compared with RIVPACS II, despite the wider range of sites.

In RIVPACS III, the GB classification (Figure 8.1) has 35 end-groups, with the number of sites per group varying from 6 to 39 (mean value of 17.5, as in RIVPACS II). The NI classification (Figure 8.2) has seven groups with group size varying between 5 and 15 (mean of 10).

A detailed consideration of the RIVPACS III classifications is beyond the scope of this chapter. Whereas the seven group classification for Northern Ireland showed a progressive sequence from upland to lowland sites, the 35 group classification for Great Britain was more complex (Figure 8.1). Unlike all previous

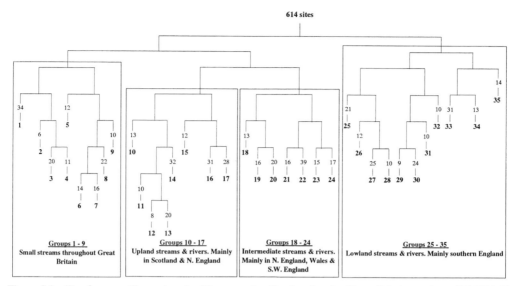

Figure 8.1   Dendrogram illustrating the 35 group classification for the Great Britain section of RIVPACS III. The number of sites in a given group is shown above the group number.

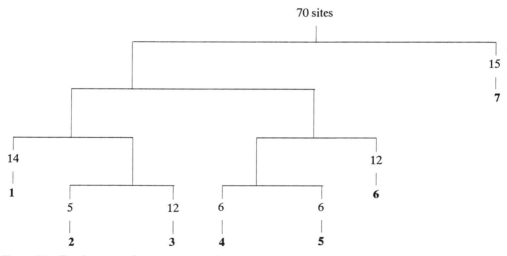

Figure 8.2   Dendrogram of the seven classification groups in the Northern Ireland section of RIVPACS III. The number of sites in a given group is shown above the group number.

classifications for GB, which displayed the typical upland to lowland sequence, the RIVPACS III classification partitioned off a major block of small stream sites (groups 1–9) on the second dichotomy. These sites occurred throughout GB and only three other groups (29, 31, 32) from the right-hand side of the first dichotomy were also small stream sites. The remaining three major blocks of classification groups (10–17, 18–24 and 25–35) exhibited the familiar sequence of change from upland to lowland.

8.4   Features of RIVPACS III

The new system sets higher standards for prediction than earlier versions as a consequence of the more comprehensive data set, rigorous site selection process and the use of a modified classification procedure.

An important feature of the system, which has been expanded in RIVPACS III, is its flexibility. Predictions can be made at a variety of taxonomic levels (species, families, BMWP families, customized) and seasons (single, paired, three seasons combined) according to need. At BMWP family level, the expected (E) values of the various BMWP indices are computed and can be compared with observed (O) values to generate O/E ratios for site appraisal. For single-season predictions only, RIVPACS III may now be used to compare observed and expected log abundance categories at family level and to calculate a new quality index with the objective of detecting early signs of environmental stress prior to major loss of taxon richness.

Predictions can be carried out interactively or in batch mode by drawing on environmental and biological data held in computer files. The general appearance of the software for RIVPACS III is similar in operation to the previous version so that current users can easily adjust to the new version. Nevertheless, it has entirely new classification and prediction systems and incorporates a large number of new features which make it more flexible and easier to use. RIVPACS III was used throughout the UK for the biological component of the 1995 General Quality Assessment.

Acknowledgements

This research was funded by the National Rivers Authority, the Scottish Office Environment Department, the Department of the Environment (Northern Ireland) and the Natural Environment Research Council. It also benefitted from the inclusion of data from high-quality sites in Great Britain, collected under contract to the former Nature Conservancy Council and the Nature Conservancy Council for Scotland. Finally, it is a pleasure to acknowledge the essential contribution made by the entire RIVPACS team to the success of this project.

References

Belbin, L. (1992). *PATN Pattern Analysis Package*. Division of Wildlife and Ecology, Commonwealth Scientific and Industrial Research Organisation, Canberra.

Hellawell, J. M. (1986). *Biological Indicators of Freshwater Pollution and Environmental Management*. Elsevier Applied Science, London and New York.

Hill, M. O. (1979). TWINSPAN-A FORTRAN program for arranging multivariate data in an ordered two-way table by classification of the individuals and the attributes. *Ecology and Systematics*, Cornell University, Ithaca, New York.

Moss, D. (1985). An initial classification of 10km squares in Great Britain from a land characteristics data bank. *Applied Geography,* **5,** 131–150.

Wright, J. F., Furse, M. T. and Armitage, P. D. (1994) Use of macroinvertebrate communities to detect environmental stress in running waters. In: Sutcliffe, D. W. (Ed.), *Water Quality and Stress Indicators in Marine and Freshwater Ecosystems: Linking Levels of Organisation (Individuals, Populations and Communities).* Freshwater Biological Association, Ambleside, 15–34.

PLATE 1: PREFERENCES AND PERCEPTIONS

1a(right) – Children's drawings of how they would like the River Ravensbourne (1c) to look (Drawings from Valley Primary School, Bromley, Kent) (see Chapter 4).

1b(bottom left) – The upper catchment of the River Ravensbourne (England). The Kyd Brook in Pond Wood, a National Trust area, is a high quality stream with pools and riffles (see Chapter 32) (Photo: C Swanwick).

1c(bottom right) – River Ravensbourne in Queen's Mead Recreation Ground, Bromley, Kent constrained in a concrete-lined channel (see Chapters 4 and 32) (Photo: S Tunstall).

PLATE 2: FRESHWATER SPECIES NATIVE TO BRITAIN

2a – Water Horsetail *(Equisetum fluviatile)* and white water-lily *(Nymphaea alba)* in Scotland (Photo: L Gill).

2b – Great crested newt *(Triturus cristatus)*, a species of amphibian protected by European legislation (Photo: L Gill).

2c – Red-throated diver *(Gavia stellata)*, a Red Data Book species which breeds in northern Scotland (Copyright RSPB).

9 PHENOTYPIC VARIATION IN BENTHIC INVERTEBRATES: AN INDICATOR OF FRESHWATER QUALITY?

I. D. Hogg, Y. de Lafontaine and J. M. Eadie

Summary

1. Studies linking phenotypic variation among benthic invertebrates with freshwater quality are reviewed, and new data presented on phenotypic and genotypic variation among *Gammarus fasciatus* (Crustacea: Amphipoda) in the St. Lawrence River, Canada.

2. Previous studies have primarily focused on one taxonomic group, the Chironomidae (Diptera), often employing complex morphological structures for assessments. Little consideration has been given to potential confounding effects of species' population genetic structure.

3. Other relatively simple and quantifiable measures (for example, fluctuating asymmetry) also show measurable spatial differences. The genetic structure of *G. fasciatus* in the St. Lawrence River was unlikely to have confounded this analysis.

4. It is concluded that phenotypic variation among benthic invertebrates may provide a simple and inexpensive means of evaluating freshwater quality.

9.1 Introduction

Benthic invertebrates are used widely in biological assessments of freshwater quality because of their sedentary existence and well-documented sensitivity to environmental perturbations (e.g., Hogg and Norris, 1991). However, taxonomic difficulties encountered in comprehensive faunal surveys have led to the development and use of more simplified techniques (Hellawell, 1986). Assessments based on individual phenotypic variation within species are becoming increasingly popular (Table 9.1).

Previous studies have used either: (a) the incidence of morphologically abnormal or deformed individuals at a particular site; or more recently, (b) measures of fluctuating asymmetry (FA)—the magnitude of difference between the left and right sides of bilaterally symmetrical characters (Table 9.1). To date, the most

Table 9.1 Studies attempting to link phenotypic variability in benthic invertebrates with environmental perturbations.

Author(s)	Year	Taxa	Measure[1]	Perturbation
Hamilton, Saether	1971	*C. tentans*[2]	DEF/mouth, body	Industrial/agricultural
Hare, Carter	1976	*C. cucini*[2]	DEF/mouth	Industrial
Tooby, Macey	1977	Hemiptera	DEF/pigment	Herbicide
Donald	1980	Plecoptera	DEF/mouth, antenna	Domestic/industrial
Koehn, Frank	1980	*C. thummi*[2]	DEF/mouth	Industrial
Simpson	1980	Trichoptera/ Plecoptera	DEF/gills	Chlorine/oil
Warwick	1980	Chironomidae[2]	DEF/mouth	Industrial/agricultural
Petersen, Petersen	1983	Trichoptera	DEF/net spinning	Heavy metals/toxic
Tennessen, Gottfried	1983	Tanypodinae[2]	DEF/mouth	Coal
Cushman	1984	*C. decorus*[2]	DEF/mouth	Coal liquid
Wiederholm	1984	Chironomidae[2]	DEF/mouth	Heavy metals
Warwick	1985	*Chironomus*[2]	DEF/antenna	Industrial/agricultural
Percy *et al.*	1986	*C. samoensis*[2]	DEF/abdomen	UV radiation
Kosalwat, Knight	1987	*C. decorus*[2]	DEF/mouth	Copper
Warwick *et al.*	1987	*C.* spp.[2]	DEF/mouth	Radioactivity/heavy metals
Warwick, Tisdale	1988	Chironomidae[2]	DEF/mouth	Industrial/agricultural
Pettigrove	1989	*Procladius*[2]	DEF/mouth	Pesticides/heavy metals
Warwick	1989	*Procladius*[2]	DEF/mouth, antenna	Organic/heavy metals
Dickman *et al.*	1990	Chironomidae[2]	DEF/mouth	Teratogens
Warwick	1990	Chironomidae[2]	DEF/mouth, antenna	Heavy metals/PCBs
Dermott	1991	Chironomidae[2]	DEF/mouth	Industrial/agricultural
Warwick	1991	*Procladius*[2]	DEF/mouth, antenna	Mercury
Camargo	1991	Trichoptera	DEF/gills, anal papillae	Chlorine
Dickman *et al.*	1992	Chironomidae[2]	DEF/mouth	Coal tar
Janssens de B. *et al.*	1992	*C.* gr. *thummi*[2]	DEF/mouth	Heavy metals
Urk, G. van, *et al.*	1992	*C.* cf. *plumosus*[2]	DEF/mouth	Toxics/heavy metals
Clarke	1993	*Chironomus*[2]	FA/mouth	Industrial
Lenat	1993	*Chironomus*[2]	DEF/mouth	Organic/toxics
Bird *et al.*	1995a	*Chironomus*[2]	DEF/mouth	Cadmium
Bird *et al.*	1995b	*C. tentans*[2]	DEF/mouth	Radioactivity/heavy metals
Gerhardt, Janssens de B.	1995	*C.* gr. *thummi*[2]	DEF/mouth	Heavy metals/organic
Hogg *et al.*	Un-published	Plecoptera	FA/legs, antenna	Temperature

[1]DEF = deformities/abnormalities, FA = fluctuating asymmetry.
[2]Chironomidae: Diptera.

commonly assessed taxa have been the chironomid Diptera (81%), and the most frequently used phenotypic traits were mouth-part or antennal morphology (84%). Assessments are based on the assumption that, given ideal (unstressed) development conditions, all individuals within a species should conform to a 'normal' (average) body plan. Phenotypic deviation, therefore, results from stress during development which in turn may be related to environmental quality. Fluctuating asymmetry may be particularly appealing because it is controlled within individuals, thus addressing recent concerns over the origin of some deformities (Bird *et al.*, 1995a, b). In theory, both the left and right sides of an organism are controlled by the same genome; hence deviation can be attributed to developmental interference (Clarke, 1993).

However, phenotypic variation could also be influenced by population genetic structure on overall levels of developmental stability. For example, populations may differ in their susceptibility to a particular perturbation because they are genetically distinct and adapted to local conditions (Jackson and Resh, 1992; Sweeney *et al.*, 1992). Furthermore, populations with greater levels of genetic variability (that is, increased heterozygosity) may be more developmentally stable (Kat, 1982).

Here, using a widespread benthic species, the level of spatial phenotypic variability is evaluated using FA, and an assessment made of whether this variability is potentially confounded by genetic differences.

9.2   Methods and Results

9.2.1   *Sample collection and study area*

The amphipod *Gammarus fasciatus* Say was selected for study based on its widespread distribution in North America, numerical abundance, and relatively simple identification. Individuals of *G. fasciatus* were collected between May 22 and 27, 1995, from seven stations along the St. Lawrence River (Figure 9.1). Sites varied in terms of physical and chemical characteristics owing to several tributaries entering the river and different land use within the study area, including large urban centres, heavy agricultural and industrial areas, as well as relatively undisturbed zones. Sites were classified according to primary anthropic influences as either Toxic, Agricultural/Municipal or Background using previous data (Warwick, 1990; Environment Canada, unpublished data). Only sexually mature *Gammarus* were selected for analyses to standardize comparisons among sites and to detect any effects of life-time environmental or genetic disturbance. *Gammarus fasciatus* were identified according to Pennak (1989).

9.2.2   *Phenotypic variability*

Sixty individuals from each site were 'scored' at 40–60 × magnification by measuring, or counting, seven bilateral characters (Figure 9.2) and subtracting the left value from the right. For each character, signed differences between the left and right sides were normally distributed (Wilk-Shapiro statistic) about a mean of zero (paired *t*-test, $p > 0.29$ in all cases). Over the size range examined, there was no correlation between mean character size ($[l_i + r_i]/2$) and the absolute value of left-right differences ($r^2 < 0.04$, $p > 0.2$, in all cases). Therefore, measures were not scaled for size.

To test for variability among sites, the absolute values of left minus right differences (FA score), were evaluated using a Bartlett's test applied to the sample

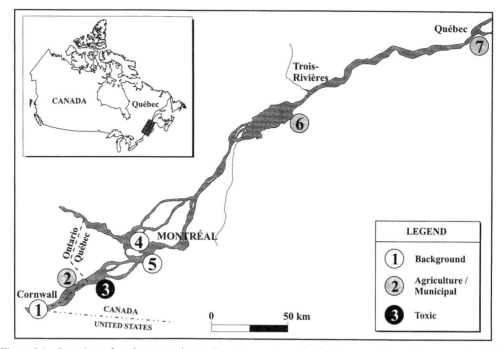

Figure 9.1   Location of study area and sampling stations along the St. Lawrence River. Sites were classified according to primary anthropic disturbances based on previous data (Warwick, 1990; Environment Canada, unpublished data).

variances (Palmer and Strobeck, 1986). Separate tests were conducted for each of the seven characters. For all characters FA scores differed significantly among sites ($p < 0.01$, in all cases). To compare differences among sites, the individual FA scores, for each character, were ranked using a Kruskal-Wallis procedure. Mean ranks were then calculated at each site for each of the seven characters and these were evaluated using a parametric one-way analysis of variance followed by

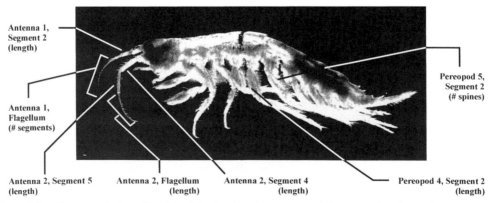

Figure 9.2   *Gammarus fasciatus* (Amphipoda), showing characters used for measuring fluctuating asymmetry (FA) for the phenotypic analyses.

a Tukey's multiple range test ($p = 0.05$). Station 3 ranked highest for six of the seven characters following the Kruskal-Wallis procedure, and for all characters combined (Figure 9.3) Station 3 had a significantly greater mean rank than all other sites ($p = 0.05$, $F = 7.41$, d.f. $= 6$) with the exception of stations 6 and 7. Probability values for all statistical tests were corrected for multiple comparisons. All statistical tests were performed using STATISTIX 4.1 (Analytical Software, Tallahassee, FL).

9.2.3 Genotypic variability

Individual *G. fasciatus* from each site were homogenized and analysed for six polymorphic enzyme loci (MPI, MDH-2, PGI, PGM, AO-1, AO-2), using cellulose acetate electrophoresis (Hebert and Beaton, 1989). At each site, calculations were made of allele frequencies and the proportion of heterozygotes observed (actual counts) and expected (based on Hardy-Weinberg equilibrium). Among populations, a coefficient of differentiation (F_{ST}: Wright, 1978) and a measure of genetic distance (Nei, 1978) were calculated. All calculations were performed using BIOSYS-1 (Swofford and Selander, 1981).

Genetic distance measures (Nei, 1978) were less than 0.01 in all cases and estimates of genetic differentiation (Wright, 1978) suggest moderate levels of present day gene flow (mean $F_{ST} = 0.014$, maximum $F_{ST} = 0.034$). Both observed and expected heterozygosity varied only slightly among sites (Table 9.2), with

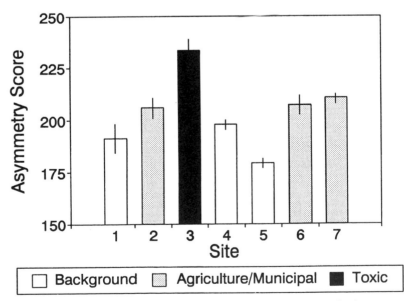

Figure 9.3   Mean Kruskal-Wallis ranks (± 1 standard error) for seven phenotypic characters of *Gammarus fasciatus*. Rankings were calculated from the absolute values of left minus right differences (FA scores) for each character; higher rankings indicate greater levels of asymmetry. Site numbers correspond to Figure 9.1.

Table 9.2 Summary of genetic variability measures for *Gammarus fasciatus* from sites in the St. Lawrence River at six polymorphic loci. Site numbers refer to Figure 9.1. Means (± 1 standard error) are shown.

Site no.	No. individuals/ locus	No. alleles/ locus	Heterozygosity Observed	Heterozygosity Expected
1	29.5 (0.3)	3.5 (0.4)	0.52 (0.09)	0.58 (0.06)
2	30.2 (0.3)	3.5 (0.5)	0.54 (0.08)	0.57 (0.05)
3	28.3 (0.7)	3.5 (0.5)	0.56 (0.08)	0.60 (0.05)
4	34.0 (0.0)	3.3 (0.5)	0.54 (0.08)	0.56 (0.07)
5	19.3 (0.3)	3.7 (0.6)	0.46 (0.09)	0.63 (0.06)
6	9.0 (0.0)	2.8 (0.5)	0.35 (0.13)	0.55 (0.08)
7	24.0 (0.0)	3.3 (0.4)	0.56 (0.08)	0.57 (0.07)

station 6 having fewer observed heterozygotes. However, this was most likely the result of the small sample size at this site ($n = 9$).

9.3 Discussion and Recommendations

Assessments of phenotypic variability within benthic taxa may provide a simple, inexpensive means of evaluating biological water quality in natural systems. However, previous assessments of phenotypic variability among populations have often relied on complex morphological characters (e.g., small mouthparts, fine antennal detail) in taxonomically complex species (e.g., Chironomidae: Diptera). This study demonstrates that even relatively simple measures (e.g., leg-spine counts, antennal length) in a readily identifiable species (*Gammarus fasciatus*) can also show measurable phenotypic differences among sites.

The genetic structure of the population was unlikely to have confounded our analyses, although few differences were expected among *G. fasciatus* within the St. Lawrence River because of their relative mobility and the continuous nature of the system. Comparisons using less mobile species or across heavily fragmented habitats could reveal considerably greater levels of genetic differentiation (e.g. Sweeney *et al.*, 1992; Hogg *et al.*, 1995). Accordingly, others are urged to consider the genetic structure of populations on a case-by-case basis.

Having considered genetic differences among populations, phenotypic differences among the sites can be examined in relation to environmental factors. Interestingly, higher levels of FA recorded at station 3 correspond to an area of known PCB contamination (Environment Canada, unpublished data). Sites considered as 'background' had among the lowest levels of FA. As part of a continuing evaluation of FA, the authors are currently undertaking further field and laboratory analyses in an effort to link elevated concentrations of toxic compounds to increased FA.

It may be concluded that phenotypic indicators in benthic invertebrates merit serious consideration for evaluating freshwater quality. However, further development and use of the technique could be enhanced by: (a) focusing on easily identifiable species, (b) employing simplified protocols (e.g. FA); and (c) greater consideration of the underlying genetic structure of benthic taxa.

Acknowledgements

We thank P. J. Boon for comments on the manuscript, and F. Boudreault, G. Ibarguchi and M. Stutman for expert technical assistance. Research was funded through the St. Lawrence Vision 2000 Plan of Environment Canada.

References

Bird, G. A., Rosentreter, M. J. and Schwartz, W. J. (1995a). Deformities in the menta of chironomid larvae from the Experimental Lakes Area, Ontario. *Canadian Journal of Fisheries and Aquatic Sciences,* **52,** 2290–2295.

Bird, G. A., Schwartz, W. J. and Joseph, D. L. (1995b). The effect of ^{210}Pb and stable lead on the induction of menta deformities in *Chironomus tentans* larvae and on their growth and survival. *Environmental Toxicology and Chemistry,* **14,** 2125–2130.

Camargo, J. A. (1991). Toxic effects of residual chlorine on larvae of *Hydropsyche pellucidula* (Trichoptera, Hydropsychidae): a proposal of biological indicator. *Bulletin of Environmental Contamination and Toxicology,* **47,** 261–265.

Clarke, G. M. (1993). Fluctuating asymmetry of invertebrate populations as a biological indicator of environmental quality. *Environmental Pollution,* **82,** 207–211.

Cushman, R. M. (1984). Chironomid deformities as indicators of pollution from a synthetic, coal-derived oil. *Freshwater Biology,* **14,** 179–182.

Dermott, R. M. (1991). Deformities in larval *Procladius* spp. and dominant Chironomini from the St. Clair River. *Hydrobiologia,* **219,** 171–185.

Dickman, M., Brindle, I. and Benson, M. (1992). Evidence of teratogens in sediments of the Niagara River watershed as reflected by chironomid (Diptera: Chironomidae) deformities. *Journal of Great Lakes Research,* **18,** 467–480.

Dickman, M., Lan, Q. and Matthews, B. (1990). Teratogens in the Niagara River watershed as reflected by chironomid (Diptera: Chironomidae) labial plate deformities. *Water Pollution Research Journal of Canada,* **24,** 47–79.

Donald, D. B. (1980). Deformities in Capniidae (*Plecoptera*) from the Bow River, Alberta. *Canadian Journal of Zoology,* **58,** 682–686.

Gerhardt, A. and Janssens de Bishtoven, L. (1995). Behavioural, developmental and morphological responses of *Chironomus* gr. *thummi* larvae (Diptera, Nematocera) to aquatic pollution. *Journal of Aquatic Ecosystem Health,* **4,** 205–214.

Hamilton, A. L. and Saether, O. A. (1971). The occurrence of characteristic deformities in the chironomid larvae of several Canadian Lakes. *Canadian Entomologist,* **103,** 363–368.

Hare, L. and Carter, J. C. H. (1976). The distribution of *Chironomus* (s.s.)? *cucini* (*salinarius* group) larvae (Diptera: Chironomidae) in Parry Sound, Georgian Bay, with particular reference to structural deformities. *Canadian Journal of Zoology,* **54,** 2129–2134.

Hebert, P. D. N. and Beaton, M. J. (1989). *Methodologies for Allozyme Analysis Using Cellulose Acetate Electrophoresis,* Helena Labs, Beaumont, Texas.

Hellawell, J. M. (1986). *Biological Indicators of Freshwater Pollution and Environmental Management.* Elsevier Applied Science, London.

Hogg, I. D. and Norris, R. H. (1991). Effects of runoff from land clearing and urban development on the distribution and abundance of macroinvertebrates in pool areas of a river. *Australian Journal of Marine and Freshwater Research,* **42,** 507–518.

Hogg, I. D., Williams, D. D., Eadie, J. M. and Butt, S. A. (1995). The consequences of global warming for stream invertebrates: a field simulation. *Journal of Thermal Biology,* **20,** 199–206.

Jackson, J. K. and Resh, V. H. (1992). Variation in genetic structure among populations of the caddisfly *Helicopsyche borealis* from three streams in northern California, U.S.A. *Freshwater Biology,* **27,** 29–42.

Janssens de Bishoven, L. G. J., Timmermanns, K. R. and Ollevier, F. (1992). The concentration of cadmium, lead, copper, and zinc in *Chironomus* gr. *thummi* larvae (Diptera, Chironomidae) with deformed versus normal mentum. *Hydrobiologia,* **239,** 141–149.

Kat, P. W. (1982). The relationship between heterozygosity for enzyme loci and developmental homeostasis in peripheral populations of aquatic bivalves (Unionidae). *The American Naturalist,* **119,** 824–832.

Koehn, T. and Frank, C. (1980). Effect of thermal pollution on the chironomid fauna in an urban channel. In: Murray, D. A. (Ed.) *Chironomidae: Ecology, Systematics, Cytology and Physiology.* Pergamon Press, Oxford, 187–194.

Kosalwat, P. and Knight, A. W. (1987). Chronic toxicity of copper to a partial life cycle of the midge, *Chironomus decorus. Archives of Environmental Contamination and Toxicology,* **16,** 283–290.

Lenat, D. R. (1993). Using mentum deformities of *Chironomus* larvae to evaluate the effects of toxicity and organic loading in streams. *Journal of the North American Benthological Society,* **12,** 265–269.

Nei, M. (1978). Estimation of average heterozygosity and genetic distance from a small number of individuals. *Genetics,* **89,** 583–590.

Palmer, A. R. and Strobeck, C. (1986). Fluctuating asymmetry: measurement, analysis, patterns. *Annual Review of Ecology and Systematics,* **17,** 391–421.

Pennak, R. W. (1989). *Fresh-water Invertebrates of the United States.* John Wiley, New York.

Percy, J., Kuhn, K. L. and Kalthoff, K. (1986). Scanning electron microscope analysis of spontaneous and UV-induced abnormal segment patterns in *Chironomus samoensis* (Diptera, Chironomidae). *Roux's Archives for Developmental Biology,* **195,** 92–102.

Petersen, L.B.-M. and Petersen, R. C., Jr. (1983). Anomalies in hydropsychid capture nets from polluted streams. *Freshwater Biology,* **13,** 185–191.

Pettigrove, V. (1989). Larval mouthpart deformities in *Procladius paludicola* Skuse (Diptera: Chironomidae) from the Murray and Darling Rivers, Australia. *Hydrobiologia,* **179,** 111–117.

Simpson, K. W. (1980). Abnormalities in the tracheal gills of aquatic insects collected from streams receiving chlorinated or crude oil wastes. *Freshwater Biology,* **10,** 581–583.

Sweeney, B. W., Jackson, J. K., Newbold, J. D. and Funk, D. H. (1992). Climate change and the life histories and biogeography of aquatic insects in eastern North America. In: Firth, P. and Fisher, S. G. (Eds), *Global Climate Change and Freshwater Ecosystems.* Springer-Verlag, New York, 143–176.

Swofford, D. L. and Selander, R. B. (1981). BIOSYS-1: a FORTRAN program for the comprehensive analysis of electrophoretic data in population genetics and systematics. *Journal of Heredity,* **72,** 281–283.

Tennessen, K. J. and Gottfried, P. K. (1983). Variation in structure of ligula of tanypodinae larvae (Diptera: Chironomidae). *Entomological News,* **94,** 109–116.

Tooby, T. E. and Macey, D. J. (1977). Absence of pigmentation in corixid bugs (Hemiptera) after the use of the aquatic herbicide dichlobenil. *Freshwater Biology,* **7,** 519–525.

Urk, G. van, Kerkum, F. C. M. and Smit, H. (1992). Life cycle patterns, density, and frequency of deformities in *Chironomus larvae* (Diptera: Chironomidae) over a contaminated sediment gradient. *Canadian Journal of Fisheries and Aquatic Sciences,* **49,** 2291–2299.

Warwick, W. F. (1980). Chironomidae (Diptera) responses to 2800 years of cultural influence: a paleolimnological study with special reference to sedimentation, eutrophication and contamination processes. *Canadian Entomologist,* **112,** 1193–1238.

Warwick, W. F. (1985). Morphological abnormalities in Chironomidae (Diptera) larvae as measures of toxic stress in freshwater ecosystems: indexing antennal deformities in *Chironomus* Meigen. *Canadian Journal of Fisheries and Aquatic Sciences,* **42,** 1881–1914.

Warwick, W. F. (1989). Morphological deformities in larvae of *Procladius* Skuse (Diptera: Chironomidae) and their biomonitoring potential. *Canadian Journal of Fisheries and Aquatic Sciences,* **46,** 1255–1271.

Warwick, W. F. (1990). Morphological deformities in Chironomidae (Diptera) larvae from the Lac St-Louis and Laprairie basins of the St. Lawrence River. *Journal of Great Lakes Research,* **16,** 185–208.

Warwick, W. F. (1991). Indexing deformities in ligulae and antennae of *Procladius* larvae (Diptera: Chironomidae): application to contaminant-stressed environments. *Canadian Journal of Fisheries and Aquatic Sciences,* **48,** 1151–1166.

Warwick, W. F., Fitchko, J., McKee, P. M., Hart, D. R. and Burt, A. J. (1987). The incidence of deformities on *Chironomus* spp. from Port Hope Harbour, Lake Ontario. *Journal of Great Lakes Research,* **13,** 88–92.

Warwick, W. F. and Tisdale, N. A. (1988). Morphological deformities in *Chironomus, Cryptochironomus,* and *Procladius* larvae (Diptera: Chironomidae) from two differentially stressed sites in Tobin Lake, Saskatchewan. *Canadian Journal of Fisheries and Aquatic Sciences,* **45,** 1123–1144.

Wiederholm, T. (1984). Incidence of deformed chironomid larvae (Diptera: Chironomidae) in Swedish lakes. *Hydrobiologia,* **109,** 243–249.

Wright, S. (1978). *Evolution and the Genetics of Populations, Volume 4. Variability within and among Natural Populations.* University of Chicago Press, Chicago.

10 NEW APPROACHES TO MONITORING AND CLASSIFYING STANDING WATERS

B. Moss, P. Johnes and G. Phillips

Summary

1. The development of methods for monitoring and classifying water quality in rivers in England and Wales is reviewed. Current approaches take into account more than just the traditional emphasis on the effects of gross organic pollution, but have become very complex. This is a reflection of the grafting of modern needs onto the established practices of a long tradition.

2. Standing waters have not been monitored, nor their quality classified, on a routine basis. It is argued that an approach which classifies on the basis of degree of change from baseline standards, which are determined by sustainable use of the catchment, will be most appropriate. 'Sustainable' is defined as that use which reflects exploitation of the catchment that is determined largely by natural features (climate, topography, geology) rather than artificial economic instruments. This differs from the approach to flowing waters which sets targets (equivalent to baselines) which are determined by current use, which need not be stringent with respect to enhancement of amenity and conservation value, and in which there is no requirement for sustainability.

3. An appropriate array of variables for assessing standing water quality is suggested, the philosophy of setting baselines that reflect sustainable use of catchments is discussed, and methods for determining the baselines are outlined.

4. A pilot testing of a scheme based on these ideas has been carried out and shows a considerable deviation from their baselines in most of a sample of 90 British standing waters.

10.1 Introduction

Though species apparently exist in discrete groups for the most part, little else in the biosphere does. Continuous variation is the norm and this applies even to species when intraspecific variation is examined. Discreteness between species is preserved by natural selection and breeding barriers but there are no parallels for the environmental variables which create the stage on which these evolutionary processes are enacted.

Therein lies a problem in monitoring our own effects on these variables and the consequences for the evolutionary play. Continua are difficult to handle. In legal terms, phenomena, events or entities must be either present or not. One must be either innocent or guilty, 'not proven' being a decision not to make a decision, rather than a third category. In environmental terms, there are no such boundaries, yet boundaries must be artificially created so that human activities can be equitably controlled through law.

The onset of serious river pollution by raw sewage in the nineteenth century has led to the development of a series of systems for monitoring its effects. Some have used chemical determinands, others the microbial community, the benthic invertebrate community, or some combination of these. The outcome has generally been to set up a series of classes and to express as a class the state of a particular stretch of river.

For a decade since 1980, a system developed by the National Water Council (NWC, 1981) has been used in England and Wales. It has been based on compliance with standards for dissolved oxygen, BOD (biochemical oxygen demand), ammonia, and general toxicity to fish and has had five categories, 1a, 1b, 2, 3, 4 (Good to Bad). A parallel scheme based on the composition of the benthic invertebrate community, and dependent on the association between particular invertebrate families and degree of organic pollution, has also been used—the Biological Monitoring Working Party (BMWP) score (NWC, 1981). A biological score is calculated for each site but there have been no formal classification categories used. There is generally a good correspondence between biological score and the NWC classification but this is inevitable since both schemes ultimately rest on the effects of gross organic pollution.

10.2   The Water Resources Act 1991 and Water Quality Objectives

With sufficient expenditure, the majority of water quality problems can be overcome. However, in a world of finite economic, as well as environmental resources, some rationalization of approach to water-quality management is inevitable. Whilst monitoring can tell us much about our impact on the environment, the results, *per se*, do not assist in directing management. To overcome this, many of the former regional Water Authorities in England and Wales set water-quality targets based on the NWC classification. Progress towards, or away from, these targets was assessed at five-year intervals in 1980, 1985 (NWC, 1981; Kinnersley, 1988) and finally in 1990 by the National Rivers Authority (NRA, 1991b).

The importance of classification and target setting was reinforced in the Water Resources Act (1991). The Act prescribes, in Section 82, that 'The Secretary of State may ... by regulations prescribe a system of classifying the quality of those [controlled] waters according to criteria specified in the regulations.' The criteria may be general or specific concerning concentrations of substances required to be present or absent and there may be other specific requirements. In Section 83 the Secretary of State may establish objectives for water quality by specifying a classification for the controlled water and unlike previous target setting, such objectives would have a status in law.

In a continuously varying environment, many sites will lie close to class boundaries, moving in and out of compliance with targets in response to random events. An element of subjectivity in the application of the former NWC classes provided some smoothing of this problem but such an approach does not sit comfortably within a statutory framework.

Following recommendations by the NRA (1991a), the Department of the Environment proposed a scheme of water quality objectives (WQOs) for rivers. The scheme proposed five use-related categories (River Ecosystem, Special Ecosystem, Abstraction for Potable Supply, Abstraction for Agricultural and Industrial use, and Watersports) (Department of the Environment and Welsh Office, 1992) with a WQO to be specified for each river stretch based on one or more of these categories. It is intended that similar use-related objectives will be applied to other controlled waters, although the Secretary of State has, as yet, established regulations for WQOs for only one of these categories, River Ecosystem (RE). The water quality criteria, which are applied with more rigorous statistical treatment than formerly (NRA, 1994), are the traditional ones associated with organic pollution (oxygen concentration, BOD, ammonia), together with standards for pH (6.0–9.0 as a 95 percentile) and two heavy metals (copper and zinc) required by the EC Freshwater Fisheries Directive. There are five categories to be used as objectives (RE 1–5).

Although the establishment of use-related targets provides a pragmatic approach to achieving a desired water quality, there is also a need to assess the overall quality of the water, which may change with time, irrespective of use. In rivers this is being achieved through a General Quality Assessment (GQA). It is intended that GQAs will have four components (general chemistry, nutrients, aesthetics and biology), of which only the first and last have yet been specified in any detail. The general chemistry includes the familiar indicators of organic pollution (oxygen, BOD, ammonia) and the biological component is the BMWP score. It is intended that the score will be compared with that predicted for the site in an unpolluted state by use of the RIVPACS scheme (Wright *et al.*, 1993, this volume). This has used a large sample of presumed pristine sites to establish links between physical characteristics of the river and invertebrate community, and has thus established a baseline against which perturbed sites can be compared.

Thus in current approaches to managing river water quality, two components are important. There is the setting of targets (which, in current thinking, are normally use-related) and the assessment of change through space and time. The former needs to be carried out in such a way that change introduced by random events does not influence compliance and thus future investment, while the latter represents a 'snapshot' in time. Targets (WQOs) may change in response to varied human need or expectation, but progress, or its lack, must be measured against a fixed baseline if the assessment is to have long-term value. This baseline may either be an absolute one (e.g. RIVPACS) or a pragmatic one based on a particular date (e.g. 1990, adopted by the NRA for the start of the river General Quality Assessment).

The element of comparison with a target or baseline is also inherent in other schemes such as that devised by Petersen (1992) in Sweden for the assessment of the state of lowland rivers. This scheme depends greatly on visible characteristics of the system and includes an assessment of the channel characteristics which have frequently been greatly altered by river engineering. No water chemistry is used but a correlation has been established between assessments made by this scheme and others dependent on the benthic community. The present state of the river is compared with a baseline determined from the characteristics of lowland rivers unaltered by human influence. A score is assigned which essentially describes the deviation of the site from the baseline state.

A similar approach, AMOEBA, dependent on degree of change, is being adopted in Holland (Ten Brink *et al.*, 1991; Ministry of Transport, Public Works and Water Management, 1992). The Swedish and Dutch schemes, together with the UK's approach to biological classification (RIVPACS) thus have a common philosophical thread in that they measure the deviation from a relatively 'natural' state. In doing so they attempt to measure the degree to which human activities have influenced the water in question and its ecological quality. This theme was picked up in the proposed EC Directive on The Ecological Quality of Water, which, if retained, is likely to drive water quality classification further in this direction.

10.3   Water Quality Objectives for Standing Waters

The Water Resources Act (1991) does not distinguish between flowing and standing waters but gives the Environment Agency responsibilities related to inland and coastal waters, and land associated with those waters, under Sections 82 and 83. Clearly, the criteria for establishing WQOs for standing waters and estuaries must be quite different from those appropriate to rivers and streams. The UK has not monitored standing water quality to anything like the extent it has for flowing waters and does not have appropriate systems in place. The way is thus open for considering suitable approaches and perhaps also for containing the complexity which seems to have been imposed by history on current river schemes.

Any thinking on this topic should be applicable to north-west Europe as a whole, not just England and Wales, despite the geographical strictures of the Water Resources Act, but there is no lack of standing waters even in the area covered by the Act. There are few large lakes but there are a myriad of smaller bodies, many of which are extremely important sites for the general public. The Serpentine in Hyde Park, London, for example, is seen by millions more people than the vastly larger Wastwater in the Lake District, and the quality of the local fishing pond may be as much an issue as that of Lake Windermere.

Traditional monitoring of river quality has not ignored the smaller streams, and monitoring standing waters should not confine itself to a few hundred larger lakes. Overall there are 12,500 water bodies above about 2 ha in size in England and Wales and perhaps 50,000 of 1 ha or more (Smith and Lyle, 1979; Johnes *et al.*, 1994). There may be as many as 300,000 standing water bodies in England and Wales overall, and standing waters have suffered from human impact as much as flowing ones. Recent surveys show considerable damage from eutrophication (Carvalho and Moss, 1995) and acidification (Rimes *et al.*, 1994) and a simple qualitative list of existing impacts and threats to the ecosystem of Loch Lomond (Table 10.1, Hamilton, 1987), which is perceived by many people, at least south of the Scottish border, as tucked away out of harm, is revealing.

What sort of approach might be used to develop WQOs for standing waters? Some basis already exists in that lake classification schemes have been a central theme of pioneering limnology (Elster, 1958) and the concept of ultra-oligotrophic, oligotrophic, mesotrophic, eutrophic and hyper-eutrophic (hypertrophic) lakes has wide currency. The Organisation for Economic and Cooperative Development (OECD, 1982) was able to prescribe ranges for each of these 'types' in total phosphorus and chlorophyll-*a* and it would be simple to use these categories as a basis for a WQO scheme. However, standing waters vary along many more axes than that of simple trophic state (Hutchinson, 1957). An alternative might be to use alkalinity and pH, as has been used by the former Nature Conservancy Council (NCC) (Palmer *et al.*, 1992). However, if both the OECD and NCC schemes are applied to one lake, Oakmere, in Cheshire (Table 10.2), the lake is classified in very different categories when the different schemes are applied, and also differently in different years.

Moreover, using any such scheme, lakes with presently similar characteristics are classified together irrespective of whether they might naturally possess these features or have acquired them as a result of human influence. South Walsham Broad in Norfolk and Whitemere in Shropshire both classify as hypertrophic on the OECD scheme (Table 10.3), but the former is such because of the sewage

Table 10.1   Existing and imminent impacts on Loch Lomond (based on Hamilton, 1987).

1. Bank erosion by motor boats
2. Suspended solids pollution
3. Eutrophication (particularly from increased summer tourist population)
4. Afforestation with exotic conifers in catchment
5. Deforestation of native hardwoods
6. Water abstraction
7. Water level regulation
8. Water transfer from adjoining basins
9. Acidification of the northern inflows
10. Dumping of roadworks spoil
11. Proposed pumped storage electricity generation
12. Impacts of introduction of fish such as ruffe on the native coregonid population

Table 10.2   Classification of Oakmere, Cheshire, according to Nature Conservancy Council and OECD schemes. Data from Carvalho (1993).

Variable	1990–1991	1991–1992
Mean total phosphorus (μg L^{-1})	66	58
Mean chlorophyll-*a* (μg L^{-1})	8.4	7.0
Maximum chlorophyll-*a* (μg L^{-1})	30.1	17.0
Mean pH (log units)	6.1	5.1
Mean total alkalinity (meq L^{-1})	0.04	0.03
Class (OECD, 1982)	Eutrophic	Mesotrophic
Class (NCC: Palmer *et al.*, 1992)	Oligotrophic	Dystrophic

Table 10.3   Characteristics of the naturally hypertrophic Whitemere (no significant anthropic P loading) and the artificially hypertrophic South Walsham Broad (main P loading from sewage effluent). Data from Moss *et al.* (1989) and Moss *et al.* (1994).

Variable	Whitemere	South Walsham Broad
Mean total phosphorus (μg L^{-1})	1,456	255
Mean chlorophyll-*a* (μg L^{-1})	15.3	132
Maximum chlorophyll-*a* (μg L^{-1})	35	428
Maximum nitrate-N (mg L^{-1})	0.54	3.65
Class (OECD, 1982)	Hyper-eutrophic	Hyper-eutrophic

effluent that has been abundantly discharged into it in the past several decades, whilst the latter has been hypertrophic for millennia (S. McGowan, unpublished data). This is perhaps because of natural mechanisms for the retention of phosphorus. South Walsham Broad might be restored and managed; it will probably be futile to attempt to change Whitemere.

10.4   Spatial State and State (Value) Changed Schemes

Schemes which classify by a single factor or group of auto-correlated factors thus have severe limitations. Such an approach for standing waters would be compounded by the greater complexity of such systems, as they are not controlled by a single over-riding physical factor to the extent that rivers are by water flow. It would be desirable to develop a single scheme, which uses a range of variables, in an open-ended way that allows introduction of new variables without disrupting the scheme, as knowledge increases. Such a scheme should acknowledge that standing waters have reached their present states by a variety of pathways and degrees of change. It should also avoid creating categories such as those of the former NWC classification for rivers and the current River Ecosystem WQO scheme, which are ultimately arbitrary.

The traditional approach to water monitoring can be referred to as a spatial state classification, the alternative as state-changed or value-changed. The former has a role in that it is important to ascertain if present quality meets presently perceived needs or aspirations for use. In this way spatial state classifications can be used for comparison against use-related targets (WQOs). Yet the same data can be used in a farther-reaching way through the state-changed approach, in which the present state is compared with a baseline for the particular water body. An additional benefit of the latter is that a knowledge of a natural baseline state will assist in setting achievable targets.

There are elements of state-changed approaches in the use of RIVPACS, River Habitat Survey (Raven *et al.*, this volume) and in the Petersen scheme for rivers, so the concept is already accepted. The Dutch AMOEBA system is based on it and the Swedish system for standing waters has parallel spatial state and value-changed indices (degree of anthropogenic perturbation: DAP) (Swedish Environmental Protection Agency, 1991).

10.5   Design of an Appropriate System

In designing a state-changed system for standing waters there are several key questions. First, what variables best, but most succinctly, describe the quality of a standing water system and how frequently need they be measured? Second, on what basis should baseline state be defined? and third, how might the characteristics of a particular water body be determined for this baseline state?

10.5.1   *Variables describing standing water systems*

Like all ecosystems, standing water systems are complex and influenced by millions of geographical, morphometric, physical, inorganic chemical, organic chemical and biological variables, and all the potential multiple interactions between them. The extent of this variability is such that, for example, no one has yet fully analysed a natural water, nor documented the entire degree of variation of even a single bacterial species in a single site. A perfect descriptive summary of the state of a system should encompass all features and is clearly impossible. The state would have changed by the time the work of description was complete.

There are, however, some features which, in our present understanding, describe characteristics basic to many such systems and which underlie important functional processes (e.g. production, nutrient cycling) in standing waters. In the UK, all lakes have inflows and outflows of liquid water (as opposed to the sole loss of water as vapour from lakes in many arid regions). Thus, the nature of the catchment is important in influencing features of water chemistry. Geochemical considerations determine that phosphorus and nitrogen compounds, in particular, are frequently key limiting nutrients in controlling phytoplankton production.

The properties of water itself place such constraints on organisms that physical and chemical influences are perhaps more important in determining community composition, and competitive and other biological interactions less so, than in terrestrial habitats. Yet physical determinism is confounded by the nature of standing waters as unstable islands which, in many cases, have been in existence for a relatively short period. They are vulnerable to water-level changes, which may severely isolate them or interconnect them with other bodies for short periods, promoting local extinction and colonization. Overall then, physical and chemical variables are, for the most part, more reliable descriptors of lake state than community composition. Yet in describing an ecosystem, biological variables cannot be ignored.

Additional items that should be considered are as follows. Variables should be sampled and compared relatively quickly, in a standard way among sites. Use of boats can greatly extend sampling times, for example. A robust scheme will not be strongly dependent on taxonomic expertise in a wide variety of groups, and any biological variables used need to be sampled in a standard way that is not dependent on a standard habitat (e.g. rocky littoral) being present in all sites. Furthermore, the value of each variable must be able to be determined in the baseline state.

Moss *et al.* (1996) have proposed an array of variables which seem to satisfy these considerations. The array includes: water retention time, maximum depth, conductivity, inflow and lake total phosphorus and nitrogen concentrations, winter inflow nitrate concentration, lake nitrogen : phosphorus ratio, Secchi disc depth, total alkalinity, pH, lake calcium concentration, maximum phytoplankton chlorophyll-*a* concentration, plant score, and potential for the maintenance of at least one fish species. All of these are easily measurable but examination of existing data sets indicates that at least six evenly distributed samplings will be necessary to obtain values of the current status of most of these within $\pm 50\%$ of their true means. Fewer visits would be necessary for some, but more would be desirable for others.

Plant score is an index based on the array of submerged and emergent aquatic plants present in summer and is derived from a scheme developed by Palmer *et al.* (1992). All variables can be determined directly without use of a boat except maximum depth and existence of a fish population or community. Maximum depth is particularly important in a few cases of reservoirs in severely eroding peaty catchments which are rapidly filling in, but can be ignored (i.e. it is a constant) in most lakes. The presence of fish can be determined by local enquiry in most cases.

10.5.2   The baseline state

With what baseline should the current state of a water body be compared to assess degree of change? There are three approaches to this: chronological, pragmatic, and functional.

Chronological comparisons might include the state of the site immediately after formation of the basin (*ca* 10,000 BC in many cases), just before colonization (say 3000 BC), just before the Industrial Revolution (1750) or just before the intensification of agriculture which took place in the UK after 1940. The baseline state of the water body must be able to be determined and increasing quantification of palaeolimnological determinations, which would be essential for all but the latter data, might be sophisticated enough to do this (Birks *et al.*, 1990; Bennion, 1994).

Taking and dating sediment cores, however, is expensive and would not be feasible for more than a handful of the total array of water bodies. More fundamental is that because lakes change constantly in response to changes in their catchments, including the greater 'catchment' of the atmosphere which also influences them, no single date is intrinsically more appropriate than any other. Moreover, because the UK will, barring geocatastrophe, remain an urban and agricultural country whose entire land surface will continue to be influenced strongly by human activities, a baseline which depends on pre-settlement conditions is unlikely to be generally acceptable.

The second approach, of pragmatism, is to set the baseline conditions arbitrarily according to the use that is intended for the particular water body. This is essentially the philosophy behind the setting of water quality objectives for rivers (see above). A general baseline can be set (the River Ecosystem baseline has been set mostly with angling in mind as the central use) but many sites would need to have different baselines for different uses, and those uses might change in response to the changing values of society.

Thus, given the sophistication of water treatment technology, a baseline might be set for potable water or industrial abstractions which would require far less stringent standards than those for amenity and conservation. With, say, the demise of local industry, aspirations for more sensitive use of the site could not be met without remedial work and legal revision of the baseline. There is always a danger that political and economic considerations might drive down standards and enforce baselines that are too modest. The resolution of these difficulties is essentially a political one, but the baseline here is clearly used as a management target. In planning for a future in which quality of the environment will become increasingly important, it will be crucial, however, to have the higher standards in place.

The higher standards are those which give maximum conservation value (those that maintain the highest potential habitat and species diversity), preserve functional values (such as fisheries, natural flood storage, harvesting or traditional products) and maintain high amenity. Since in the UK people are almost everywhere, even if only as tourists, almost all sites are in the public view and are important components of local amenity. The philosophy of the baseline, therefore, should be one of determining the state which reflects the highest possible quality, consonant with maintenance of current populations and of agricultural use of the catchment. This constitutes the third, functional, approach to setting the baseline state.

10.5.3 The functional approach to setting baselines

There is ample evidence of much acidification damage to standing waters through energy consumption and vehicle use and consequent atmospheric deposition of acidic pollutants (Rimes *et al.*, 1994). People also cause eutrophication damage by sewage effluent discharge (Carvalho and Moss, 1995). Equally the development of agriculture to present intensive levels has contributed eutrophicating nutrients and brought about drainage schemes which, in removing floodplains and wetlands, has removed natural devices for the regulation of nutrients (Shoard, 1980).

There are, however, existing technologies for extracting acid gases from industrial furnaces and power stations, developing technology for removing nitrogen oxides from vehicle exhausts, and existing technology for stripping phosphorus from sewage effluent. There is a realization that current agricultural practice is in negative energy balance and unnecessary for maintenance of adequate food supplies. There is also increasing public concern about environmental standards, which makes it increasingly unlikely that current practices in all of these respects will be acceptable in the future.

A sensible functional basis on which to determine baselines for standing water quality is thus one of sustainable land use. This may be defined as one in which the buffering capacities of the soils are not exceeded by atmospheric inputs of hydrogen ions, and in which it is unnecessary to discharge substantial amounts of phosphorus or nitrogen from sewage treatment works. It is also one in which agricultural systems are largely determined by the natural capacities of the land that result from climate, topography, and geology, supplemented by systems of cultivation and fertilization in which virtually all of the fertilizer added is used by the crop and does not run off.

The precise water quality and state of the ecosystem would be difficult to determine for individual sites given such general requirements. However, a reasonable working approximation might be the state of the systems in the immediate pre-Second World War period (say around 1930) which just preceded the enormous rise in energy consumption and intensification of farming which have dominated the state of the British environment in general for most of this century. It is fortunate, but coincidental, that the water quality can be inexpensively determined (hindcast) for this period using existing databases and this introduces the third question of how this might be done.

10.5.4 Determining the baseline state

Among the variables proposed above for the characterization of standing waters are four key variables that underpin many of the others. These are retention time, conductivity, and inflow total nitrogen and phosphorus concentrations. Retention time requires knowledge of the approximate volume of the basin, but given this it can be calculated as a long-term average from meteorological data (precipitation rate, actual evaporation rate), area of catchment and volume of basin. These are readily available from the Meteorological Office (1989), maps and simple survey.

Conductivity can be hindcast from geological maps and databases (Moss *et al.*, 1996) linking run-off and groundwater chemistry with rock type. Different rocks in a catchment are taken to contribute proportionally to their areas of surface occurrence. The databases indicate a range of conductivities for each rock type, and regressions comparing calculated with measured values indicate highly significant correlations with values calculated from either extremes or the mean of the range. The greatest accuracy is obtained using the high end of the ranges, the slope of the regression line being 0.99, $n = 90$, $r^2 = 0.76$ and $p < 0.0001$ (Moss *et al.*, 1996).

Total nitrogen and phosphorus concentrations in the inflow water can be determined from the total amounts of these elements exported from the catchment and the water discharge. Total export can be hindcast from export coefficient models (Reckhow and Simpson, 1980; Beaulac and Reckhow, 1982) based on land-use data, stock numbers and human population (Johnes, 1990, in press; Johnes and Heathwaite, submitted; Heathwaite and Johnes, submitted; Johnes *et al.*, in press). Land-use data and stock numbers may be obtained from the Annual Agricultural Censuses (Clark, 1982), human population data from population censuses.

There is a substantial literature covering the annual release of nitrogen and phosphorus from animals, people, and different crops and semi-natural vegetation (Johnes *et al.*, in press). The calculations from such export coefficient models can be calibrated and validated using existing measurements of water chemistry for different catchments. Regressions using 10 catchments and three or four separate years of data from each give highly significant relationships ($r^2 > 0.9$, $p < 0.0001$) and slopes close to 1 for a variety of models based on individual catchment or regional calculations (Johnes *et al.*, in press).

From these four key variables and a set of regression models, the other variables can be hindcast for a baseline state (Moss *et al.*, 1996). The relationships for pH and calcium are less close than those for nutrient-related variables, but an alternative approach for hindcasting a baseline for acidification-related variables might be the use of critical loads (calculated loads of H^+ that can be accommodated by the buffering capacity of the catchment rocks and soils) (Battarbee *et al.*, 1994).

10.6   Testing a Pilot Scheme

A scheme designed according to the above principles has been devised and tested by Moss *et al.* (1996). It used existing data for the current state of 90 lakes in Britain, though these data were generally less reliable than required for an operational use of the model (with at least six sampling occasions during a year). Baseline states were calculated on a regional basis. This means that calculations were made for nutrient export and conductivity for the natural land-use regions delineated by Dudley Stamp (1941) and all standing waters within each region were assumed to be similar in the baseline state. This assumption was justified because calculations made on this basis showed a very high correlation with similar calculations made for individual lake catchments (Johnes *et al.*, in press).

Calculation of baseline states assumed the land use, stocking densities and fertilizer practice of 1931 (Ministry of Agriculture, Fisheries and Food, 1968) and that virtually all sewage effluent phosphorus can be retained at the sewage treatment works. Values of pH calculated for the baseline depend only on geology and soil water in equilibrium with unpolluted precipitation. Pumped storage reservoirs, in which the water quality bears no relationship to the surrounding land, and for which the baseline would have to be that for the catchment from where the water originates, were not included in the sample. Reservoirs storing local water, but constructed since 1930, were included. The baseline is not a chronological reconstruction but a hypothetical state based on sustainable use of the land, so the date of origin of a reservoir is immaterial.

The scheme may give misleading results in certain lakes where internal processes may determine lake state as much as, or more than, the catchment. These include shallow, macrophyte dominated lakes and some stratified, groundwater-fed, deep basins with very long retention time, in which internal recycling of nutrients is important. Examples are included in the sample tranche but refinements of the scheme will be necessary to give accurate results for these.

The results from such a large tranche are voluminous and given in detail in Johnes *et al.* (1994) and Moss *et al.* (1996). They are only summarized here in terms of degree of change compared with the hindcast baseline and are shown in Figure 10.1. Change from the baseline is calculated for groups of variables linked to eutrophication, those linked to acidification, and for an overall index. Change is expressed as the difference between contemporary and baseline value divided by baseline value expressed as a percentage. For calculation purposes, pH was converted to H^+ concentration and calculations were included in the acidification index for lakes whose baseline pH was calculated as 6.0 or lower. All pH changes were included in calculating the overall index. For most variables, negative change was treated as zero; for pH in the overall calculation, sign was ignored.

The preliminary results indicate large degrees of change. A 100% change means a doubling in magnitude of the variable and nearly half of the lakes in the tranche have undergone this degree of disturbance. More than three-quarters have suffered more than a 50% change and only 4.4% can be considered to be insignificantly perturbed from their calculated baselines. Most interesting is that lakes which lie in upland regions, including the Cumbrian Lake District, have undergone severe change compared with their baselines. On spatial state schemes, such as the OECD trophic scheme, such lakes classify in the oligotrophic or mesotrophic category (Table 10.4) and might not be thought to have serious problems. The state-changed approach suggests that stringent targets for improvement are appropriate.

10.7 Conclusions

There is perhaps a general feeling among many non-limnologists analogous to that of the pigs in George Orwell's (1945) *Animal Farm*, i.e. 'Four legs good, two legs bad'. The parallel is 'Oligotrophic good, mesotrophic OK, eutrophic bad'.

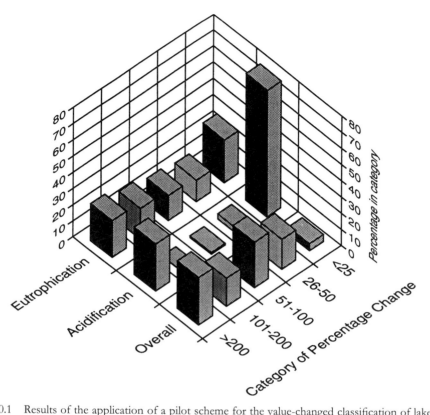

Figure 10.1   Results of the application of a pilot scheme for the value-changed classification of lakes using data from a tranche of 90 British lakes. The percentage change from calculated baselines is shown for groups of variables related to eutrophication, to acidification, and for overall change (all variables available included— these relate not only to acidification and eutrophication but to salinity change and morphometric change). The tranche included a very wide variety of lakes within the following ranges of variables: Area (ha), 0.5– 7,120; Mean depth (m), 1–36.9; Retention time (days), 2–10,600; Secchi depth (m), 0.35–3.75; Conductivity (μS cm^{-1}), 9.2–5,000; Ca^{2+} (mg L^{-1}), 0.2–204; pH (log units), 5.08–8.64; total alkalinity (meq L^{-1}), 0.02– 3.43; Inflow total P (μg L^{-1}), 55–275; Lake total P (μg L^{-1}), 5–1,450; Inflow total N (mg L^{-1}), 0.63–11.5; Lake total N (mg L^{-1}), 0.21–32.6; N:P ratio (by weight), 2.4–248; Total oxidized N (essentially nitrate-N) in winter (mg L^{-1}), 0.2–5.88; Maximum chlorophyll-*a* (μg L^{-1}), 0.5–234. For further details, see Moss *et al.* (1996).

Use of a state-changed scheme rather than a spatial state scheme for assessing the state of standing waters allows avoidance of such simple errors, gives sensible targets for setting water quality objectives, provides a relatively straightforward and easily understandable scheme, and, with a baseline set around sustainable use, is proactive for the political climate likely to be extant in the future.

The scheme presented represents a significant change in the British approach to water quality management. It has been widely debated within and outside the Environment Agency and has received a cautious welcome. Several issues remain to be resolved but the new Agency is currently developing the approach in a more intensive pilot testing of approximately 80 lakes.

Table 10.4 Mean percentage change from their hindcast baseline states in variables linked with eutrophication in some upland lakes, compared with the classification these lakes would receive, based on maximum chlorophyll-*a* in the OECD classification.

Lake	Percentage change in eutrophication variables	Current maximum chlorophyll-a ($\mu g\,L^{-1}$)	OECD class
Llyn Gwernan	104	0.73	Ultra-oligotrophic
Craig Goch Reservoir	88	1.8	Ultra-oligotrophic
Blelham Tarn	173	68	Eutrophic
Esthwaite Water	394	212	Hyper-eutrophic
Wastwater	74	5.3	Oligotrophic
Tarn Hows	91	4.8	Oligotrophic
Bassenthwaite	185	3.3	Oligotrophic
Ullswater	176	9.2	Mesotrophic
Yew Tree Tarn	175	5.1	Oligotrophic

It is a scheme that should also be applicable in other north temperate countries. The state-changed approach is internationally applicable. The details of calculating or otherwise setting baseline states may need to vary in different countries, but many have long-term records of land use or other information that could be used. Even if such data are not available in a detailed form, a baseline target could still be set from comparative studies of the literature from countries with analogous climate, geology and topography.

The state-changed approach also has the strength that any number of variables can be included—heavy metals, organic micropollutants, measures of tourist pressure, fish catch—provided only that baseline values can be determined, either from past data or from informed opinion. It is a vastly more informative and flexible approach to water and ecosystem quality than spatial state assessments and if accepted could form a rational basis for the future safeguarding of standing waters.

Acknowledgements

Financial support was provided by the National Rivers Authority for this work but the views expressed are not necessarily those of the Authority or of its successor.

References

Battarbee, R. W., Allott, T. E. H., Bull, K., Christie, A. E. G., Curtis, C., Flower, R. J., Hall, J., Harriman, R., Jenkins, A., Juggins, S., Kreiser, A., Metcalfe, S. E., Ormerod, S. J. and Patrick, S. T. (1994). Critical loads of acid deposition for UK freshwaters. *Environmental Change Research Centre Research Papers,* **11**, 1–139.

Beaulac, M. N. and Reckhow, K. M. (1982). An examination of land use–nutrient export relationships. *Water Resources Bulletin,* **18**, 1013–1024.

Bennion, H. (1994). A diatom-phosphorus transfer function for shallow, eutrophic ponds in southeastern England. *Hydrobiologia,* **275/276,** 391–410.

Birks, H. J. B., Line, J. M., Juggins, S., Stevenson, A. C. and Ter Braak, C. J. F. (1990). Diatoms and pH reconstruction. *Philosophical Transactions of the Royal Society of London,* **327,** 263–278.

Carvalho, L. C. (1993). 'Experimental Limnology of Four Cheshire Meres'. Unpublished Ph.D. thesis, University of Liverpool, Liverpool.

Carvalho, L. C. and Moss, B. (1995). The current status of a sample of English Sites of Special Scientific Interest subject to eutrophication. *Aquatic Conservation: Marine and Freshwater Ecosystems,* **5,** 191–204.

Clark, G. (1982). *The Agricultural Census—United Kingdom and United States.* Concepts and Techniques in Modern Geography, **35,** Geo Books, Norwich.

Department of the Environment and Welsh Office (1992). *River Quality, the Government's Proposals: a Consultation Paper.* HMSO, London.

Dudley Stamp, L. (1941). *The Land of Great Britain. Vols I–IX.* HMSO, London.

Elster H. J. (1958). Das limnologische Seetypensystem, Rückblick und Ausblick. *Verhandlungen der Internationalen Vereinigung für theoretische und angewandte Limnologie,* **13,** 101–120.

Hamilton, J. D. (1987). Recent human influences on the ecology of Loch Lomond, Scotland. *Verhandlungen der Internationalen Vereinigung für theoretische und angewandte Limnologie,* **25,** 403–413.

Heathwaite, A. L. and Johnes, P. J. (submitted) The contribution of catchment sources of nitrogen and phosphorus to stream water quality. *Water Resources Research.*

Hutchinson, G. E. (1957). *A Treatise on Limnology Vol. 1,* John Wiley, New York.

Johnes, P. J. (1990). 'An Investigation of the Effects of Land Use upon Water Quality in the Windrush Catchment'. Unpublished D.Phil. thesis, University of Oxford, Oxford.

Johnes, P. J. (in press). Evaluation and management of the impact of land use change on the nitrogen and phosphorus load delivered to surface waters. 1. The export coefficient modelling approach. *Journal of Hydrology.*

Johnes, P. J. and Heathwaite, A. L. (submitted). Evaluation and management of the impact of land use change on the nitrogen and phosphorus load delivered to surface waters. II The role of catchment hydrology, *Water Resources Research.*

Johnes, P. J., Moss, B. and Phillips, G. L. (1994). *Lakes—Classification and Monitoring. A Strategy for the Classification of Lakes.* National Rivers Authority R&D Project Record 286/6/A, Bristol.

Johnes, P. J., Moss, B., and Phillips, G. L. (in press). The determination of total nitrogen and total phosphorus concentrations in freshwaters from land use, stock headage and population data—testing of a model for use in conservation and water quality management. *Freshwater Biology.*

Kinnersley, D. (1988). *Troubled Water. River Policies and Pollution.* Shipman, London.

Meteorological Office (1989). *Climatological Data for Agricultural Land Classification: Gridpoint Data Sets of Climatic Variables and 5 km Intervals for England and Wales.* Bracknell.

Ministry of Agriculture, Fisheries and Food (1968). *A Century of Agricultural Statistics: Great Britain 1866–1966.* HMSO, London.

Ministry of Transport, Public Works and Water Management (1992). *Speaking of Sustainable Development ... Towards a Method of Measuring the Quality of Nature in Salt Water Habitats, the 'Amoeba'.* The Hague, Netherlands.

Moss, B., Booker, I., Balls, H. R. and Manson, K. (1989). Phytoplankton distribution in a temperate floodplain lake and river system. 1. Hydrology, nutrient sources and phytoplankton biomass, *Journal of Plankton Research,* **11,** 813–838.

Moss, B., Johnes, P. J. and Phillips, G. L. (1996). The monitoring of ecological quality and the classification of standing waters in temperate regions: a review and proposal based on a worked scheme for British waters. *Biological Reviews,* **71,** 301–319.

Moss, B., McGowan, S. and Carvalho, L. (1994). Determination of phytoplankton crops by top-down and bottom-up mechanisms in a group of English lakes, the West Midland meres. *Limnology and Oceanography,* **39,** 1020–1029.

National Rivers Authority (1991a). *Proposals for Statutory Water Quality Objectives.* Water Quality Series, **5,** Bristol.

National Rivers Authority (1991b). *The Quality of Rivers, Canals and Estuaries in England and Wales.* Water Quality Series, **4,** Bristol.

National Rivers Authority (1994). *Water Quality Objectives: Procedures Used by the NRA for the Purpose of the Surface Waters (River Ecosystem) (Classification) Regulations 1994*. Bristol.

National Water Council (1981). *River Quality—the 1980 Survey and Future Outlook*. London.

OECD (1982). *Eutrophication of Waters: Monitoring, Assessment and Control*. Paris.

Orwell, G. (1945). *Animal Farm*. Secker and Warburg, London.

Palmer, M., Bell, S. L. and Butterfield, I. (1992). A botanical classification of standing waters in Britain: applications for conservation and monitoring. *Aquatic Conservation: Marine and Freshwater Ecosystems, 2*, 125–144.

Petersen, R. C. (1992). The RCE: a riparian, channel and environmental inventory for small streams in the agricultural landscape. *Freshwater Biology, 27*, 295–306.

Raven, P. J., Fox, P., Everard, M., Holmes, N. T. H. and Dawson, F. H. (This volume). River Habitat Survey: a new system for classifying rivers according to their habitat quality.

Reckhow, K. H. and Simpson, J. J. (1980). A procedure using modelling and error analysis for prediction of lake phosphorus concentration from land use information. *Canadian Journal of Fisheries and Aquatic Sciences, 37*, 1439–1448.

Rimes, C. A., Farmer, A. M. and Howell, D. (1994). A survey of the threat of surface water acidification to the nature conservation interest of fresh waters on sites of Special Scientific Interest in Britain. *Aquatic Conservation: Marine and Freshwater Ecosystems, 4*, 31–44.

Shoard, M. (1980). *The Theft of the Countryside*. Temple Smith, London.

Smith, I. and Lyle, A. (1979). *Distribution of Freshwaters in Great Britain*. Institute of Terrestrial Ecology, Cambridge.

Swedish Environmental Protection Agency (1991). *Quality Criteria for Lakes and Watercourses*. Naturvardsverket, Solna, Sweden.

Ten Brink, B. J. H., Hosper, S. H. and Colijn, F. (1991). A quantitative method for description and assessment of ecosystems: the AMOEBA approach. *Marine Pollution Bulletin, 23*, 265–270.

Wright, J. F., Furse, M. T. and Armitage, P. D. (1993). RIVPACS—a technique for evaluating the biological quality of rivers in the UK. *European Water Pollution Control, 3*, 15–25.

Wright, J. F., Moss, D., Clarke, R. T. and Furse, M. T. (This volume). Biological assessment of river quality using the new version of RIVPACS (RIVPACS III).

11 DEFINING THE QUALITY OF SCOTTISH FRESHWATER LOCHS

I. R. Fozzard, C. R. Doughty and T. M. Leatherland

Summary

1. A scheme for the classification of Scottish standing waters has been drawn up in response to locally identified needs and a recommendation of the Sixteenth Report of the Royal Commission on Environmental Pollution. The components of the scheme are described and its operation outlined.

2. The scheme is default-based and designed to minimize sampling and analytical requirements. It examines lochs along three gradients influenced by human activities: phosphorus concentration (indicating nutrient enrichment), acid neutralizing capacity (indicating acidification), and the concentration of toxic substances. Lochs are assigned to four classes, this final classification corresponding to the most serious impact along any one of the three gradients examined.

3. The scheme has been used in Scotland for classifying freshwater lochs $> 1\,km^2$ as part of the 1995 quinquennial water quality survey. Three examples of the use of the scheme are presented in outline, illustrating banding along the three environmental gradients and the overall classification.

11.1 Introduction

The Sixteenth Report of the Royal Commission on Environmental Pollution (RCEP) dealt with freshwater quality (RCEP, 1992). Recommendation number 6 of that report stated: 'UK standing waters of 0.4 hectares and above should be surveyed and classified on a regular basis and . . . as far as possible the classification should adopt an internationally recognized system such as the OECD one'. For the 1995 quinquennial classification of Scottish waters, freshwater lochs were classified using a new scheme distinct from that used for rivers and streams. The procedure adopted was to identify the impacts relevant to standing waters in Scotland, investigate what methodologies were already available for the assessment of these impacts, and assemble these components into a scheme based around a decision tree.

The classification scheme centres on the extent to which human activity has altered or downgraded water quality and aquatic ecology on a site-by-site basis. This temporal 'changed state' approach is necessary because of the wide spectrum of natural loch geomorphology, hydrology, biology and chemistry (Moss *et al.*, 1994, this volume). For example, nutrient concentrations which would be entirely natural and expected in a shallow lowland loch could be indicative of pollution in a deeper highland loch.

The scheme classifies lochs along three gradients; *phosphorus concentration* (indicating nutrient enrichment), *acid neutralizing capacity* (indicating anthropic acidification), and presence of *toxic substances*. The decision tree provides all the stages necessary for classifying a standing water. A water body is assessed in relation to these impacts, resulting in three quality bandings, with the overall class of the water being that of the lowest quality band. The structure of the classification scheme has been designed to minimize the amount, and hence cost, of new monitoring and modelling requirements. Thus, where relatively simple and inexpensive measures clearly demonstrate current good quality, further measurements and hindcasting are not required. Presently available data indicate that this will apply to most of the larger Scottish lochs. Only where lochs have been significantly polluted by human activities will more data be required to discriminate between classes.

11.2 Class Descriptors

Output from the scheme is an overall classification into four classes, based upon the lowest of the three bands for nutrient enrichment, acidification, and toxic substances. The general character of the lochs within each of the classes is described in Table 11.1.

11.3 A Guide to the Scheme

It is not possible to give a fully detailed account of the scheme, including the decision tree and all the appendices, in this chapter. Copies of the full document (Association of Directors and River Inspectors of Scotland, 1995) are available from the authors. This section briefly outlines the contents, and a simplified decision tree is reproduced as Figure 11.1.

Table 11.1 Class descriptors.

Class 1	Lochs whose water quality and aquatic ecology are not significantly altered by human activity.
Class 2	Lochs whose water quality and/or ecology are significantly altered by human activity.
Class 3	Lochs whose water quality and ecology are seriously downgraded by human activity.
Class 4	Severely polluted lochs incapable of supporting fisheries due to gross anthropic enrichment, acidification, presence of toxins, or deoxygenation.

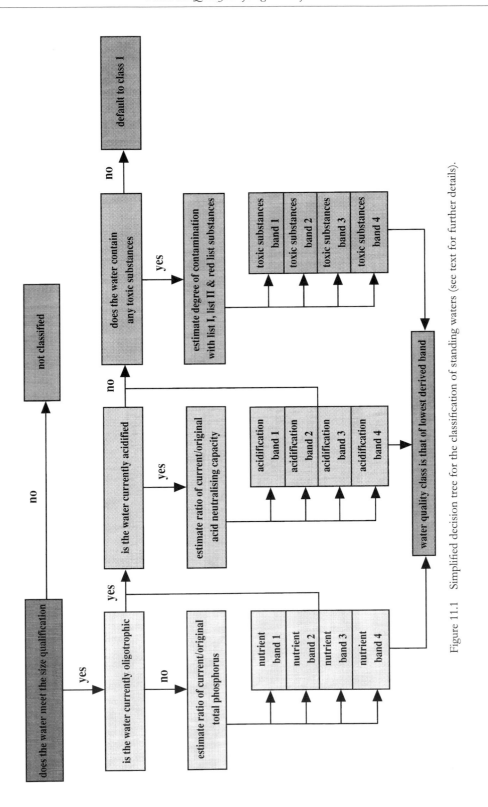

Figure 11.1 Simplified decision tree for the classification of standing waters (see text for further details).

11.3.1   The decision tree

The decision tree provides all the stages necessary for classifying a standing water and is designed to allow the most efficient route to the final quality classification. Reference to the individual quality bandings is *via* separate appendices which are described below. The scheme is default based: lochs which are currently deemed oligotrophic, have an alkalinity greater than 2 mg L^{-1}, and whose waters comply with local, national, and international environmental quality standards for toxic substances, default to class 1. This makes application of the scheme cost-effective in identifying those waters which have suffered significant impacts, permitting targeting of resources. Where data indicate that a water body may not meet these primary criteria, further data collection and hindcasting are used to determine the quality banding along the appropriate gradient. This does not imply that the water will be lower than class 1, as further analysis may still result in a band 1 designation. After this process, the water body is banded for the three quality gradients, and the overall class is that of the lowest derived band.

11.3.2   Nutrient banding

Nutrient banding is determined using total phosphorus, a pragmatic necessity since the possibilities for hindcasting are centred on this parameter. Furthermore, in northern temperate lakes, phosphorus is generally regarded as being the factor limiting biomass development of most planktonic algae (Vollenweider, 1968). It is also the factor which has been most modified by human activities and is most amenable to control.

The current trophic status of a loch is assessed ideally by an evaluation of a suite of parameters including algal biomass (high algal production may not be regarded as an environmental impact if it does not result in high standing crop), other biota, total and dissolved phosphorus, colour and turbidity. For the purposes of this scheme the mean annual total phosphorus (TP) concentration derived from monthly samples over one year is the preferred option, provided it is in agreement with the inferences made from other available data. Where TP data are not available, a surrogate value may be inferred from available chemical and biological data.

The baseline trophic status of a loch may be assessed in a variety of ways, again dependent on the data readily available. Ongoing research (Ferrier *et al.*, this volume) should produce a workable methodology for hindcasting the baseline trophic status employing land-use categories and phosphorus loss coefficients. This methodology has produced hindcast phosphorus values for all lochs classified in the 1995 survey. The reconstruction of historical TP changes by using sub-fossil diatom frustules from the dated strata of lake sediments (Battarbee, this volume) is of considerable interest and provides a potential validation for the land use/loss coefficient method adopted.

When current and hindcast TP concentrations have been calculated or esti-mated, the ratio of these two values is employed to determine the degree of change. Band 1 represents a $TP_{(current)} : TP_{(hindcast)}$ ratio $\leqslant 2$, Band 2 a ratio of 2–6, Band 3 a ratio of 6–20, and Band 4 a ratio > 20.

11.3.3 Acidification banding

The influences of geology and peat accumulation mean that many Scottish lochs are naturally acidic. A quality classification scheme must be based, therefore, on a comparison between present acidification status and the natural pre-industrialization baseline level. Empirical models (e.g. Wright and Henriksen, 1983; Henriksen *et al.*, 1992) may be used to hindcast baseline alkalinity or acid neutralizing capacity (ANC), or historical pH changes can be reconstructed from sub-fossil diatom frustules from the dated strata of lake sediments (e.g. Flower and Battarbee, 1983). The former methodology employing ANC has been adopted for the purposes of this scheme, but it is intended that where possible a comparison will be made between both methods. Lochs may be classified on a minimum of two water samples, from spring and autumn.

The decision tree (Figure 11.1) incorporates two-stage screening before the hindcasting of ANC is required. If current alkalinity is equal to or greater than 2 mg L^{-1} then the loch defaults to Band 1. If alkalinity is less than 2 mg L^{-1}, then current ANC is calculated from alkalinity and dissolved organic carbon (the latter takes account of the additional buffering provided by humic substances) using an empirical relationship (Cantrell *et al.*, 1990). If ANC is equal to or greater than 40 μeq L^{-1} then the loch defaults to Band 1. If both of these steps indicate greater acidity, then hindcasting of acidification status is necessary. Two methods are given for the calculation of baseline ANC, the simpler of which ignores base cation leaching and background sulphate concentration. These methods are based on the observation that in non-acidified waters, bicarbonate alkalinity is approximately equivalent to the total base cation concentration (excluding that derived from sea salts). If certain assumptions are made, baseline ANC may be estimated from present base cation concentrations.

Lochs are placed into one of four bands according to the difference between present and hindcast ANC as illustrated in Table 11.2. The band boundaries take into account the relationship between present-day ANC and fishery status derived from Norwegian lakes (Henriksen *et al.*, 1992).

Table 11.2 Allocation of acidification banding by ANC difference (estimated to the nearest whole number).

Baseline ANC (μeq L^{-1})	Present ANC (μeq L^{-1})					
	$\geqslant 40$	39–20	19–0	-1–-20	-21–-40	< -40
$\geqslant 40$	Band 1	Band 2	Band 2	Band 3	Band 3	Band 4
20–39		1	2	3	3	4
0–19			1	2	3	4

Table 11.3 Allocation of toxic substances banding.

Criterion	100% EQS compliance of samples	Annual EQS compliance of samples	Exceedence of any List II EQS only	Exceedence of any List I or Red List EQS
Allocated band	Band 1	Band 2	Band 3	Band 4

100% EQS compliance means all samples must be at or below the Environmental Quality Standard value. Annual EQS compliance means that the annual average must be at or below the Environmental Quality Standard. For more details of List I, List II, and Red List substances, see Edwards (1992).

11.3.4 Toxic substances banding

In their natural state, standing waters would contain no xenobiotic trace organic substances, but traces of naturally occurring toxic substances such as ammonia and metals (e.g. cadmium, mercury) would be present due to natural weathering and cycling processes. The simple presence of a toxic substance is therefore insufficient to justify downgrading. Exceedence of local, national and international (EC) Environmental Quality Standards (EQSs) for 'List I', 'List II', or other hazardous substances (*Official Journal of the European Communities*, 1976; Department of the Environment, 1990; North Sea Task Force, 1990) would generally indicate a substantial change from the natural state and result in downgrading. The bandings for toxic substances are derived as outlined in Table 11.3.

11.4 The 1995 Classification Exercise

It is estimated that there are 3,788 freshwater lochs over 4ha in Scotland (Smith and Lyle, 1979), and in terms of the Royal Commission recommendation, there are estimated to be over 30,000 waters of over 0.4ha. Resource constraints prevented classifying all of these in one year, so in 1995 the classification was restricted to those lochs over $1 km^2$ and those smaller lochs considered to be of local concern. A total of 173 freshwater lochs were classified, with the Western Isles being the only area of the country not covered by this scheme. The results of the 1995 quinquennial water quality survey should be published during 1996 by the Scottish Office. To illustrate the scheme three examples are presented here: one loch affected by acidification, and two lochs affected by differing degrees of nutrient enrichment, one of which is also affected by a toxic substance.

11.4.1 Examples (Table 11.4): Lake of Menteith, Loch Gelly and Loch Muick

The Lake of Menteith lies 22km west of Stirling in the Forth catchment. The lake is a designated wildlife site (a Site of Special Scientific Interest, or SSSI), a commercial rainbow trout fishery, and a tourist destination. Algal blooms over the past two decades have raised concerns over nutrient enrichment, and the Scottish Environment Protection Agency has consequently imposed phosphorus limits on consented discharges to the lake.

Table 11.4   Worked examples of the classification process: Lake of Menteith, Loch Gelly and Loch Muick. Chemical data are means for the period 1990–1995 (1986–1988 for Loch Muick—data courtesy of North East RPB).

	Menteith	Gelly	Muick
Physical data			
Dimensions (km)	2.6×1	1×0.6	3.5×0.8
Surface area (km^2)	2.64	0.58	2.20
Mean depth (m)	6	1.8	35.4
Maximum depth (m)	23.5	2.5	78
Water residence time (yr)	0.8	0.16	1.25
Altitude AOD (m)	17	107	400
Chemical data			
pH	7.4	8.2	5.97
Alkalinity (mg L^{-1})	19	103	1.30
TON (mg L^{-1})	0.14	2.08	0.19
TP (μg L^{-1})	18	1,071	8
chl a (μg L^{-1})	6.1	24	—
Ammonia (mg L^{-1})	—	0.72	—
Ca^{2+} (mg L^{-1})	—	—	1.08
Mg^{2+} (mg L^{-1})	—	—	0.42
Cl$^-$ (mg L^{-1})	—	—	2.92
SO$_4^{2-}$ (mg L^{-1})	—	—	3.25
TOC (mg L^{-1})	—	—	2.1
Banding and classification			
Current TP (μg L^{-1})	18	1,071	—
Nutrient status	Mesotrophic	Hypertrophic	—
Hindcast TP (μg L^{-1})	12	31.5	—
Nutrient status	Mesotrophic	Mesotrophic	—
Nutrient band (see Section 11.3.2)	1	4	—
Current ANC (μeq L^{-1})	—	—	35.5
Hindcast ANC (μeq L^{-1})	—	—	52.2
ANC band (see Section 11.3.3)	—	—	2
NH$_4$-N (mg L^{-1}, 95 percentile)	—	1.25	—
NH$_4$-N (EQS)	—	0.78	—
Toxic substances band (see Section 11.3.4)	—	3	—
Overall class	1	4	2

Loch Gelly is a small shallow loch, situated in Fife. The main feeder stream receives the treated sewage effluent from Cowdenbeath Sewage Treatment Works. Engineering works are in progress to divert this effluent. Crops of phytoplankton are relatively low, but *Enteromorpha* and *Potamogeton pectinatus* are abundant. Figure 11.2 shows Loch Gelly in August 1995.

PLATE 3: NON-NATIVE FRESHWATER SPECIES ESTABLISHED IN BRITAIN

3a(right) – Giant hogweed *(Heracleum mantegazzianum)* in the Tweed catchment (Scotland). Introduced as an ornamental garden plant, it is now the dominant plant species on some river banks in Britain (Photo: M Smith).

3b(below) – Australian swamp stonecrop *(Crassula helmsii)* completely covering a small pond in the New Forest (England). This popular aquarium plant is now commonly found in the wild where it displaces native species (Photo: H Dawson).

3c(bottom) – North American signal crayfish *(Pacifastacus leniusculus)*, a species imported for aquaculture but now established in the wild where it displaces the native crayfish species by competitive exclusion, predation or disease (Photo: D Fox/D Holdich).

PLATE 4: THE GEOMORPHOLOGICAL DIVERSITY OF DYNAMIC RIVERS

4a(main picture) – The braided River Dee (Scotland) and its undeveloped floodplain – now an uncommon feature of British river systems (Photo: L Gill).

4b(inset right) – The alluvial fan of the River Feshie (Scotland), protected by British legislation because of its relative intactness and continued dynamic nature (Photo: V Brazier) (see Chapter 23).

4c(inset top left) – The Rapa Valley, Sarek National Park (Sweden), illustrating a range of freshwater features resulting from glaciation (Photo: P Hanneberg) (see Chapter 29).

4d(inset bottom left) – An active, gravel-bed river in the Middle Hills of Nepal, supplying water for rice-field cultivation (Photo: S Ormerod) (see Chapter 21).

Figure 11.2   Loch Gelly, summer 1995, illustrating dense growths of the filamentous alga *Enteromorpha*. (Photo: I. R. Fozzard).

Loch Muick is a mountain loch on granite at high altitude near Lochnagar in the Grampian mountains. Some angling takes place on the loch, and the surrounding moorland is part of a sporting estate. The main inflow and outflow have been sampled since 1986 and as a result of these data, the loch is regarded as a clearwater acid loch affected by acid deposition.

11.5   Conclusions

One function of environmental quality classification schemes should be to translate sometimes complex scientific data into simple terms which can be readily understood by non-scientists. Quality classification schemes thus provide a means of informing policy makers and the public in clear, non-technical language, of progress made towards the attainment of objectives. The scheme provides the water manager with a simple, cost effective, overall classification of standing waters into four quality classes. The three major pollution threats to the quality of standing waters in Scotland are incorporated into the scheme and their contribution to the overall quality class is explicit.

A consequence of this initiative to classify standing waters according to their 'changed state' has been to focus attention on the adequacy of existing techniques for hindcasting water quality variables. More work is needed in this area. Testing the classification scheme on selected lochs of differing quality has produced an output likely to be recognized as appropriate by freshwater scientists and members of the public.

Acknowledgements

The Standing Waters Classification Scheme is the product of a group comprising: Dr. Tom Leatherland (Chair), Ian Fozzard (Secretary), Ross Doughty, Dr. Roger Owen, and Dr. Julian Hunter. Thanks are due to Ron Harriman of the Freshwater Fisheries Laboratory, Pitlochry, for comments and advice on the acidification aspects of the scheme.

References

Association of Directors and River Inspectors of Scotland (1995). 'Quality Classification of Scottish Standing Waters'. Unpublished Report, ADRIS sub-group on Classification of Standing Waters.

Battarbee, R. W. (This volume). Freshwater quality, naturalness and palaeolimnology.

Cantrell, K. J., Serkiz, S. M. and Perdue, E. M. (1990). Evaluation of acid neutralising capacity data for solutions containing natural organic acids. *Geochimica et Cosmochimica Acta,* **54,** 1247–1254.

Department of the Environment (1990). *United Kingdom North Sea Action Plan 1985–1995.* London.

Edwards, P. (1992). *Dangerous Substances in Water: A Practical Guide.* Environmental Data Services Ltd., London.

Ferrier, R. C., Owen, R., Edwards, A. C., Malcolm, A. and Morrice, J. G. (This volume). Hindcasting of phosphorus concentrations in Scottish standing waters.

Flower, R. J. and Battarbee, R. W. (1983). Diatom evidence for recent acidification of two Scottish lochs. *Nature,* **305,** 130–133.

Henriksen, A., Kamari, J., Posch, M. and Wilander, A. (1992). Critical loads of acidity: Nordic surface waters. *Ambio,* **21,** 356–363.

Moss, B., Johnes, P. and Phillips, G. (1994). August Thienemann and Loch Lomond—an approach to the design of a system for monitoring the state of north-temperate standing waters. *Hydrobiologia,* **290,** 1–12.

Moss, B., Johnes, P. and Phillips, G. (This volume). New approaches to monitoring and classifying standing waters.

North Sea Task Force (1990). *Final Declaration of the Third International Conference on the Protection of the North Sea.* The Hague.

Official Journal of the European Communities (1976). *Council Directive on Pollution caused by Certain Dangerous Substances Discharged into the Aquatic Environment of the Community* (76/464/EEC). European Commission, Brussels.

Royal Commission on Environmental Pollution (1992). *Freshwater Quality.* HMSO, London.

Smith, I. R. and Lyle, A. (1979). *Distribution of Freshwaters in Great Britain.* Institute of Terrestrial Ecology, Cambridge.

Vollenweider, R. A. (1968). *Scientific Fundamentals of the Eutrophication of Lakes and Flowing Water, with Particular Reference to Phosphorus and Nitrogen as Factors in Eutrophication.* Organisation for Economic Cooperation and Development, Paris.

Wright, R. F. and Henriksen, A. (1983). Restoration of Norwegian lakes by reduction in sulphur deposition. *Nature,* **305,** 422–424.

12 HINDCASTING OF PHOSPHORUS CONCENTRATIONS IN SCOTTISH STANDING WATERS

R. C. Ferrier, R. Owen, A. C. Edwards, A. Malcolm and J. G. Morrice

Summary

1. A methodology has been developed to determine historical land cover change within catchments selected as part of the Scottish Standing Waters Classification Scheme.

2. Phosphorus loss coefficients association with 30 types of present day and reconstructed historical land cover have been used to calculate the diffuse catchment inputs of phosphorus to the lochs studied.

3. The ratio of total phosphorus concentration under current conditions to the total phosphorus concentration of the water body under 'hindcast' historical conditions allows for the determination of changed state, and classification into one of four bands of sensitivity.

4. This chapter describes the waters included in the Standing Waters Classification Scheme, the rationale and methodology of hindcasting, and how the hindcasting methodology operates in an example catchment (the Davan catchment, NE Scotland).

12.1 Introduction

A new standing water classification scheme was developed for the 1995 quinquennial Scottish Water Quality Survey. The scheme is based upon the extent to which human activity has altered or downgraded water quality and aquatic ecology, and it focuses on three main forcing functions. These are: change in nutrient status, acidification classification, and presence of toxic substances (defined as those on Lists I and II of the EC Dangerous Substances Directive, and Red List substances identified by the inter-governmental North Sea Task Force). The Standing Waters Classification Scheme identifies four classes of water quality, and has established standards for each class within the three main criteria. The classes range from Class 1 (lochs whose water quality and aquatic ecology is not significantly altered by human activity), to Class 4 (severely polluted lochs incapable of supporting fisheries due to gross anthropic enrichment, acidification, presence of toxins, or deoxygenation). Further details are provided by Fozzard *et al.* (this volume).

A changed-state temporal framework was adopted in order to produce a quality classification of the nutrient status of standing waters. This compares current condition with that pertaining to a date before the import of phosphorus into catchments caused any significant change. The parameter selected for this analysis is mean total phosphorus concentration (TP), although it is accepted that this is not a direct measure of eutrophication. Algal biomass, which is generally of most direct relevance, is influenced by other factors besides phosphorus concentration, such as turbidity, colour, residence time, and climatic factors. General algal productivity of lakes increases with increasing concentration of phosphorus, rather than nitrogen (Schindler, 1977). However, it is considered that without any practical method for deriving hindcast algal biomass or chlorophyll values, total phosphorus appears to represent the best alternative (Fozzard, *et al.*, this volume). The water quality change associated with nutrient enrichment is therefore determined in the scheme by the ratio of current and hindcast total phosphorus concentration ($TP_{current}/TP_{original}$), and this is separated into one of four classes (Figure 12.1).

12.2   Waters Included in the Hindcasting Scheme

The scheme developed for the 1995 classification was only for those lochs and reservoirs with a surface area exceeding $1 km^2$, although in principle the scheme is equally applicable to smaller standing water bodies. Indeed, some lochs of special interest which are less than $1 km^2$ have been included. Present TP concentrations in the study lochs sampled to date can be classified into five broad trophic categories. Lochs with TP $< 10 \mu g L^{-1}$ would be considered oligotrophic (90 sites); those with TP $10–40 \mu g L^{-1}$ mesotrophic (45 sites); TP $40–100 \mu g L^{-1}$ eutrophic (12 sites), and those $> 100 \mu g L^{-1}$ hypertrophic (five sites). All trophic states are represented in the Standing Waters Classification Scheme, but nearly 60% of the lochs studied would be considered oligotrophic. Chemical data for the remaining lochs is currently being assimilated by the Scottish Environment Protection Agency.

12.3   Hindcasting Rationale and Procedure

Eutrophication of standing water bodies is an extremely rare natural condition, and almost always represents an entirely anthropic phenomenon. This condition can arise from alterations in land use which lead to increased nutrient release, and the presence in the catchment of substantial quantities of highly concentrated phosphorus in the form of fertilizers or excreta from humans or livestock. It is important to realize, therefore, that water quality in standing water bodies changes through time. Thus, although existing lake conditions may be important in

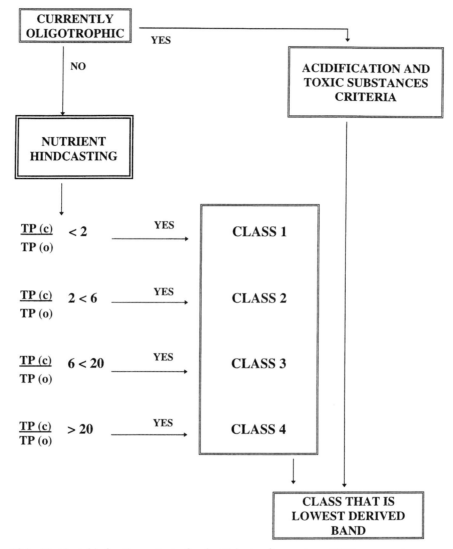

Figure 12.1 Nutrient hindcasting criteria for Scottish standing waters. TP(c) represents current mean phosphorus and TP(o) the hindcast mean phosphorus from diffuse sources.

determining appropriate current water uses, they cannot be used in isolation to draw conclusions about their present status or potential for change without reference in some way to the history of the lake (Johnes *et al.*, 1994). An assessment of change in trophic status can also be used to determine which water bodies will require active catchment management in order to stabilize or remediate water quality.

The determination of hindcast TP is most conveniently carried out by using phosphorus loss coefficients for different land uses, and a protocol for determining current and historical land use change (Moss *et al.*, this volume). Initially, catchment boundaries and loch margins are digitized, then the Land Cover of Scotland 1988 data (LCS88) (Macaulay Land Use Research Institute, 1992) are overlain. The LCS88 data set contains 126 different categories of land use, with over 1200 mosaics of land use where no particular cover is dominant. This database has been reduced to 30 dominant types which have been allocated the best available phosphorus loss coefficient (M. Marsden, personal communication). This allows for the determination of diffuse TP load (as kg ha^{-1}), and following the inclusion of data on individual catchment point sources and discharge characteristics, modelled total current phosphorus concentration is calculated (TP$_{derived}$). At present, an analysis of TP$_{derived}$ to TP$_{current}$ (from recent water quality surveys) is being undertaken over the whole spectrum of TP$_{current}$ concentrations to assess model fit.

Hindcast phosphorus concentrations are determined by subsequent overlaying of the extent of ancient woodland (c.1850) coverage, and a re-interpretation of land cover categories into natural and semi-natural units. This is achieved using relationships between mapped soil information, data on the Hydrology of Soil Types (HOST) (Boorman *et al.*, 1995), and spatial information on the historical land cover of Scotland. This allows for the re-calculation of diffuse loads (all point source inputs of phosphorus are removed), before calculation of TP$_{original}$, following conversion of flux to concentration using the most appropriate equation from OECD (1982) and information on loch volumes and retention times.

12.4 An Example Catchment—the Davan, NE Scotland

The present-day and historically reconstructed land cover in the Davan catchment have been compared using a Geographic Information System. The specific features which emerge from the land-cover analysis in this catchment are:

- Regeneration of small areas of native woodland on moorland.
- Large-scale expansion of commercial coniferous afforestation.
- Loss of small pockets of ancient woodland to improved grassland and arable land.
- Development of wetlands on lock fringe and a reduction in total loch area.
- Increased intensification of farming practices (both arable and improved pasture).

The preliminary hindcasting calculation (Table 12.1) for the Davan catchment suggests that the net effect of historical land-use change is to increase mean TP concentration from $16 \mu g \, L^{-1}$ to $33 \mu g \, L^{-1}$. This would result in Loch Davan being classified as Class 2 for nutrients in the Standing Waters Classification Scheme i.e., a loch whose water quality and/or ecology has been significantly altered by human activity.

12.5 Future Research Aims

A further development of the hindcasting protocol will include the calibration of TP$_{derived}$ to TP$_{current}$ for all lochs, spanning the spectrum of trophic status from oligotrophic to hypertrophic. Uncertainty in modelled total phosphorus (TP$_{derived}$)

Table 12.1 Hindcasting calculation for the Davan catchment.

Point sources	30 kg
Diffuse load (present day)	675 kg
Diffuse load (c.1850)	243 kg
Discharge	$0.49\,\mathrm{m^3\,s^{-1}}$
$TP_{derived}$	$43\,\mu\mathrm{g\,L^{-1}}$
$TP_{current}$	$33\,\mu\mathrm{g\,L^{-1}}$
$TP_{original}$	$16\,\mu\mathrm{g\,L^{-1}}$
$TP_{current}/TP_{original}$	2.1
Class	2

is most strongly influenced by the determination of appropriate loss coefficients for land-cover types, and available data on the nature and quantification of point sources of phosphorus, but also through the accurate determination of TP given natural seasonal fluctuations and the lack of accurate field data. Following refinements in the land-use model, all $TP_{original}$ concentrations will be recalculated and all waters classified for change in nutrient status.

Acknowledgements

The research team would like to acknowledge the invaluable assistance, expertise and information supplied by the seven former Scottish River Purification Boards (Clyde, Forth, Highland, North East, Tay, Tweed, and Solway); the Department of the Environment for Northern Ireland (Environment Service); and the Orkney and Shetland Islands Councils. This research was funded by the Scotland and Northern Ireland Forum for Environmental Research (SNIFFER).

References

Boorman, D. B., Hollis, J. M. and Lilly, A. (1995). *The Hydrology of Soil Types; a Hydrologically Based Classification of the Soils of the UK.* Institute of Hydrology Report No. 126, IH, Wallingford.

Fozzard, I. R., Doughty, C. R. and Leatherland, T. M. (This volume). Defining the quality of Scottish freshwater lochs.

Johnes, P., Moss, B. and Phillips, G. (1994). *Lakes—Classification and Monitoring.* NRA R&D Note 253, Bristol.

Macaulay Land Use Research Institute (1992). *The Land Cover of Scotland 1988.* Aberdeen.

Moss, B., Johnes, P. and Phillips, G. (This volume). New approaches to monitoring and classifying standing waters.

OECD (1982). *Eutrophication of Waters: Monitoring, Assessment and Control.* Paris.

Schindler, D. W. (1977). Evolution of phosphorus limitation in lakes. *Science*, **195**, 260–262.

13 POLISH PRACTICE IN LAKE QUALITY ASSESSMENT

D. Kudelska, H. Soszka and D. Cydzik

Summary

1. Lake quality assessment and monitoring in Poland is performed according to the Lake Quality Evaluation System developed by the Institute of Environmental Protection in Warsaw. The system represents an ecosystem approach to lake quality evaluation, considering not only the characteristics of the water contained in the lake basin but also the morphometric, hydrographic and catchment parameters on which the state of the lake is dependent.

2. This system, which has three principal classes of water quality and three categories of lake sensitivity to degradation, gives general guidelines on how lakes should be managed, protected and restored. The Lake Quality Evaluation System is widely used in lake monitoring in Poland, and has proved to be a useful decision-making tool for effective lake quality control and management.

13.1 Introduction

The sustainable use of lake water resources requires the appropriate management of a lake/catchment system, since lakes are integrated parts of the entire catchment. The elaboration of appropriate lake water criteria was considered to be an important requirement in Poland, and the Institute of Environment Protection designed for decision makers an ecosystem approach to lake classification and management. This kind of approach takes into account not only the characteristics of water within the lake basin, but also morphometric, hydrographic and catchment parameters on which lake water quality is obviously strongly dependent.

13.2 The Lake Quality Evaluation System

From the numerous data collected and analysed, a Lake Quality Evaluation System (LQES) was developed and tested on a sample of 130 lakes from different Polish lakelands (Kudelska *et al.*, 1981). Representative temperate lowland lakes were carefully selected from a wide trophic spectrum, with different surroundings (arable land and forest), and subject to different urban and industrial impacts and tourism use.

The system has three principal classes of water quality and three categories of lake sensitivity to degradation. The water quality classes are based on different ranges of 18 parameters (physical, chemical and biological) indicative of general water conditions in the lake (Table 13.1). Among them are commonly used indices of trophic status, such as concentration of phosphate and total phosphorus, inorganic and total nitrogen, chlorophyll-*a*, hypolimnetic oxygen saturation, Secchi disc readings, specific conductivity, COD, and BOD_5, as well as coliform density and concentration of toxic chemicals. Most of the values are representative for surface and bottom layers and they are averaged either seasonally or specifically for spring and/or summer periods. The range of variables indicates that class I is equal to oligotrophic and mesotrophic in limnological terminology, class II represents moderately eutrophic lakes, and class III represents highly eutrophic water bodies. Hypertrophic lakes are known in the LQES as 'off class'.

13.3 The Classification Process

The first element, classification of water quality, is done in the following way:

1. Values of parameters obtained from analyses and field measurements are referred to corresponding classes (Table 13.1).
2. For each parameter, the class derived above is allocated points according to a simple scale: for class I—1 point; class II—2 points; class III—3 points; 'off class'—4 points.
3. The average value of points is calculated.
4. The average is referred to the following ranges indicative of the resulting class of water quality:
   class I ⩽ 1.5 points
   class II > 1.5 ⩽ 2.5 points
   class III > 2.5 ⩽ 3.25 points
   'off class' > 3.25 points.

When massive mortalities of aquatic organisms (e.g. fish kills) are visibly detected in the lake, they may place the lake 'beyond' the principal three classes. These phenomena are a crucial part of this classification, as they are the best indicators of poor water quality (being more sensitive than chemical analysis), and do not necessarily reflect the lake's trophic status. Toxic chemicals, when exceeding permissible standards, also place the lake beyond the three principal classes. Finally, the sanitary index has a controlling importance in establishing the quality class determined by all other data. If the *E. coli* number indicates a water quality class lower than that evaluated according to the physical, chemical and biological indices, the final classification is based on the *E. coli* number.

Biological surveys are an integral part of the water-quality assessment process. These include a descriptive analysis of the phytoplankton (algal blooms, occurrence of cyanobacteria) and zooplankton, quantitative and qualitative analyses of benthic

Table 13.1   Ranges of lake water quality variables for three classes of lake waters.

Variable		Period and sampling point	Class of water quality		
			I	II	III
Hypolimnetic O_2 saturation (mean %) (s.l.)		Summer Hypolimnion	$\geqslant 40$	$\geqslant 20$	$\geqslant 5$
Dissolved oxygen (ns.l.)	$mgO_2\ L^{-1}$	Summer Surface layer	$\geqslant 4.0$	$\geqslant 2.0$	$\geqslant 1.0$
COD, dichromate method (s.l.+ns.l.)	$mgO_2\ L^{-1}$	Summer Surface layer	$\leqslant 20$	$\leqslant 30$	$\leqslant 50$
BOD_5 (s.l.+ns.l.)	$mgO_2\ L^{-1}$	Summer Surface layer	$\leqslant 2$	$\leqslant 4$	$\leqslant 8$
BOD_5 (s.l.)	$mgO_2\ L^{-1}$	Summer Bottom layer	$\leqslant 2$	$\leqslant 5$	$\leqslant 10$
$P-PO_4$ (s.l.+ns.l.)	$mgP\ L^{-1}$	Spring Surface layer	$\leqslant 0.020$	$\leqslant 0.040$	$\leqslant 0.080$
$P-PO_4$ (s.l.)	$mgP\ L^{-1}$	Summer Bottom layer	$\leqslant 0.020$	$\leqslant 0.040$	$\leqslant 0.080$
Total P (s.l.)	$mgP\ L^{-1}$	Summer Bottom layer	$\leqslant 0.060$	$\leqslant 0.150$	$\leqslant 0.600$
Total P (s.l.+ns.l.)	$mgP\ L^{-1}$	Spring, summer (mean value) Surface layer	$\leqslant 0.050$	$\leqslant 0.100$	$\leqslant 0.200$
Inorganic N ($N_{NH4}+N_{NO3}$) (s.l.+ns.l.)	$mgN\ L^{-1}$	Spring Surface layer	$\leqslant 0.20$	$\leqslant 0.40$	$\leqslant 0.80$
Ammonia (s.l.)	$mgN\ L^{-1}$	Summer Bottom layer	$\leqslant 0.20$	$\leqslant 1.00$	$\leqslant 5.00$
Total N (s.l.+ns.l.)	$mgN\ L^{-1}$	Spring, summer (mean value) Surface layer	$\leqslant 1.0$	$\leqslant 1.5$	$\leqslant 2.0$
Conductivity	$\mu S\ cm^{-1}$	Spring Surface layer	$\leqslant 250$	$\leqslant 300$	$\leqslant 350$
Chlorophyll (s.l.+ns.l.)	$\mu g\ L^{-1}$	Spring, summer (mean value) Surface layer	$\leqslant 8$	$\leqslant 15$	$\leqslant 25$
Dry mass of seston (s.l.+ns.l.)	$mg\ L^{-1}$	Spring, summer (mean value) Surface layer	$\leqslant 4$	$\leqslant 8$	$\leqslant 12$
Secchi disc readings (s.l.+ns.l.)	m	Spring, summer (mean value)	$\geqslant 4$	$\geqslant 2$	$\geqslant 1$
E. coli titre (s.l.+ns.l.)		Spring, summer Surface and bottom layer (the worst result)	$\geqslant 1.0$	$\geqslant 0.1$	$\geqslant 0.01$
Biological field observations (s.l.+ns.l.)		All year Whole lake	Occurrence of fish kills or mass mortality of other aquatic organisms (both in littoral and pelagic) puts the lake 'off class' regardless of the range of other parameters.		

s.l.—Stratified lakes.

ns.l.—Non-stratified lakes.

Table 13.2 Ranges of morphometric, hydrographic and catchment variables for three categories of lakes according to their sensitivity to degradation.

Parameters and units*	Category		
	I	II	III
Mean depth (m)	$\geqslant 10$	$\geqslant 5$	$\geqslant 3$
Vl/Ll (m^3 1000 m^{-1})	$\geqslant 4$	$\geqslant 2$	$\geqslant 0.8$
Stratification (%)	$\geqslant 35$	$\geqslant 20$	$\geqslant 10$
Pb/Ve (m^2 m^{-3})	$\leqslant 0.10$	$\leqslant 0.15$	$\leqslant 0.30$
Water renewal (% yr^{-1})**	$\leqslant 30$	$\leqslant 200$	$\leqslant 1000$
Schindler's index (Pl+Pw)/Vl(m^2 m^{-3})	$\leqslant 2$	$\leqslant 10$	$\leqslant 50$
Catchment land use ***(%)	$\geqslant 60$% forests	< 60% cultivated fields < 60% forests	$\geqslant 60$% cultivated fields

*Vl—lake volume, Ll—length of shoreline, Pb—area of active bottom surface, Ve—epilimnion volume, Pl—lake area, Pw—catchment area.

**If a lake is supplied by an inflow of better quality than the water in the lake, then water renewal rate is not included in lake categorization.

***If local authorities record point sources of sewage pollution in the catchment *without* nutrient removal, then the lake category can only predict the effectiveness of protective or restorative action *after* removing or diverting the nutrient input. 'Resilient' lakes with favourable Category I characteristics have better chances of recovery than more 'vulnerable' Category III lakes.

invertebrate community composition, and observations in the littoral zone (occurrence of filamentous algae and higher plants).

The second element of the LQES concerns the lake's sensitivity to degradation. This shows how easily the water body could respond to various human impacts, such as pollution, according to its morphometric and hydrographic properties and catchment land use. The three successive categories correspond to decreasing values of mean depth, the ratio of lake volume to shoreline length, and the relative volume of the unmixed layer, and to increasing values of the water renewal coefficient, Schindler's index (Schindler, 1971), and the percentage area of cultivated fields vs. forest in the catchment (Table 13.2). The values of these lake sensitivity parameters are transferred into a point scale and, as in the water quality classification method, a cumulative index determines the category of the lake (I–III) (Table 13.2). These categories are indicative respectively of 'very good', 'good' and 'unfavourable' natural lake characteristics. Lakes with very unfavourable natural features exceed the limits of the point scale and are deemed to be 'off category', which indicates their extreme sensitivity to degradation and the limited possibilities for their use and successful restoration.

13.4 Management Applications

The application of LQES to lake quality assessment gives, by comparison of the respective class and category, general guidelines on how the lake should be managed, protected and restored (Table 13.3). The Lake Quality Evaluation System is used for enforcement purposes by the State Inspectorate of Environmental Protection in Poland. The lake monitoring programme, designed and supervised by the Institute of Environmental Protection, is conducted by the Regional Inspectorates of Environmental Protection, following the published manual on the application of LQES in basic lake monitoring (Kudelska *et al.*, 1994). The primary objectives of this programme are the characterization of lake quality, the identification of problem waters, and evaluation of the effectiveness of pollution control measures. A total of almost 700 of Poland's most valuable lakes,

Table 13.3   General guidelines for management, control and restoration of lakes in different combinations of water quality classes and categories of sensitivity to degradation.

Class	Category		
	I	*II*	*III*
I	Lakes having clean water and favourable morphometric and catchment conditions. Control of the present state is needed, and use according to 'special protection' principles.	Lakes with clean water but rather sensitive to degradation. Maintenance of the present state is needed. Catchment land use and sewage disposal activities probably require corrective action.	Lakes which still remain clean but very sensitive to degradation. To maintain this state, land use in the catchment and sewage discharges to the tributaries should both be controlled.
II	Lakes with favourable morphometric and catchment conditions, but poor water quality. Catchment land use should be controlled, as well as sewage discharges into the lake.	Lakes of intermediate water quality but rather sensitive to further degradation. Improved land use and sewage disposal in the catchment is needed to prevent further worsening of water quality.	Lakes which still have intermediate water quality but are very sensitive to further degradation. Catchment management must be urgently improved together with sewage diversion. Some restoration techniques necessary if improvement of water quality is desired.
III	Lakes which have favourable catchment and morphometric conditions but very poor water quality, probably due to improper management in the past. Adequate catchment management (with total sewage diversion) is essential, but restoration techniques appropriate to natural lake characteristics may also be required.	Highly polluted lakes which are sensitive to degradation. Only a combination of different restoration techniques according to lake-specific properties could improve the situation. Fundamental changes in the use of the catchment are also essential.	Highly polluted lakes having the worst catchment situation and morphometric properties. Most are hypertrophic. Fundamental changes in the use of lake and catchment absolutely necessary, with restoration activities such as the removal of the upper layer of bottom sediments probably the most effective.

comprising more than 60% of the country's lakewater resources, have already been evaluated according to LQES.

All data are stored and processed in a computer database, and the results of the investigations are published in five-yearly *Atlases of the Quality of Lakes in Poland* (Cydzik *et al.*, 1982, 1992, 1995; Cydzik and Soszka, 1988). Data are intended to be used for a variety of resource management purposes by state and regional water resource managers, planners, fisheries and agricultural corporations as well as local government planning and zoning agencies.

References

Cydzik, D., Kudelska, D. and Soszka, H. (1982). *The Atlas of the Quality of Lakes in Poland for 1974–1978*. Institute of Environmental Development, Warsaw. (In Polish).

Cydzik, D., Kudelska, D. and Soszka, H. (1992). *The Atlas of the Quality of Lakes in Poland for 1984–1988*. State Inspectorate of Environmental Protection and Institute of Environmental Protection, Warsaw. (In Polish).

Cydzik, D., Kudelska, D. and Soszka, H. (1995). *The Atlas of the Quality of Lakes in Poland for 1989–1993*. State Inspectorate of Environmental Protection and Institute of Environmental Protection, Warsaw. (In Polish).

Cydzik, D. and Soszka, H. (1988). *The Atlas of the Quality of Lakes in Poland for 1979–1983*. Wydawnictwa Geologiczne, Warsaw. (In Polish).

Kudelska, D., Cydzik, D. and Soszka, H. (1981). Design of a lake quality evaluation system. (In Polish, English summary). *Wiadomosci Ekologiczne*, **27**, 149–173.

Kudelska, D., Cydzik, D. and Soszka, H. (1994). *Basic Lake Monitoring: a Methods Manual*. State Inspectorate of Environmental Protection, Warsaw. (In Polish).

Schindler, D. W. (1971). A hypothesis to explain differences and similarities among lakes in the experimental lakes area, Northwestern Ontario. *Journal of the Fisheries Research Board of Canada*, **28**, 295–301.

14 FRESHWATER QUALITY, NATURALNESS AND PALAEOLIMNOLOGY

R. W. Battarbee

Summary

1. Freshwater quality for lakes is defined as the extent to which they have changed compared with their natural baseline status.

2. Although other historical sources can be invaluable where they are available, changes in lake systems are most reliably assessed using palaeolimnological techniques.

3. A full assessment of changing lake quality requires not only measures of pollution (acidification, eutrophication) but also a measure of lake habitat disturbance.

4. Changes in these largely independent causal mechanisms can be visualized using a naturalness matrix that illustrates changes over baseline and the extent to which critical thresholds have been exceeded.

5. Changes due to acidification and eutrophication can be quantified separately using diatom-pH and diatom-TP transfer functions respectively, or combined using a diatom species turnover approach.

6. Assessment of habitat disturbance remains a qualitative exercise, but a knowledge of lake and catchment history derived from both documentary and palaeo-limnological sources can be used to make approximate categorizations.

7. The combination of all these measures within the framework of the naturalness matrix can then be used to generate a state-changed lake classification system for water quality.

14.1 Introduction

Environmental quality is regarded here as the degree to which natural systems have deviated, as a result of human impact, from their natural state. Ratcliffe (1971) proposed naturalness as one of the main criteria for the selection of nature reserves, but, as Birks (1996) points out, it is often a difficult criterion to apply.

For most systems, there is a general lack of historical data of sufficient accuracy and antiquity for the natural state of an ecosystem to be defined, and it is rarely possible to infer naturalness from a knowledge only of the present. However, palaeoecological techniques for reconstructing past environmental change are developing rapidly (Birks *et al.*, 1990; Birks, 1993; Williams and Williams, this volume), and for most lakes the degree of naturalness can now be assessed using palaeolimnology (Battarbee, 1991; Charles *et al.*, 1994).

Palaeolimnology is a science concerned with how and why lakes have changed and are changing through time, principally from an analysis and understanding of their sediment record. In the last few decades there has been a rapid development of techniques for coring, dating, analysing and interpreting lake sediment data, and this form of historical reconstruction is now almost always the most consistent, universal and reliable means of assessing lake history. In addition, for some lakes this approach can be most usefully supplemented by studies of available instrumental and documentary records both for the lake and its catchment.

This chapter presents a conceptual basis for understanding lake naturalness and describes how lake naturalness can be defined and quantified using the lake sediment and other records. It is principally concerned with the twin pollution problems of acidification and eutrophication, but also points out the threat to naturalness from habitat disturbance, an aspect of aquatic conservation ecology that has been less studied.

14.2 The Naturalness Matrix, Human Impact and Baselines

It can be argued that fresh waters and other ecosystems are threatened from two relatively independent sources, pollution and habitat disturbance. Following Schneiders *et al.* (1993) these can be represented graphically as shown in Figure 14.1.

The pollution axis refers essentially to chemical change that causes or may cause a biological change. For lakes the primary changes of importance are eutrophication (increases in phosphorus and nitrogen), and acidification (increases in sulphur and nitrogen), although contamination by toxic trace metals, persistent organics and radionuclides also occurs and in some cases these substances may be present in sufficiently high concentrations to cause biological change (exceed the 'critical load'). Almost all these changes are recorded by lake sediments, and it is now possible to quantify their impact by calculating the extent of change over the baseline (Section 14.3).

The habitat disturbance axis in Figure 14.1 is more difficult to define. Ecologically important disturbances include both physical changes (shoreline alteration, water-level regulation, inwash of catchment soils) and direct biological disturbance such as the impact of species introductions, and over-fishing. Many of these changes can be identified and documented, although it may be particularly difficult to quantify their impact on the overall structure and functioning of the system. Nevertheless, for any individual case it is often possible using available documentary and sediment records, to differentiate between disturbances that have had no discernible effect on the lake's biology from those that have caused a change in species composition and abundance (or exceeded a 'critical limit').

On this basis the pristine (natural baseline or natural state) of a lake is the one that combines an absence of pollution and habitat disturbance (Figure 14.1). If this is a state where the biodiversity of indigenous taxa is maximized (Hambler and Speight, 1995), then defining the natural baseline has added importance for ecocentric lake management. These baseline conditions can be used to define future chemical and biological target conditions, or if these are unobtainable because irreversible change has taken place, alternative targets that approximate natural conditions ('target box', Figure 14.1) can be defined.

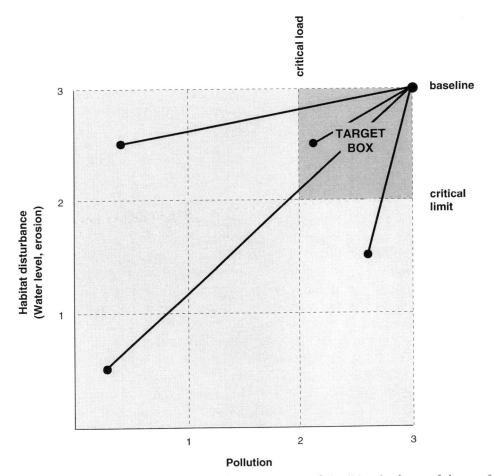

Figure 14.1 The 'naturalness matrix'. The matrix presents a way of visualizing the degree of change of a system over a natural, historical baseline. The y axis represents degree of habitat disturbance, the x axis the degree of pollution. A completely natural system is indicated by the baseline point. The critical load and critical limits are the points at which a biologically significant threshold is passed, and the target box represents the target status for restoration. The vectors represent hypothetical lake time trajectories.

14.3 Establishing Baseline Conditions from Lake Sediment Records

Almost all natural lakes contain soft, organic muds that have accumulated continuously over time, since the formation of the lake basin. In the glaciated parts of north-west Europe, including most of the UK, this covers approximately the last 10000–14000 years. Over this time scale the sediment column chronicles the recolonization of lake catchments by forests after deglaciation, the development of catchment soils, the removal of the forests by early agriculturalists, and long-term trends in the character of the lake itself. Except in rare cases, e.g. Dissmere (Fritz, 1989), analyses of these records on a Holocene time scale show that human impact on lake water quality is imperceptible or slight. This is in marked contrast to the record of vegetation change for terrestrial systems shown by pollen analysis (e.g. Pennington, 1974; Birks *et al.*, 1988).

The uppermost sediment of most British lakes, on the other hand, contains a remarkably vivid record of the most recent lake and catchment history, including evidence for acidification, eutrophication, catchment erosion, and atmospheric contamination (Battarbee, 1991). Consequently, it is relatively easy from the lake sediment record to identify the pre-disturbance period where little change occurred, or where change occurred only slowly, from the later pollution period of the last 100–200 years, when human activity becomes the dominant influence on water quality.

14.3.1 Sediment coring and dating

It is this recent sediment that varies from the top 3 cm in ultra-oligotrophic mountain lakes to more than 1 m in some hypertrophic lakes or lakes with eroding catchments, that must be sampled most carefully so that the record is not disturbed in any way. There are many methods now available including gravity coring (Glew, 1991), piston coring (Mackereth, 1969) or freeze coring (Renberg, 1981). The sediment cores are finely sliced (e.g. into contiguous 2 mm or 5 mm sections) and then subdivided for dating and for various physical (grain-size, rock magnetics), chemical (major ions, trace metals, trace organic pollutants, etc.), biochemical (pigments, organic macromolecules) and biological (diatom, cladoceran, chironomid, ostracod, pollen) analyses (Berglund, 1986; Battarbee, 1991).

Cores are dated using a variety of techniques, but the most universally useful is based on measurements of the radionuclide ^{210}Pb which has a half-life of approximately 26 years (Appleby *et al.*, 1987). The technique has good precision and it allows age-depth curves to be constructed over the last 100–150 years. Peak concentrations of the fallout radionuclides ^{137}Cs and ^{241}Am dating to 1963 can also be fixed and used to reinforce the ^{210}Pb dates. Figure 14.2 shows a typical series of dates for a core from Llyn Llagi, North Wales.

14.3.2 Training sets and transfer functions

One of the goals of palaeolimnology is to use the fossil record to reconstruct the changing structure and function of lake ecosystems, especially in response to

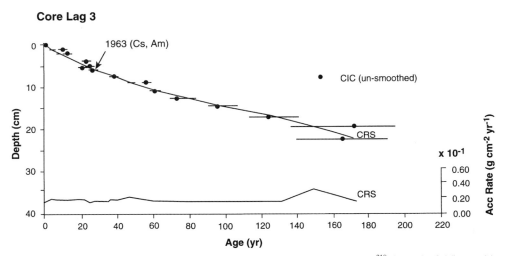

Figure 14.2   An example of lake sediment for a core from Llyn Llagi using the ^{210}Pb method. The position of the 1963 peak in the radionuclides ^{137}Cs and [241]Am is also shown (from Battarbee *et al.*, 1988).

medium and long-term changes in the environment. Although substantial progress is being made in this respect (Leavitt *et al.*, 1994; Jeppeson *et al.*, in press) much of the emphasis of palaeolimnologists over recent years has been the use of the fossil record to reconstruct past environments, especially the hydrochemical environment.

Diatoms are perhaps the most useful and powerful indicators of water chemistry, and techniques are now available for reconstructing past lake pH and total P values, with a high degree of certainty. The method is based on large-scale surveys of modern diatom distributions, in which the relative abundance of diatom taxa in relation to pH, total phosphorus (TP) and other important chemical variables are established. From these surveys, modern calibration training sets can be generated that allow the optimum pH or TP for each taxon to be calculated using weighted averaging (Birks *et al.*, 1990; Bennion *et al.*, in press). These values can then be used to estimate the probable pH or TP of lakes in the past according to the changing composition of diatom assemblages in sediment cores.

14.4   Surface Water Acidification and pH Reconstruction

Although Eville Gorham had, in the 1950s, already suggested that the acidity of rainfall was sufficient to cause acidification of tarns (e.g. Gorham, 1958) international concerns about lake acidification began in Scandinavia in the late 1960s (Odén, 1968). From the beginning it was clear that the record of acidification potentially contained in lake sediments would play an important role in the scientific and political debate. The use of diatoms as indicators of water acidity is long established, stemming from the early work of Hustedt (1937–1939) and Nygaard (1956) in particular. However, the importance of acid rain research in the 1980s in the USA and in north-west Europe led to the rapid development of the methodology (Renberg and Hellberg, 1982; Battarbee, 1984) and the production by the late 1980s of robust, quantitative methods of pH reconstruction (Birks *et al.*, 1990).

Although it is now known that substantial areas of the uplands of the UK are acidified (Critical Loads Advisory Group, 1995), the first region to be studied in any detail was Galloway in south-west Scotland. In Galloway, extremely acid lakes are found (pH < 5.0) especially associated with the areas of granitic rocks to the south and west of the town of New Galloway. The sediments of most of these lakes have been studied, with specific attention being given to the Round Loch of Glenhead (Flower and Battarbee, 1983; Jones *et al.*, 1989; Allott *et al.*, 1992).

14.4.1 *The Round Loch of Glenhead: an acidification example*

The Round Loch of Glenhead is a small, very acid (pH = 4.8), upland loch in Galloway, south-west Scotland. A small number of indigenous brown trout (*Salmo trutta*) are still present in the lake but some adjacent lakes are fishless. The lake and its catchment are situated entirely on granitic bedrock and the catchment has mainly peaty soils and a moorland vegetation which is grazed by sheep and periodically burned.

Figure 14.3 shows a diatom diagram from a core collected in 1985. The core has been dated by the ^{210}Pb method using gamma spectrometry (Appleby *et al.*,

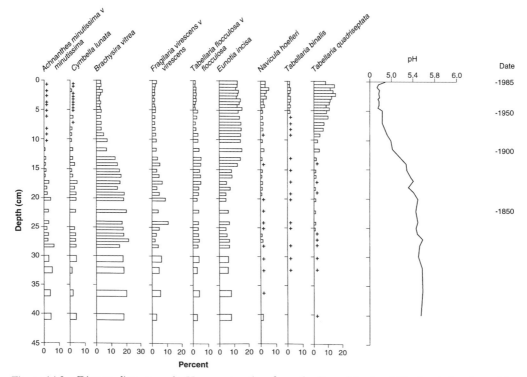

Figure 14.3   Diatom diagram and pH reconstruction from the Round Loch of Glenhead showing a lake acidification sequence (from Jones *et al.*, 1989 and Birks *et al.*, 1990).

1987) and the proportion of the main diatom species at successive sediment levels has been calculated. The diagram shows that there has been little change in the diatom flora of this lake until the mid-nineteenth century when diatoms characteristic of circumneutral water such as *Brachysira vitrea* began to decline and be replaced by more acidophilous species. Acidification continued through the twentieth century and by the early 1980s the diatom flora of the lake was dominated only by acid-tolerant taxa such as *Tabellaria quadriseptata* and *Tabellaria binalis*.

The reconstructed pH curve since 1700 shows a stable pH of about 5.4 until 1850, followed by a reduction of almost 1 pH unit in the following 130 years to 1980. The site has been part of the UK Acid Waters Monitoring Network (Patrick *et al.*, 1991) since 1988 and consequently it is sampled frequently for chemical and biological analyses. Data covering the first five years of monitoring have been published by Patrick *et al.* (1995).

14.5 Eutrophication and TP Reconstruction

Eutrophication has been recognized as a major problem for lakes for a longer period than acidification. Hasler (1947) was responsible for bringing the problem to attention by reviewing evidence for eutrophication for a range of American and European lakes, including Zürichsee (Minder, 1938) and Windermere (Pennington, 1943).

In the 1960s and 1970s eutrophication became a major issue throughout the world as improvements in sanitation and the introduction of synthetic detergents in the post-war period caused major increases in the loading of P to watercourses from sewage works (Vollenweider, 1968).

Attempts to quantify the changes from palaeolimnological data at the time were based not on transfer functions but on estimates of the changing accumulation rate of diatoms in sediments as indicators of productivity change (Battarbee, 1973, 1978; Bradbury and Waddington, 1973). However, following the successful developments of transfer functions for pH for soft, upland waters, recent work on eutrophication has focused on developing similar methodology with respect to phosphorus reconstruction for lowland eutrophic lakes (Anderson *et al.*, 1993; Bennion, 1994).

14.5.1 *Lough Augher: a eutrophication example*

Lough Augher is a small (9.3 ha), eutrophic lake in County Tyrone, Northern Ireland. It has a maximum depth of about 14 m, and the lake has been the recipient of nutrient-rich effluent from a creamery between about 1900 and the mid-1970s. The recent sediments of the lake have been studied in detail, and they chronicle both the increase in nutrient enrichment and the subsequent recovery following diversion of the effluent in 1974 (Anderson, 1986, 1989; Anderson *et al.*, 1990; Anderson and Rippey, 1994). Analysis of a single ^{210}Pb dated core from the point of maximum depth showed that the diatom flora changed markedly from an assemblage dominated by *Aulacoseira ambigua*, *Asterionella formosa* and *Fragilaria crotonensis* in the early twentieth century to one dominated by small *Stephanodiscus* species after the Second World War. These floristic changes clearly indicate a process of rapid eutrophication over recent decades, and parallel the known increase in the disposal of creamery waste (Anderson, 1986).

Using a calibration training set of Ulster lakes spanning a gradient of nutrient concentrations, Anderson (Anderson *et al.*, 1993) was able to calculate the optimum TP values for each of the diatoms in the lakes and use these data to reconstruct past changes in TP in the sediment core (Figure 14.4). The results show that the baseline TP concentrations for Augher at the beginning of the present century were approximately $30 \mu g L^{-1}$, and that levels rose to between 100 and $150 \mu g L^{-1}$ in the 1960s. Creamery effluent no longer enters the lough, and nutrient levels are now declining, an improvement that is also recorded in the most recent sediment (Anderson *et al.*, 1990; Anderson and Rippey, 1994).

Further development of this methodology has been carried out by Bennion, who has developed a training set for highly eutrophic ponds in south-east England (Bennion, 1994), and by Bennion *et al.* (in press) who have now developed a TP transfer function for north-west Europe of 152 lakes, spanning a TP gradient

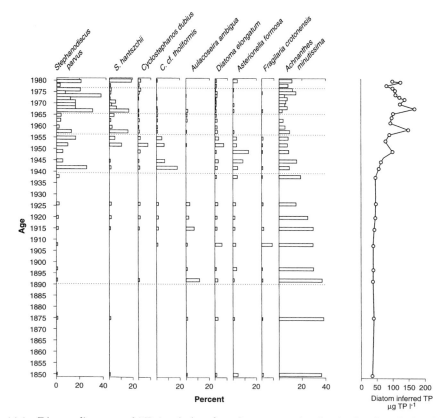

Figure 14.4   Diatom diagram and TP (total phosphorus) reconstruction for Augher Lough showing a lake eutrophication sequence (from Anderson, personal communication).

from 5–$1,190 \mu g L^{-1}$, using a weighted averaging partial least squares method (ter Braak and Juggins, 1993).

14.6 Hydrochemical Reconstruction and Species Turnover as Alternative Measures of Pollution Severity

So far more than 50 lakes in the UK have been analysed for pH reconstruction, and more than 25 will soon have been analysed for TP. Table 14.1 presents data from a subset of seven of these sites, showing baseline values, current values and degrees of change. It is apparent that the baseline pH of most acidified sites has varied between approximately 5.5 and 6.5 Circumneutral and alkaline lakes are usually too strongly buffered to be affected by acid deposition. Consequently, although the severity of biological change depends on the part of the pH scale where change has occurred, the most appropriate definition of change for acidification is 'change in pH over the baseline' expressed in pH units (Table 14.1). This could alternatively be expressed in terms of critical load exceedance at sites where the deposition of total acidity is known (Critical Loads Advisory Group, 1995).

For total phosphorus, absolute values are less important as nutrient enrichment can occur in almost all lakes, i.e. whatever the baseline value. In this case it is perhaps more useful to assess the extent of enrichment as change in TP over the baseline expressed as a multiple of the baseline value (Table 14.1).

Whilst this approach allows the extent of acidification or eutrophication to be compared between sites, it does not provide an overall measure of the severity of pollution that can be used at any site. One way of addressing this issue is to express the degree of change on the pollution axis using the 'species turnover' concept.

In community ecology Gauch has argued that a species 'appears, rises to its

Table 14.1 Data for a selection of British lakes showing degree of change over an 1850 baseline using (a) diatom-pH transfer function for sites sensitive to acidification; (b) diatom-TP transfer function for enriched sites; (c) diatom species turnover calculations for all sites. [1]Species turnover is expressed in units of standard deviation (SD); [2]value refers to 1900 not 1850 AD. NB TP and SD values are provisional and may change as models are improved.

Site	pH			TP			SD[1]
	1850	1990	ΔpH	1850	1990	ΔTP	
Loch Uisge	6.3	6.3	0.0	—	—	—	0.80
Loch Corrie nan Arr	6.1	5.8	0.3	—	—	—	0.96
Lochnagar	5.5	5.1	0.4	—	—	—	1.76
Round Loch of Glenhead	5.5	4.8	0.7	—	—	—	1.85
Loch Ness	6.6	6.6	0.0	8	8	0	1.33
Marsworth Reservoir	—	—	—	200[2]	400	×2	1.36
Loch Leven	—	—	—	40	120	×3	2.40

mode, and disappears over a span of about four standard deviations, and a full turnover in species composition of samples likewise occurs in about four standard deviations' (Gauch, 1982, p.155). If this essentially spatial response is applied to a temporal one, species turnover can be calculated from the changes in diatom assemblages in sediment cores (Table 14.1). On the assumption that species turnover in acidified and enriched lakes represents equal severity of pollution, this statistic provides a direct and unified biological assessment of pollution extent over baseline. Species turnover can be easily derived using ordination methods. The most appropriate method is detrended constrained correspondence analysis (DCCA) in which the core data are constrained by depth. The length of axis one is then related to the floristic difference between the bottom and top samples in the core and this is expressed in units of standard deviation.

Values for the subset of seven sites are shown in Table 14.1. The data show that the most acidified site (Round Loch of Glenhead) and the most enriched site (Loch Leven) have the highest scores and that the scores are directly related to the degree of pH or TP change. However, of note is the score of 0.8 for Loch Uisge where the pH reconstruction shows no change, and the higher score of 1.33 for Loch Ness for which both pH and TP reconstruction techniques also suggest no change. Inspection of the diatom diagrams suggests that there have been significant species changes at both these sites. For Loch Uisge it is a slight change that may or may not be the result of incipient acidification, whereas for Loch Ness the species change is very clear and almost certainly reflecting the onset of eutrophication. In these cases it appears that the species turnover approach may be a more sensitive measure of change than the transfer function approach. On the other hand, it is also possible that species changes may occur for reasons unrelated to either acidification or eutrophication, in which case it could be important to use both approaches in a complementary way.

14.7   Assessing Habitat and Community Disturbance

A complete assessment of the naturalness of a lake requires study not only of the impact of pollution, but also the extent of habitat and community disturbance. Although such disturbances can be relatively easy to identify or are often well-recorded, e.g. in the case of lakes used as reservoirs, the biological impact of such disturbances is more difficult to assess. Nevertheless, some important distinctions can often be made, based on a knowledge of the lake and catchment history from the use of both documentary and sediment records. A quality assessment could be attempted as follows.

Category 3.   Undisturbed.
This would include all sites that are either completely undisturbed or where any physical disturbance to the lake or its catchment has not caused a biological impact on the lake. In other words these are sites where the disturbance has not exceeded any 'critical limit' (Figure 14.1). Two subcategories should then be distinguished:

Category 3a. Pristine.

In the UK only some of the Scottish mountain lochs could be confidently placed in this category. The high corrie lochs in the Cairngorms are, perhaps, the least disturbed, although even here there is evidence from some sites, e.g. Lochnagar, that there have been recent increases in the rate of sediment accumulation as a result of accelerated catchment erosion (Jones *et al.*, 1993). Corrie an Lochan and Lochan Uaine (Cairntoul), although slightly polluted from acid deposition, appear to be otherwise completely undisturbed.

Category 3b. Physical disturbance not leading to a biological change.

This category applies to many lakes in the UK where physical modifications such as minor alterations to the shoreline, small-scale water abstraction, small water-level adjustments, or soil inwash have occurred without causing any apparent change in the composition and abundance of the lake's biota. These changes are usually well documented, and the impact on the lake can often be seen in the sediment record from the presence of clay bands, changes in sediment accumulation rate, and so on. The significance of such disturbances is generally proportional to the size of the lake, and again their impact on the lake's biology can be assessed from the fossil record. For example, although the construction of the Caledonian Canal constituted major engineering, and the level of Loch Ness was changed during the nineteenth century, the overall impact on the loch, judging from the diatom record of the sediment, was minimal (Jones *et al.*, unpublished). Likewise the diversion of the headwaters of the Dargall Lane into Loch Dee in the 1930s increased discharge to the loch but appears to have had no impact on water quality (unpublished data).

Category 2. Lake or catchment disturbance leading to a change in the composition and/or abundance of the lake's biota.

In many cases physical disturbance to lakes and their catchments can lead to biological changes. Perhaps the most common problem is water-level change that leads to changes in the distribution and composition of littoral species, and that can also cause reworking of marginal sediments and disturbance to profundal habitats.

The water level of Loch Corrie nan Arr was raised by 20 cm in 1991 to improve the flow regime of the outflow stream. Regular monitoring at this site indicated that the lake level rise caused a slight inundation of the peaty shoreline and may have been responsible for the lack of *Carex rostrata* in the lake in 1992 (Patrick *et al.*, 1995).

Accelerated soil erosion can also have a biological impact through increasing water turbidity, siltation of benthic habitats and increasing the rate of marginal hydroseral development. Figure 14.5 shows sediment evidence for both the disturbance and its impact on the diatom and macrophyte community of Loch Fleet in Galloway. Deep drainage of catchment blanket peats in the early 1960s prior to afforestation caused massive peat and soil erosion and the acceleration of

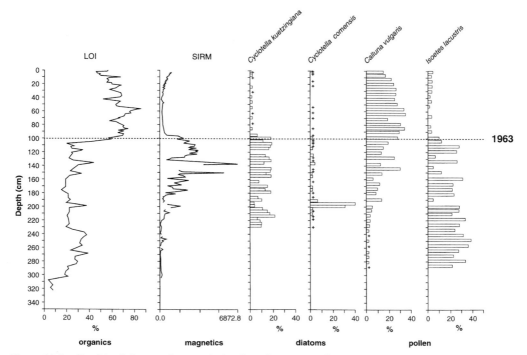

Figure 14.5   Combined diagram from analysis of a sediment core from Loch Fleet, showing evidence for a major inwash of peaty catchment soils (loss on ignition, saturated isothermal remanent magnetisation, *Calluna vulgaris* pollen) and evidence for the biological response to the disturbance (loss of planktonic diatoms, and decline in the aquatic macrophyte *Isoetes lacustris*.

sediment accumulation in the loch by two orders of magnitude. At the same time the planktonic diatom *Cyclotella kuetzingiana* disappeared and the submerged macrophyte *Isoetes lacustris* decreased markedly. Because there was no change in the assemblage of epilithic diatoms it was clear that these changes recorded in the sediment were due to the physical disturbance caused by erosion rather than acidification (Anderson *et al.*, 1986).

Category 1.   Major disturbance leading to changes in the ecological functioning of the lake. Some lakes have been so severely disturbed that not only have there been changes to community structure, but there has also been an alteration in the way the systems function. This often occurs when lakes are converted into water-storage reservoirs for hydroelectric generation, when large, frequent and irregular water-level drawdown may eliminate littoral communities and distort planktonic ones. New disruption of lake systems in this way is now relatively rare, although a significant number of such sites occur especially in Scotland as a result of engineering schemes carried through in the earlier part of the twentieth century (e.g. the Galloway (R. Dee) and Grampian (R. Tummel) schemes (Johnson, 1994). Other examples occur in Wales and Ireland.

14.8 Assessing the Impact of Invasions and Introductions

A full assessment of lake naturalness needs to consider changes to lake biology as a result of species invasions, introduction of alien taxa, fish stocking, and over-fishing. There are many alien aquatic macrophytes, invertebrates and fish in UK lakes (Maitland *et al.*, 1994) either deliberately or accidentally introduced, and in most cases, where such species become abundant, it can be assumed that they pose a significant threat to native taxa through competition, e.g. the introduction of ruffe (*Gymnocephalus cernua*) to Loch Lomond (Maitland and East, 1989). The stocking of lakes for angling and commercial fishing may also cause competition, impose top-down changes on prey communities, and potentially impoverish genetic diversity of indigenous populations.

Ideally the naturalness matrix (Figure 14.1) requires a third axis to represent such direct biological disturbances, and any site assessment would need to differentiate clearly biological change brought about by pollution, physical changes to the habitat, and direct alteration of species composition. However, for the sake of simplicity these kinds of change can be combined with those of physically-induced changes and represented by the y-axis of the naturalness matrix. In most cases lakes with alien species and/or commercially important fisheries would be placed in Category 2.

14.9 Applying the Naturalness Matrix to a Subset of UK Lakes

Figure 14.6 uses the data in Table 14.1 to illustrate the application of the naturalness matrix to a number of UK lakes with respect to habitat disturbance and pollution, and shows how the matrix might be used for classifying lake quality according to the degree of change from the baseline.

Values on the y (habitat disturbance) axis for the seven sites are provisional, and indicate a simple subjective allocation to one of the three main categories described above based on a knowledge of the seven sites.

Values on the x (pollution) axis are also provisional, but on the other hand they are objectively derived. Figure 14.6a shows changes for acid and acidified sites, Figure 14.6b refers to nutrient-enriched sites, and Figure 14.6c shows how the species turnover approach allows both the acidified and enriched groups of lakes to be plotted together on the same axes.

Figure 14.6d shows how, by combining scores on both axes, a numerical state-changed classification scheme (Moss *et al.*, 1996, this volume) might be generated. A score of 10 would indicate a pristine site, whereas 9 would refer to sites where some physical or chemical change may have occurred without causing an identifiable biological change. It could be argued that this represents the highest quality of water body attainable in the UK, and should be the chief objective of water quality management. In such cases, the baseline sediment record can be used to define some of the key biological characteristics of the restored lake, not only with respect to diatoms, but also in relation to zooplankton and the profundal benthos that are found in abundance in the microfossil record.

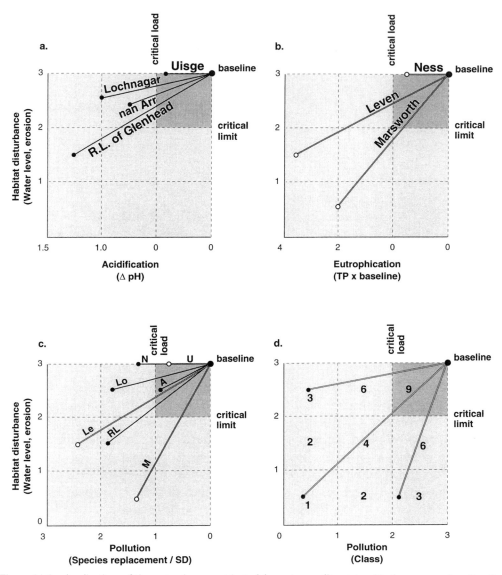

Figure 14.6   Application of the naturalness matrix to lake water quality status (a) change over baseline for four acid lakes based on a diatom-pH transfer function; (b) change over baseline for three eutrophic lakes based on a diatom-TP transfer function; (c) changes over baseline for the seven lakes in (a) and (b) using a 'species turnover' calculation; (d) an example of the use of the naturalness matrix to develop a state-changed lake classification scheme where the natural baseline scores 10 and the most disturbed sites score 1 (see text for further explanation). Vectors are hypothetical.

14.10   Conclusions

Knowing how and why lakes are changing through time over years, decades and centuries is essential if the current status of a lake is to be assessed. For most lakes, such knowledge can now be derived from the analysis of sediment records. Lake sediments integrate information in time and space. Trends in key chemical variables, such as pH and TP, can be projected back in time using diatom-based transfer functions, whilst physical disturbances to the lake and its catchment, such as water-level change and soil erosion, are indicated by changes in sediment lithology, mineralogy and rock magnetic records. Using these techniques it is possible to identify the point in the past when changes in lake chemistry and biology first occurred as a result of human activity. In this way a pre-disturbance baseline picture of the lake can be revealed for comparison with the present. The degree of change can be expressed in different ways, but it is useful to separate changes caused by chemical pollution (mainly acidity and nutrients) from those caused by physical disturbances. If these are represented by the different axes of a matrix, and the changes are calibrated in terms of 'species turnover rate', lakes of different kinds can be classified and compared on the same basis.

Although this general approach to the definition of lake-water quality can be defended on the basis now of a considerable research literature, many of the details presented are provisional. In particular the use of the 'species turnover' concept as a constant measure of disturbance needs evaluation, and identifying, quantifying and assessing the biological impact of physical disturbances requires much more study. Nevertheless, it is clear that the sediment record contains a detailed inbuilt history of ecosystem change that allows the water quality of lakes to be defined in a unique way.

Acknowledgements

The work presented here is based on palaeolimnological research carried out by colleagues and collaborators over many years in the ECRC, and I should like to thank them for their help and for their contribution to the ideas presented here. In addition I am most grateful to Tim Allott for calculating the species turnover data shown in Table 14.1 and John Anderson for permission to use data from L. Augher. I should also like to thank Guy Baker for drawing the diagrams.

References

Allott, T. E. H., Harriman, R. and Battarbee, R. W. (1992). Reversibility of acidification at the Round Loch of Glenhead, Galloway, Scotland. *Environmental Pollution,* **77,** 219–225.

Anderson, N. J. (1986). 'Recent Sediment Accumulation in a Small Lake Basin, with Special Reference to Diatoms'. Unpublished Ph.D. thesis, University of London, London.

Anderson, N. J., Battarbee, R. W., Appleby, P. G., Stevenson, A. C., Oldfield, F., Darley, J. and Glover, G. (1986). Palaeolimnological evidence for the recent acidification of Loch Fleet, Galloway. *Palaeoecology Research Unit Report* No. 17, University College London.

Anderson, N. J. (1989). A whole-basin diatom accumulation rate for a small eutrophic lake in Northern Ireland and its palaeoecological implications. *Journal of Ecology,* **75,** 926–946.

Anderson, N. J., Rippey, B. and Stevenson, A. C. (1990). Change to a diatom assemblage in a eutrophic lake following point-source nutrient re-direction: a palaeolimnological approach. *Freshwater Biology,* **23,** 205–217.

Anderson, N. J., Rippey, B. and Gibson, C. E. (1993). A comparison of sedimentary and diatom-inferred phosphorus profiles: implications for defining pre-disturbance nutrient conditions. *Hydrobiologia,* **253,** 357–366.

Anderson, N. J. and Rippey, B. (1994). Monitoring lake recovery from point-source eutrophication: the use of diatom-inferred epilimnetic total phosphorus and sediment chemistry. *Freshwater Biology, 32,* 625–639.

Appleby, P. G., Nolan, P. J., Gifford, D. W., Godfrey, M. J., Oldfield, F., Anderson, N. J. and Battarbee, R. W. (1987). ^{210}Pb dating by low background gamma counting. *Hydrobiologia, 143,* 21–28.

Battarbee, R. W. (1973). A new method for estimating absolute microfossil numbers, with special reference to diatoms. *Limnology and Oceanography, 18,* 647–653.

Battarbee, R. W. (1978). Observations on the recent history of Lough Neagh and its drainage basin. *Philosophical Transactions of the Royal Society, London, B,* **281,** 303–345.

Battarbee, R. W. (1984). Diatom analysis and the acidification of lakes. *Philosophical Transactions of the Royal Society, London, B,* **305,** 451–477.

Battarbee, R. W. (1991). Recent palaeolimnology and diatom-based environmental reconstruction. In: Shane, L. C. K. and Cushing, E. J. (Eds), *Quaternary Landscapes.* University of Minnesota Press, Minneapolis, 129–174.

Battarbee, R. W., Anderson, N. J., Appleby, P. G., Flower, R. J., Fritz, S. C., Haworth, E. Y., Higgitt, S., Jones, V. J., Kreiser, A., Munro, M. A. R., Natkanski, J., Oldfield, F., Patrick, S. T., Richardson, N. G., Rippey, B. and Stevenson, A. C. (1988) *Lake Acidification in the United Kingdom 1800–1986: Evidence from Analysis of Lake Sediments.* Ensis, London.

Bennion, H. (1994). A diatom-phosphorus transfer function for shallow, eutrophic ponds in southeast England. *Hydrobiologia,* **275/276,** 391–410.

Bennion, H., Juggins, S. and Anderson, N. J. (1996). Predicting epilimnetic phosphorus concentrations using an improved diatom-based transfer function, and its application to lake eutrophication management. *Environmental Science and Technology,* **30,** 2004–2007.

Berglund, B. E. (Ed.) (1986). *Handbook of Holocene Palaeoecology and Palaeohydrology.* John Wiley, Chichester.

Birks, H. H., Birks, H. J. B., Kaland, P. E. and Moe, D. (Eds) (1988). *The Cultural Landscape—Past, Present and Future.* Cambridge University Press, Cambridge.

Birks, H. J. B., Line, J. M., Juggins, S., Stevenson, A. C. and ter Braak, C. J. F. (1990). Diatoms and pH reconstruction. *Philosophical Transactions of the Royal Society, London, B,* **327,** 263–278.

Birks, H. J. B. (1993). Quaternary palaeoecology and vegetation science—current contributions and possible future developments. *Review of Palaeobotany and Palynology,* **79,** 153–177.

Birks, H. J. B. (1996). The contribution of Quaternary palaeoecology to conservation biology. *Journal of Vegetation Science,* **7,** 89–98.

Bradbury, J. P. and Waddington, J. C. B. (1973). The impact of European settlement on Shagawa Lake, northeastern Minnesota, USA. In: Birks, H. J. B. and West, R. G. (Eds), *Quaternary Plant Ecology.* Blackwell, Oxford, 289–307.

Charles, D. F., Smol, J. P. and Engstrom, D. R. (1994). Paleolimnological approaches to biological monitoring. In: Loeb, S. L. and Spacie, A. (Eds), *Biological Monitoring of Aquatic Systems.* CRC Press, Boca Raton, 233–293.

Critical Loads Advisory Group (1995). *Critical Loads of Acid Deposition for United Kingdom Freshwaters,* Critical Loads Advisory Group sub-group report on freshwaters. Institute of Terrestrial Ecology, Edinburgh.

Flower, R. J. and Battarbee, R. W. (1983). Diatom evidence for recent acidification of two Scottish lochs. *Nature, 20,* 130–133.

Fritz, S. C. (1989). Lake development and limnological response to prehistoric and historic land-use in Diss, Norfolk, UK. *Journal of Ecology,* **77,** 182–202.

Gauch, H. G. (1982). *Multivariate Analysis in Community Ecology.* Cambridge University Press, Cambridge.

Glew, J. (1991). Miniature gravity corer for recovering short sediment cores. *Journal of Paleolimnology,* **5,** 285–287.

Gorham, E. (1958). The influence and importance of daily weather conditions in the supply of chloride, sulphate and other ions to freshwaters from atmospheric precipitation. *Philosophical Transactions of the Royal Society, London, B,* **241,** 147–178.

Hambler, C. and Speight, M. R. (1995). Biodiversity conservation in Britain: Science replacing tradition. *British Wildlife,* **6,** 137–147.

Hasler, A. D. (1947). Eutrophication of lakes by domestic drainage, *Ecology,* **28,** 383–395.

Hustedt, F. (1937–1939). Systematische und ökologische Untersuchungen über den Diatomeen-Flora von Java, Bali, Sumatra. *Archiv für Hydrobiologie,* **(Suppl.) 15 and 16.**

Jeppeson, E., Madsen, E. A., Jensen, J. P. and Anderson, N. J. (1996). Reconstructing the past density of planktivorous fish and trophic structure from sedimentary zooplankton fossils: a surface sediment calibration data set from shallow lakes. *Freshwater Biology*, **36**, 115–127.

Johnson, F. G. (1994). Hydro-electric generation. In: Maitland, P. S., Boon, P. J. and McLusky, D. S. (Eds), *The Fresh Waters of Scotland: a National Resource of International Significance*. John Wiley, Chichester, 297–316.

Jones, V. J., Stevenson, A. C. and Battarbee, R. W. (1989). Acidification of lakes in Galloway, south-west Scotland: a diatom and pollen study of the post-glacial history of the Round Loch of Glenhead. *Journal of Ecology*, **77**, 1–23.

Jones, V. J., Flower, R. J., Appleby, P. G., Natkanski, J., Richardson, N., Rippey, B., Stevenson, A. C. and Battarbee, R. W. (1993). Palaeolimnological evidence for the acidification and atmospheric contamination of lochs in the Cairngorm and Lochnagar areas of Scotland. *Journal of Ecology*, **81**, 3–24.

Leavitt, P. R., Sanford, R. R., Carpenter, S. R. and Kitchell, J. F. (1994). An annual fossil record of production, planktivory and piscivory during whole-lake manipulations. *Journal of Paleolimnology*, **11**, 133–149.

Mackereth, F. J. H. (1969). A short core sampler for subaqueous deposits. *Limnology and Oceanography*, **14**, 145–151.

Maitland, P. S. and East, K. (1989). An increase in numbers of Ruffe, *Gymnocephalus cernua (L.)* in a Scottish loch from 1982 to 1987. *Aquaculture and Fisheries Management*, **20**, 227–228.

Maitland, P. S., Boon, P. J. and McLusky, D. S. (Eds) (1994). *The Fresh Waters of Scotland: a National Resource of International Significance*. John Wiley, Chichester.

Minder, L. (1938). Der Zürichsee als Eutrophierungsphänomen. Summarische Ergebnisse aus fünfzig Jahren Zürichseeforschung. *Geologie der Meere und Binnengewässer*, **2**, 284–299.

Moss, B., Johnes, P. and Phillips, G. (1996). The monitoring of ecological quality and the classification of standing waters in temperate regions: a review and proposal based on a worked scheme for British waters. *Biological Reviews*, **71**, 301–319.

Moss, B., Johnes, P. and Phillips, G. (This volume). New approaches to monitoring and classifying standing waters.

Nygaard, G. (1956). Ancient and recent flora of diatoms and chrysophyceae in Lake Gribso. Studies on the humic, acid Lake Gribso. *Folia Limnologica Scandinavica*, **8**, 32–94.

Odén, S. (1968). *The Acidification of Air Precipitation and its Consequences in the Natural Environment*. Energy Committee Bulletin, 1. Swedish Natural Sciences Research Council, Stockholm.

Patrick, S. T., Juggins, S., Waters, D. and Jenkins, A. (1991). *The United Kingdom Acid Waters Monitoring Network. Site Descriptions and Methodology Report*. ENSIS Ltd, London.

Patrick, S. T., Monteith, D. T. and Jenkins, A. (1995). *UK Acid Waters Monitoring Network: The First Five Years. Analysis and Interpretation of Results, April 1988–March 1993*. Ensis Publishing, London.

Pennington, W. (1943). Lake sediments: the bottom deposits of the north basin of Windermere, with special reference to the diatom succession. *New Phytologist*, **42**, 1–27.

Pennington, W. (1974). *The History of British Vegetation*, English Universities Press, London.

Ratcliffe, D. A. (1971). Criteria for the selection of nature reserves. *Advancement of Science*, **27**, 294–296.

Renberg, I. (1981). Improved methods for sampling, photographing and varve-counting of varved lake sediments. *Boreas*, **10**, 255–258.

Renberg, I. and Hellberg, I. (1982). The pH history of lakes in southwestern Sweden, as calculated from the subfossil diatom flora of the sediments. *Ambio*, **11**, 30–33.

Schneiders, A., Verhaert, E., Blust, G. D., Wils, C., Bervoets, L. and Verheyen, R. F. (1993). Towards an ecological assessment of watercourses. *Journal of Aquatic Ecosystem Health*, **2**, 29–38.

ter Braak, C. J. F. and Juggins, S. (1993). Weighted averaging partial least squares regression (WA-PLS): an improved method for reconstructing environmental variables from species assemblages. *Hydrobiologia*, **269/270**, 485–502.

Vollenweider, R. A. (1968). *Scientific Fundamentals of the Eutrophication of Lakes and Flowing Waters with Particular Reference to Nitrogen and Phosphorus as Factors in Eutrophication*. OECD, Paris.

Williams, N. E. and Williams, D. D. (This volume). Palaeoecological reconstruction of natural and human influences on groundwater outflows.

15 PALAEOECOLOGICAL RECONSTRUCTION OF NATURAL AND HUMAN INFLUENCES ON GROUNDWATER OUTFLOWS

N. E. Williams and D. D. Williams

Summary

1. Examining the fossil remains of aquatic insect larvae in sediments below freshwater springs enables reconstruction of the past history of source aquifers and their catchments, thus supplying human impact data on previously pristine systems.

2. A core taken from the bed of a spring in southern Ontario, Canada, shows that over the past 200 years the surrounding land use has changed from pre-European settlement forest, through a land clearing/agricultural phase, to a present-day increase in urban development.

3. Over this period, fossil sclerites of caddisflies (Trichoptera) and chironomids (Diptera) depict an early decline in the importance of river species, a gradual decline in the percentage representation of pond species, and a corresponding increase in the proportion of spring species, although the latter are well represented throughout the entire core. While the numbers of spring chironomids were maximal before human settlement, maximum diversity occurred well after settlement (around 1900). Caddisfly numbers and diversity increased gradually to a peak around 1900.

4. While the data presented do not reveal a complete and comprehensive analysis of groundwater quality *per se*, they are meant to establish the potential and credibility of the protocols involved in detecting changes that are likely to influence groundwater.

15.1 Introduction

The Quaternary (approximately 2 million years ago to the present) is perhaps the most intensively studied of all periods of the past, doubtless because of the large and rapid fluctuations of climate that took place throughout its history (Shotton, 1977). Alongside the latter were marked changes in organism populations and distributions as species attempted to migrate, adapt or otherwise mitigate the effects of these fluctuations. Study of the fossil remains of plants and animals preserved in Quaternary sediments has proved highly successful in reconstructing the past environments of this time. Whereas the remains of vertebrates and plants (including pollen) dominated early work, in the last 30 years considerable effort has been devoted to the interpretation of invertebrate fossils, in particular insects (Coope, 1977). Most recently, the potential of aquatic insects and microcrustaceans has been realized (Williams, 1988; Delorme, 1990).

Not only have aquatic invertebrate remains been used successfully to discern major changes in the environment, such as glacial/interglacial transitions (e.g. Williams and Eyles, 1995), but their potential for use on smaller temporal and spatial scales is now being recognized (e.g. Warwick, 1991). It is the latter that illustrates the tremendous potential of certain taxa in enabling the acquisition of baseline data on water quality and ecosystem health—data which essentially have been lost from contemporary sampling programmes due to the advanced state of degradation of most water bodies. Records retained in sediments deposited by water bodies can aid, therefore, in evaluating and tracking a variety of recent, human-driven environmental perturbations.

Subsurface waters, in particular, are being degraded at an alarming rate and are a leading environmental issue. Globally, point and non-point contaminant sources of primarily industrial, agricultural and household origin pose a threat to ground-water supplies used for domestic consumption. Part of the problem is that the extent of contamination of subsurface waters is poorly known—even in regions where major urban centres draw the majority of the municipal water supplies from the ground.

Groundwater contamination poses a challenge for the research community— to predict the likely subsurface behaviour of contaminants and to develop remedial action and aquifer management that can alleviate or eliminate the problem. From a *technological* standpoint, it is possible to produce exhaustive organic, inorganic, isotopic and biological assessments of discrete volumes of water. From a *practical* standpoint, however, there are currently no cost-effective methods for assessing, with confidence and on a routine basis, the toxicological quality of groundwater (Cherry, 1987). This problem stems from the difficulties and costs of analysing the entire (and expanding) spectrum of chemicals that may occur in groundwater. Such compounds may vary in abundance over time so that concentrations may be misjudged at low sampling frequency. Furthermore, there is limited knowledge of the synergistic effects of chemicals that occur individually at 'safe' levels.

This chapter describes the assessment of groundwater quality by means of the communities of invertebrates that live in springs. Such species live there permanently, integrating the effects of geology, vegetation, climate and human activity in space and time, and should thus be able to provide an especially accurate index of the water quality of individual aquifers, just as benthic invertebrate communities have been used to assess the condition of surface waters (Cairns and Pratt, 1993). Furthermore, skeletal remains of past communities, retrieved from sediment cores taken from the spring bed, should enable the history of an aquifer's water quality to be reconstructed, together with major changes in its catchment.

15.2 Practical Considerations

In practical terms, that is in order to make time spent on sorting and identification of fossils worthwhile in water quality assessment, the invertebrate groups used for palaeoenvironmental reconstruction must meet a number of criteria: they must be consistently found in the type of water body in question (in this case springs); their remains must be abundant and well-preserved in sediments; they must be good indicators of specific environmental conditions; and they must be easily identified to a level of use in describing environmental conditions. No one group meets all of these criteria perfectly but the combination of caddisflies and chironomids comes reasonably close. Few chironomid head capsules can be identified to species level, and current knowledge of larval ecology limits the information that can be derived from some genera, but on the other hand they are virtually always abundant and can supply some information. Caddisflies are less consistently abundant as fossils, but a large proportion can be identified to species level and provide useful habitat information. Many species and genera are known to have fairly narrow habitat requirements.

Caddisfly remains comprise disarticulated pieces of chitin from the larval exo-skeleton, especially from the head and thorax. Particularly abundant are fronto-clypeal sclerites (dorsal covering of the head) and pronotal sclerites (dorsal covering of the first thoracic segment), both of which can be used to identify specimens, often to species (Williams, 1989). Chironomid remains are restricted to entire head capsules although, with the exception of mandibles, many of the smaller appendages (e.g. antennae, premandibles and labral setae) upon which specific identifications are based (Wiederholm, 1983) have usually become detached.

In order to obtain sufficient fossil material to establish the 'natural' or 'pre-treatment' fauna of a spring, a core (or cores) must be taken from a depositing area below the source to a depth sufficient to include sedimentation that took place before industrial, agricultural or urban influences in question. A ponded area is ideal for coring but successful samples can be obtained also by coring directly in soft sediment areas of the spring bed itself. Because sedimentation rates vary, it is useful to date at least one level of the core. Radioisotope methods may be expensive and/or unsuitable for the relatively recent time periods involved. A more practical means of dating shallow cores is to search for pollen spectrum markers or other sedimentary markers related to known recent human impact or natural events. In North America, for example, a rapid rise in the proportion of ragweed (*Ambrosia*) pollen is related to land clearing by nineteenth century settlers. Precise settlement dates can be established from written records.

15.3 Case Study

This technique may be illustrated by a summary of the reconstructed invertebrate community structure of a small spring in southern Ontario over the past 200 years. In this part of Canada, the period includes pre-European settlement times until the present. Although the spring is located in a forested valley, surrounding land use has undergone a series of changes related to agriculture and urban development. In addition, the groundwater source has been affected by influxes of salt resulting from winter road de-icing practices during the last 40 years. The data presented do not reveal a complete and comprehensive analysis of water quality *per se*; rather they are meant to establish credibility of the protocols involved in detecting changes likely to influence groundwater.

15.3.1   The site

Valley Spring (43°45′N; 79°15′W) is a small, first order stream that arises from a single point issue in an 81 ha, hilly woodland comprising a mixture of deciduous and coniferous trees. The discharge is between 1,800 and 2,300 litres hr^{-1} and emanates from a large, shallow aquifer located in sandy sediments. The annual water temperature range in the spring is from 7 to 18°C. The stream flows for about 60 m before entering the much larger Highland Creek. A full description of the site and spring is given by Hogg and Williams (1996).

15.3.2   Methods of sampling and analysis

Approximately 10 m below the source, the stream bends to the east and at this point a small (now dry) pond, 4 m in diameter existed. Fragments of dead invertebrates, together with some inorganic materials from the source, had accumulated in this region of reduced flow over many years. It was at this position that the sedimentary material was sampled.

A vertical sequence of sediment was extracted from the ponded section using a combination of: (a) direct digging, cleaning off the exposed sides, and removing a continuous column of sediment from the wall of the resulting hole using a trowel; and (b) driving a corer, consisting of a 6 cm diameter metal pipe (3 mm wall) directly into the pond bed. In this way, a 1 m deep sequence was removed. On site, the gross characteristics of the sedimentary profile (e.g. colour, texture, prominence of organic material, presence of macrofossils, thickness of layers, etc.) were recorded before cutting the cores carefully into 5 cm sections and placing them in polyethylene bags. In the laboratory, each section was washed through a series of sieves and the material retained on the 90 μm and 250 μm sieves examined with the aid of a dissecting microscope. Approximately 360 cm^3 of sediment were processed at each level. Aquatic insect fossils (primarily larval caddisfly and chironomid exoskeletons) were picked from the debris, mounted on microscope slides and identified to species or genus level. These taxa together with their known, modern-day environmental requirements were then compared among different levels in the sedimentary profile; hereafter referred to as 'the core'.

15.3.3   Results

Approximately 16 different caddisfly taxa and 60 chironomid taxa were recovered from the core with maximum species richness values at any one level of seven for

Trichoptera, eight for each of the chironomid sub-families Tanypodinae and Orthocladiinae, and 12 for Chironominae. Numbers of chironomid head capsules recovered, as exemplified by the Chironominae, were highest at the 81–86 cm level, while caddisfly sclerites were most abundant higher up in the core (56–61 cm; Figure 15.1). A major flood was manifest in the core by a layer of sand and gravel between 16 and 41 cm, and this accounts for a temporary reduction in fossil numbers and diversity to near zero. When this event is disregarded, there were no major trends in fossil abundance or diversity except for a gradual decline in the diversity of the Chironominae (Figure 15.1). When the insects are classified into spring, river and pond species, with the exception of the flood period, there was: (a) a gradual upwards decline in the percentage representation of fossils from pond species; (b) an early decline in the importance of river species; and (c) a corresponding increase in the proportion of spring species, although the latter group is well represented throughout the core (Figure 15.2).

Dating of the core was established by examining the pollen spectrum at each level. The rise in ragweed (*Ambrosia*) pollen at about 75 cm from the top of the

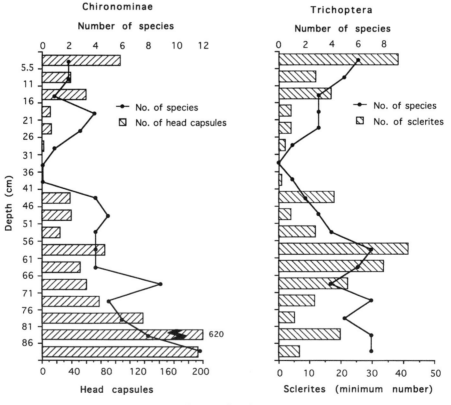

Figure 15.1 The numbers of species of chironomids and caddisflies identified from a standard volume of sediment at 5 cm intervals in the Valley Spring core. Also shown are the total numbers of larval chironomid head capsules and larval caddisfly sclerites retrieved.

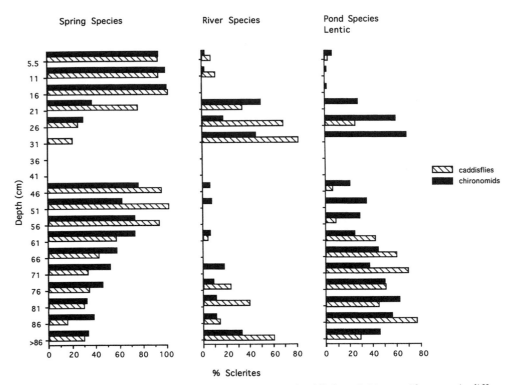

Figure 15.2   Percentages of spring, river and pond species of caddisfly and chironomid present in different parts (5 cm intervals) of the Valley Spring core.

core identifies the beginning of land clearing by settlers (farmers) around 1840. This marker, along with written and photographic historical records, allows us to be reasonably certain that the sequence of sand and well-rounded gravel between 41 and 16 cm represents material brought by flooding of Highland Creek, caused by Hurricane Hazel in 1954. Historical records indicate also that before 1840, Highland Creek was a much larger river deep enough to accommodate a 97 tonne schooner. The decline in river species at the time of the ragweed rise suggests that river sediment no longer reached the sampling site on a regular basis, probably as a result of lowered water table related to land clearing.

The decline in lentic water species was more gradual, although caddisflies disappeared more quickly than chironomids. It seems likely that the 'pond' was initially large and fed annually from river overflow during high water periods. Subsequent shrinking of the river contributed also to a diminishing pond. The complete drying of the pond was actually an artefact caused by manipulation of Valley Spring, in 1989, as part of a global warming study (Hogg and Williams, 1996).

Since the numbers of fossil species that are known crenophiles are high throughout the core, we have a good basis for consideration of community dynamics over approximately the past two centuries. While numbers of spring chironomids are at a maximum before European settlement, near the bottom of the core, maximum diversity occurs well after settlement (around 1900). At least part of these increases might be accounted for by the fact that the spring source would be closer to the sampling site after land clearing, as a result of the drop in the water table, effectively meaning that more spring fossils would be likely to reach the pond sediments. Remains of the caddisfly *Lepidostoma vernale*, and the chironomids *Meropelopia* sp. and *Metriocnemus* sp., for example, were first found at the peak level (56–61 cm). *Lepidostoma vernale* is known to occur most abundantly, now, near the spring source. Above this peak level, the numbers and diversity both of caddisflies and chironomids declined. Notably, among the caddisflies, *Ptilostomis* sp. declined to low levels while *Clostoeca* nr. did not recur. Similarly, the chironomids *Acricotopus* and *Micropsectra* became much rarer.

In recent times (post-1954), species diversity again increased in both insect groups, despite a steady increase in chloride ions in the groundwater to a present day peak of 177 ppm. In addition, in the uppermost sample, maximum numbers of caddisfly fossils occurred while chironomid head capsules reached near maximum numbers. *Lepidostoma* species were the numerically dominant caddisflies in the upper two samples as well as in the modern spring community, overtaking *Frenesia* which was consistently dominant in the lower samples. Both genera are detritivores but the former tends to be associated with finer particles, perhaps indicating increased FPOM (fine particulate organic matter) in the spring.

A summary of the major events associated with Valley Spring and its catchment, and therefore likely to have affected the local groundwater, is presented in Table 15.1.

15.4   Conclusions

The fauna of Valley Spring has undergone various changes in terms of taxa found and their relative abundance. It is clear that forestry, agriculture and urban development have, at times, each contributed to these changes through qualitative and quantitative shifts in the local vegetation and associated physical and chemical characteristics of the spring. Although the data do not tell us whether the recent changes are related to the increasing salinity of the groundwater, they do suggest that one means of determining whether salinity has yet been an important factor would be to test experimentally the salt tolerance of the species whose abundance has changed recently. Such specific *post hoc* testing may, in itself, reduce the amount of bioassay work associated with contamination studies.

Since deep cores are not required, coring below springs can be done with simple and inexpensive equipment—plexiglass tubing or basic metal corers. Caddisfly and chironomid fossils have been recovered successfully from cores taken below the origins of other southern Ontario springs, including one high salinity spring (>1100 ppm) with a presently impoverished fauna, and another that is high in nitrate (15.5 ppm) with a recently reduced complement of caddisfly species. Fossil taxonomy for the two groups is relatively well-established; consequently, by combining fossil data with sedimentary data and information available on local history,

Table 15.1   Summary of the major faunal and habitat changes in Valley Spring over the past 200 years.

Probable time	Sediment	Fauna	Dominant spring taxa	Habitat
1993	Sand, silt, organics, patches of rounded gravel	Diverse caddis	*Lepidostoma vernale* *Meropelopia* *Parametriocnemus* *Thienemanniella* *Micropsectra*	Forested spring stream, increasing salinity
1955–1989	Silt, organics	Increasing diversity of caddis and chironomids	*Lepidostoma* sp. 2 *Meropelopia* *Zavrelimyia* *Parametriocnemus* *Micropsectra* *Prodiamesa* at top	Forested spring stream and small pond
1954 Hurricane Hazel	Sand, rounded gravel, silt	Sparse river forms		Major flooding of river
Pre-1954 Post-1850	Dark brown organics, ragweed pollen	Pond caddis abundant in lower part; chironomid numbers moderate, diversity high	*Frenesia* *Zavrelimyia* *Parametriocnemus* *Micropsectra*	Pond fed by springstream, pond size decreasing
~1840	Grey-brown silt	Caddis sparse; lentic chironomids abundant and diverse	*Frenesia* *Zavrelimyia* *Micropsectra* *Ptilostomis* nr. *Clostoeca*	Pond fed by springstream ?occasional river overflow ?oxbow
~1800	Grey clay, sand, shells	Caddis sparse but diverse river species; chironomids abundant, maximum diversity, especially lentic	*Acricotopus* *Micropsectra* *Apatania* *Rhyacophila*	Larger river, slow flow, frequent overflow

a good record and interpretation of changes in spring faunas can be obtained. Although still being tested and refined, the protocol shows considerable promise for relating faunal changes to human impact and natural changes in spring habitats, their catchments, and the quality of local groundwater.

References

Cairns, J. and Pratt, J. R. (1993). A history of biological monitoring using benthic macroinvertebrates. In: Rosenberg, D. M. and Resh, V. H. (Eds), *Freshwater Biomonitoring and Benthic Macroinvertebrates*. Chapman and Hall, New York, 10–27.

Cherry, J. A. (1987). Groundwater occurrence and contamination in Canada. In: Healey, M. C. and Wallace, R. R. (Eds), *Canadian Aquatic Resources*. Canadian Bulletin of Fisheries and Aquatic Sciences No. 215, Ottawa, 387–426.

Coope, G. R. (1977). Quaternary Coleoptera as aids in the interpretation of environmental history. In: Shotton, F. W. (Ed.), *British Quaternary Studies: Recent Advances*. Clarendon Press, London, 55–68.

Delorme, L. D. (1990). Freshwater Ostracodes. In: Warner, B. G. (Ed.), *Methods in Quaternary Ecology*. Geoscience Canada, Reprint Series 5, St. John's, 93–100.

Hogg, I. D. and Williams, D. D. (1996). Response of stream invertebrates to a global warming thermal regime: an ecosystem-level manipulation. *Ecology*, **77**, 395–407.

Shotton, F. W. (1977). *British Quaternary Studies: Recent Advances*. Clarendon Press, London.

Warwick, W. F. (1991). Indexing deformities in ligulae and antennae of *Procladius* larvae (Diptera: Chironomidae): application to contaminant-stressed environments. *Canadian Journal of Fisheries and Aquatic Sciences*, **48**, 1151–1166.

Wiederholm, T. (Ed.) (1983). Chironomidae of the Holarctic Region: Keys and diagnoses, Part I. Larvae. *Entomologica Scandinavica Supplement No. 19*, 1–457.

Williams, N. E. (1988). The use of caddisflies (Trichoptera) in paleoecology. *Palaeogeography, Palaeoclimatology, Palaeoecology*, **62**, 493–500.

Williams, N. E. (1989). Factors affecting the interpretation of caddisfly assemblages from Quaternary sediments. *Journal of Paleolimnology*, **1**, 241–248.

Williams, N. E., and Eyles, N. (1995). Sedimentary and paleoclimatic controls on caddisfly (Insecta: Trichoptera) assemblages during the last interglacial-to-glacial transition in southern Ontario. *Quaternary Research*, **43**, 90–105.

16 REMOTE SENSING AS A TOOL FOR MONITORING INLAND WATERS

T. J. Malthus, S. Bennett, S. North and C. J. Place

Summary

1. Greater use could be made of remote-sensing technologies for monitoring inland water environments. Airborne digital imaging has particular promise, offering flexible deployment capabilities and images obtained at higher spatial and spectral resolutions.

2. Remote sensing allows for the accurate prediction of important surface-water quality parameters in lakes through their effects on the shape of spectral reflectance from lakes.

3. Applications also exist in monitoring change in fluvial systems. In combination with the spatial analytical capabilities of geographical information systems, airborne remote sensing techniques could be used to automate retrieval of certain types of information required in river corridor survey.

4. The physical basis of the technique and its relevance to water quality monitoring is reviewed, examples of applications are presented, and directions for further research are discussed.

16.1 Introduction

The optimum management of the world's inland waters, be it for conservation or exploitation, necessitates knowledge about water quality. However, conventional lake or river-based water quality sampling programmes are point based, offering little information on the spatial variation of water quality parameters in what can be highly dynamic and variable environments. Remote sensing represents a technique with considerable potential for monitoring the spatial extent of surface water quality and other features of lakes and rivers. The technique offers a synoptic view which allows for the generation of digital maps depicting the two-dimensional structure of surface-water quality features.

This chapter presents an introduction to the exciting potential of digital remote sensing technologies as a new source of information for the evaluation of water quality and water habitats. For a more complete scientific review of the applications of remote sensing to inland water quality assessment the reader is directed to the article by Dekker *et al.* (1995).

16.2 Physical Basis: Spectral Reflectance from Lakes

The principles of remote sensing of water quality are soundly physically based. However, a knowledge of the effects of optically important water constituents on the underwater optical properties is important in understanding their influence on measured optical parameters. Figure 16.1 illustrates that commonly measured optical properties of water (so-called *apparent* properties) are modified by constituents in the water column through their effects on the *inherent* optical properties of absorption and scattering (Kirk, 1994).

Figure 16.2 shows spectra of subsurface reflectance from different Dutch water bodies of widely ranging trophic status. These measurements were made using a portable spectroradiometer adapted for underwater measurements. The figure indicates that reflectance increases with higher turbidity as a result of increased scattering of light caused predominantly by the particles suspended in the water column. The complex shape of reflectance is the result of absorption due mainly to dissolved colour and photosynthetic pigments contained in phytoplankton.

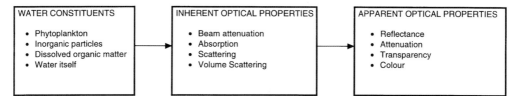

Figure 16.1   The relationship between optical water quality parameters and inherent and apparent optical properties (modified from Davies-Colley, 1983).

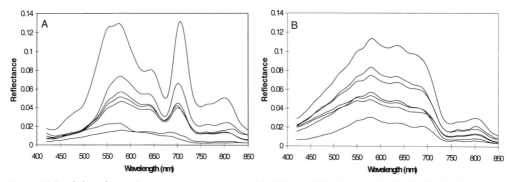

Figure 16.2   Subsurface reflectance spectra measured in different inland waters in the Netherlands covering a wide range of water turbidities: (A) lakes in which phytoplankton are the dominant particulate matter (chlorophyll-*a* concentrations ranging from 1 to 125mg m^{-3}); (B) lakes in which inorganic suspended sediment is the dominant particulate material (dry weight concentration ranging from 5 to 30mgL^{-1}).

Reflectance is low at short wavelengths (400 to 500 nm) as a result of strong light absorption by phytoplankton pigments and dissolved humic substances. Beyond 500 nm reflectance is markedly affected by the nature and concentration of particulate matter within the water column. Lakes rich in phytoplankton have reflectance curves punctuated by absorption features due to different photosynthetic pigments in phytoplankton. For example, the strong reduction in reflectance around 670 nm is due to absorption of red light by chlorophyll-*a*. Reflectance is relatively low above approximately 720 nm because in this region water itself is a strong absorber of light. The remote sensing of optical water quality parameters is therefore restricted to a wavelength region of light between approximately 400 to 800 nm. This is a relatively narrow waveband compared with other remote sensing applications, for example terrestrial vegetation (400–2500 nm).

Other factors will affect the utility of the reflectance signal when measured by a sensor carried by either an aircraft or a satellite platform. These factors include the prevailing atmospheric conditions, the state of the water surface and the angle of incidence of the sunlight.

16.3   Algorithms

The reflectance from inland waters can be seen, therefore, as having a distinct spectral shape. For the successful application of remote sensing to the determination of inland water quality, algorithms are required to resolve individual water quality parameters from the compound reflectance signal. Different wavelengths of spectral reflectance can be combined to form indices for the estimation of water quality parameters. As an example, Figure 16.3 shows the relationship between a ratio of subsurface reflectances at 705 and 670 nm and measured chlorophyll-*a* concentrations for the reflectance spectra displayed. The ratio shows a high level

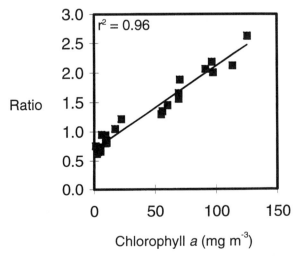

Figure 16.3   Relationship between the ratio of subsurface reflectances at 705 and 670 nm and phytoplankton chlorophyll-*a* concentration for the data displayed in Figure 16.2.

of correlation and may be used to estimate surface chlorophyll to a high level of accuracy.

Remote sensing is capable of directly monitoring those properties which either affect or describe water optical properties (e.g. phytoplankton, suspended sediments, dissolved humus, detritus, transparency, attenuation, water depth). In previous studies, algorithms have principally been derived using empirical or semi-empirical methods in which statistical relationships have been sought between measured water quality parameters and spectral reflectances (e.g. Dekker *et al.*, 1991). However, with these approaches causal relationships between the parameters and reflectance may not necessarily exist. Similarly, the statistical coefficients calculated will only be applicable to the data from which they were derived, limiting their application in any multi-temporal comparison. Currently, considerable research is focused on the development of analytical algorithms for a range of water quality parameters through the use of models linking underwater optical properties to remotely sensed reflectance (Dekker, 1993). This approach will ensure multi-temporal applicability; allowing true comparisons of images obtained on different dates.

16.4   Imaging Instrumentation

The applications of particular satellite and airborne sensors in water quality studies was extensively reviewed by Dekker *et al.* (1995). The suitability of a particular sensor to monitoring features in inland waters will not only depend on the size of the water body but on the spectral, spatial, radiometric and temporal characteristics of each individual sensor (Table 16.1). Satellite sensors, such as the Landsat TM and SPOT HRV sensors, have been frequently used (e.g Baban, 1993; Dekker and Peters, 1993). These sensors have a high spatial resolution (20 to 30 m) but are limited in their application to the accurate estimation of water quality parameters because of poor spectral band width and location with respect to the underlying spectral features. In addition, because the sensors are largely designed for relatively bright land-surface features, signals from the relatively dark water targets also show low contrast. Ocean colour sensors, such as the Coastal Zone Colour

Table 16.1   The suitability of currently available spaceborne and airborne optical sensors for remotely sensing inland waters based on a comparison of general instrument characteristics.

Characteristic	'Terrestrial' Sensors (e.g. Landsat TM, SPOT HRV)	Oceanographic Satellite Sensors (e.g. CZCS, SeaWIFS)	Airborne sensors (e.g. ATM, CASI)
Spatial resolution	Good (20–30 m)	Poor (km scale)	High (0.5 to 20 m)
Spectral resolution	Poor (3 to 4 bands)	Better (6 to 8 bands)	Best (8 to 288 bands)
Radiometric resolution	Poor (256 brightness levels)	Good (1024 brightness levels)	Good (256 to 4092 brightness levels)
Temporal resolution	Poor (18 to 26 days)	Good (6 days)	Flexible

Scanner (CZCS) and Sea Viewing Wide Field of View Sensor (SeaWIFS), have more precisely placed spectral bands and show high contrast over water targets, but have a poor spatial resolution (41 km) which limits their application only to large lakes. The temporal resolution of most satellite instruments is also a limiting factor; a high temporal frequency of measurements is needed to study the dynamic nature of inland water systems.

Airborne sensors include line spectrometers, multispectral scanners (e.g. Airborne Thematic Mapper, ATM) and imaging spectrometers (e.g. Compact Airborne Imaging Spectrometer, CASI). Lower altitude airborne sensors allow the measurement of reflectance at much higher spatial resolutions enabling adequate measurement of the spatial features of small lakes. Generally, they are capable of imaging at a higher spectral resolution allowing the full potential of the reflectance signal to be utilized. They may also be flexibly deployed to take advantage of favourable overhead conditions, thus improving on the temporal limitations of satellite-based sensors. Generally, such instruments are capable of imaging at a higher spectral resolution with a greater number of spectral bands which, depending on the instrument, may be tailored to match the spectral features of interest in the reflectance spectrum from inland waters.

16.5   Applications of Airborne Imaging

Plate 8 demonstrates a range of applications of the ATM multispectral scanner for monitoring inland waters. Plate 8a illustrates the spatial pattern of Secchi disk transparency for the northern basin of Loch Lomond (Central Scotland), and shows two large regions of low transparency, apparently as a result of turbid inputs from river inflows. Plate 8b illustrates the predicted spatial pattern of phytoplankton biomass (as chlorophyll-*a* concentration) in Loch Leven. High chlorophyll concentrations are shown in the west of the loch with an intricate structure evident, probably as a result of the processes of wind-driven surface currents, differences in surface temperature and varying nutrient concentrations. These figures illustrate the power of remote sensing to provide understanding of the spatial scales of lake dynamics as was also illustrated by George (1993) and George and Allen (1994). Such understanding may be used to determine optimum scales for routine application of remote sensing in lake management, and appropriate spatial and temporal scales for lake-based sampling strategies and water quality models.

Airborne remote sensing also has wide application in monitoring change in fluvial systems. Numerous applications were reviewed by Muller *et al.* (1993) and Milton *et al.* (1995). Plate 8c illustrates the use of ATM imagery in river corridor assessment for the River Tay. Information can be obtained on water depth and channel morphometry as well as vegetation types on the river margins. The level of information retrieved will be determined by the size of the river under study, the spatial resolution of the imagery (1 m pixel size is the highest resolution for ATM) and the season in which it was obtained. The date of acquisition of the imagery may be important when dense river bank vegetation may mask other significant channel features. Fixed waveband scanners, such as the ATM, may also be limited in their spectral characteristics; further investigation is required on the shape, variability and separability of the spectral signatures of the numerous features of fluvial systems. Information retrieval and analysis may be significantly enhanced when the remotely sensed data are combined with other sources of information (such as elevation data) within a Geographical Information System (GIS).

16.6   Conclusion and Further Research

Remote sensing represents a powerful tool for monitoring inland water environments. It allows for the accurate prediction of important surface-water quality parameters (e.g. phytoplankton biomass, transparency) through the effects of such parameters on the spectral shape of reflectance from lakes. However, the coarser spectral and spatial resolutions of current satellite sensors limits their application to large area surveys at the catchment and regional scales. Airborne imaging is currently the best technique available for routinely monitoring surface-water quality in lakes and for monitoring change in riverine systems at more local scales (e.g. Hilton, 1984). From a management perspective, the capability to monitor large areas synoptically and quickly may lead to savings through reduced requirements for expensive conventional lake-based sampling programmes.

There is thus considerable scope for greater use of remotely sensed data in studies of water quality. Current research is focused on a variety of applications with emphasis placed on understanding the physical basis of the factors contributing to above-surface reflectance and how this may be interpreted to yield useful information. Much of this research focuses on the applicability of high spectral resolution techniques and frequently involves modelling of the underwater optical processes. Topics currently under investigation include: the use of Monte Carlo modelling procedures to simulate spectral reflectance from lakes as an aid to algorithm development (Harwar *et al.*, 1995); the remote sensing of algal taxonomic groups through their effects on reflectance based on differences in pigmentation; and the use of geostatistics to investigate the structure of the dynamic spatial features observed in lakes as an aid to understanding the role of various environmental variables, including lake morphometry. Other topics meriting further investigation include the applications of digital airborne remote sensing (in conjunction with GIS) to river corridor/habitat analysis, and digital remote sensing techniques for aquatic macrophyte survey as investigated by Malthus and George (1993).

References

Baban, S. M. J. (1993). Detecting water quality parameters in the Norfolk Broads, UK, using Landsat imagery. *International Journal of Remote Sensing,* **14,** 1247–1267.

Davies-Colley, R. J. (1983). Optical properties and reflectance spectra of 3 shallow lakes obtained from a spectrophotometric study. *New Zealand Journal of Marine and Freshwater Research,* **17,** 445–459.

Dekker, A. G. (1993). 'Detection of Optical Water Quality Parameters for Eutrophic Waters by High Resolution Remote Sensing'. Unpublished Ph.D. thesis, Free University, Amsterdam.

Dekker, A. G., Malthus, T. J. and Hoogenboom, H. J. (1995). The remote sensing of inland water quality. In: Danson, F. M. and Plummer, S. E. (Eds), *Advances in Environmental Remote Sensing*. John Wiley, Chichester, 123–142.

Dekker, A. G., Malthus, T. J. and Seyhan, E. (1991). Quantitative modeling of inland water quality for high-resolution MSS systems. *IEEE Transactions on Geosciences and Remote Sensing*, **29,** 89–95.

Dekker, A. G. and Peters, S. W. M. (1993). The use of the Thematic Mapper for the analysis of eutrophic lakes: a case study in the Netherlands. *International Journal of Remote Sensing*, **14,** 799–821.

George, D. G. (1993). Physical and chemical scales of pattern in freshwater lakes and reservoirs. *The Science of the Total Environment*, **135,** 1–15.

George, D. G. and Allen, C. M. (1994). Turbulent mixing in a small thermally stratified lake. In: Beven, K. J., Chatwin, P. C. and Millbank, J. H. (Eds), *Mixing and Transport in the Environment*. John Wiley, Chichester, 2–15.

Harwar, M. D., Malthus, T. J., Dekker, A. G. and Trueman, I. C. (1995). Reflectance from inland waters: Modelling the effects of varied non-living suspended sediment concentration on the spectral features attributed to chlorophyll-*a*. In: *Proceedings of the Annual Conference of the Remote Sensing Society*, University of Southampton, 466–473.

Hilton, J. (1984). Airborne remote sensing for freshwater and estuarine environments. *Water Research*, **18,** 1195–1223.

Kirk, J. T. O. (1994). *Light and Photosynthesis in Aquatic Ecosystems*. Cambridge University Press, Cambridge.

Malthus, T. J. and George, D. G. (1993). Remote sensing of aquatic macrophytes in lakes. In: *Proceedings of the NERC Airborne Remote Sensing Symposium,* University of Dundee. Natural Environment Research Council, Swindon, 57–69.

Milton, E. J., Gilvear, D. J. and Hooper, I. D. (1995). Investigating change in fluvial systems using remotely sensed data. In: Gurnell, A. and Petts, G. (Eds), *Changing River Channels*. John Wiley, Chichester, 277–301.

Muller, E., Décamps, H. and Dobson, M. K. (1993). Contribution of space remote sensing to river studies. *Freshwater Biology,* **29,** 301–312.

17 WATER QUALITY ASSESSMENT BASED ON BENEFICIAL USE IMPAIRMENT

M. A. Zarull and J. H. Hartig

Summary

1. The development of use-based objectives provides a common foundation for assessment, rehabilitation and protection of the Laurentian Great Lakes Basin ecosystem.

2. The first step in this process was the development of narrative objectives based on cumulative scientific research, followed by a process of peer review and public consultation.

3. The next step was the development of numerical criteria or indicators that provide quantification of the identified use. These indicators are area-specific (although they may apply to more than one area) and are developed by specialists working in the geographic area along with local stakeholders.

17.1 Introduction

The Laurentian Great Lakes have a combined surface area of approximately $246,000 \text{ km}^2$ and hold almost one-fifth of the total surface liquid fresh water of the earth. The drainage basin population exceeds 37×10^6 with more than 24×10^6 depending on the lakes for drinking water. Due to the availability of abundant fresh water, for consumption, transportation, irrigation and waste disposal, the region became the industrial heartland of North America. Approximately 50% of the USA's steel production and 62% of Canada's comes from this area. However, this development and accompanying prosperity has not been without environmental cost. The lakes have been, and continue to be, stressed by the presence of excess nutrients, oxygen-consuming wastes, eroded soil and persistent toxic substances. They also have experienced severe losses of wetlands and other habitats, invasions and impacts from many exotic species, and significant losses of natural biodiversity from these and other human-induced stresses (Hartig and Zarull, 1992; Allan and Zarull, 1995). Perhaps the greatest or more obvious expression of impact from these stresses has been in the nearshore embayments, harbours and river mouths adjacent to the human population centres.

Canada and the USA have signed a series of water-quality agreements for the Laurentian Great Lakes in 1972, 1978 and 1987, as part of their 1909 Boundary Waters Treaty (USA and Canada, 1972, 1978, 1987). The purpose of these agreements is to restore and maintain the chemical, physical and biological integrity of the waters of the Great Lakes Basin ecosystem. As part of this process, the two countries adopted some common, general and specific objectives to assess water quality. These objectives are used to determine both the need for remedial and preventative actions and their effectiveness. The latest Agreement also committed the governments to develop plans and take specific actions to remediate contaminated nearshore areas, which are referred to as Areas of Concern. These are defined as areas that fail to meet the general or specific objectives of the Agreement, and where such failure has caused or is likely to cause impairment of beneficial use(s) or impairment of the areas' ability to support aquatic life.

This approach attempts to reconcile general and specific water quality objectives (which can be different among the eight Great Lakes states, the Province of Ontario and the two federal governments) with an ecosystem, use-based assessment. However, the Agreement does not provide detailed definitions of impairments or guidance on their quantification. Recently, attempts have been made to quantify ecosystem integrity and the beneficial use impairments identified in the Agreement, through a series of scientific symposia and workshops, and through the use of public review and comment.

17.2 Goals and Objectives

The statements of beneficial use impairment, contained in the Agreement, provide a common means of defining existing problems along with their causes and a standard way of assessing future conditions throughout the lakes. The absence of a single numeric expression for each impairment acknowledges the need for site-specific indicators. The process includes developing a narrative objective which, when achieved, will satisfy or indemnify a particular use goal, and then developing a quantitative indicator that identifies the achievement of the objective. The process is often iterative. Once a better understanding of the state and functioning of the system is gained, the indicator may need to be revised.

The 14 beneficial uses described in the Agreement can be grouped into four aspects of ecosystem health or performance: human health, societal value, economic value and biological or ecological performance. These groupings also illustrate the need to have a variety of professionals and the public collectively involved in the process, to ensure their effectiveness through technical accuracy and consensual development. The following sections provide a summary of the narrative objectives for the Laurentian Great Lakes and selected examples of local numeric indicators that have been established to demonstrate the achievement of those objectives.

17.2.1   Restrictions on fish and wildlife consumption

The use is deemed to be impaired when contaminant levels in fish or wildlife populations, due to contaminant input from the watershed, exceed current standards, objectives or guidelines, or public health advisories that are in effect for human consumption of fish or wildlife.

17.2.2   Tainting of fish and wildlife flavour

The use is considered impaired when ambient water quality standards, objectives, or guidelines, for the anthropic substance(s) known to cause tainting, are being exceeded or survey results have identified tainting of fish or wildlife flavour.

17.2.3   Degraded fish and wildlife populations

This beneficial use is impaired when fish and wildlife management programmes have identified degraded fish or wildlife populations due to a cause within the watershed. In addition, this use will be considered impaired when relevant, field-validated, fish or wildlife bioassays, with appropriate quality assurance/ quality controls, confirm significant toxicity from water column or sediment contaminants.

In Hamilton Harbour (Lake Ontario), the overall objective is to shift from a fish community indicative of eutrophy, to a self-sustaining community indicative of mesotrophy. Quantitative fishery targets include: 200–250 kg ha^{-1} total biomass of fish in littoral habitats; 40–60 kg ha^{-1} piscivore biomass in littoral habitats; 70–100 kg ha^{-1} specialist biomass in littoral habitats; 30–90 kg ha^{-1} generalist biomass in littoral habitats; native piscivores representing 20–25% of total biomass; 80–90% native species; and a species richness of six to seven species per survey transect (Hamilton Harbour Remedial Action Plan Writing Team, 1992).

17.2.4   Fish tumours or other deformities

When the incidence rates of fish tumours or other deformities exceed rates at unimpacted control sites or when survey data confirm the presence of neoplastic or pre-neoplastic liver tumours in bullheads or suckers (demersal fish), this use is declared impaired.

17.2.5   Bird or animal deformities or reproductive problems

When wildlife survey data confirm the presence of deformities (e.g. cross-bill syndrome) or other reproductive problems (e.g. egg-shell thinning) in sentinel wildlife species, this beneficial use is regarded as being impaired.

In the Fox River and Green Bay (Lake Michigan, Wisconsin), historical discharges from the world's largest concentration of pulp and paper mills are believed to be the primary source of 30,000 kg of PCBs that reside in river sediments downstream of Lake Winnebago and up to 15,000 kg of PCBs in Green Bay. Studies have demonstrated avian exposure to contaminants through aquatic food chains. A 1983 study of two colonies of Forster's tern showed reproductive success of a lower Green Bay colony to be significantly impaired when compared with a relatively clean reference colony on Lake Poygan, upstream from industrial activities in the Fox River. Based on the 1983 study and an additional study in 1988, reproductive success was defined using four criteria: hatching rate (90% success rate), fledging rate (one chick/pair), incubation time (23 days), and chick growth rate.

17.2.6   Degradation of benthos

This use is deemed impaired when benthic macroinvertebrate community structure significantly diverges from unimpacted control sites of comparable physical and chemical characteristics. In addition, this use will be considered impaired when toxicity (as defined by relevant, field-validated, bioassays with appropriate quality assurance and quality controls) of sediment-associated contaminants at a site is significantly higher than controls.

In Canada, site-specific guidelines for benthos are being established from a reference site database (biological attributes and environmental variables) using multivariate techniques, such as cluster and ordination analysis (Reynoldson and Zarull, 1993). Reference site benthic communities are grouped using cluster analysis. The site environmental variables, which are not affected or minimally affected by human activity, are then used as predictors to group the sites into the appropriate biological clusters. The benthic community structure and the same nine environmental variables (depth, NO_3, silt, aluminium, calcium, loss on ignition, alkalinity, sodium, pH) are measured at the test sites. Using the environmental predictors and the discriminant model (derived from the reference site database), each site is assigned to a biological cluster. The benthic invertebrate data are then similarly analysed. If the site in the Area of Concern lies outside the reference site cluster, then that site is judged to be impaired. In the Great Lakes, 335 sites have been sampled and the multivariate 'model' developed from this database correctly predicts benthic invertebrate communities with 90% accuracy (Reynoldson *et al.*, 1995). In addition, acute and chronic measures of 'toxicity' (including growth and reproduction) performed at these same sites provide measures of background performance for the appropriate, indigenous organisms that are to be used in assessing sediment toxicity (see Section 17.2.7).

17.2.7   Restrictions on dredging activities

When contaminants in sediments exceed standards, criteria, or guidelines such that there are restrictions on dredging or disposal activities, this use is viewed as impaired.

Great Lakes dredging guidelines were developed to provide protection against the short and long-term impacts associated with the disposal of dredged sediments. These guidelines employ bulk chemistry measurements for a few parameters that are assessed using either water quality equivalent standards or background concentration classifications (International Joint Commission, 1982; Zarull and Reynoldson, 1992). More recently, the Ontario Ministry of Environment and

Energy (OMOE) has released biologically-based, sediment contaminant concentration guidelines for use in assessing bottom sediments in Areas of Concern and for use in assessing dredged material disposal. These chemical concentration guidelines are also supported through the use of site-specific bioassays (OMOE, 1992). In many areas outside the Great Lakes, the Sediment Quality Triad Approach (i.e. chemistry, benthos community structure, and bioassays) is being used to assess sediment problems and recommend remedial actions (Chapman, 1990). A similar method has been recommended for use in the Great Lakes (International Joint Commission, 1987, 1988; Zarull and Reynoldson, 1992).

End-points for benthos community structure are being established as described in Section 17.2.6, using reference sites throughout the nearshore Great Lakes. Sediment bioassays (using species such as *Chironomus riparius*, *Hexagenia limbata*, *Hyallela azteca*, and *Tubifex tubifex*) provide confirmation that sediment is the source of the impact, rather than the water column or other factors, which are integrated by the benthos. As with community structure, a reference site (bioassay) database has been established (Reynoldson *et al.*, 1995).

17.2.8   Eutrophication or undesirable algae

When there are persistent water quality problems (e.g. dissolved oxygen depletion of bottom waters, nuisance algal blooms or accumulation, decreased water clarity, etc.) attributed to cultural eutrophication, the use is considered impaired.

In Saginaw Bay, Lake Huron, modelling phosphorus loading/phosphorus concentration-threshold odour value relationships has led to establishment of a $15 mg L^{-1}$ total phosphorus (TP) concentration for the inner bay (Bierman *et al.*, 1983). The TP loading target is $440 t yr^{-1}$, which will result in threshold odour values <3 and a TP concentration of $15 mg L^{-1}$ (US Public Health Service Standard).

17.2.9   Restrictions on drinking water consumption or taste or odour problems

This use is impaired when treated drinking water supplies are impacted to the extent that: (a) densities of disease-causing organisms or concentrations of hazardous/toxic chemicals or radioactive substances exceed human standards, objectives or guidelines; (b) taste and odour problems are present; or (c) the treatment needed to make raw water suitable for drinking is beyond the standard treatment used in comparable portions of the Great Lakes, which are not degraded (settling, coagulation, disinfection).

17.2.10   Beach closings

This use is deemed impaired when waters, which are commonly used for total body-contact or partial body-contact recreation, exceed standards, objectives, or guidelines for such use.

17.2.11   Degradation of aesthetics

When any substance in water produces a persistent objectionable deposit, unnatural colour or turbidity, or unnatural odour (e.g. oil slick, surface scum), this use is considered impaired.

In New York, narrative standards for suspended sediment and colour are set at 'none' that would adversely affect the waters for their best use (New York State, 1991). For turbidity, the standard is no increase that would cause a visible contrast from natural conditions and, for oil and floating substances, it is no residue that would be visible. If conditions are attributable to unnatural causes and sources, New York ambient water quality standards are used to establish reduction targets in order to make a determination. Examples of quantitative targets that have been established for dischargers causing such conditions include: $3.0 \, mgL^{-1}$ for suspended solids, and $15 \, mgL^{-1}$ for oil and floating substances.

17.2.12 *Added costs to agriculture or industry*

This use is judged as impaired when there are additional costs required to treat the water prior to use for agricultural purposes (including, but not limited to, livestock watering, irrigation and crop spraying) or industrial purposes (that is, intended for commercial or industrial applications and non-contact food processing).

17.2.13 *Degradation of phytoplankton and zooplankton populations*

When phytoplankton or zooplankton community structure significantly diverges from unimpacted control sites of comparable physical and chemical characteristics, this use is impaired. In addition, this use will be considered impaired when relevant, field-validated, phytoplankton or zooplankton bioassays (e.g. *Ceriodaphnia*; algal fractionation bioassays) with appropriate quality assurance/quality controls confirm toxicity in ambient waters.

Limited attempts have been made to qualify objectives based on zooplankton and phytoplankton community structure, due to the expensive and time-consuming nature of plankton identification and enumeration. Bioassay end-points are more frequently used. Degraded zooplankton populations were identified as an impaired use in the Cuyahoga River (Ohio) due to chronic toxicity of ambient waters below the Akron Wastewater Treatment Plant. Toxicity was measured by the seven-day, three brood *Ceriodaphnia* test. *Ceriodaphnia* are easily cultured, found in the Great Lakes, sensitive to toxic substances and have a short maturation time. Based on standard *Ceriodaphnia* bioassay protocols (International Joint Commission, 1987), zooplankton populations were considered not impaired when there was no significant difference in survival and number of young per female relative to controls ($p < 0.05$).

17.2.14 *Loss of fish and wildlife habitat*

This use is impaired when fish and wildlife management goals have not been met as a result of loss of fish and wildlife habitat due to a perturbation in the physical, chemical or biological integrity of the Boundary Waters, including wetlands.

Approximately 80% of the wetlands in Hamilton Harbour, Lake Ontario have been lost to development. The water use goal for the fishery is 'that water quality and fish habitat should be improved to permit an edible, naturally-reproducing fishery for warmwater species, and water and habitat conditions in Hamilton Harbour should not limit natural reproduction and the edibility of cold water species'. This water use goal has been translated into the following targets for fish habitat (Hamilton Harbour Remedial Action Plan Writing Team, 1992): increase the quantity of emergent and submerged aquatic plants in the Hamilton Harbour, Cootes Paradise, Grindstone Creek delta, and Grindstone Creek marshes to approximately 500 ha in accordance with the Fish and Wildlife Habitat Restoration Project; rehabilitate 344 ha of littoral fish habitat; rehabilitate 39 ha of pike spawning marsh and nursery habitat; provide additional 10 km of littoral shore by creating 5 km of narrow islands; and achieve water clarity as measured by Secchi disc during the summer season of 3.0 m in the harbour and 1.0 m in Cootes Paradise and Grindstone Creek.

17.3   Conclusions

To restore and maintain the chemical, physical and biological integrity of an aquatic ecosystem, traditional, single-chemical, concentration objectives and standards should be replaced with ecosystem objectives and quantitative indicators or targets based on beneficial uses. These objectives and their quantitative targets should be developed openly and consensually, using input from both technical experts and the public.

References

Allan, R. J. and Zarull, M. A. (1995). Conservation and protection of lake ecosystems and natural biodiversity: lessons learned from the lower Great Lakes. *Proceedings of the 6th International Conference on the Conservation and Management of Lakes—Kasumigaura '95*, Vol. 1, 174–177.

Bierman, V. J., Dolan, D. M., and Kasprzyk, R. (1983). Retrospective analysis of the response to Saginaw Bay, Lake Huron, to reductions in phosphorus loadings. *Environmental Science and Technology*, **18**, 23.

Chapman, P. C. (1990). The sediment quality triad approach to determining pollution-induced degradation. *The Science of the Total Environment*, **97/98**, 815.

Hamilton Harbour Remedial Action Plan Writing Team (1992). *Remedial Action Plan for Hamilton Harbour. Goals, Options and Recommendations*, Vol. 2, Main Report. Stage II RAP, Burlington, Ontario, Canada.

Hartig, J. H. and Zarull, M. A. (1992). *Under RAPs—Toward Grassroots Ecological Democracy in the Great Lakes Basin*. The University of Michigan Press, Ann Arbor, Michigan.

International Joint Commission (1982). *Guidelines and Register for Evaluation of Great Lakes Dredging Projects*. Windsor, Ontario.

International Joint Commission (1987). *Guidance on Characterization of Toxic Substances Problems in Areas of Concern in the Great Lakes*. Windsor, Ontario.

International Joint Commission (1988). *Procedures for the Assessment of Contaminated Sediment Problems in the Great Lakes*. Windsor, Ontario.

New York State (1991). *New York State Codes. Rules, Regulations, Title 6, Chapter X, Part 701.19, Water Quality Regulations for Surface Waters and Groundwaters*. New York State Department of Environmental Conservation, Albany, New York.

OMOE (1992). *Guidelines for the Protection and Management of Aquatic Sediment Quality in Ontario*. Toronto, Ontario.

Reynoldson, T. B. and Zarull, M. A. (1993). An approach to the development of biological sediment guidelines. In: Francis, G., Kay, J. and Woodley, S. (Eds), *Ecological Integrity and the Management of Ecosystems*. St. Lucie Press, Florida, 177–200.

Reynoldson, T. B., Bailey, R. C., Day, K. E. and Norris, R. H. (1995). Biological guidelines for freshwater sediment based on BEnthic ASsessment of SedimenT (the *BEAST*) using a multivariate approach for predicting biological state. *Australian Journal of Ecology*, **20,** 198–219.

United States and Canada (1972). *Great Lakes Water Quality Agreement.* International Joint Commission, Windsor, Ontario.

United States and Canada (1978). *Great Lakes Water Quality Agreement of 1978.* International Joint Commission, Windsor, Ontario.

United States and Canada (1987). *Revised Great Lakes Water Quality Agreement of 1978. As Amended by Protocol.* International Joint Commission, Windsor, Ontario.

Zarull, M. A. and Reynoldson, T. B. (1992). A management strategy for contaminated sediment: assessment and remediation. *Water Pollution Research Journal of Canada*, **27,** 871.

PART THREE
NATURE CONSERVATION ASSESSMENT

18 PRINCIPLES OF NATURE CONSERVATION EVALUATION

M. B. Usher

Summary

1. Over the last 20 years many criteria have been proposed for undertaking conservation evaluations. These are reviewed briefly, but it is shown that two—species richness and rarity—are most frequently used.

2. For dealing with large data-sets, computer algorithms have been developed so that optimal selections of areas to protect for nature conservation can be made. These algorithms can incorporate most criteria, but again rarity and species richness are most frequently used.

3. More recent developments include greater taxonomic awareness ('Should all species be counted equally?') and a focus on 'hotspots'—areas which have unusually large assemblages of species.

4. In any evaluation work, classification is an essential first step. Classifications establish classes on the basis of their fauna, flora and/or physical characteristics.

5. Nature is dynamic, and what might be valued today may increase or decrease in value in the future. This dynamism in nature implies that nature conservation may need to invoke the precautionary principle, since a minimalist approach now may mean a sub-standard set of protected areas in the future.

6. There is a greater need to incorporate socio-economic activity with nature conservation. This is not necessarily part of the evaluation process, but is important in the long-term management of sites selected on the basis of their biodiversity.

18.1 Introduction: the Search for Objectivity

It could be said that an intuitive feeling for what has value is all that is needed. If one possesses an antique or a work of art, then a valuer's intuition gives an assessment of its worth. This assessment can be tested in the market-place, usually at an auction, when the price realized can be compared with the valuation. Intuition is based on experience of both the market-place and the taste of the public at that particular time. However, the question that needs to be asked is 'was that valuation based on a set of criteria that anyone could apply, or was it solely based on intuition and experience?'.

In conservation evaluation, assessments tend to be different because there is usually no competitive market-place for sites that hold more (or less) wildlife, for sites that are nearer to (or further from) a natural condition, for sites with more (or fewer) rare species, etc. Intuitive feelings cannot then be tested in the market place and it becomes more important that the criteria used for evaluation are defined and broadly agreed and accepted. Given a strong degree of definition and acceptance, the criteria can then be applied in a way that is objective in the sense that the selection of a site, or series of sites, is repeatable, rigorous, and not personally biased.

A rigorous analysis of the criteria that could be used for the selection of sites for nature conservation purposes in Britain was undertaken by Ratcliffe (1977). Although 'representativeness' was not one of the 10 criteria that he used (see Table 18.1), it was perhaps implicit since the evaluation was carried out on the basis of six broad habitat types—woodlands, uplands, peatlands, grasslands, coastal sites and open waters. The criterion of 'representativeness' is difficult to apply in practice, as discussed by Austin and Margules (1986). Ratcliffe's (1977) aim was the 'selection of a series of sites adequately representing the national range of variation' (pp. 12–13) in relation to a series of ecological features, as well as climate, landform, soils and the influences of human populations. The review of criteria was advanced by Margules and Usher (1981) and Usher (1986b), who analysed the 'popularity' of various criteria internationally (Table 18.1).

Table 18.1 Criteria that have been used internationally for conservation evaluation (derived from the 17 studies reviewed by Usher, 1986b). The 10 criteria used by Ratcliffe (1977) are indicated by being set in bold type.

Criteria	Frequency of use
Richness (of habitats and/or species)	16
Naturalness, rarity (of habitats and/or species)	13
Area (or size, extent)	11
Threat of human interference	8
Amenity value, education value, representativeness	7
Scientific value	6
Recorded history	4
Population size, **typicalness**	3
Ecological fragility, position in ecological/geographical unit, potential value, uniqueness	2
Archaeological interest, availability, importance for migratory wildfowl, **intrinsic appeal**, management factors, replaceability, silvicultural gene bank, successional stage, wildlife reservoir potential	1

This early work of setting out criteria and questioning how they might be applied has led in two directions. First, in Britain it has led to a focus on individual sites, the Sites of Special Scientific Interest (SSSIs are declared by the statutory nature conservation agencies in Britain, and hence the suite of them forms the core of site-based nature conservation activities). Usher (1980) compared a number of the proposed criteria and examined their application within a large upland SSSI (4593 ha) in northern England. Guidelines for the selection of biological SSSIs were eventually published (Nature Conservancy Council, 1989), very much on the basis of the Ratcliffe criteria. These guidelines, together with their subsequent revisions, ensure that the national series of SSSIs is more objectively selected and that sites are not chosen on the basis of the whims of a few selectors. The second direction was the search for greater objectivity. This can be encapsulated by the mathematical expression:

$$V = f(C_1, C_2, C_3, \ldots, C_n)$$

where V is the conservation value, C_i are the values of the n criteria being used, and f is an appropriate mathematical function. Despite the simple appeal of such a mathematical approach, there are several difficulties. The two most important relate to the values placed on the criteria (the extent of a site can be measured in, say, hectares, and hence a number can be used; but how is the potential value, intrinsic appeal, or even naturalness, to be measured numerically?) and the form of the function f (how do you combine the number of species occurring on a site with its fragility, for example?).

Despite such difficulties, Margules and Usher (1984) designed an experiment to determine such equations for a panel of conservation assessors and, after a more detailed study (Margules, 1984), it became apparent that the equations were tremendously variable from assessor to assessor. However, Margules (1984) considered that most assessors intuitively followed a three-stage process: site rarity and fragility appeared to be the criteria used first, species richness and geographical location were used second, and more management-based criteria third. Although other criteria were used at the first and second stages as part of an individual's personal filtering process, it was interesting that, before the publication of the Nature Conservancy Council's (1989) guidelines, a hierarchical approach to assessment appeared to be used by many people in Britain.

Much research has been undertaken to find quicker, cheaper and more reliable ways of assessing the criteria. For example, Lesica (1993) sampled the vegetation around 82 ponds in eight areas, and on the basis of a classification, recommended that in designing reserves it was preferable to use measures of species richness as well as representativeness (i.e., select those ponds with the greatest number of species in each category of the classification). However, Estabrook (1991) warned that the longevity of plants was important and this led him to advocate habitat quality as the primary criterion in reserve design. These are just two examples from a large literature where only small numbers of criteria have been used or advocated. Evaluations are best performed, however, on the basis of as wide a range of criteria as possible—the resulting selection of sites, reserves, etc., is therefore conceived in a multidisciplinary framework rather than reflecting only one or a few interests.

The search for objectivity in conservation evaluation essentially began in the 1970s. During the 1980s attempts were made to define attributes of protected areas, to devise criteria to assess these attributes, and then to place values on each criterion. In many cases this was successful, and some of the selection schemes based on criteria devised in the 1970s and 1980s remain in use today (a large number of examples are given in Usher, 1986a). However, many of these approaches were not fully objective, and the search for greater objectivity continues. There is frequently an acknowledgement that one uniform system of evaluation is an unrealistic goal, and that has led to suggestions that reserves should be selected on the basis of each of several criteria used individually (e.g. Idle, 1986). Such an approach recognizes that the selected sites will then be the best for a whole range of criteria, but it does mean that optimization over the range of criteria has been lost. This leaves the dilemma of whether to select on the basis of a single criterion or on the basis of multiple criteria—each selector tends to have their own personal preferences.

This underlines one of the difficulties of any study of evaluation techniques; it is difficult to eliminate the personal element. An aim of this review is to attempt to separate personal preferences from more scientifically based concepts. What is the evaluation to be used for? In this review the focus is on selecting series of nature conservation sites, though of course there are many other purposes for which evaluations can be used.

18.2   Can Objectivity be Automated?

The search for automation has focused on defining sets of decision rules that could be applied by computers to large data sets. If, for example, one takes a series of 75 habitat fragments (the limestone pavements discussed by Margules *et al.*, 1994b), it could be argued that it is not a difficult task to look through the 75 species lists to find the site with the greatest species richness, or the greatest number of rare species, and so on. However, if the aim is to select two sites that will maximize the total number of species or the number of rare species, then there are 2,775 comparisons to be made (the sum of the series 74+73+...+1, since there are 74 sites to compare with site 1, 73 sites with site 2 because site 1 has already been compared with it, etc.). This may be possible by hand, but the task becomes more difficult if a selection of three sites is to be made (it is essentially optimizing from the 67,525 ways of selecting three sites). There are nearly 1.25×10^6 ways of selecting four sites, and there are huge numbers of possible selections for larger numbers of sites. Clearly there are benefits in formulating sets of decision rules and then writing a computer algorithm so that an optimal selection of sites can be made.

The development of such algorithms (e.g. Margules *et al.*, 1988; Margules, 1989; Nicholls and Margules, 1993; Pressey *et al.*, 1993; Margules *et al.*, 1994b) has focused on clarifying potential ambiguities in the decision rules. Take, for example, one of the earlier algorithms shown diagrammatically in Figure 18.1, which is based particularly on two criteria—number of species and rarity. Step 1 is used to select all those sites that have a unique species, that is, a species that occurs on one site and on no other site. These sites will obviously contain a variety of other species, some of which may only occur on two or three sites in total, whilst others will be ubiquitous, occurring on all or most sites; all species occurring on the selected sites are now described as 'represented', leaving a set of species that are 'unrepresented'. Step 2 essentially asks the question 'are all species now represented?'. If the answer is 'no', step 3 continues the focus on rarity by selecting the rarest 'unrepresented' species (say species R) and choosing a site on which it occurs. If there are several possible sites on which species R is present, the number of 'unrepresented' species on each site is counted, and the site with the largest number of 'unrepresented' species is chosen. The lists of 'represented' and 'unrepresented' species are then adjusted, and steps 2 and 3 are repeated, selecting a site for the new rarest species, say species S. However, if two or more candidate sites for species R have the same number of 'unrepresented' species, the algorithm passes to step 4. From these candidate sites, the one with the least frequent group of species (defined as that group having the smallest sum of frequencies of occurrence in the remaining unselected sites) is selected, and once again the algorithm returns to steps 2 and 3. However, if there is no single site with the least frequent group of species, the algorithm goes to step 5 and selects the first site on the list. This is unsatisfactory since it is order-dependent, that is, dependent on the order of the sites in the two-dimensional table of species and sites. Of course, the algorithm could have selected one of these sites at random, thus overcoming the order-dependence. Neither approach is satisfactory since the selection is arbitrary, but it does highlight one of the two essential features of such algorithms.

First, there must be a rule for choosing between equals. Even with sophisticated algorithms some rule has to be introduced if all other decision criteria are equal; the order-dependence occurs, for example, in step 10 of the upgraded algorithm of Nicholls and Margules (1993), but this could equally have been a random selection. Second, there has to be a rule for stopping the procedure. There are at least four possibilities for creating a stopping rule:

(a) Stop when all sites have been selected (i.e., all the sites have been placed in priority order).
(b) Stop when a predetermined number of sites has been selected (say three sites or 10 sites).
(c) Stop when each species is represented on a site (i.e., there are no longer any species which are 'unrepresented').
(d) Stop when each species is represented on at least n ($n \geqslant 2$) sites, assuming that all species which occur on less than n sites will have their sites included in the selection.

In step 2 in Figure 18.1 the generic question 'have sufficient sites been selected?' is asked, but this needs to be related to a specific stopping rule, such as those indicated above.

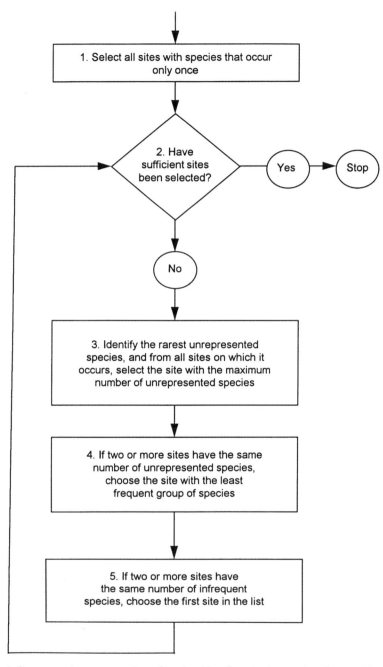

Figure 18.1   A diagrammatic representation of an algorithm for selecting a suite of potential protected areas from a long list of candidate sites. The algorithm is based on that described by Margules *et al.* (1988).

The most recent developments of these algorithms have incorporated many other decision criteria that diverge from the focus on rarity and species richness. For example, the concept of communities can be introduced, as well as spatial aspects (e.g. 'if there is a choice, select the site that is nearest geographically to a site already selected); or resource constraints on the funding agency (e.g. 'if there is a choice, select the smallest site' or 'if there is a choice, select the site that will be least expensive to manage').

All of these automated methods rely on good quality data, which implies that the inventory work has been undertaken to a high standard and is complete. The analyses are all performed on the basic data matrix of sites with their species occurrence, perhaps with supplementary data on community occurrence on the sites, extent of the sites, geographical location, site management costs, etc. It is all too frequently assumed, usually implicitly, that once such a data matrix has been gathered it is constant, and that these algorithms will make the 'best' selection of potential areas from all of the candidate sites. It has to be remembered, however, that species occurrences are likely to change from year to year, and that the inventory data may contain errors. The implications of such dynamic behaviour, whether real or due to observer errors, are explored in analyses of the selection of limestone pavements in Northern England by Margules *et al.* (1994b).

The answer to the question that heads this section is certainly that algorithms can be devised to automate the selection of a 'best' set of sites. However, this selection depends both upon the decision criteria that are embedded in the algorithm and on the quality (and stability) of the data set that is analysed.

18.3. Other Considerations

18.3.1 *Is there a taxonomic component?*

Leaving aside uncertainties of what is a species, the question essentially focuses attention on the value of each species present. If one species is native and another species is non-native, should they each count as one species in assessing species richness? If this is taken to absurd lengths, botanical and zoological gardens are the most species-rich localities that will be encountered! This leads to a feeling that only native species should be counted in areas to be chosen for protection— but why? If two species are very closely related, say sibling species, do they contribute as much as two species that are only distantly related? On the one hand, both are pairs of species and should count as two; on the other hand, the two unrelated species are likely to be more diverse genetically and hence could be more valued than two sibling species—but why? If we are concerned with conserving, say, blanket bogs, should the species confined to blanket bogs (say *Andromeda polifolia* or some of the *Sphagnum* mosses) be given greater weight than the species that occur in a wide variety of habitats (for example *Calluna vulgaris*)? These are difficult questions to address and there is, as yet, no consensus about the answers.

An example of the taxonomic relatedness of species (Williams *et al.*, 1993) concerns the various diversity measures that can be used (Figure 18.2). Species richness is simple: each of the 10 sites has three of the six possible species, and hence its richness is represented as 50%. The taxonomic root weight attaches importance to ancestral species, and hence site H, with the three most ancestral species, has the largest diversity index and site J, with the least ancestral species, has the lowest. A progression from this is the diversity of higher taxa, measured by comparisons between all pairs of species. This is maximized in Figure 18.2 for sites B, D and H, and is again minimized for site J. The spanning-tree length measures how much of the cladogram is occupied by the fauna of any site. As the total 'width' of the cladogram in Figure 18.2 is spanned by sites A, B and C, these have the highest diversity measure, whereas sites H, I and J have the smallest, irrespective of whether species are classified as 'ancestral' or 'recent'. Finally, the taxonomic dispersion is an extension of this concept, giving very similar results to the spanning-tree length, though site A has a slightly greater dispersion than sites B and C. The methods of calculating these five measures of diversity are given by Williams *et al.* (1993). The subject has been further discussed by Williams *et al.* (1994), who referred to taxonomic, genetic and ecological attributes as 'currencies', and by Humphries *et al.* (1995).

These kinds of analysis have considerable theoretical interest, but they have yet to be applied to practical conservation considerations at the local level. Analyses such as those by Pressey *et al.* (1993) on the world's owls or Williams *et al.* (1993) on bumble bees of the *sibiricus* group indicate areas of the world where reserves to protect these groups should be located, but such locational work has not yet

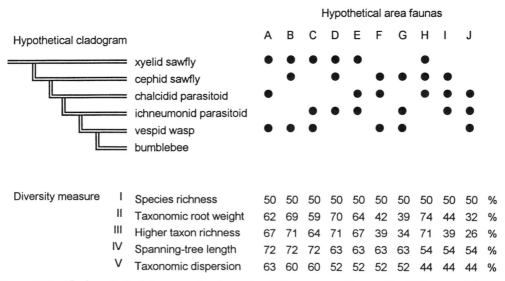

Figure 18.2   The hypothetical cladogram for six species of Hymenoptera discussed by Williams *et al.* (1993). The upper part of the diagram indicates the cladogram, and the occurrence of the species on 10 sites, lettered A to J. The lower part of the diagram indicates five measures of diversity, which are discussed in the text.
The diagram is reproduced with permission from both CAB International and the authors.

begun. How close a correlation might there be if different groups of species were to be analysed? Using cells of 5° latitude and 10° longitude, 12 cells are identified as being important for the bees and over 50 cells for the owls. Interestingly, only three cells coincide in the two analyses; the third most important for bees is the fourth most important for owls, the ninth for bees is the second for owls, and the tenth for bees is the forty-eighth for owls. Undoubtedly if enough cladograms existed for enough groups of organisms, most of the $5° \times 10°$ cells of the planet could be classified as important for one or more groups of organisms (except for Antarctica, where there are so few terrestrial organisms that all diversity indices would take low values, except possibly for the Acari).

The question of whether the number of species should be considered, and whether some taxonomic moderation should be applied, is becoming increasingly important. Williams and Gaston (1994) analysed numbers of families, and found that this correlated with the numbers of species (for a number of disparate taxonomic groups in Britain, Australia and Central America). This relationship could also be important in finding ways of minimizing the future loss of biodiversity (Witting and Loeschcke, 1995) and it relates closely to the problems of conserving genetic diversity (e.g. Crozier, 1992), especially when that diversity is difficult (and expensive) to measure in natural populations. However, it comes back to the question of whether the species is the most appropriate biological unit for conservation. Is species conservation a surrogate for the conservation of genetic diversity? Has the modern emphasis towards habitat conservation (see the European Union's 'Habitats Directive' of 1992) moved even further away from conserving genetic diversity, or are habitats important because the species that have become adapted to living in several habitat types have a greater genetic diversity than species that occur in only one habitat type? There are many theoretical questions that have still to be addressed and incorporated into criteria used for deciding what should be protected and conserved.

To the practical conservationist these questions may seem remote, but they could be important in deciding national or regional strategies to minimize the loss of biodiversity. Three questions are particularly urgent given the current state of taxonomic knowledge:

(a) Should non-native species be considered as part of an area's diversity?
(b) Should species characteristic of the habitat type that is to be protected be valued more than non-characteristic species that are, perhaps incidentally, occurring on the site?
(c) What should be done to conserve the diversity of species that are poorly known taxonomically (for example, the soil microbes, the soil fauna or marine nematodes)?

The answers to these questions are not simple, and each can be approached from a number of directions. There are strongly held views about alien and invasive species, about aiming conservation measures at identified species or habitats or at the wider countryside, etc. Until there are answers, a blend of theory and pragmatism is required in devising schemes of biodiversity conservation, and in deciding the areas that most need protecting and conserving.

18.3.2   Should 'hotspots' be identified?

In the examples quoted in the preceding section, three of the $5° \times 10°$ cells were important both for bumble bees and owls; in a sense these could be termed 'hotspots' of biodiversity. One was on the western coast of South America (in the Peru/Ecuador region), and the other two in the eastern Himalayan region. There has been much speculation that if the planet were viewed as a whole, then the greatest species richness would be found in the tropical forest zones of South America and Asia. However, although globally these may be 'hotspots' of biodiversity, the concept can also be used at more local scales, within nations or regions.

Within Britain there tends to be a decline in species richness from south to north. Analysis of the 10 km squares of the National Grid led Prendergast *et al.* (1993) to demonstrate that this assertion was not true for all taxonomic groups. Plotting the 5% of the grid squares with the greatest numbers of species demonstrated that the assertion held true for butterflies and dragonflies, since all of the species-rich squares lie south of a line from the Humber to the Mersey, and the majority lie south of a line from the Wash to the Severn. For aquatic plants (Figure 18.3) and breeding birds some of the species-rich squares are in northern England and Scotland, but for the liverworts Scotland has the greatest species richness. In relation to the evaluation of freshwater habitats the dragonflies and aquatic plants are two important indicator groups. Why are there relatively few dragonflies in the north, and why is the species richness of aquatic plants more evenly distributed in Britain? Is the latter related to the diversity of water bodies—

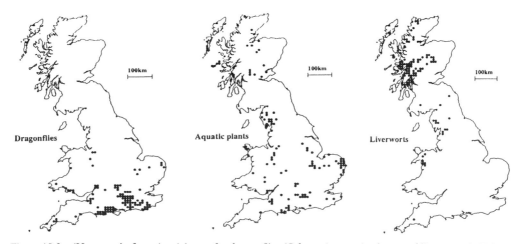

Figure 18.3   'Hotspots' of species richness for dragonflies (Odonata), aquatic plants and liverworts in Britain. The maps are taken from Prendergast *et al.* (1993) and are reproduced with permission from *Nature*, Macmillan Magazines Limited.

running and still water, oligotrophic and eutrophic waters, etc., found in different geographical regions?

A focus on 'hotspots' once again brings the number of species to prominence in conservation evaluation. All species are equally weighted, and hence considerations such as rarity and commonness, native and non-native, or taxonomic status and cladistic position, are excluded from the analysis. In many ways the focus on species richness, one of Ratcliffe's (1977) criteria, has been re-expressed as a 'hotspot'. However, the data collected in biological recording schemes can be used more proactively. Rather than choosing between a set of pre-identified candidate sites, the emphasis in the analysis of 'hotspots' has focused on geographical areas of the country ($100\,m^2$ cells) where the biodiversity is unusually large, and it is perhaps within these cells that sites could be sought and assessed for their nature conservation potential.

18.4 Conservation Evaluation of Freshwater Habitats: Some Thoughts

Freshwater habitats are essentially no different from any other habitats if their value for nature conservation is to be assessed. In Ratcliffe's (1977) consideration of a series of key nature conservation sites in Britain, fresh waters are one of the six broad habitat groupings that he used. However, there is a difference, and that relates to the need to establish a classification of fresh waters. In terrestrial habitats, classification is usually done on the basis of the assemblage of plants that grow in an area. The classification of these assemblages into associations or communities is therefore on the basis of the plant species themselves, focusing on either the dominant species or species that are characteristic of (or are of high fidelity to) that community. To some extent this also applies to fresh waters (e.g. Rodwell, 1995), but there tends also to be a much greater emphasis on the physical environment: on whether the water is flowing or not, on the nutrient status and pH of the water, or on the nature of the sediment, be it sandy, muddy or rocky. This is recognized in Naiman *et al.*'s (1992) review of the classification of rivers for their conservation potential.

However, there is an increasing interest in the use of biological features for the classification of freshwater habitats. To choose two recent studies, Palmer *et al.* (1992) devised a botanical classification and Foster *et al.* (1992) devised a classification based on 15 families of water beetles. Both studies used similar statistical methods, employing TWINSPAN (Hill, 1979) to divide the species lists from a large number of sampling localities into a number of groups of similar sites. For the aquatic plants in Britain (samples from Cornwall to Shetland), 10 groups were selected; for the water beetles of Ireland (also with good geographical coverage) again 10 groups were identified. The fact that both studies chose 10 groups is interesting, since the water beetle analysis was based on 289 lists with a total of 165 species, whereas the plant analysis was based on 1124 lists with 104 species of submerged and floating plants (the number of emergent species was not given).

What do these studies indicate? Is it true that there is as yet no agreed classification of water bodies that is satisfactory for conservation evaluation? Will a classification ever be mutually acceptable to all interested groups, perhaps combining the physical features with different components of the biota, especially the plants and invertebrates? The invertebrate fauna is arguably particularly important, and is now widely used in the assessment of the biological quality of running water sites in the UK (see Wright *et al.*, this volume, for a description of the use of the invertebrate fauna in the RIVPACS III software package).

Increasingly, classifications are being used within software packages, and the quest for automating evaluations is continuing. The development of an expert system was the aim of O'Keeffe *et al.* (1987) and Danilewitz *et al.* (1988) in their assessments of the river systems of South Africa. Their River Conservation System (RCS) was described as an automated, semi-numerical model, providing a framework within which results from huge data sets can be obtained. A similar automated system, being developed in the UK by Boon *et al.* (1994 and this volume), is known as the System for Evaluating Rivers for Conservation (SERCON). These systems have two features which need to be assessed critically. First, there is the quality of the data themselves; no system can be better than the data on which it is based. Good quality data in turn means good survey or inventory work, and hence quality assurance on the input data is important. Second, there is the handling of both qualitative and quantitative data by the software package itself. The algorithms used do need to be assessed, and it is important that these packages are not just 'black boxes' but are transparent, allowing the users to understand just how evaluations are being carried out.

18.5 Discussion: Dynamic Nature vs. Changing Human Attitudes

For many years arguments have been published about whether one large reserve or several small reserves should be selected (SLOSS—single large or several small; see Simberloff, 1986) and about the shape of reserves (SION—shape important or not; see Usher, 1991). All of the studies arguing one way or another have assumed static conditions; the number of species is assessed at one time, and then comparisons are made and conclusions drawn. However, nature is not static, and the individual species may come and go, or the inventory work may be inaccurate so that species are recorded that are not there, or, more usually, species that are present are not recorded. It is always possible to prove that a species is present on a site by seeing it (unless an individual has been misidentified), but it is almost impossible to prove that a species is not present—the lack of observations may be indicative, but it is not conclusive. The study of the flora of 74 limestone pavements (Margules *et al.*, 1994b) indicated a considerable degree of dynamism, either real or apparent because of observer errors, over an 11 year period. So an important question is whether an evaluation carried out today will still be valid at some time in the future. Because of the inherent dynamism of nature it is perhaps essential to err on the cautious side, to apply what is termed as the 'precautionary principle' and conserve rather more than the absolute minimum.

Only rarely have repeat surveys been carried out. As Margules *et al.* (1994b) showed, if the aim of the first of their two surveys had been to make a selection of pavements that included all 50 species, then that selection of pavements would only have 32 of these species 11 years later. In other words, if a minimalist approach had been taken, the set of sites chosen to represent all 50 species would only have had 64% of these species 11 years later at the time of the second survey. This is a sobering thought, and raises the question as to whether these limestone pavement habitats are particularly dynamic, or if nature is as dynamic as this in other habitat types.

The limestone pavements are particularly small habitat types in otherwise much more extensive grassland. They were chosen for study because of the increasing interest in fragmentation. Although fragmentation is less likely to affect freshwater habitats than terrestrial ones, the way that species richness behaves in the face of fragmentation is an important area for research. The Australian experiment (Margules, 1992) on the fragmentation of *Eucalyptus* forest is important in this respect because it is using three different fragment sizes, each replicated five times. Preliminary results (Margules *et al.*, 1994a) indicated that different arthropod species reacted to fragmentation in different ways; will there ever be a single type of reaction when organisms are faced with responding to an ever-changing environment? In the *Eucalyptus* forest, scorpions seemed to be unaffected by fragmentation, whilst an amphipod was adversely affected, especially in the smaller fragments. More experimental work will be required if we are to understand whether habitat fragments have much conservation value; initial indications from farm woodlands are that fragments of less than 1.5 ha have virtually no true woodland species, whereas patches of more than 5 ha can be expected to have a reasonably complete complement. These area thresholds come from studies in the Vale of York (Usher, 1995), but more experimental work in other geographical areas is required if their generality is to be established.

The human dimension has not yet been considered. Although the human species cannot be excluded from considerations of naturalness (Margules and Usher, 1981), the presence of ever-increasing numbers of people can have a substantial influence (Perrings *et al.*, 1992). Macdonald *et al.* (1989) showed clearly for a number of biomes in Africa and North America that the number of non-native species increased proportionately with increasing numbers of visitors to protected areas. If the native biota is to be conserved, the presence of more and more non-native species is likely to lead to diminished population sizes of the native species, and possibly to their extinction. Kitihara and Fujii's (1994) studies on butterflies in and around Tsukuba in Japan indicated that human disturbance was associated with the loss of the specialist species. Butterfly species richness declined with increasing disturbance, even though the number of generalist species remained constant. In other words, with an increasing human population and increasing human disturbance, is the world likely to become increasingly dominated by a few generalist species whilst the specialist species are increasingly lost? This is a fascinating hypothesis to test, and one that might account for the demise of so many island species (which would generally be classified as specialist).

These are so many aspects to conservation evaluation that it is impossible to specify a series of principles. The attempt has been to define criteria, and then to measure these criteria in a quantitative way, if that is possible. To this extent we are operating in a scientific environment. However, the definition of the criteria, and their quantification, poses questions that are not easy to answer. 'What are the effects of fragmentation?', or 'Is the biodiversity of a site dynamic?' are questions that can be addressed by the design and execution of appropriate experiments. There are many other questions that can only be answered by considering the values of society at large. 'What is the value of a golden eagle?' or 'Is the soil biota to be valued?' are examples of these, as would be the actual values that attach to the criteria that have been chosen. For example, which is the more important, a site with a few rare species or a site with an unusually large number of common species?

It is this integration of scientific and socio-economic factors which will be important in deciding what should be conserved today. As Norton and Ulanowicz (1992) concluded:

> Economic activities that complement and enhance, rather than oppose and degrade, ecological processes are to be preferred and encouraged. Recognizing that natural systems will react creatively to change, we should develop economic incentives to encourage development that mimics natural disturbances.

It is this socio-economic dimension that is lacking in the range of methods that have been developed for conservation evaluation. This dimension should certainly be considered when management plans are being written for sites that have been evaluated and selected. But, more importantly, biodiversity cannot be maintained just on the basis of a few protected areas. To retain in perpetuity the range of species, and their genotypes, requires biodiversity conservation to be a facet of all forms of land use, and hence the integration of ecological and socio-economic sciences is essential. This is, however, a wider topic than nature conservation evaluation, which is still very much an ecological science.

Acknowledgements

I am grateful to Dr P. J. Boon for drawing my attention to some of the freshwater literature that has been cited in this review, and for commenting on a draft manuscript.

References

Austin, M. P. and Margules, C. R. (1986). Assessing representativeness. In: Usher, M. B. (Ed.), *Wildlife Conservation Evaluation*. Chapman and Hall, London, 45–67.

Boon, P. J., Holmes, N. T. H., Maitland, P. S. and Rowell, T. A. (1994). A system for evaluating rivers for conservation ('SERCON'): an outline of the underlying principles. *Verhandlungen der Internationalen Vereinigung für theoretische und angewandte Limnologie*, **25**, 1510–1514.

Boon, P. J., Holmes, N. T. H., Maitland, P. S., Rowell, T. A. and Davies, J. (This volume). A system for evaluating rivers for conservation (SERCON): development, structure and function.

Crozier, R. H. (1992). Genetic diversity and the agony of choice. *Biological Conservation,* **61,** 11–15.

Danilewitz, D. B., O'Keeffe, J. H. and Bradshaw, J. A. (1988). An expert interface to an ecological model. *South African Journal of Science,* **84,** 189–194.

Estabrook G. F. (1991). The size of nature reserves and the number of long lived plant species they contain. *Coenoses,* **6,** 39–45.

Foster, G. N., Nelson, B. H., Bilton, D. T., Lott, D. A., Merritt, R., Weyl, R. S. and Eyre, M. D. (1992). A classification and evaluation of Irish water beetle assemblages. *Aquatic Conservation: Marine and Freshwater Ecosystems,* **2,** 185–208.

Hill, M. O. (1979). *TWINSPAN: a Fortran Program for Arranging Multivariate Data in an Ordered Two-way Table by Classification of the Individuals and Attributes.* Cornell University, Ithaca, New York.

Humphries, C. J., Williams, P. H. and Vane-Wright, R. I. (1995). Measuring biodiversity value for conservation. *Annual Review of Ecology and Systematics,* **26,** 93–111.

Idle, E. T. (1986). Evaluation at the local scale: a region in Scotland. In: Usher, M. B. (Ed.), *Wildlife Conservation Evaluation.* Chapman and Hall, London, 181–198.

Kitihara, M. and Fujii, K. (1994). Biodiversity and community structure of temperate butterfly species within a gradient of human disturbance: an analysis based on the concept of generalist vs. specialist strategies. *Researches on Population Ecology,* **36,** 187–199.

Lesica, P. (1993). Using plant community diversity in reserve design for pothole prairie in the Blackfeet Indian Reservation, Montana, USA. *Biological Conservation,* **65,** 69–75.

Macdonald, I. A. W., Loope, L. L., Usher, M. B. and Hamann, O. (1989). Wildlife conservation and the invasion of nature reserves by introduced species: a global perspective. In: Drake, J. A., Mooney, H. A., di Castri, F., Groves, R. H., Kruger, F. J., Reymánek, M. and Williamson, M. (Eds), *SCOPE 37, Biological Invasions: a Global Perspective.* John Wiley, Chichester, 215–255.

Margules, C. R. (1984). Conservation evaluation in practice, II. Enclosed grasslands in the Yorkshire Dales, Great Britain. *Journal of Environmental Management,* **18,** 169–183.

Margules, C. R. (1989). Introduction to some Australian developments in conservation evaluation. *Biological Conservation,* **50,** 1–11.

Margules, C. R. (1992). The Wog Wog habitat fragmentation experiment. *Environmental Conservation,* **19,** 316–325.

Margules, C. R., Milkovits, G. A. and Smith, G. T. (1994a). Contrasting effects of habitat fragmentation on the scorpion *Cercophonius squama* and an amphipod. *Ecology,* **75,** 2033–2042.

Margules, C. R., Nicholls, A. O. and Pressey, R. L. (1988). Selecting networks of reserves to maximise biological diversity. *Biological Conservation,* **43,** 64–76.

Margules, C. R., Nicholls, A. O. and Usher, M. B. (1994b). Apparent species turnover, probability of extinction and the selection of nature reserves: a case study of the Ingleborough limestone pavements. *Conservation Biology,* **8,** 398–409.

Margules, C. and Usher, M. B. (1981). Criteria used in assessing wildlife conservation potential: a review. *Biological Conservation,* **21,** 79–109.

Margules, C. R. and Usher, M. B. (1984). Conservation evaluation in practice, I. Sites of different habitats in north-east Yorkshire, Great Britain. *Journal of Environmental Management,* **18,** 153–168.

Naiman, R. J., Lonzarich, D. G., Beechie, T. J. and Ralph, S. C. (1992). General principles of classification and the assessment of conservation potential in rivers. In: Boon, P. J., Calow, P. and Petts, G. E. (Eds), *River Conservation and Management.* John Wiley, Chichester, 93–123.

Nature Conservancy Council (1989). *Guidelines for Selection of Biological SSSIs.* Peterborough.

Nicholls, A. O. and Margules, C. R. (1993). An upgraded reserve selection algorithm. *Biological Conservation,* **64,** 165–169.

Norton, B. G. and Ulanowicz, R. E. (1992). Scale and biodiversity policy: a hierarchical approach. *Ambio,* **21,** 244–249.

O'Keeffe, J. H., Danilewitz, D. B. and Bradshaw, J. A. (1987). An 'expert system' approach to the assessment of the conservation status of rivers. *Biological Conservation,* **40,** 69–84.

Palmer, M. A., Bell, S. L. and Butterfield, I. (1992). A botanical classification of standing waters in Britain: applications for conservation and monitoring. *Aquatic Conservation: Marine and Freshwater Ecosystems,* **2,** 125–143.

Perrings, C., Folke, C. and Mäler, K.-G. (1992). The ecology and economics of biodiversity loss: the research agenda. *Ambio,* **21,** 201–211.

Prendergast, J. R., Quinn, R. M., Lawton, J. H., Eversham, B. C. and Gibbons, D. W. (1993). Rare species, the coincidences of diversity hotspots and conservation strategies. *Nature,* **365,** 335–337.

Pressey, R. L., Humphries, C. J., Margules, C. R., Vane-Wright, R. I. and Williams, P. H. (1993). Beyond opportunism: key principles for systematic reserve selection. *Trends in Ecology and Evolution,* **8,** 124–128.

Ratcliffe, D. A. (Ed.) (1977). *A Nature Conservation Review, Volume 1.* Cambridge University Press, Cambridge.

Rodwell, J. S. (Ed.) (1995). *British Plant Communities, Volume 4. Aquatic Communities, Swamps and Tall-herb Fens.* Cambridge University Press, Cambridge.

Simberloff, D. (1986). Design of nature reserves. In: Usher, M. B. (Ed.), *Wildlife Conservation Evaluation.* Chapman and Hall, London, 315–337.

Usher, M. B. (1980). An assessment of conservation values within a large Site of Special Scientific Interest in North Yorkshire. *Field Studies,* **5,** 323–348.

Usher, M. B. (Ed.) (1986a). *Wildlife Conservation Evaluation.* Chapman and Hall, London.

Usher, M. B. (1986b). Wildlife conservation evaluation: attributes, criteria and values. In: Usher, M. B. (Ed.), *Wildlife Conservation Evaluation.* Chapman and Hall, London, 3–44.

Usher, M. B. (1991). Habitat structure and the design of nature reserves. In: Bell, S. S., McCoy, E. D. and Muskinsky, H. R. (Eds), *Habitat Structure: the Physical Arrangement of Objects in Space.* Chapman and Hall, London, 373–391.

Usher, M. B. (1995). Species richness and the application of island biogeography theory to farm woodlands. In: Ferris-Kaan, R. (Ed.), *Managing Forests for Biodiversity.* Forestry Commission (Edinburgh) Technical Paper, **8,** 22–27.

Williams, P. H. and Gaston, K. J. (1994). Measuring more of biodiversity: can higher-taxon richness predict wholesale species richness? *Biological Conservation,* **67,** 211–217.

Williams, P. H., Gaston, K. J. and Humphries, C. J. (1994). Do conservationists and molecular biologists value differences between organisms in the same way? *Biodiversity Letters,* **2,** 67–78.

Williams, P. H., Vane-Wright, R. I. and Humphries, C. J. (1993). Measuring biodiversity for choosing conservation areas. In: LaSalle, J. and Gauld, I. D. (Eds), *Hymenoptera and Biodiversity.* CAB International, Wallingford, 309–328.

Witting, L. and Loeschke, V. (1995). The optimization of biodiversity conservation. *Biological Conservation,* **71,** 205–207.

Wright, J. F., Moss, D., Clarke, R. T. and Furse, M. T. (This volume). Biological assessment of river quality using the new version of RIVPACS (RIVPACS III).

19 RIVER HABITAT SURVEY: A NEW SYSTEM FOR CLASSIFYING RIVERS ACCORDING TO THEIR HABITAT QUALITY

P. J. Raven, P. Fox, M. Everard, N. T. H. Holmes and F. H. Dawson

Summary

1. River Habitat Survey (RHS) has been developed in response to the need for a nationally applicable classification of rivers based on their habitat quality. This has been driven primarily by the need to establish an objective basis for assessing the state of river habitats. River management by the Environment Agency and other equivalent bodies, in the form of regulation, operational works and advice to planning authorities, can then take full account of the need to protect highly valued sites, implement appropriate measures to enhance degraded reaches, and identify relevant mitigation where development proceeds.

2. When fully developed and implemented, RHS will comprise four distinct but related outputs: (a) a standard field survey method; (b) a computer database, containing information from a national reference network of UK sites; (c) a classification of river types based on a predictive model of physical structure; and (d) a scheme for assessing habitat quality.

3. This chapter outlines project development to date, the general approach to future development, and some preliminary results.

19.1 Introduction and Background

River management requires a sound technical basis, so that actions to protect the best wildlife sites and those to enhance degraded ones are appropriate, cost-effective and closely match the real rather than the perceived need. The Environment Agency is responsible for water management and pollution control in England and Wales. It has a high public profile and an obligation to spend taxpayers' and charge payers' money wisely. It is against this background that development of River Habitat Survey (RHS) must be viewed. The features in RHS include those which are well established and considered to be important for wildlife (Harper *et al.*, 1995). What makes RHS novel is that the approach is based on establishing a national inventory of these features, deriving a classification of river types, and establishing a habitat quality assessment scheme on a semi-objective basis.

From 1 April 1996 the Environment Act 1995 established an Environment Agency (EA) for England and Wales, bringing together the functions of the National Rivers Authority (NRA), Her Majesty's Inspectorate of Pollution, and the Water Regulatory Authorities. The EA is a non-departmental public body with statutory powers and duties in respect of pollution control, water resource management, flood defence, freshwater and migratory fisheries and, for certain rivers, navigation in England and Wales. The EA has statutory duties to have regard to, and to further, conservation in carrying out its pollution control, and other functions, respectively. It also has a duty generally to promote so far as it considers desirable, the conservation of flora and fauna dependent on the water environment and also to promote recreation on waters.

The EA operates through an integrated river basin management approach and its activities and priorities are set out in Local Environment Agency Plans. One of the current weaknesses in these plans is the lack of a standard descriptive assessment of physical structure to complement those developed for water quality and quantity. Without this capability it is difficult to set targets for habitat quality, or measure the success or otherwise of river management techniques. The EA currently reports on chemical water quality through published surveys every five years. Development of its General Quality Assessment scheme will allow reporting on other aspects of water quality, including invertebrate biology, nutrients and aesthetic quality (NRA, 1994). Physical structure is one of the primary determinants of ecosystem quality, so to complete the picture, a reporting mechanism of this aspect is clearly needed.

In 1996, the EA employed 86 full-time equivalent conservation staff out of a total workforce of 9,450. The bulk of their workload represents a technical audit and quality assurance role to ensure that site-based proposals for river management, by the Agency itself or other parties, are screened for their potential impacts. This role is primarily focused on three key activity areas: (a) regulation; through appraising applications for water abstraction or impoundment, discharge of pollutants, land drainage works and fish movements, (b) operational works; by applying best environmental practice for designing, constructing and maintaining flood defences and other structures, and (c) advisory; through comments as a consultee to local planning authorities (NRA, 1993). In a year, these conservation staff screen more than 9,000 applications for land drainage, fisheries, and discharge consents and abstraction licences, plus a similar number of planning applications (NRA, 1995).

The collective responsibility for land, air and water quality, including reporting on the state of the environment, linked *inter alia* with government commitments on biodiversity and sustainability, reinforce the need for a sound methodology for classifying the quality of river habitats.

The draft EC Directive on the Ecological Quality of Water (COM(93)680 Final) (see Preface) proposed a broad approach to assessing and reporting quality, taking account of *physical* as well as *chemical* conditions of inland waters, including the contribution made by the riparian zone. Furthermore, it stated that the national systems adopted by member states must be notified to the scientific community and that the details should be published. The EC Habitats Directive (92/43/EEC) and the establishment of *Natura 2000* sites is another major influence, since member states are required to monitor the state of Special Areas of Conservation (SACs) with a view to maintaining, or where necessary, restoring favourable conservation status. The state of habitats within river SACs will have to be monitored as part of this process.

The UK Biodiversity Action Plan (Department of the Environment *et al.*, 1994), published as a result of the 1992 Earth Summit Conference in Rio de Janeiro, places significant emphasis on the need to evaluate, report and monitor biodiversity. The use of physical structure as a surrogate measure for biodiversity is likely to be an important aspect in reporting on the state of running freshwater habitats, a key component of the British landscape.

19.2   Development of RHS

The need for a nationally applicable system to measure, classify and report on the physical structure of rivers has been matched only by the lack of a suitable methodology. A number of current techniques partly fulfil the requirements but fail to deliver the appropriate output.

For example, RIVPACS (Wright *et al.*, 1984, this volume) is focused on the association between invertebrate communities and environmental features, HABSCORE (Milner *et al.*, 1993) on salmonid fishery rivers and PHABSIM (Johnson *et al.*, 1993) on measuring flow requirements at an intensity of detail that is prohibitively expensive for a national survey. The classification of rivers developed by Holmes (1989) is based solely on aquatic plant communities.

The aim from the outset was to develop a system to assist river management decisions. It would be based on the ability to predict, with statistical probability, those physical features which ought to occur in unmodified examples for the full range of river types in England and Wales. The scheme for assessing habitat quality would comprise a simple five-band classification (excellent, good, fair, poor, bad) derived from the comparison between *observed* features in the site and those *expected* for that particular river type in an unmodified state. Development of this system therefore had to fulfil the following basic requirements:

(a) A robust, tried and tested field method.
(b) An objective sampling strategy to establish a statistically valid national inventory.
(c) Appropriate computer database facilities with the analytical capability to derive a statistically valid and recognizable river typology from the data.
(d) Compatibility with existing methods.

(e) Practical and simple outputs, easily understood by river managers and amenable to reporting at catchment and national scales.

(f) A tool providing significant input to the environmental appraisal process.

(g) Acceptance by external organizations, notably the conservation agencies.

(h) With the European Directives in mind, applicability in the UK and beyond.

19.3   Survey Methodology

19.3.1   Field survey

RHS is essentially an assessment of the physical structure of watercourses. Procedures for field survey have been established and refined by extensive trials and subsequent analysis of data. RHS does not require specialist geomorphological or botanical expertise, but consistent recognition of features included on the field survey form is essential. An illustrated manual has been produced, and accreditation of field surveyors will be ensured through attendance at approved RHS training courses.

Analysis of field data collected from 'spot check' transects located 10 m apart throughout three 1 km long sample blocks of the River Derwent, Cumbria in 1993 indicated that for physical features the optimum sample length for maximum information gain in minimum time is 500 m (Figure 19.1a). This is consistent with unit length currently used for river corridor surveys and aquatic macrophyte classifications and enables better use of each component and their conjunctive use and cross-validation (Holmes, 1989; NRA, 1992). Further analysis of the same Derwent data set indicated that 10 'spot-checks' per 500 m yielded at least 69% of recorded features (Figure 19.1b). Since each spot check takes approximately two minutes to complete, a pragmatic decision to use 10 spot checks per 500 m (site) was taken to ensure efficient and effective data capture, particularly since infrequent features not occurring at spot checks are recorded via a 'sweep-up' checklist.

19.3.2   Data collection

The RHS form is four pages long and simple to fill in. The form requires input of selected information obtained from maps and other readily available sources, plus field data. Background information for each 500 m site includes grid reference, altitude, slope, solid and drift geology, mean annual flow and distance from source. Features recorded on site are associated with the channel, banks and riparian corridor to 50 m either side of the river (Table 19.1). The method of recording ensures maximum information content and accuracy without excessive time penalty. Features that broadly characterize the site (e.g. valley form, and adjacent land use) set the scene. Bankfull and water width, together with bankfull height and water depth, are measured at one selected location because the width: depth ratio, taken in the context of other physical features, provides information about geomorphological processes acting on the site.

Attributes such as channel substrate type, presence of key habitat features,

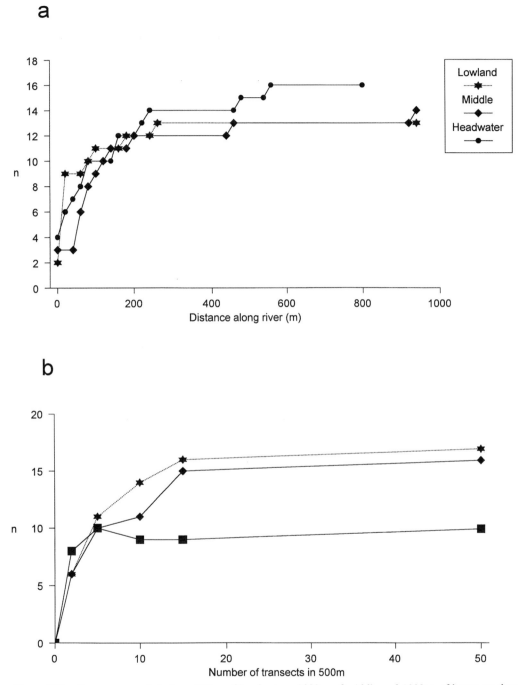

Figure 19.1   Features recorded along 800m of headwaters, 1000m of middle and 1000m of lower reaches of the River Derwent, Cumbria: (a) cumulative number (n) of new features recorded by transects 10m apart; (b) cumulative number (n) of features related to number of transects within 500m.

Table 19.1   The main features recorded during an RHS survey.

Feature	Spot checks	Sweep-up
Channel dimensions (*at one predetermined point*)		
Predominant valley form		✓
Predominant channel substrate	✓	
Predominant bank material	✓	
Flow type	✓	✓
Channel and bank modifications	✓	✓
Bankface vegetation structure (*uniform/simple/complex*)	✓	
Channel vegetation types	✓	✓
Bank profile (*unmodified and modified*)	✓	✓
Bankside trees and associated features		✓
Channel habitat features	✓	✓
Artificial features	✓	✓
Features of special interest on the floodplain		✓
Notable nuisance plant species		✓
Land use	✓ (*Banktop*)	✓

aquatic vegetation types, complexity of bank vegetation structure and type of artificial modification are recorded at each of 10 equidistant spot checks along the 500m. The format is simple, and coded two-letter abbreviations for attributes are entered into a matrix. These codes are included on a spot check key which acts as a prompt card for the surveyor. Each feature is also illustrated in a photo gallery included in the RHS manual. The discipline of doing 10 spot checks improves accuracy of data capture since the observer does not have to remember or estimate the extent of features over long distances, a method which is notoriously inaccurate and can be a major source of error in river corridor survey maps (Gurnell *et al.*, 1994).

A 'sweep-up' checklist within the 500m length ensures that the presence of features occurring between the spot checks is fully accounted for (Table 19.1). The actual number of selected key geomorphological features (e.g. riffles, point bars) is recorded, as well as the type and extent of artificial modifications to the channel and banks. Space is also provided for a brief descriptive sentence to provide a rapid thumbnail sketch of the site.

The RHS survey form is easy to use and requires little additional training (2–3 days) beyond that of a sound biological background and familiarity with rivers. The data set is amenable to rapid transfer to the RHS computer database, either manually or via optical reading from hard copy. Adaptation onto portable data-logging devices for use in the field is also possible. The time taken to survey a 500m length of river varies according to the complexity of the site and ease of access, inherent factors which affect any type of river-based sampling. Simple sites may take as little as 35–40 minutes to complete, while those of complex character and difficult access may take an hour or more. The average time taken on site in 1994 was 57 minutes ($n = 1,521$ sites).

Considerable effort has been made to minimize surveyors' variation in recording different features through training and clear guidance with accompanying photographs in the RHS manual. There are more than 100 different features in total and analysis of responses indicates that inter-surveyor variation is low. Moreover, experimental alteration of the positions of spot checks within the 500m still produces a consistent output in terms of assessing overall site character. Duplicate sampling of randomly selected sites by different surveyors is being carried out in 1995 and 1996 to provide the necessary confidence limits, quality assurance and control. Seasonal changes are also being monitored on a bi-monthly basis at selected sites.

19.3.3   *Establishing a site reference network*

One of the principal objectives during the development phase of the project was to establish a national reference network of sites chosen on a stratified random basis. These sites would therefore provide an objective database to establish (a) a national inventory of features and (b) a statistically valid basis for a classification of river types. Thereafter, any site in the country surveyed using RHS could be categorized on the basis of river type and the observed features compared with a national or regional 'norm'.

In common with other census-type surveys (e.g. breeding birds), the 10×10 km grid square has been used as the basis for the site reference network. For convenience, all squares with $>50\%$ of land below high water mark have been omitted from the sample. On this basis, there are 1523 sample squares in England and Wales. To provide a truly national (UK) context, 779 squares in Scotland and 133 in Northern Ireland have also been included.

Rivers and streams from source to tidal limit indicated on 1 : 250,000 scale topographical maps represent the 'sample population'. Sample sites are selected on the basis of the random selection of a 2×2 km tetrad within the 10km square. The main qualifying criterion for England and Wales is that the watercourse is classified for water quality as indicated by the published 1985 River Quality Map based on the National Water Council (NWC) classification (NWC, 1981). Where no such classified watercourses exist within a 10km square, unclassified watercourses qualify. In the few cases that no watercourses appear on the 1 : 250,000 scale map, unclassified watercourses shown on the 1 : 50,000 scale Ordnance Survey map qualify. Two sample squares in Southern England contain no rivers.

For England and Wales, three reference sites per 10km square, one sampled in each of three years 1994–1996, will form the network. When complete, coverage by the reference network will comprise 4,569 sites, representing 2,284km of watercourse or 6.6% of the total length classified for water-quality purposes. Analysis of the 1994 tranche of reference sites using the Strahler (1957) method for stream order, indicates a similar distribution to that for streams and rivers across the UK calculated by Smith and Lyle (1979) (Table 19.2). This indicates that the RHS network is a good representative sample in terms of size, distribution and geographical range.

Table 19.2   Frequency distribution (%) of stream order: a comparison between the UK distribution calculated by Smith and Lyle (1979) and the 1994 RHS reference network, based on the method of Strahler (1957).

Stream order	Smith and Lyle (1979)	RHS (1994) (n = 1,521)
1	75	70*
2	20	17
3	4	10
4	1	3

*Represents 'zero order' (not shown on 1 : 625,000 scale map), plus first order streams.

For Scotland, where the basis for water-quality assessment sampling is different, the main qualifying criterion for RHS network sites is that the watercourse indicated on the 1 : 250,000 scale map has a minimum average discharge of 63 L s^{-1}. This criterion was selected to conform with the minimum qualifying size of watercourses for the draft EC Directive on the Ecological Quality of Water. In Scotland and Northern Ireland one reference site per 10 km square will contribute to the network by 1996.

19.3.4   Catchment strategy

To identify an optimum RHS sampling strategy for catchment purposes, the entire length of the River Wyre in NW England was surveyed in 1994. Analysis of the results indicated that a frequency of one 500 m length in four, together with a sweep-up inventory between provided the most efficient way of describing the river (Sansbury, unpublished). Further comparative work on this aspect is being carried out on the River Frome, Dorset and River Dee in north-east Scotland.

19.4   A Classification of River Types

A cornerstone of RHS is the derivation of a working classification of river types from a subset of the reference site data which displays semi-natural physical characteristics. This in turn forms the basis for the predictive model and the basis for assessing habitat quality (Figure 19.2). In essence, the primary aim is to identify those determinants which shape and influence watercourses represented by the network sites. The RHS computer database provides the analytical capability, containing both map-derived and field data. A key requirement is the ability to divide whole rivers into one or more types (segments) of similar physical character. Each watercourse can then be classified according to type, and the semi-natural physical character of the channel in each segment type predicted on the basis of map-derived information. This allows for cross-comparison of similar river types nationally, and an estimate of the extent and quality of the resource to be produced. A detailed description of the approach and results will appear in a separate paper, but a simplified summary is provided here.

RHS FORM

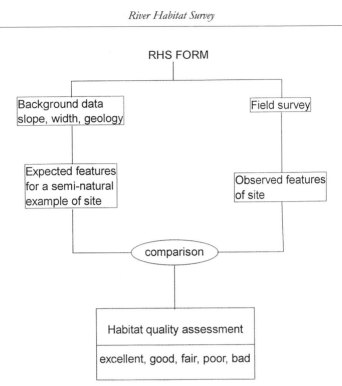

Figure 19.2   An overview of how RHS works.

The first exercise was to isolate those sites in the 1994 database with little or no obvious artificial modification affecting structure or flow. Using these criteria, only 478 of the 1,521 sites qualified for analysis. Interrogation of the data produced four consistent descriptors influencing the physical character of sites: solid geology, altitude, slope, and size expressed as flow category. Not surprisingly, all four are inter-related so it is difficult to quantify the influence of each feature. Moreover, it is virtually impossible to be certain of discrimination between types based on physical features alone. Nevertheless, a working classification had to be developed and tested.

Using discriminant and cluster analysis of the data, together with photographs of sites, the 478 sites yielded 67 individual 'types'. Each could be determined on the basis of mathematical rules regarding geology, altitude, slope, and flow category. In order to make the classification manageable on a national basis, the cluster analysis dendrogram was used to aggregate the 67 segment sub-types into 11 segment types (Table 19.3). Rules for these 11 river segment types have been used to produce, for the first time, a working map of river categories in England and Wales based on predicted semi-natural physical character of the channel (NERC, 1995). The map will be refined as the 1995 and 1996 site reference data are incorporated into the analysis and the original rules are modified. The intention is to produce a classification of river types applicable to the UK as a whole, using the reference network sites in Scotland and Northern Ireland. It is important to note that (a) the 11 segment types are preliminary categories for reporting, and

Table 19.3   A working classification of river types in England and Wales, based on 1994 River Habitat Survey data.

Segment type	Descriptor	Predominant distribution in England and Wales
1	Low altitude, low-gradient rivers on soft geology	Central and S England
2	Low altitude, low-gradient rivers on mixed geology	Cornwall, SW Wales, also scattered in Wales and in N England
3	Low altitude, low-gradient streams on soft geology	Midlands, Southern and SE England
4	Low altitude, steep-gradient streams on mixed geology	Devon and Cornwall, scattered elsewhere
5	Medium altitude, low-gradient rivers on soft geology	N England and Devon; a few in Wales
6	Medium altitude, moderate-gradient rivers on mixed geology	N England and Wales
7	Medium altitude, moderate-gradient streams on soft geology	Mid-Wales and Midlands
8	Medium altitude, steep-gradient streams on mixed geology	N England, SW Wales, Cornwall
9	High altitude, moderate-slope rivers on mixed geology	Pennines, Wales, Devon
10	High altitude, steep-slope streams on mixed geology	Pennines, Wales, Devon
11	High altitude, high-slope streams on hard geology	Pennines, Wales, Devon

Mean altitude (m): low = 38; medium = 103; high = 253.
Mean slope (m km^{-1}): low = 3.6; moderate = 9.7; steep = 25.0; high = 69.0.

(b) the site-based 67 'sub-segment' types represent the building blocks for RHS day-to-day river management.

19.5   Preliminary Results

A wealth of data has been generated by the RHS reference network, and this will be used by the EA to present a state of the environment report on river habitats, but some preliminary results for England and Wales can be presented here.

The bulk of watercourses in the reference network are small streams (more than 50% are < 10.0 m bankfull width), largely reflecting proximity to source, while altitude and slope reflect the topographic distribution of relief throughout the country (Figure 19.3). The predominant channel substrate (36% of all spot checks; $n = 15210$) is gravel-pebble (2–64 mm diameter), with bedrock and boulders more closely associated with steep upland streams. Silt tends to be associated with low-altitude gently-sloping streams, but not exclusively so (Figure 19.4). The predominant flow type is determined by slope and controlling influences such as natural or artificial obstructions. The most frequently occurring flow types in

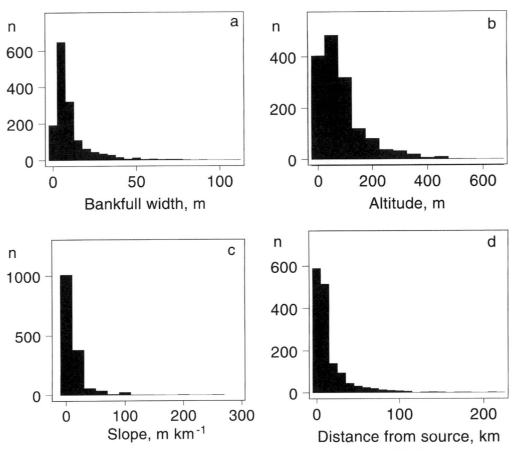

Figure 19.3   Frequency distributions of (a) stream width, (b) altitude, (c) slope, and (d) distance from source of the 1994 RHS reference network sites in England and Wales.

unimpounded sites are those associated with riffles (67% of sites), and runs and glides (61%).

The influence of human modification is illuminating (Table 19.4). Only 9% of the reference sites are pristine, that is, *completely* free of any artificial feature or modification. Some 17% of sites have no artificial modifications recorded in their spot checks and could therefore be categorized as predominantly semi-natural in character. However, since no obvious artificial modifications were recorded for 82% of all spot checks, the indication is that the majority of sites have some artificial modification but only affecting a small proportion of their length. The occurrence of selected features traditionally valued as important for wildlife is shown in Table 19.5, whilst the distribution pattern of bankside trees, usually a good indicator of habitat quality, is shown in Table 19.6.

19.6   Towards a Scheme for Assessing Habitat Quality

A key output from RHS will be a scheme for assessing habitat quality. The basis of such a scheme depends upon (a) the ultimate aim, (b) the ability to calibrate,

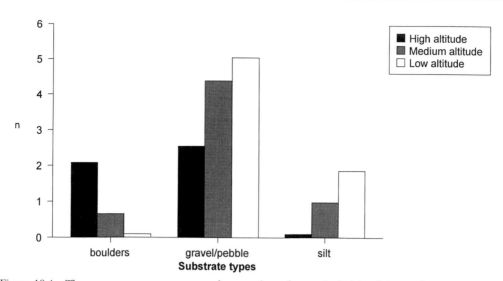

Figure 19.4   The mean occurrence, expressed as number of spot checks(n), of three substrate categories recorded in high, medium and low altitude segment types of semi-natural rivers in England and Wales in 1994.

Table 19.4   The occurrence of artificial features at the 1994 RHS reference sites in England and Wales.

Feature	Occurrence as % of all sites (n = 1,521)
Culverts	13
Reinforced bank(s)*—concrete, brick, rip-rap, etc.	9
Resectioned bank(s)*	20
Flood embankments—either bank	7
Bridges—road and foot	48
Weirs—barriers to flow	19
Outfalls	23

Figures to nearest integer.

*More than three spot checks within site.

and (c) the level of confidence in categorizing a site. The development of a working classification of river types for England and Wales (Table 19.3), and the representative nature of the sites in the RHS reference network provides the necessary elements. A classification based on predicted physical structure in the unmodified state allows for a characteristic 'fingerprint' of features for individual segment types to be established. Not surprisingly, many features are common to several segment types, but distinctive associations should allow for sufficient discrimination and assessment of habitat quality at the site (500 m) level.

Any classification system with a predictive approach has to be flexible enough to account for variations in the occurrence of 'constant' features which should

Table 19.5 The occurrence of features of importance to wildlife recorded at the 1994 RHS reference sites in England and Wales.

Features	Importance to wildlife	% occurrence (n = 1,521)
Riffles	Invertebrates, spawning redds	67 (20)
Underwater tree roots	Invertebrates, fish fry	43 (3)
Coarse woody debris	Invertebrates	56 (4)
Exposed boulders	Dipper	26 (4)
Submerged vegetation	Invertebrates, fish	93 (13)
Emergent reeds/sedges/rushes	Invertebrates, warblers	90 (13)
Mid-channel and/or point bars	Invertebrates	19 (1)
Exposed bankside tree roots	Otter	51 (7)*
Vertical earth cliffs	Kingfisher, sand martin	30 (26)*

Figures to nearest integer. Those in brackets represent percentage occurrence where feature is extensive, that is, > 33% of site.
*Either bank.

Table 19.6 Distribution pattern of bankside trees at the 1994 RHS reference sites in England and Wales.

Bankside trees	% occurrence (n = 1,521)	
	One bank	Both banks
None/isolated/scattered	35	20
Regular, single	2	1
Occasional clumps	17	8
Semi-continuous	27	16
Continuous	19	12

always be present, and those which are frequently or sometimes present. An important factor is the influence of *scale* on the occurrence and repeat pattern of features such as riffles. Fewer features are likely to be present in a 500 m length of a large (> 50 m wide) semi-natural river than a smaller one (Leopold *et al.*, 1964; Newson, 1992). A classification capability based on the occurrence of features at the site level (67 segment 'subtypes'), but applicable to the current 11 segment types used for national reporting, is therefore likely to be more robust than one derived the other way round. This reflects the needs of river managers who require information at the site or subcatchment/catchment level rather than the national scale.

Each site has the potential to be described in terms of both extent of artificial modification and habitat quality. The modification descriptor can be derived from a set of arbitrary rules. An index of habitat quality is dependent upon the ability to calibrate the difference between the expected and observed occurrence of features known to be associated with semi-natural examples of individual segment

Table 19.7   Features which will contribute to the habitat quality assessment of rivers.

Feature	Example(s)
Flow/biotope pattern	Step-pool; riffle-run; riffle-pool
In-channel features	Boulders, cobbles, gravel, bars, islands
Channel vegetation type	Liverworts/mosses; emergent, submerged, fine-leaved macrophytes
Bank features	Earth cliffs
Bank vegetation structure	Uniform/simple/complex
Trees	Extent of tree roots, coarse woody debris
Land use	Water-dependent habitats such as fen

types. In order to calibrate habitat quality, a number of known top quality 'benchmark sites' have been surveyed, selected on the basis of the 11 segment types. Since benchmark sites were selected subjectively, the survey data are not included in the site reference network part of the RHS database.

The assessment of habitat quality will build on the 'functional habitat' approach of Harper *et al.* (1995) and concentrates on those features which are representative of individual river segment types and are particularly influenced by artificial modification. Movement between classes (e.g. good to fair, and *vice versa*) will need to be determined by modifiable attributes. Features which are resilient will not be so useful in constructing an assessment scheme *per se*. Preliminary analysis indicates that a relatively small number of features will determine the rules governing the assessment scheme (Table 19.7)

Interrogation of the database enables, for the first time, an appraisal of the relative occurrence of physical features associated with different river segment types. More importantly, it allows evaluation of how river management practices affect these features. This is a particularly powerful tool regarding the correlation of features such as earth cliffs and bankside vegetation structure with unmodified and modified banks. A major factor to consider is intra-site variation, because within a 500 m length there can be good and bad quality components. Interrogation of the spot check data will allow this variation to be described, both in terms of modification and habitat quality. The classification outputs can also be shaped by the ability to discriminate between, or combine, the physical character of the channel banks and adjacent corridor.

19.7   Discussion

The pitfalls and limitations of classification schemes imposing arbitrary divisions in what is essentially a continuum such as a river system, are comprehensively explored by Kondolf (1995). In particular, wider temporal and spatial aspects which determine geomorphological processes need to be taken into consideration for a full understanding of a site. In this respect, RHS is pitched at a level of detail which provides information on physical character at site level that can then prompt specialist surveys by, for example, geomorphologists or botanists.

There have been numerous attempts worldwide to classify rivers with a view to conservation management. A key problem is one of scale, with different processes influencing features from the catchment to microhabitat level (e.g. Frissell *et al.*, 1986; Mitchell, 1990; Kershner and Snider, 1992; Naiman *et al.*, 1992; Hawkins *et al.*, 1993; Rosgen, 1994). Another problem has been how to link physical and biological features which together comprise the 'stream ecosystem'. For example, analysis of physical data collected as part of macrophyte surveys used to classify British rivers (Holmes, 1989) did not produce a feasible habitat-only based equivalent, despite the similar survey length of 500 m (Rowell *et al.*, 1995). Reasons for this included the fact that the plant-based survey sites were located on the best rivers, thereby avoiding large, managed rivers and those with poor water quality. Furthermore, the great variety of features within most 500 m lengths of river make it difficult to relate precisely the occurrence of macrophytes to physical features. It is clear that there is no practical basis or use for a single classification of river types. Rather, it is better to identify a standard high-level framework for classification of physical features derived from geomorphological principles and tailor specialist needs (e.g. plant or animal distribution) within the framework, based on particular aspects of river management.

The use of GIS at an appropriate scale, and map-derived and other available information, is crucial to RHS. It provides the necessary framework and context for river typing, thereby underpinning the predictive element upon which the assessment of habitat quality is based.

The RHS reference site network includes a considerable number of headwater streams, which have in the past been largely ignored by other routine sampling methods (Figure 19.3). However, bias exists with respect to minimum size criteria, classification for water-quality purposes in England and Wales, and the omission of 10 km squares where more than half the area is either a permanent freshwater lake or tidal water. It will be necessary to review whether these squares need to be included in future. The current network also contains a disproportionate skew in 'semi-natural' sites between the uplands and lowlands. The almost complete absence of unmanaged reaches of large lowland rivers in England and Wales will mean incorporating subjective elements in the approach to ensure their adequate representation in the system.

Another key issue will be classification of river types regarding completely artificial channels such as those in East Anglia and the Somerset Levels. In addition, subjectivity is always a problem in trying to determine the value of ecosystems. To this end, the specialist group approach of the SERCON project with regard to weighting various attributes will provide invaluable guidance for the habitat quality assessment (Boon *et al.*, 1994, this volume).

19.7.1 *Synergy with other systems*
19.7.1.1   SERCON
RHS is not a conservation classification, but has been developed in close parallel with a desk-based computer evaluation system known as SERCON (System for

Evaluating Rivers for Conservation). SERCON utilizes existing habitat and species data for a multiple of river corridor attributes and applies classic conservation assessment criteria such as diversity, naturalness, representativeness, rarity, and so on, in a more rigorous manner than has been done in the past (Boon *et al.*, 1994). For the assessment of many river corridor attributes, SERCON depends on outputs from either RHS or river corridor surveys, unless data of a similar nature are available from other sources. Generally, SERCON is intended to work at a larger scale (catchment and subcatchment) than RHS to provide an overview of conservation interest in the broadest terms. However, a consistent framework for data gathering can be provided by the RHS classification of river types and sampling strategy for catchment purposes.

19.7.1.2 River corridor survey

River Corridor Survey is principally a map-based system of surveying 500 m lengths of river. It provides information about the location of habitats and plant assemblages within river channels, margins, banks and corridor. Such surveys have been used to identify lateral boundaries for river Sites of Special Scientific Interest (SSSIs) in Britain (Nature Conservancy Council, 1989). The system was developed in the early 1980s when the prime requirement was to provide information for stretches of river where management work was proposed, so that the most important habitat features and rare communities could be conserved and maximum benefit derived from enhancing degraded habitats. Many thousands of kilometres of rivers in England and Wales have been surveyed using the standard method (NRA, 1992) and the data used in a variety of ways, including environmental auditing and post-project appraisal. For these purposes, as with SERCON, interpretation of maps is not an ideal way of retrieving and analysing data, nor for objectively comparing sites, even though valuable information is contained within them.

For the most detailed site appraisal, and as a prescriptive (site-specific) management tool, the tried and tested methodology cannot be rivalled. RHS represents a logical development from river corridor survey, providing a computer database, national inventory, classification of river types and habitat quality assessment. RHS can be undertaken in conjunction with corridor surveys with little extra time investment but major benefit in terms of information retrieval.

19.7.1.3 RIVPACS

RIVPACS (River InVertebrate Prediction And Classification System) requires broadly similar environmental data to RHS which is acquired from maps and site units but focuses on a shorter length of river. The information is then used for the prediction of aquatic invertebrate communities. Comparison of observed and expected invertebrate communities provides a basis for water quality assessment (Wright *et al.*, 1994, this volume). Much of the background information (such as altitude and slope) collected for RIVPACS and RHS is the same. Indeed, the environmental quality index approach, comparing predicted and observed features, is similar (Figure 19.2). However, RHS is able to provide predictions of river habitat structure in a broader context. It is intended to combine RHS and RIVPACS data analysis in future so that sites can be assessed in both water quality and habitat terms and influences acting on invertebrate communities can be more clearly determined.

19.7.1.4   HABSCORE

HABSCORE is a stream habitat assessment method which expresses habitat quality in terms of predicted salmonid fish populations based on empirical models derived for more than 600 sites, mainly in north-east England and Wales (Milner *et al.*, 1993). The system applies to river sites that contain resident salmonids and which can be electrofished (that is < 15m channel width). Both the habitat features recorded and transect (spot check) method of survey are similar to RHS but the sample unit is variable, usually 30–100m in length. Background catchment information is used to construct a predicted fish community structure. Since many of the features recorded are common to both systems, RHS can provide a basic framework for HABSCORE.

19.7.1.5   PHABSIM/IFIM

A recent development in water resource management in the UK is the use of the computer model PHABSIM (Physical Habitat Simulation System) which implements the Instream Flow Incremental Methodology (IFIM). IFIM uses the results of hydraulic survey at the microhabitat scale to relate flow requirements of certain river plants, invertebrates and fish to discharge regimes (Bovee, 1982; Johnson *et al.*, 1993). The method is at present highly specific and extremely resource intensive. However, RHS data from the reference network may well be able to provide a potentially significant saving, by providing data input to simplified versions involving the characteristic hydraulic behaviour of flow over and around specific morphological elements of the channel. Since these morphological elements are inventoried by RHS and form the basis of the classification of river types, it is hoped that ecologically acceptable flows in channel networks can be estimated by a hierarchical synthesis at much more reasonable cost (Newson, personal communication).

19.8   Conclusions

At this stage in its development, taking account of achievements to date and refinements needed in future, it is anticipated that RHS will provide the following potential benefits for river management and conservation:

- A tried and tested field survey method which is easy to use and complements existing systems.
- A computer-based method for collecting and managing data to enable rivers to be classified against an expected background, and compared on the basis of physical features with particular reference to those of value to wildlife.

- A national inventory of habitat features on a UK basis.
- The necessary context for any 500 m stretch of river, thereby enabling river managers to (a) assess objectively the likely impact of proposed physical modifications to the site, (b) identify how much effort to invest in protecting or rehabilitating sites, and (c) determine appropriate enhancement and rehabilitation activities.
- The catchment context of a site in terms of habitat uniqueness/frequency which will enable the importance of specific features to be placed in an area, regional and national context, thereby determining priorities for protection and enhancement.

Better-informed decision-making is the main benefit of RHS since the system will provide a more objective means for advising river managers or external developers on the local, regional or national value of individual sites with regard to physical features. It will also provide a powerful tool, delivering an inventory of river habitats, amenable to rapid data retrieval and interrogation which can contribute to the prediction of change within an environmental impact assessment. Although not yet in its final form, RHS should provide the best basis for a semi-quantitative habitat survey of river corridors. As such, it will bring greater objectivity to survey work and be valuable for *comparative* purposes.

RHS will also assist in developing a better understanding of fluvial geomorphological links between riverine habitats and different river types. It will also provide a better basis for identifying the relative degrees of degradation within these types, and what habitat features should be present and at what frequency.

The national inventory enables RHS to provide the vital missing link between the existing well-tried, tested and accepted map-based river corridor surveys which develop site-specific management proposals, and the larger-scale assessment of conservation 'value' derived through SERCON. RHS provides a strategic tool, allowing assessment of temporal and spatial trends. All sites can be classified using a nationally consistent method, and habitat quality assessed as a backdrop to different river management functions. These may include fisheries (e.g. spawning gravels, extent of cover), flood defence (asset evaluation and the potential of the river reach for floodwater attenuation), and water resources (flow levels, water storage, changes in velocity and depth). Opportunities for optimizing field surveys and production of catchment data with common features amongst RHS, HABSCORE, RIVPACS, etc., will yield significant efficiency savings in that the current practice of broadly similar surveys carried out by different Environment Agency functions will be minimized.

RHS will fulfil the original requirements which precipitated its development. It will be able to deliver outputs of immediate use to river managers and has already been used for environmental appraisal purposes. It will also provide a hitherto unavailable capacity for reporting on the state of river habitats for national and European purposes.

References

Boon, P. J., Holmes, N. T. H., Maitland, P. S. and Rowell, T. A. (1994). A system for evaluating rivers for conservation ('SERCON'): an outline of the underlying principles. *Verhandlungen der Internationalen Vereinigung für theoretische und angewandte Limnologie*, **25**, 1510–1514.

Boon, P. J., Holmes, N. T. H., Maitland, P. S., Rowell, T. A. and Davies, J. (This volume). A system for evaluating rivers for conservation (SERCON): development, structure and function.

Bovee, K. D. (1982). *A Guide to Stream Habitat Analysis Using the Instream Flow Incremental Methodologies*. US Fish and Wildlife Service Instream Flow Information Paper No. 12 Report No. FWS/OBS-82/26, USFWS Instream Flow Group, Fort Collins.

Department of the Environment *et al.* (1994). *Biodiversity: the UK Action Plan*. Command 2428. HMSO, London.

Frissell, C. A., Liss, W. J., Warren, C. E. and Hurley, M. D. (1986). A hierarchical approach to classifying stream habitat features: viewing streams in a watershed context. *Environmental Management*, **10**, 199–214.

Gurnell, A. M., Angold, P. and Gregory, K. J. (1994). Classification of river corridors: issues to be addressed in developing an operational methodology. *Aquatic Conservation: Marine and Freshwater Ecosystems*, **4**, 219–231.

Harper, D. M., Smith, C., Barham, P. and Howell, R. (1995). The Ecological Basis for the Management of the Natural River Environment. In: Harper, D. M. and Ferguson, A. J. D. (Eds), *The Ecological Basis for River Management*. John Wiley, Chichester, 219–238.

Hawkins, C. P., Kershner, J. L., Bisson, P. A., Bryant, M. D., Decker, L. M., Gregory, S. V., McCullough, D. A., Overton, C. K., Reeves, G. H., Steedman, R. J. and Young, M. K. (1993). A hierarchical approach to classifying stream habitat features. *Fisheries*, **18**, 3–12.

Holmes, N. T. H. (1989). British rivers: a working classification. *British Wildlife*, **1**, 20–36.

Johnson, I. W., Elliott, C. R. N., Gustard, A., Armitage, P. D., Ladle, M., Dawson, F. H. and Beaumont, W. R. C. (1993). *Ecologically Acceptable Flows: Assessment of Instream Flow Incremental Methodology*. R&D Note 185. National Rivers Authority, Bristol.

Kershner, J. L. and Snider, W. M. (1992). Importance of a habitat level classification system to design instream flow studies. In: Boon, P. J., Calow, P. and Petts, G. E. (Eds), *River Conservation and Management*. John Wiley, Chichester, 179–192.

Kondolf, G. M. (1995). Geomorphological stream channel classification in aquatic habitat restoration: uses and limitations. *Aquatic Conservation: Marine and Freshwater Ecosystems*, **5**, 127–141.

Leopold, L. B., Wolman, M. G. and Miller, J. P. (1964). *Fluvial Processes in Geomorphology*. Freeman and Co., San Francisco and London.

Mitchell, P. (1990). *The Environmental Condition of Victorian Streams*. Internal Report to Department of Water Resources, Victoria, Australia.

Milner, N., Wyatt, R. J. and Scott, M. D. (1993). Variability in the distribution and abundance of stream salmonids, and the associated use of habitat models. *Journal of Fish Biology*, **43**(Supplement A), 103–109.

Naiman, R. J., Lonzarich, D. G., Beechie, T. J. and Ralph, S. C. (1992). General principles of classification and the assessment of conservation potential in rivers. In: Boon, P. J., Calow, P. and Petts, G. E. (Eds), *River Conservation and Management*. John Wiley, Chichester, 93–124.

Natural Environment Research Council (1995). Annual Report. Swindon.

Nature Conservancy Council (1989). *Guidelines for Selection of Biological SSSIs*. Peterborough.

Newson, M. D. (1992). *Land, Water and Development*. Routledge, London.

NRA (1992). *River Corridor Surveys. Methods and Procedures*. Conservation Technical Handbook No. 1. Bristol.

NRA (1993). *NRA Conservation Strategy*. Bristol.

NRA (1994). *The Quality of Rivers and Canals in England and Wales (1990 to 1992)*. Water Quality Series No. 19. HMSO, London.

NRA (1995). *Annual Report and Accounts 1994/95*. Bristol, 47–48.

NWC (1981). *River Quality—The 1980 Survey and Future Outlook*. London.

Rosgen, D. L. (1994). A classification of natural rivers, *Catena*, **22**, 169–199.

Rowell, T., Jeffers, J. and Holmes, N. T. H. (1996). River morphology and plant relationships, *R&D Note 483*. National Rivers Authority, Bristol.

Sansbury, J. (1994). 'The Applicability of River Habitat Survey for Catchment Management Planning'. Unpublished report to the National Rivers Authority, North West Region, Warrington.

Smith, I. and Lyle, A. (1979). *Distribution of Freshwaters in Great Britain*. Institute of Terrestrial Ecology, HMSO, London.

Strahler, A. N. (1957). Quantitative analysis of watershed geomorphology. *Transactions, American Geophysical Union,* **38,** 913–920.

Wright, J. F., Moss, D., Armitage, P. D. and Furse, M. T. (1984). A preliminary classification of running water sites in Great Britain based on macro-invertebrate species and prediction of community type using environmental data. *Freshwater Biology,* **14,** 221–256.

Wright, J. F., Furse, M. T. and Armitage, P. D. (1994). Use of macro-invertebrate communities to detect environmental stress in running waters. In: Sutcliffe, D. W. (Ed.), *Water Quality and Stress Indicators in Marine and Freshwater Ecosystems: Linking Levels of Organisation (Individuals, Populations and Communities)*. Freshwater Biological Association, Ambleside, 15–34.

Wright, J. F., Moss, D., Clarke, R. T. and Furse, M. T. (This volume). Biological assessment of river quality using the new version of RIVPACS (RIVPACS III).

20 RIVER HABITAT SURVEY IN SCOTLAND

I. R. Fozzard, M. Davidson and G. Moffett

Summary

1. River Habitat Survey (RHS) is a new system to classify rivers according to their physical character initiated by the National Rivers Authority (NRA). Initial survey and development work was limited to England and Wales.

2. During 1994 the NRA surveyed some 1500 sites in England and Wales, this being the first tranche of sites in a three-year programme to establish a river typology, based upon a subset of natural/semi-natural sites within the total of some 4,500 sites surveyed. To ensure that Scottish sites were included on the database, a survey programme of 760 sites began in May 1995, covering both mainland Scotland and the Western and Northern Isles.

3. Site survey was to be undertaken largely within existing resources and spread over 1995 and 1996. By the end of September 1995 26% of sites had been surveyed.

4. Preliminary results indicate that in the lowlands, at least, Scottish rivers have been extensively modified. The degree of physical habitat modification will be a factor, both directly and indirectly, in determining the overall environmental quality of Scottish rivers.

20.1 Introduction

The principal duty of the river purification authorities (RPAs) is to promote the cleanliness of rivers, other inland waters, and tidal waters, and to conserve water resources. The basic duties to improve water quality have been expanded by subsequent Acts, and from direction of the Scottish Office, culminating in the Environment Act (1995) which makes it a clear duty to promote the conservation of flora, fauna, and the natural heritage of Scotland. The conservation of the natural environment is a legitimate use of fresh waters, along with drinking water supply, industrial abstraction, fisheries, etc. Protection of these uses is the cornerstone of the RPA duty to conserve water resources, concepts that are now widely accepted. It is similarly accepted that the maintenance and conservation of the physical architecture of the aquatic environment is at least as important as the maintenance of the chemical and physical properties of the water. River Habitat Survey (see Raven *et al.*, this volume) is a key tool in this task.

River Habitat Survey (RHS) is a new system to classify rivers according to their physical character currently being developed by the Environment Agency (EA) and initiated by its predecessor, the National Rivers Authority (NRA). Initial development work was limited to England and Wales. The Scottish RPAs were represented, through the Association of Directors and River Inspectors for Scotland (ADRIS), on the steering group of SERCON (System for Evaluating Rivers for Conservation, see Boon *et al.*, this volume), and through this became aware of, and involved in, the development of RHS during 1993. It was evident that there were mutual benefits to be gained by widening the scope of RHS to include the whole of the UK, not least the provision of a national typology of rivers, and through this a UK reporting base. The environmental obligations of the planned Scottish Environment Protection Agency (SEPA), the successor organization to the RPAs from April 1996, were further factors stimulating interest in RHS.

During 1994 the NRA sampled 1,500 sites in England and Wales, this being the first tranche of sites in a three-year programme to establish a site reference network of 4,500 sites. The effectiveness of RHS is dependent on the development of a river typology, based upon a subset of natural and semi-natural examples from these 4,500 sites. The geology, climate, and topography of Scotland have produced river types not well represented elsewhere in the UK. To permit a truly national typology, it was imperative that rivers in Scotland, the Scottish Islands, and Northern Ireland be included in the RHS database. Following approval by ADRIS, staff of the RPAs carried out RHS during the summer of 1995, and a commitment was given to complete the survey of the reference network sites by the end of 1996.

20.2 The Need in Scotland

The RPAs (river purification boards on the mainland and local authorities on the islands) have achieved considerable success in improving water quality since being set up some 40 years ago (Hammerton, 1994). The return of salmon (*Salmo salar*) to the Clyde, sparling (*Osmerus eperlanus*) to the Forth, and the general high quality of Scotland's rivers, lochs and tidal waters bear witness to their efforts. Nevertheless, some aspects of Scotland's environment have been poorly served by legislation, possibly because it was deemed that there was little in the way of a threat to quality. Freshwater fisheries, for example, except those for migratory salmonids, are relatively unmanaged, as is the physical architecture of Scottish rivers. RHS has the potential to fulfil both operational and reporting needs for physical habitat quality, the latter in both a national and European context.

Operationally, RHS will provide a comparative evaluation of river habitats in a local, regional, and national context. More specifically, RHS will provide input data on the physical habitat of rivers for SERCON, the system developed by Scottish Natural Heritage (SNH) to aid the assessment of the conservation value of rivers (Boon *et al.*, this volume). Such evaluation is likely to be of increasing importance to SEPA. RHS also has the potential to form an essential component of catchment management plans (CMPs). Combined with the assessment of water quality and water quantity, the RHS assessment of physical habitat quality will enable CMPs to form the basis for comprehensive integrated river basin management. For reporting purposes it is anticipated that RHS will meet part of the UK obligation under the proposed EC framework Directive on water policy (see Preface), and may fulfil part of the reporting requirements of the Habitats Directive (92/43/EEC) and the UK Biodiversity Action Plan (Department of the Environment, 1994). RHS also has the potential to provide an assessment of physical habitat quality of rivers to complement chemical, biological, and any other components, in an overall assessment for national reporting.

The adoption of RHS in Scotland will have further additional benefits, namely the implementation of a cost-effective, tested methodology, which has the potential to link with other systems in use within the UK. In addition to SERCON, RHS has similar field survey requirements to several other systems, such as RIVPACS (Wright *et al.*, 1993, this volume), HABSCORE (Milner, 1991), and River Corridor Survey (NRA, 1992). There are opportunities here for efficiency savings by optimizing the collection of field survey data.

20.3   Site Selection

Sites selected for the RHS reference database must be chosen objectively. To meet this requirement it was decided that one site would be chosen in each 10 km × 10 km square with ⩾50% land area on the 1:250,000 Ordnance Survey Travelmaster maps. From this stratified sample, a point on a watercourse was chosen randomly using the prescribed method. The method of site selection is described below.

1. Divide the selected 10 km square into 25 tetrads and select one of these using a random number table.
2. Identify the point on a watercourse nearest to the centre of the tetrad, or select another tetrad if there is no watercourse shown.
3. The selected watercourse must meet the following additional criteria:
   (a) long-term mean discharge $>63 \, \mathrm{L \, s^{-1}}$.
   (b) <2 km from nearest vehicle track.
4. If all criteria are met, the centre point of the survey site is marked on the 1:50,000 OS Landranger map. The survey section extends 250 m upstream and downstream from this point.

Criterion 3(a) was selected to conform with the minimum qualifying size of watercourses for the draft EC Directive on the Ecological Quality of Water (94/C222/060) (now likely to be subsumed by the framework Directive).

The RPAs have identified 779 qualifying 10 km squares throughout mainland Scotland and the Western and Northern Isles. It is expected that approximately 760 sites will be surveyed during 1995 and 1996. Some squares have failed to

Table 20.1 A comparison of the distribution of stream orders (%) in the whole of Scotland with those selected for RHS in the Clyde, Forth and Tay RPB areas and in Orkney and Shetland.

Strahler stream order	Scotland (Smith and Lyle, 1979), 1:625,000	Sample of Scottish RHS sites transformed to 1:625,000
1	77	72
2	18.5	16
3	3.4	7.3
4	0.66	2.9
5	0.07	1.4

generate a suitable site either because of the lack of a qualifying watercourse or reasonable access.

20.4 Site Representativeness

To assess whether the sites selected were representative of the population of different sized watercourses in Scotland, a comparison was made with data calculated by Smith and Lyle (1979). Table 20.1 compares the percentages of watercourses of different stream order in the whole of Scotland, with the stream orders of the RHS sites selected in the Clyde, Forth, and Tay RPB areas, and for those sites in Orkney and the Shetland Isles ($n = 274$). Stream order data were not available for the remaining Scottish sites. Stream orders (Strahler, 1957) were estimated from 1:50,000 OS Landranger maps and transformed to the 1:625,000 scale employed by Smith and Lyle. The sites selected generally reflect the distribution of stream orders in Scotland, especially orders 1 and 2. The higher order streams seem to be progressively over-represented and this may be due to the site selection procedure. A higher order stream or river is likely to occupy several of the 25 tetrads in a 10km × 10km square and is therefore more likely to be chosen. The lower size limit of a discharge of 63L s^{-1} for streams, and the exclusion of many coastal 10km × 10km squares, may have also contributed to the apparent bias in the sites selected. However, the object of the survey was not to gather data on a statistically unbiased group of sites, but rather on a geographically representative basis, thus building a database of all river types in Scotland.

20.5 Extent of Modification of Scottish Rivers

RHS methodology permits an assessment of both the nature and degree of modification of the river channel within the 500m survey section. Data from the limited number of sites surveyed to date (207 from the 779 possible, 26%, at 31 October 1995), suggest that most rivers and streams away from the uplands have some degree of modification. Typically this comprises minor work for prevention of channel movement by farmers (bank reinforcement, often with rubble or rough stone), or (with greater implications for environmental quality), channel deepening, straightening, and embanking to aid agricultural drainage. Watercourses in urban areas and on sites of open cast coal mining are invariably the most seriously affected. In these latter cases extensive reinforcement and diversions may have serious consequences for environmental quality.

20.6   Prediction of River Segment Type

The current (mid-1995) RHS predictive model utilizes solid geology, slope, altitude, and discharge as predictors. These 'fixed' parameters permit a prediction of the segment type and the associated suite of fluvial and riparian features. Using this predictive model, the River Teith (Central Region) and the Lochty Burn (Fife) are both classified as Type 2—rivers that are gravel/pebble dominated, with 60% of sites being predominantly riffle/pool. The Lochty Burn is very different from this, its channel having undergone a considerable degree of modification. Analysis of the predicted and recorded fluvial and riparian features of an RHS reach will generate a habitat quality index (Raven *et al.*, this volume). 'Benchmark' sites, that is sites of the highest quality, are employed in the development of the habitat quality index to provide calibration. Sites in the north and west of Scotland were visited during September 1995 for this purpose.

Further RHS development work in Scotland is being carried out as part of the Dee Catchment Management Project (DeeCAMP). This is a prototype catchment management tool of the Aberdeenshire Dee, funded by the North-east RPB, the Dee District Salmon Fishery Board, the Dee Salmon Fishing Improvement Association, Grampian Region Council Water Services, and SNH. NRA and SNH funding has contributed to the project during 1995, financing the application of RHS on a catchment wide basis. Outputs from DeeCAMP should assist in refining RHS catchment sampling strategy (Webb and Bacon, 1995).

20.7   Conclusions

The inclusion of Scottish river sites, together with those from Northern Ireland, makes River Habitat Survey a national system suitable for reporting on a UK basis. The typology derived from the semi-natural river types in the reference site network will incorporate the unique river types found in Scotland. Agencies within Scotland will benefit from the substantial R&D input by the NRA (and the EA) and the access to the UK database. The Scottish Environment Protection Agency will have access to a developed, tested, national system for assessing the physical quality of the riverine environment suitable for the reporting requirements of several international obligations.

References

Boon, P. J., Holmes, N. T. H., Maitland, P. S., Rowell, T. A. and Davies, J. (This volume). A system for evaluating rivers for conservation (SERCON): development, structure and function.

Department of the Environment *et al.* (1994). *Biodiversity: the UK Action Plan.* Command 2428. HMSO, London.

Hammerton, D. (1994). Domestic and industrial pollution. In: Maitland, P. S., Boon, P. J. and McLusky, D.

S. (Eds), *The Fresh Waters of Scotland: a National Resource of International Significance.* John Wiley, Chichester, 347–364.

Milner, N. J. (1991). *Field Manual for 'HABSCORE' Stream Habitat Assessment.* National Rivers Authority, Caernarfon.

NRA (1992). *River Corridor Surveys. Methods and Procedures.* Conservation Technical Handbook No. 1, Bristol.

Raven, P. J., Fox, P., Everard, M., Holmes, N. T. H. and Dawson, F. H. (This volume). River Habitat Survey: a new system for classifying rivers according to their habitat quality.

Smith, I. R. and Lyle, A. (1979). *Distribution of Freshwaters in Great Britain.* Institute of Terrestrial Ecology, Cambridge.

Strahler, A. N. (1957). Quantitative analysis of watershed geomorphology. *Transactions of the American Geophysical Union,* **38,** 913–920.

Webb, A. and Bacon, P. J. (1995). *DeeCAMP: Deeside River Survey, Recommendations to DeeCAMP Clients.* Institute of Terrestrial Ecology. Contract Report T 0805004. ITE, Banchory.

Wright, J. F., Furse, M. T. and Armitage, P. D. (1993). RIVPACS—a technique for evaluating the biological quality of rivers in the UK. *European Water Pollution Control,* **3,** 15–25.

Wright, J. F., Moss, D., Clarke, R. T. and Furse, M. T. (This volume). Biological assessment of river quality using the new version of RIVPACS (RIVPACS III).

21 RIVER HABITAT SURVEY AND BIODIVERSITY IN THE NEPAL HIMALAYA

S. J. Ormerod, H. S. Baral, P. A. Brewin, S. T. Buckton, I. Jüttner,

H. Rothfritz and A. M. Suren

Summary

1. Seventy-six rivers in the Himalaya of Nepal were sampled to assess whether River Habitat Survey (RHS) detected influences by land use. Effects were significant, but habitat structure and land use both changed with altitude so that cause-effect relationships were unclear.

2. The survey also assessed whether RHS provided information on biodiversity. The taxon richness and community composition of diatoms, bryophytes, invertebrates and birds correlated strongly with RHS data, but patterns were again covariant with altitude. Changes along gradients in habitat structure varied between taxonomic groups because their habitat requirements differed.

3. Further work is needed to assess whether there is a causal basis to these correlative patterns. The results are nevertheless valuable in indicating that complex gradients in habitat structure can be represented by RHS in ways that are meaningful ecologically.

4. It is suggested that RHS might be valuable for quality assessment in other parts of the world if it is modified to suit local conditions. The importance of measuring biodiversity and river habitat structure at a compatible geographical scale, of maximizing the ecological relevance of RHS measurements, and of accounting for annual dynamism in regions with pronounced seasonal floods, are all discussed.

21.1 Introduction

Schemes for surveying and assessing the quality of river habitats, such as River Habitat Survey (RHS) described in this volume by Raven *et al.*, have several basic aims. One is to record river structure in a way that reveals the intrinsic conservation value of important geomorphological features (see McEwen *et al.*, this volume). Another is to assess the status of rivers as habitats for organisms, for example because structural diversity might reflect biological diversity (MacArthur and

MacArthur, 1961). If this were true, habitat surveys could indicate the biological effects of physical degradation (Karr, 1991), and habitat typologies could help bring an ecological focus to river restoration (e.g. Brookes, 1994). Equally, quantitative relationships between habitat structure and community composition might improve biological models used in detecting pollution and other types of adverse change (e.g. Armitage, 1994; Wright, 1995).

In reality, however, the extent to which RHS can satisfy these aims still requires extensive field analysis. Particularly for the purposes of nature conservation and biological monitoring, there is a need to establish the following:

(a) Whether RHS data can be simplified into habitat variates that are ecologically meaningful.
(b) Whether RHS data represent natural influences on river structure, for example from altitude.
(c) Whether RHS data reflect human influences on river structure, for example from change in land use.
(d) Whether RHS data provide correlates with alpha (richness) and beta (turn-over) components of biological diversity (Whittaker, 1967).
(e) Whether RHS data provide information of relevance to important species or groups.

More ambitiously, there is a need to assess whether RHS could be applicable under a wider range of physical conditions than those in the UK. There would be particular benefits if RHS could detect the types of pronounced physical degradation that sometimes occur in the less developed world, where many major problems in river conservation arise (Dudgeon, 1992).

Such assessments are currently in progress in the Himalaya of Nepal and India (see Plate 4d). Besides providing one of the largest altitudinal ranges on earth, and hence challenging test conditions, the region has been the site of dramatic changes in land use which have probably affected rivers and their catchments (e.g. Ives and Messerli, 1989). As part of a larger ongoing study (Rundle *et al.*, 1993; Tyler and Ormerod, 1993; Brewin and Ormerod, 1994; Ormerod *et al.*, 1994; Suren, 1994; Brewin *et al.*, 1995; Wilkinson *et al.*, 1995), a modified RHS was applied along 76 streams in the Simikot, Dunai and Makalu regions of Nepal (Figure 21.1). This chapter assesses whether the resulting RHS data illustrate natural and anthropic effects on river habitats. It provides the first assessment of whether variables derived from RHS correlate with the diversity of aquatic organisms. In so doing, it presents a methodology and comparative data set which will act as a basis for similar studies that are now required in the UK.

21.2 Methods

All the rivers were in different subcatchments crossed during surveys in November and December 1994. They covered an altitudinal range from 350 to 4,000 m above sea level, and all were remote, reached by each of three survey teams walking for approximately 200 km. Methods for RHS largely followed those recommended by

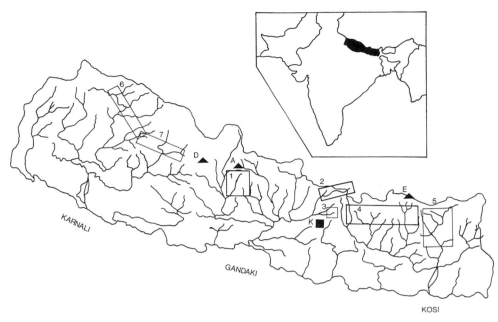

Figure 21.1   The major river systems of Nepal, showing sites of hydrobiological work in the Annapurna (1), Langtang (2), Likhu Khola (3), Everest (4), Makalu (5), Simikot (6) and Dunai (7) regions. Areas 5, 6 and 7 figured in this study. Everest (E), Annapurna (A), Dhaulagiri (D) and Kathmandu (K) are also indicated.

the Environment Agency (see Raven *et al.*, this volume), except that conditions in the field restricted survey reaches to 200m, with 'spot checks' every 20m. Spot checks in this context refer to specific RHS variables describing attributes of the substratum, bank, riparian zone and land use recorded at these fixed intervals. 'Sweep-up' variables, in contrast, refer to more integrated measures of features over the whole 200m reach (see Tables 21.1, 21.2 and Raven *et al.*, this volume). River birds were surveyed over this same 200m reach, but other taxa were recorded from samples removed at single points within it. The full biological methods will be described in more detail elsewhere, but in outline involved kick-sampling in margins and riffles for invertebrates (see Plate 7b), brushing stone surfaces for diatoms, collecting aquatic bryophytes by hand, and counting birds along the river channel. These methods were designed to produce measures of alpha and beta diversity, the latter represented as change in community composition shown by DECORANA ordination scores (Hill, 1979). Birds, diatoms and bryophytes were identified to species for these purposes, while invertebrates were identified to family. For the most species-rich group, the diatoms, Shannon-Wiener's indices of diversity and evenness were also calculated in order to assess changes in the patterns of dominance (Gray, 1989).

21.3   Results

RHS measures could be reduced to principal components (called RHS PCs; Tables 21.1, 21.2), which were correlated linearly between the 'sweep-up' and

Table 21.1 Principal components (RHS PCs) derived from the River Habitat Survey 'sweep-up' procedure at 76 sites in Nepal: Listings, by rank order, of variables that contributed most to the first four principal components.

PC 1 (20%)	PC 2 (12%)
Water width (− ve)	Waterfalls (−)
Bank width (−)	Overhanging boughs (−)
Woody debris (+)	Trees (−)
Depth (−)	Boulders (−)
Leaf litter (+)	Gravel (+)
Shade (+)	Fallen trees (−)
No. of riffles (+)	Shade (−)
Unvegetated side bars (−)	Bank height (−)
Bank height (−)	Bankside roots (−)
Underwater roots (+)	Torrential flow (−)
Laminar flow (−)	Sand (+)
Bankside roots (+)	Silt (+)
Fallen trees (+)	Debris dams (−)
Boulders (−)	Exposed bedrock (−)
Pebbles (+)	
Unvegetated mid-bars (−)	
Debris dams (+)	

PC 3 (8%)	PC 4 (7%)
Vegetated side bars (−)	Mature islands (+)
Cobbles (+)	Unvegetated mid-bars (+)
No. of unvegetated point bars (+)	Vegetated mid-bars (+)
Slack flow (−)	No. of riffles (+)
Vegetated mid-bars (−)	Laminar flow (+)
Waterfalls (−)	Riparian vegetation (+)
Sand (−)	Trees (−)
Outfalls (−)	No. of unvegetated point bars (+)
Boulders (−)	Sand (+)
	Underwater roots (−)
	Torrential flow (+)
	Boulders (−)

'spot-check' procedures (e.g. PC1, $r = -0.79$, $n = 76$, $p < 0.001$). This inter-correlation indicated site-to-site consistency in data collection, but also some redundancy in effort, since both sets of measures illustrated the same major trend. For both, there were strong and highly significant trends with altitude on the first PC (Table 21.3). For example, PC1 from the sweep-ups represented an altitudinal shift from large streams with laminar flow, boulders and vegetated or unvegetated side bars, to small, pebbly streams with features related to trees. Trends of this type for all the RHS PCs are outlined in Tables 21.1 and 21.2.

In several instances, RHS PC scores varied significantly between streams bor-

Table 21.2 Principal components (RHS PCs) derived from the River Habitat Survey by the 'spot-check' procedure at 76 sites in Nepal: Listings, by rank order, of variables that contributed most to the first four principal components.

PC 1 (12%)	*PC 2 (10%)*
Earth banks (−)	Banks with side bars (−)
Riffle flow (−)	Banks with no features (−)
Complex riparian zone (+)	Torrential flow (+)
Simple land use (−)	Stable cliffs (+)
Complex land use (+)	Boulder/cobble substratum (+)
Boulder/cobble banks (+)	Gravel/pebble banks (+)
Simple riparian zone (−)	Uniform banks (+)
Reinforced banks (+)	Cascading flow (−)
Eroding cliff (−)	Exposed rocks and boulders (+)
Stable cliff (−)	Reinforced banks (−)
Bedrock banks (+)	Simple banks (−)
	Pools (−)

PC 3 (8%)	*PC 4 (7%)*
Uniform land use (+)	Cobbles/pebbles (+)
Bare banks (−)	No channel modification (+)
Simple riparian zone (−)	Dams (−)
Reinforced banks (+)	Resectioned banks (−)
Point bars (+)	No bank modifications (+)
Substratum not visible (−)	Substratum silt (+)
Cascading flow (−)	Riparian zone uniform (−)
Dams (−)	Simple banks (+)
	Sand/gravel (+)
	Complex land use (+)
	Complex riparian zone (+)
	Stable cliffs (+)

dered by different land uses (Table 21.4). In part, this pattern reflected the correlation between PC1 and altitude, since altitude also affected land use. None of the other RHS PCs were likely to have been spuriously affected in this way, since no other RHS PCs varied altitudinally.

Many of the sites were rich biologically, with up to 50 diatom species, seven bryophyte species, 10 river bird species, and 32 invertebrate families. Several measures describing the taxon richness, evenness and community composition of these groups correlated highly significantly with the RHS PCs (Table 21.3). Perhaps predictably, however, patterns contrasted between organisms; on sweep-up PC1, for example, diatom and bryophyte species richness increased, bird species richness declined, while the number of invertebrate families remained unchanged. Among invertebrates, community composition changed significantly along 'sweep-up' PC1, but taxon richness did not. In contrast, changes along PC1 in the species richness of diatoms were stronger than changes in community composition.

Table 21.3   Correlations between measures of biodiversity in contrasting groups of organisms and the first four principal components from **River Habitat Surveys** in Nepal (see Tables 21.1 and 21.2 for habitat trends). Relationships with altitude are also shown. (All $n > 70$; *$P < 0.05$; **$P < 0.01$; ***$P < 0.001$). 'R' and 'M' for invertebrates indicate 'riffle' and 'margin' samples, respectively.

	'Sweep-up' scores				'Spot-check' scores				Altitude
	PC 1	PC 2	PC 3	PC 4	PC 1	PC 2	PC 3	PC 4	
Diatoms:									
Species richness	0.56***	0.10	−0.18	0.24*	−0.45***	−0.15	0.02	0.06	0.37**
Diversity	0.55***	0.06	−0.27*	0.23	−0.42***	−0.17	0.00	0.01	0.38**
Evenness	0.44***	0.07	−0.30*	0.19	−0.34**	0.10	−0.02	−0.06	0.31**
Ordination axis 1	−0.32**	0.11	−0.43***	−0.03	0.34**	−0.31**	−0.04	−0.02	−0.58***
Ordination axis 2	−0.60***	−0.04	0.06	−0.29	0.48***	0.05	−0.19	0.10	−0.51***
Invertebrates:									
No. of families (R)	0.03	−0.33**	−0.34**	−0.06	0.14	−0.34**	−0.16	−0.02	−0.13
No. of families (M)	0.00	−0.27*	−0.34**	−0.08	0.13	−0.34**	−0.12	0.11	−0.03
Ordination axis 1 (R)	−0.59***	0.15	−0.27*	−0.11	0.51***	−0.24*	−0.08	0.02	−0.79***
Ordination axis 2 (R)	0.18	0.35**	0.16	−0.09	−0.25*	0.09	0.13	0.12	0.11
Ordination axis 1 (M)	0.56***	0.07	0.36**	0.09	−0.59***	0.32**	0.14	−0.04	0.79***
Ordination axis 2 (M)	0.09	0.36**	−0.04	0.25*	−0.12	0.00	0.36**	−0.03	−0.03
Bryophytes:									
Species richness	0.44***	−0.10	−0.24*	0.05	−0.18	−0.33**	−0.23	0.11	0.36**
Birds:									
Species richness	−0.62***	0.16	0.04	0.03	0.35**	0.15	−0.17	−0.09	−0.69***
Ordination axis 1	0.54***	0.07	−0.17	−0.05	−0.34**	−0.08	0.20	−0.10	0.42***
Ordination axis 2	0.11	0.18	−0.16	0.04	−0.09	−0.14	0.12	0.14	0.01
Altitude	0.74***	0.01	0.12	0.07	−0.62***	0.10	0.11	0.01	

Table 21.4 Significant variations between different land uses in principal components (see Tables 21.1 and 21.2) derived from River Habitat Surveys at 76 sites in Nepal. *F* ratios and significance levels were determined by ANOVA.

| | | Mean score (with SD) on: | | | |
| | | RHS Sweep-up PCs: | | | RHS Spot-check PCs: |
Land Use	PC1	PC2	PC4	PC1	PC3
Sal forest (*n* = 8)	−3.0 (1.1)	0.9 (0.9)	0.8 (2.3)	1.4 (0.9)	−1.2 (1.8)
Terrace (11)	−0.7 (2.3)	1.2 (2.5)	0.5 (1.1)	0.0 (1.5)	1.7 (1.6)
Rough pasture (28)	0.6 (2.4)	0.3 (2.5)	0.4 (1.6)	−0.9 (2.1)	0.5 (2.1)
Mixed forest (29)	0.5 (3.0)	−0.9 (1.4)	−0.8 (1.4)	0.5 (2.9)	−0.8 (1.1)
F	5.0**	4.5**	4.2**	3.0*	8.3***

Notes:

1 For this analysis, one site with conifer forest was treated as mixed forest.

2 Influences by land use on RHS PC1 in both cases disappeared when covariant effects by altitude were taken into account.

As with land use, spurious relationships between biological trends and RHS PCs could not be ruled out because of covariance with altitude. Twenty out of the 41 statistically significant correlations, and 14 of 15 highly significant correlations ($p < 0.001$, with $r^2 > 0.16$) involved PC1, which in turn varied altitudinally. Only seven correlations with PC1 remained significant after the effects of altitude were partialled out by regression; all these cases involved diatoms, for which RHS PC1 provided a stronger correlate with diversity than altitude alone (see Table 21.3).

21.4 Discussion

These data show that variates derived from RHS changed with both altitude and land use in Nepali river systems. Although covariance between altitude, land use and RHS PCs prevented a clear understanding of cause-effect relationships, the RHS at least allowed a linear representation of complex structural changes between different Himalayan rivers. In other words, changes from large to small streams, laminar to turbulent or cascading flow, boulders to pebbles, and vegetated or unvegetated side bars to none, might all be regarded as the kinds of simultaneous structural changes that occur with increasing altitude in the Himalaya. Equally, the structural characteristics of rivers in different land use appear, for example, to include silt, sand and gravelly substrata in sal forest and terracing, but boulder substrata, exposed bedrock, torrential flow, waterfalls and tree-related features in mixed forest (see sweep-up PC2, Table 21.4). Patterns of this type will have indicator value where land-use changes begin to impinge on river structure.

Do these structural trends represent features to which biological communities respond? RHS PCs were significantly related to change in the community composition (beta diversity) and taxon richness (alpha diversity) of river organisms. This is a valuable result, indicating that RHS can represent structural changes that are meaningful ecologically. It has particular value in the context of this volume, because both alpha and beta diversity are important measures through which nature conservation quality is defined. One conclusion would be that RHS might be an important tool in conservation assessment. At the same time, however, there are two important lessons and caveats that underpin it.

First, not all organisms, nor all features of their diversity, responded in the same way to habitat changes. This will prevent RHS being used to provide a simple measure of biodiversity or habitat quality, because different organisms clearly have different habitat requirements: put simply, a river with appropriate habitats for birds will not necessarily have a large diversity of diatoms or invertebrates, and vice versa. Even within groups, the abundances of different species, genera and families changed in different ways with the RHS PCs (Ormerod *et al.*, unpublished data). One positive corollary is that RHS measures might provide models through which the abundance or diversity of different groups can be predicted. Using such models, a river engineer may choose how to structure river habitats for desired communities or species.

Second, there was strong covariance between altitude, RHS PCs, and biological features, which prevented a clear understanding of causal effects by changing structure alone. Thus, while the RHS PCs might have represented habitats that influenced the altitudinal distribution of some organisms, ecological influences by other altitudinal factors are likely to have been involved: climatic patterns, discharge variability, chemistry and energetic regime are all possibilities (e.g. Ormerod *et al.*, 1994). For this reason, the correlations between RHS PCs and biological trends should be viewed as a basis for hypothesis testing and further investigation, rather than proof that RHS is valuable.

If this, or other allied work, progresses to the stage of assessing cause-effect links between RHS data and biodiversity, three other general observations from this study might be valuable. The first is that the geographical scales of assessments for biodiversity and RHS were not wholly compatible; only birds were recorded over the same 200m reach as the RHS data. In contrast, diatoms, bryophytes and macroinvertebrates were derived from spot measurements within each reach on the assumption that the resulting data were representative. This assumption, made often in studies of river biota, will need careful examination where RHS reaches are internally variable. Second, a view expressed by RHS recorders during this survey was that more biological relevance could be built into the RHS features currently recorded. In particular, not all potentially important habitat features are coded with the same attention to scale, size, heterogeneity and material. As an example, small mid-bars of fine sand may well have different ecological character from large mid-bars of large boulders; in Nepali rivers, the latter can reach many metres in width and have an important role in structuring whole reaches. Yet, these mid-bar habitats would be categorized together in RHS coding. Thus, although RHS data are already complex, they may not be complex enough. Third, one other important feature absent from this work was that of temporal change, which sometimes confounds attempts to assess relationships between physical and biotic measures of river quality (e.g. Shields *et al.*, 1995). In rivers on the lower slopes of the Himalaya, seasonal floods associated with the annual monsoon have major effects on habitat structure, flow conditions and aquatic communities (Brewin, 1993); yet, the approach here assumes an element of equilibrium in all these features. While such regular and natural disturbances may well be less pronounced in other river systems where RHS is applied, temporal dynamism over relatively short periods may require careful scrutiny.

Acknowledgements

We thank Dick Johnson and Alan Jenkins of the Institute of Hydrology for the unmissable opportunity to carry out this work, funded by the Darwin Initiative for the Survival of Species. The Geology Department of Tribhuvan University collaborated in the surveys. Paul Raven, Peter Fox and Cath Beaver of the Environment Agency gave us essential help in the use of RHS. We particularly thank Geraldine Daly for identifying the need for this work.

References

Armitage, P. D. (1994). Prediction of biological response. In: Calow, P. and Petts, G. E. (Eds), *The Rivers Handbook, Volume 2*. Blackwell Scientific Publications, Oxford, 254–275.

Brewin, P. A. (1993). 'The Density, Micro-habitat Distribution and Drift of Invertebrates in Nepalese Hillstreams with Reference to Monsoon Flooding and Altitude'. Unpublished M.Sc. thesis, University of Wales, Cardiff.

Brewin, P. A., Newman, T. and Ormerod, S. J. (1995). Patterns of macroinvertebrate distribution in relation to altitude, habitat structure and land use in streams of the Nepalese Himalaya. *Archiv für Hydrobiologie*, **135**, 79–100.

Brewin, P. A. and Ormerod, S. J. (1994). The drift of macroinvertebrates in streams of the Nepalese Himalaya. *Freshwater Biology*, **32**, 573–584.

Brookes, A. (1994). River channel change. In: Calow, P. and Petts, G. E. (Eds), *The Rivers Handbook, Volume 2*. Blackwell Scientific Publications, Oxford, 55–75.

Dudgeon, D. (1992). Endangered ecosystems: a review of the conservation status of tropical Asian rivers. *Hydrobiologia*, **248**, 167–191.

Gray, J. S. (1989). Effects of environmental stress on species of rich assemblages. *Biological Journal of the Linnean Society*, **37**, 19–32.

Hill, M. O. (1979). *DECORANA—A FORTRAN Program for Detrended Correspondence Analysis and Reciprocal Averaging*. Cornell University, Ithaca, New York.

Ives, J. D. and Messerli, B. (1989). *The Himalayan Dilemma: Reconciling Development and Conservation*. Routledge, New York.

Karr, J. R. (1991). Biological integrity: a long neglected aspect of water resource management. *Ecological Applications*, **1**, 66–84.

MacArthur, R. H. and MacArthur, J. (1961). On bird species diversity. *Ecology*, **42**, 594–598.

McEwen, L. J., Brazier, V. and Gordon, J. E. (This volume). Evaluating the geomorphology of fresh waters: an assessment of approaches.

Ormerod, S. J., Rundle, S. D., Wilkinson, S. M., Daly, G. P., Dale, K. M. and Jüttner, I. (1994). Altitudinal trends in the diatoms, bryophytes, macroinvertebrates and fish of a Nepalese River System. *Freshwater Biology*, **31**, 309–322.

Raven, P. J., Fox, P., Everard, M., Holmes, N. T. H. and Dawson, F. H. (This volume). River Habitat Survey: a new system for classifying rivers according to their habitat quality.

Rundle, S. D., Jenkins, S. and Ormerod, S. J. (1993). Macroinvertebrate communities in streams in the Himalaya, Nepal. *Freshwater Biology*, **30**, 169–180.

Shields, F. D., Knight, S. S. and Cooper, C. M. (1995). Use of the index of biotic integrity to assess physical habitat degradation in warmwater streams. *Hydrobiologia,* **312,** 191–208.

Suren, A. M. (1994). Macroinvertebrate communities of streams in western Nepal: effects of altitude and landuse. *Freshwater Biology,* **32,** 323–336.

Tyler, S. J. and Ormerod, S. J. (1993). The ecology of river birds in Nepal. *The Forktail,* **9,** 59–82.

Whittaker, R. H. (1967). Gradient analysis of vegetation. *Biological Reviews,* **49,** 207–264.

Wright, J. F. (1995). Development and use of a system for predicting the macroinvertebrate fauna in flowing waters. *Australian Journal of Ecology,* **20,** 181–197.

Wilkinson, S. M., Brewin, P. A., Rundle, S. D. and Ormerod, S. J. (1995). Observations on the behaviour of a *Dineutus* whirligig beetle (Gyrinidae) in a Nepalese hillstream. *The Entomologist,* **114,** 131–137.

22 Biotopes and their Hydraulics: A Method for Defining the Physical Component of Freshwater Quality

C. L. Padmore

Summary

1. This chapter introduces the biotope as the basic unit of instream physical habitat. As biotopes can be identified in the field at a scale relevant to ecology and geomorphology, they are practical for identifying and classifying physical habitat.

2. Field identification by dominant flow type is explained, and biotope mapping described as a method which may be applied to physical habitat inventories.

3. Incorporating biotopes into River Habitat Surveys provides a standard method by which the physical habitat of different river sectors may be determined as one component of freshwater quality.

22.1 Introduction

The ecological concept of freshwater quality involves two components which provide a context for the study reported here. First, 'quality' includes the physical, structural features in addition to water chemistry; second, in order to assess quality there must be a set of objective standards against which rivers may be compared.

Classification is essential in order to avoid confusion arising from comparisons between rivers of different types (O'Keeffe, this volume). River Habitat Surveys (RHS) undertaken by the Environment Agency (EA) in England and Wales are being used to classify reaches into segments, as a basis for comparing the physical habitat features within a particular segment type (Raven *et al.*, this volume). Recording the type and distribution of physical features requires a standard, objective approach, and the need to define with clarity physical features of the instream environment requires a standard terminology. Traditionally, the focus has been towards riffles and pools. More recently, the perception of marginal habitat importance has increased (Petts *et al.*, 1995); as has that of macrophyte vegetation as a structural habitat element in lowland rivers (Wright *et al.*, 1994; Harper and Smith, 1995). The 'marriage' of ecology and fluvial geomorphology in recent river management (Petts *et al.*, 1995) has broadened the terminology associated with instream environments. However, confusion still exists and identification procedures are far from standardized (Wadeson, 1994).

22.2 The Physical Biotope: Identification by Dominant Flow Type

Research at Newcastle University involving the identification, and habitat hydraulics, of instream physical features has been adopted by the EA's River Habitat Survey (Raven *et al.*, this volume), and is the first stage in a proposed methodology for establishing catchment-scale environmentally acceptable flows.

The basic unit of instream habitat is the physical biotope. Classification at this scale allows standardized field identification of 'habitat units' based on dominant flow type, as summarized in Figure 22.1. It incorporates the microhabitat variables to which biota adapt—notably substrate particle size, depth, velocity and vegetation—at a scale relevant to RHS.

Study sites were selected to include a range of geomorphological channel features and biotopes. They were located near flow gauging stations in order to relate biotopes to discharge but at sites where weirs did not influence flow. Sites chosen in north-east England are representative of nine of the 11 segments

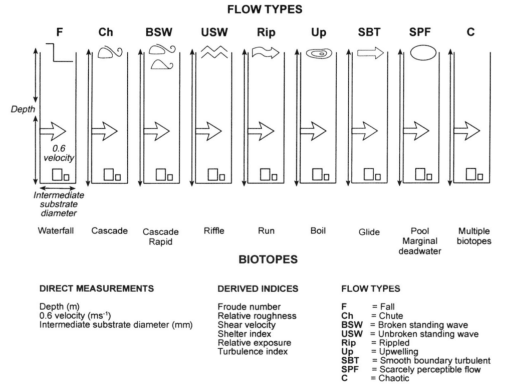

Figure 22.1   Identifying physical biotopes: flow type and hydraulic calibration.

identified by the EA's classification of river segment types (National Rivers Authority, 1996).

22.3 Biotopes as Hydraulically Discrete Units

Hydraulic characterization of physical biotopes allows statistical testing of the subjective classification by flow type. Data were collected at 1 m intervals across regularly spaced transects using procedures detailed in Padmore *et al.* (in press). Biotopes change both across a transect and longitudinally; thus accurate hydraulic characterization requires classification at the biotope scale. To achieve this, the variables listed in Figure 22.1 were collected at 1 m intervals, and the flow type recorded at each point or 'cell' within the sampling 'grid'. Transects were located every 5 or 10 m upstream depending on hydraulic diversity within a biotope. In addition, a transect-level classification of biotopes was determined by the dominant flow type across a transect. This is consistent with data recording in RHS (Raven *et al.*, this volume), and allows gross flow-related changes of biotopes to be mapped by field observation (see section 22.4).

22.3.1 *Testing the subjective classification of biotopes*

Combined hydraulic indices are calculated for each cell, to determine statistically whether particular flow types—and thus physical biotopes—have discrete, hydraulic characteristics. The Froude number has proved to be a good discriminator of physical biotopes in New Zealand and South Africa (Jowett, 1993; Wadeson, 1994). Other additional indices are calculated which may discriminate between biotopes, and which may have ecological relevance. Indices are dimensionless and independent of discharge, thus permitting comparisons between different sites and discharges. The indices, all calculated as ratios, include relative roughness (substrate:depth), relative exposure (depth:substrate), shelter index (substrate:Froude number) and turbulence index (stream power:substrate) (see Figure 22.1). Formulae for calculations are given in Padmore *et al.* (in press).

These indices are used in a Stepwise Discriminant Analysis which tests statistically the significance of subjectively classified flow types. By considering those hydraulic indices shown to be good flow type discriminators, each 'cell' is allocated to the flow type which its hydraulics (as described by the selected indices) most closely resemble. The Froude number is the best discriminator between flow types with relative roughness, shelter index and turbulence index each accounting for roughly 10% of variation. More detailed results are given in Padmore *et al.* (in press).

22.3.2 *Results: hydraulic characterization of biotopes*

Flow types are correctly allocated in the majority of cases. At higher flows, more than 80% of cells are correctly allocated for all flow types due to increased hydraulic uniformity within a biotope. At low flows, substrate has a greater influence on local hydraulics *via* increased roughness, so slightly more cells are misclassified, notably rippled flow and unbroken standing waves. Misclassified cells are explained by the influence of the hydraulics of adjacent cells, which are identified by the dominant flow type. For example, in a cascade, a small number of rippled flow cells may be present, but their hydraulics at the *biotope scale* will be similar to those of adjacent broken standing waves. Full explanations are provided in Padmore *et al.* (in press). The significance from a management perspective is that the biotope is the smallest 'patch' with discrete hydraulics, and decisions regarding flow manipulation can then be taken to maintain the characteristic hydraulics of 'critical' biotopes for a given reach.

The ecological significance of biotopes is unknown at present, as the majority of national scale invertebrate sampling traditionally focused on differences in riffle and pool fauna. More recently, 'all habitat types' have been sampled in developing RIVPACS (Wright, 1995). The ecological relevance of biotopes is being tested as part of a Newcastle University Ph.D. study of invertebrate-biotope relations supported by the EA.

22.4   Biotope Mapping

Sites have been mapped after significant rainfall events to establish how biotope sequences alter with discharge. Biotopes alter as substrate roughness decreases and hydraulic controls are 'drowned out'. This is illustrated in Figure 22.2; as flow increases, boulders are submerged and the cascade becomes a rapid, dominated by broken standing waves. At high flows the entire site becomes one run-rapid unit. A general response of biotopes to fluctuating flow, for a range of channel types, is presented in Padmore (in press). Knowledge of flow exceedence percentiles at which biotope sequences alter for a particular reach type will allow flow management decisions to be made to ensure that the hydraulics of 'target' biotopes are maintained. 'Target' biotopes are use-dependent and require value judgements to be made; it may be that riffle spawning redds are critical, or marginal deadwaters for rare invertebrate species.

Information from biotope mapping over a range of discharges may be used together with existing River Habitat Surveys to extend the national database to higher flows. At present the RHS database is restricted to low summer flows, although a project between the EA and the Institute of Freshwater Ecology to carry out bi-monthly River Habitat Surveys is being implemented at 10 RHS sites in 1996 (H. Dawson, personal communication).

22.4.1   Flood geomorphology and biotope change

The influence of large floods on channel morphology was established by biotope mapping following high magnitude floods which occurred in north-east England in 1995. Floods with return periods between 25 and 100 years (D. Archer, personal communication) led to infilling of pools and cobble deposition in cascades. This caused a change in biotope type at equivalent pre- and post-flood discharges, as illustrated in Figure 22.2. Such events should therefore be considered in successive national habitat inventories for their role in altering channel morphology, and for their possible ecological implications.

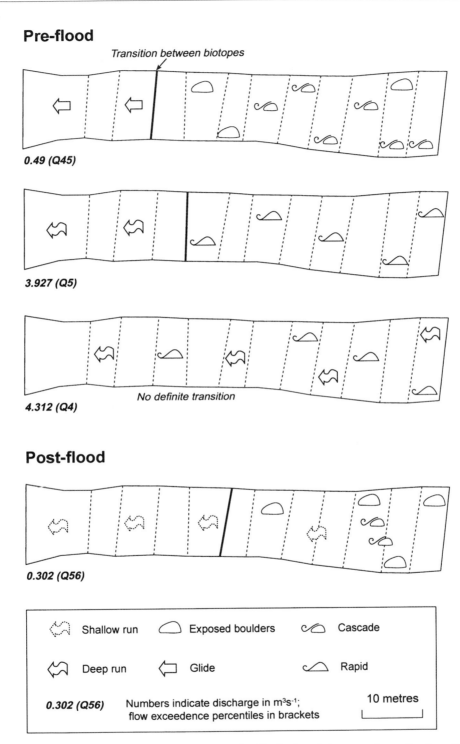

Figure 22.2   Biotope sequence at Harwood Beck, a boulder-bed reach in pre- and post-flood conditions.

22.5 Applications: Determining Physical Freshwater Quality

22.5.1 River Habitat Survey

Identification of channel features based on flow types has been adopted by the EA as part of its RHS methodology (Raven *et al.*, this volume). This national inventory of UK river habitat features is being developed within the framework of a classification of river segment types to assess the conservation potential of a given watercourse on the basis of characteristic and intrinsic value features (Raven *et al.*, this volume). Reaches may then be compared with those of a similar segment type to determine the impacts of channel modification, or set targets for river enhancement.

22.5.2 River restoration

Biotope mapping has been carried out on two British rivers selected for restoration as part of an EC-funded 'Life' project (Nielsen, in press). An inventory of physical biotopes before and after restoration works on the Rivers Skerne (Darlington) and Cole (Swindon) will enable the success of the project to be assessed. In addition, the influence of macrophyte vegetation on physical biotopes in low gradient, fine-gravel channels was investigated by biotope mapping and taking detailed velocity profiles at both sites.

22.5.3 Flood defence maintenance engineering

An inventory of physical biotopes on a 6 km reach of the River Swale (North Yorkshire) between Catterick and Great Langton Bridge revealed high biotope diversity within an unstable sedimentation zone. The ecological importance of this reach was considered within flood defence maintenance proposals, following large floods which damaged local farmland and adjacent properties in 1995. Rather than removing excess sediment from the channel (as requested by landowners), it was considered essential to retain the range of biotopes associated with mid-channel bars. Proposals to remove gravel only from an overheightened bar upstream of historic flood defence structures allowed both flood defence and conservation objectives to be met.

22.5.4 River regulation and biotope change

Studies on the Colorado River, USA, suggest that stage reductions have had an impact on backwater biotopes (J. Pitlick, personal communication) and on sediment transport frequencies (Pitlick, 1994). Biotope mapping has been recommended as part of a project carried out by the University of Colorado. An inventory of physical biotopes will be compared with historical air photographs to investigate the possible consequences of impoundment on biotope type and distribution, which will then be related to changes in native fish populations.

22.6 Conclusions

The biotope has been identified as the basic unit of hydraulic instream habitat. Biotope mapping within the framework of River Habitat Surveys has been adopted as a standard technique for comparing rivers at the reach scale. Further research regarding the biotope concept will involve developing the following points of relevance to conservation management:

(a) Biotope sequences to characterize reaches within the classification of river segment types.

(b) Biotope 'patchiness' and 'diversity' indices for inclusion in Habitat Quality Indices.

(c) The ecological significance of biotopes in terms of invertebrate communities.

This research will be carried out within an applied framework, with reference to recent theoretical developments in stream ecosystem theories, notably 'patch dynamics' and 'disturbance-recovery' theories (White and Pickett, 1985; Milner, 1994).

References

Harper, D. M. and Smith, C. D. (1995). 'Habitats in British Rivers: Biological Reality and Practical Value in River Management'. Unpublished report. National Rivers Authority, Bristol.

Jowett, I. G. (1993). A method for objectively identifying pool, run and riffle habitats from physical measurements. *New Zealand Journal of Marine and Freshwater Research,* **27,** 241–248.

Milner, A. M. (1994). System recovery. In: Petts, G. E. and Calow, P. (Eds), *The Rivers Handbook Volume 2.* Blackwell Scientific, Oxford, 76–97.

National Rivers Authority (1996). *River Habitats in England and Wales: a National Overview.* Bristol.

Nielsen, M. B. (in press). River restoration: report of a major EU Life demonstration project. *Aquatic Conservation: Marine and Freshwater Ecosystems.*

O'Keeffe, J. (This volume). Methods of assessing conservation status for natural fresh waters in the Southern hemisphere.

Padmore, C. L. (in press). The role of physical biotopes in determining the conservation status and flow requirements of British rivers. *Journal of Aquatic Ecosystem Health.*

Padmore, C. L., Newson, M. D. and Charlton, M. E. (in press). Instream habitat in gravel bed rivers: identification and characterization of biotopes. *Gravel Bed Rivers in the Environment (International Workshop).* Oregon State University.

Petts, G. E., Maddock, I., Bickerton, M. and Ferguson, A. J. D. (1995). Linking hydrology and ecology: the scientific basis for river management. In: Harper, D. M. and Ferguson, A. J. D. (Eds), *The Ecological Basis for River Management.* John Wiley, Chichester, 1–16.

Pitlick, J. (1994). Coarse sediment transport and the maintenance of fish habitat in the upper Colorado River. In: Cotromeo, G. V. and Rumer, R. R. (Eds), *Proceedings of the American Society of Civil Engineers Conference on Hydraulic Engineering.* ASCE, New York, 855–859.

Raven, P. J., Fox, P., Everard, M., Holmes, N. T. H. and Dawson, F. H. (This volume). River Habitat Survey: a new system for classifying rivers according to their habitat quality.

Wadeson, R. A. (1994). A geomorphological approach to the identification and classification of instream flow environments. *South African Journal of Aquatic Sciences,* **20,** 1–24.

White, P. S. and Pickett, S. T. A. (1985). Natural disturbance and patch dynamics: an introduction. In: White, P. S. and Pickett, S. T. A. (Eds), *The Ecology of Natural Disturbance and Patch Dynamics.* Academic Press, New York, 3–13.

Wright, J. F., Blackburn, J. H., Clarke, R. T. and Furse, M. T. (1994). Macroinvertebrate-habitat associations in lowland rivers and their relevance to conservation. *Verhandlungen der Internationalen Vereiningung für theoretische und angewandte Limnologie,* **25,** 1515–1518.

Wright, J. F. (1995). Development and use of a system for predicting the macroinvertebrate fauna in flowing waters. *Australian Journal of Ecology,* **20,** 181–197.

23 EVALUATING THE GEOMORPHOLOGY OF FRESH WATERS: AN ASSESSMENT OF APPROACHES

L. J. McEwen, V. Brazier and J. E. Gordon

Summary

1. This chapter assesses several approaches (mainly focused on the UK) to the evaluation of geomorphological quality of rivers: earth science conservation, river restoration and rehabilitation, and habitat and ecological evaluation. Integral to such evaluation are the fundamental characteristics of river behaviour, including spatial and temporal changes, the links between processes, and responses at different scales and geomorphological sensitivity.

2. Five key elements involved in geomorphological evaluation are: environmental context, type of geomorphological system, linkages between different elements of the catchment system, the ability to aggregate descriptive and interpretative detail into larger units, and the effective assessment of system change.

3. No single approach allows a comprehensive answer to river evaluation. Evaluation systems for earth science conservation are a useful point of departure and in particular, the Geological Conservation Review provides a helpful conceptual framework and classification which deserve wider application. In contrast, the geomorphological components of habitat and ecological surveys have a weaker theoretical basis, but are better designed for simple and practical application.

4. A more comprehensive approach to river evaluation should be firmly based on an understanding of the fundamental characteristics of river behaviour, the scale dependencies of landform patterns and processes and the nature of change in river systems.

5. A more integrated approach to river evaluation is advocated, incorporating both geomorphological and ecological components, so that the physical underpinning is fully incorporated in the development of river conservation strategies and management planning.

23.1 Introduction

Geomorphology encompasses the study of the physical processes of landform development and the features that these processes produce, modify and rework over time. In essence, deposits and landforms resulting from past and present geomorphological processes underpin all freshwater habitats to varying degrees. The effective representation of significant attributes of geomorphological systems is important in both landform and habitat-based evaluations of the quality of freshwater geomorphology. This chapter reviews the scientific robustness of a range of evaluative techniques, using the example of rivers, and assesses what lessons can be learned from earth science conservation, river rehabilitation/river management and ecological habitat assessments, where different forms of geomorphic evaluation are employed.

Significant variations exist between the approaches of different disciplines (e.g. geomorphology, hydrology, civil engineering and ecology) to the geomorphological assessment of rivers, and the different evaluation procedures with contrasting foci and purpose can result in marked differences in the interpretation of the 'quality' of a river site. Through the comparison of the geomorphological elements in different systems of evaluation, the aim of this paper is to identify what is needed to evaluate effectively the geomorphological attributes of rivers. The focus is primarily on evaluation schemes within the UK, but many of the principles and issues discussed are transferable. A comparison between the information requirements for geomorphological evaluation and the geomorphological inputs needed for ecological river assessment allows areas of commonality to be identified and recommendations for good practice to be made.

23.2 River Systems: Challenges for Geomorphological Evaluation

23.2.1 Fundamental characteristics of rivers

In developing a system of geomorphological evaluation, it is important at the outset to appreciate some of the fundamental characteristics of rivers that result from their environmental setting and their susceptibility to change, both at present and in the past. Within the UK, Scotland has some of the highest energy river environments, characterized by steep slopes, large clast sizes and flashy run-off regimes (Werritty *et al.*, 1994; Werritty and McEwen, in press). Many of the controls on sediment availability and channel confinement are determined by glacial legacy and hence upland Scottish rivers are very different in character from their lowland counterparts. Classification into erosional, transportational and depositional zones (Schumm, 1977) is frequently an oversimplification when dealing with Scottish rivers (Werritty and McEwen, in press). Evaluation must therefore be sensitive to the range of channel form in different environmental settings.

River systems are inherently dynamic, and any system of geomorphic evaluation must encompass changes of river character both over space and through time.

Rates of change in upland river systems can be abrupt over short timescales, followed by periods of relative quiescence (Werritty and Ferguson, 1983), whereas lowland rivers frequently develop in a more systematic fashion through floodplain channel migration and floodplain evolution. Rivers are active across a nested hierarchy of scales of resolution from the catchment down to the level of individual bedforms associated with a specific cross-section. Different criteria for evaluation may be appropriate to a particular scale of evaluation. Change at one scale may also exert an impact across a range of other scales; for example, sediment sources within a catchment may control spatial variations in bar forms within a channel. The nature of downstream change in river form and channel bed characteristics, with increasing catchment area, is equally important (e.g. Knighton, 1987; Hoey and Ferguson, 1994). Upstream changes, such as afforestation or flow regulation, may affect the 'naturalness' of the landforming environment in downstream reaches. Establishing the interconnections between different elements of the drainage basin is central to effective evaluation, whatever the main scale of focus. In addition, the transverse relationship between a river and its corridor and floodplain has been an important focus for recent research in lowland rivers (Newson, 1992), with particular reference to river rehabilitation and the ecological value of such wetland successions (e.g. Petts *et al.*, 1992). The relationship between channel and corridor in high-energy environments is equally important although the nature and rate of the processes are different and more episodic, leading to distinctive landform assemblages.

It is also important to establish, before evaluation, an appropriate conceptual basis for understanding river system adjustment to changing controls. The notion of geomorphological sensitivity (Brunsden and Thornes, 1979; Thomas and Allison, 1993) provides a useful framework for assessing the behaviour of dynamic river systems (Newson and Sear, 1994; Werritty and Brazier, 1994). River systems may be classified as essentially robust or sensitive, depending upon their tolerance to externally driven change (Figure 23.1). Sensitive rivers are those where a comparatively minor event triggers a fundamental change in river regime. However, differentiating robust and sensitive conditions in a naturally dynamic environment is complex, particularly if limited to field evidence.

The relationships between landforms, geomorphological processes and ecological habitats is a further consideration and one that needs better definition for dynamic Scottish river environments. Within the Scottish uplands, the nature and pace of geomorphological change during the Holocene (the last 10,000 years) has, in the past, been mistakenly dismissed as insignificant by geomorphologists, geologists and ecologists alike. There has been an assumption that hillslope and river processes have had little significant effect in modifying a largely vegetated landscape, following rapid plant colonization during deglaciation at the end of the Late Devensian some 10,000 years ago. However, recent studies of the Holocene suggest that the whole landscape has continued to be both dynamic and sensitive to less dramatic environmental changes and human intervention (Werritty *et al.*, 1994).

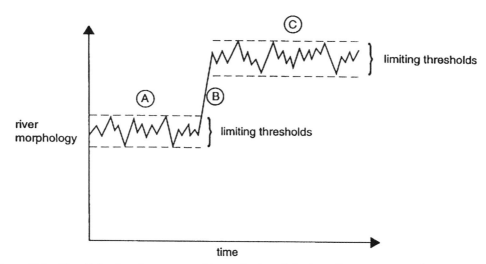

Figure 23.1 The distinctions between sensitive and robust behaviour (from Werritty and Brazier, 1994). (A), (C): *robust behaviour*—river repeatedly crossing intrinsic thresholds, but overall response stable within limiting thresholds. Negative feedback regulates change. Landforms retain stable identity as they form and reform. (B): *sensitive behaviour*—in response to externally imposed change, river moves across extrinsic threshold to new process regime. Landforms in original regime (A) destroyed and replaced by new landforms created in regime (C).

23.2.2 *Definitions: quality and geomorphology*

The term 'quality' has a range of interpretations when applied to the geomorphology of fresh waters. In abstract, the use of 'quality' in geomorphological assessment can take the following three different forms:

(a) 'Quality' can be viewed along a continuum from the common to the unique, with increasing value as a landform or landform assemblage becomes rarer within the terms of reference of the assessment. This is essentially a subjective judgement whereby a feature is assessed as unique, or very rare and therefore of exceptionally high value on the basis of existing knowledge. For example, the lower River Spey in north-east Scotland would be considered of high quality as it is the best example of a coarse-grained, braided channel in the lower reaches of any UK river (Lewin and Weir, 1977).

(b) 'Quality' can be considered in terms of representativeness, as an assessment of how good a particular landform is as an example of its class. This interpretation of quality is normally used when describing and evaluating a representative example of a commonly occurring feature. This may be a typical section of wandering gravel bed river, a characteristic river form in the Scottish uplands, or a characteristic suite of point bars associated with a regular meander train.

(c) 'Quality' is also implicit when assessing the degree of 'naturalness' associated with a landform, landforming environment or landform assemblage (see Warren, 1993). The level of quality is associated with the degree of degradation due to human intervention and reduction of naturalness or integrity of the site. This assessment of quality varies in the degree to which it is amenable to qualitative versus quantitative assessment and subjective/objective evaluation.

In practice, the interpretation of 'quality' depends on the focus, criteria for assessment and frame of reference within which it is evaluated. These definitions concur with some of those for 'quality' in ecological assessment (Ratcliffe, 1977). 'Representativeness' and 'naturalness' are conservation assessment criteria or approaches to defining quality in SERCON (see section 23.3.3.3).

23.2.3 *Different approaches for evaluating geomorphic quality of rivers: criteria for assessment*

Critical evaluation of the different schemes for the geomorphological assessment of quality requires an appropriate breakdown of key issues. These include aims and objectives, the evaluation framework and specific advantages and disadvantages. Table 23.1 provides a summary evaluation of those schemes dealt with in section 23.3. It is important to note that value judgements are not explicit in all evaluative schemes. Given the different definitions of 'quality' (section 23.2.2) and the different approaches and terms of reference within evaluation, it is possible to obtain different evaluations for the same landform assemblage, for example according to the scale of comparison. This may be illustrated by the case of a large alluvial fan formed over the last 13,000 years at the confluence of the River Feshie with the River Spey, which has been assessed as a relatively rare, internationally important, example of a dynamic system (Petts *et al.*, 1990; Werritty and Brazier, 1991; Werritty and McEwen, in press). The fan exhibits classic traits of channel switching that have generally been engineered out of many similar sites in Europe. However, at a global scale, the history of human interference in the active segment of the fan diminishes the overall quality of the site when compared with pristine alluvial fans in remote mountain areas of, for example, South America and New Zealand. By extending the geographical coverage of the evaluation to a global scale, the value of an important site for earth science conservation in Europe is reduced, without any material change on the actual site. Similarly, the highly braided planform in the lower reaches of the River Spey is exceptional in a UK context (Figure 23.2). On an international scale, however, the site is of lower geomorphological research significance when compared to the unconstrained braiding associated with outwash plains, such as Icelandic sandar.

23.2.4 *Requirements for river evaluation*

Effective evaluation of the geomorphology of rivers requires five key elements: an assessment of environmental context, type of geomorphic system, linkages within the system, the ability to aggregate units of assessment to characterize larger scale systems, and effective assessment of change.

Environmental context indicates the controls that define the balance between

Figure 23.2   Lower River Spey: the diversity of habitats reflects the geomorphological diversity of an actively changing, braided river floodplain. Overall river quality closely reflects the physical processes and landforms and their spatial and temporal changes. (Photo: L. J. McEwen).

forces of erosion and resistance within the catchment. These include slope (energy balance), inputs into the system (precipitation, forces for change) and lithology (forces of resistance). This information provides the context for the whole evaluation, and is particularly important when reviewing sensitivity of channels, especially to adverse change and degradation. The characteristic *type of geomorphological system*, for example as defined by a channel typology, is a result of adjustments within the system to its environmental setting or context. All geomorphological systems are subject to changes and adjustments over different spatial and temporal scales. A river can be considered in quasi-equilibrium if the inputs (in terms of sediment supply and discharge regime) balance the outputs over a given timescale. This does not imply that the landform is static.

Linkages between different elements of the catchment system (relationships between upstream/downstream reaches; links between channel and floodplain) must be established and interpreted. In addition, links may exist between different types of process regime with significant impacts on river channel form and stability. For example, the periodicity of sediment inputs from the colluvial activity in upland catchments will affect the availability of sediment for fluvial reworking and transport and so act as an important control on channel character at downstream sites.

Aggregation involves the ability to build up descriptive and interpretative detail into

Table 23.1   Assessment of different, predominantly field based, approaches to evaluating quality of freshwater geomorphology.

Criteria for assessment	Landform inventories			Field surveys with a morphological focus		Field surveys with an ecological focus		
Example evaluation schemes	*New Zealand landform inventory*	*Canadian landform inventory*	*Geomorphological Conservation Review GCR*	*Thorne's stream reconnaissance*	*Brookes' morphological survey*	*River Corridor Survey RCS*	*River Habitat Survey RHS*	*SERCON*
1. Aims and objectives								
• To establish research interest	Examples in class of national significance	Yes	Sites of national or international research status	No	No	No	No	No
• To identify range of morphology within a region/country	Yes	Yes	Channel typology for Scotland	No	Yes	No	Yes	Yes
• To infer morphological stability of channel	No	Yes	Channel sensitivity part of assessment	Yes	Yes	No	No	No
• To interpret channel morphology and fluvial processes operating in the channel	No	No	Yes	Yes	Yes	No	No	No
• To evaluate impacts of proposed or past engineering intervention	No	No	No	Yes (principally for river restoration)	Yes	Yes	Yes	Yes
• To provide feedback on on-going operational maintenance (make improvements)	No	No	No	Yes	Yes	Yes	No	No
• To establish permanent historical record of the channel as basis for repeat survey	No	No	No, but information will need to be updated	Yes	No	No	No	No
• To provide ecological assessment	No	No	No	No	No	Key element in assessment	Key element in assessment	Key element in assessment
2. Framework								
• Nature of information	Landform category	Landform category	Channel typology and characteristics give sites national research interest	Detailed description of valley, floodplain, channel and bed sediment	Basic description of valley, planform, channel, bank and substrate	Features in aquatic, marginal, bank and adjacent zones depicted by symbol	Numerous (including physical attributes, bank profiles)	Organized in terms of conservation criteria and attributes
• Information sources	Based on field visit, maps, aerial photographs; consultation with researchers	Based on field visit, maps, aerial photographs; consultation with researchers	Based on field visit, maps, aerial photographs; consultation with researchers	Based on field visit	Based on field visit	Based on field visit	Based on field visit	Based on field visit

continued

● Scale of evaluation (single site, nested, hierarchical)	Site-based; hierarchical	Large-scale systems	Primarily site-based; can encompass small integrated catchments	River channel segment (cross-sectional assessment) placed in catchment context	Homogeneous reach (survey may work along a series of such reaches)	Site-based	Site-based	Site-based
● Length of segment, landform unit	Variable	Variable	Variable	Variable	Variable	500 m	500 m	500 m
● Environment	Upland	Upland	Upland/ lowland	Developed for lowland rivers	Developed for lowland rivers	Upland/ lowland	Upland/ lowland	Upland/ lowland
3. Advantages and limitations								
● Usage	One-off	One-off	One-off (will need periodic update)	One-off routine	Routine	Routine	Routine	Routine
● Level of expertise (need for training?)	Expert	Expert	Expert	Specialist geomorphological skills and knowledge; training required for those inexperienced in field methods	Management interpretation requires trained fluvial geomorphologist	Should be experienced in RCS methods; NVC experience or training for field survey desirable	Non-specialist recording; largely self-explanatory (some training essential)	Non-specialist recording; largely self-explanatory (some training essential)
● Naturalness	Natural sites only	Natural sites only	Only natural sites included	Applicable to channels with varying degrees of human intervention	Applicable to channels with varying degrees of human intervention	Applicable to channels with varying degrees of human intervention	Applicable to channels with varying degrees of human intervention	Applicable to channels with varying degrees of human intervention
● Description v. interpretation v. evaluation	Description, interpretation and evaluation	Description, interpretation and evaluation	Evaluation high priority	Mixture of qualitative observation and morphometric measurement to build up a record of channel form; some interpretative observations	Mainly qualitative observations; quantitative assessment of channel description	Annotated map with mainly descriptive summary text	When RHS completed there is an element of interpretation and evaluation	Description, interpretation and evaluation

Table 23.1—*continued*

Criteria for assessment	Landform inventories			Field surveys with a morphological focus		Field surveys with an ecological focus		
Example evaluation schemes	*New Zealand landform inventory*	*Canadian landform inventory*	*Geomorphological Conservation Review GCR*	*Thorne's stream reconnaissance*	*Brookes' morphological survey*	*River Corridor Survey RCS*	*River Habitat Survey RHS*	*SERCON*
• Representativeness of cross-section	Not relevant	Not relevant	Not relevant	Decision of observer	Decision of observer	At least one representative cross-section drawn for 500m sections	Not considered	Not considered
• Ecological elements in assessment	No	No	No	Limited	Vegetation noted in terms of bank stability	Bank zone habitats; marginal vegetation on both banks; adjacent land use; habitats to be retained intact	Fluvial habitat features; substrates, bank top land use and vegetation structure; channel vegetation types; extent of trees and associated features	Fluvial habitat features; in-stream vegetation structure; substrates; bank/riparian zone vegetation; corridor land use and special features; wide range of species attributes
• Accuracy	High	High	High	Level of confidence in answers provided as %	Wide class brackets	Regular checking of the quality of RCS outputs	Confidence not assessed	DAFOR index for some attributes; subjective confidence rating
4. Requirements for river evaluation (section 23.2.4)								
• Environmental setting	Not explicit	Not explicit	Environmental setting provided Detailed	Region and valley description	Basic	Not specified	Basic; map-based	Basic
• Type of geomorphological system	N/A	N/A		Not explicit	Not explicit	Not addressed	Not addressed	Not addressed
• Linkages	None	None	Links between different geomorphological agents discussed	Structured working from valley-scale downwards	Structured working from valley-scale downwards	Not addressed	Not addressed	Not addressed
• Aggregation	N/A	N/A	Possible	Possible	Possible at basic level	Possible	Possible	Possible
• Effective assessment of change	N/A	N/A	Yes	Interpretative observations e.g. bank erosion	Basic	Not addressed	Not addressed	Replicability and ability to carry out repeat surveys are important considerations

an understanding of larger scale system dynamics (e.g. moving from the character of banks—to the propensity for bank erosion—to channel instability—to erosion of a major sediment store with implications for downstream channel form).

Effective assessment of change involves identifying the processes of change and evaluating their impact on channel form over both space and time. This includes assessing the extent of human intervention in the natural process system, site integrity and sensitivity to change. It must also encompass the potential for monitoring change within the system over time.

23.3   Geomorphological Evaluation

23.3.1   *The experience of earth science conservation*

National audits and evaluations of geomorphological heritage for earth science conservation have been carried out in several countries (e.g. Ontario Ministry of Natural Resources, 1981; Björklund, 1987; Davidson, 1988; Priestley and Crozier, 1990; Erikstad, 1994; Gordon, 1994; Smith-Meyer, 1995; Werritty and McEwen, in press). These surveys vary in type and character from simple inventories of large-scale morphological groups, to more elaborate nested hierarchies of river channel systems (Table 23.1). Some assessments are also linked to new technology with the establishment of expert systems or Geographic Information Systems (GIS) to assist in evaluation.

23.3.1.1   National landform inventories

Landform inventories developed in New Zealand and Canada are limited geographically and in comprehensiveness. The New Zealand landform inventory section on fluvial/pluvial landforms and active process environments follows a site-based approach, identifying sites from a list of 24 categories that range in scale from alluvial plains filling the whole valley floor, to rills defined as 'a very small erosion channel caused by running water' (Priestley and Crozier, 1990). Each of the 24 categories is assigned examples of key sites. For example, the category 'alluvial fan' has 13, mostly well-known areas that have one or more classic alluvial fans, such as the Mt. Binser fan in Arthur's Pass National Park. Quality here is defined as exceptional examples of a particular landform class. However, further scientific details of the geomorphological interest of each site are absent, and the level of evaluation is confined to an unsupported and apparently arbitrary three point classification of importance and vulnerability.

The Canadian approach goes beyond listing sites that are examples of particular geomorphological processes, and includes a system for classifying and evaluating potential sites and then identifying a strategy for conserving these sites. However, the section of the earth science evaluations devoted to river evaluation is brief, and again the classification is principally concerned with large-scale systems. There is little evidence of detailed site assessment criteria beyond large-scale landform assemblage classes such as 'alluvial fan' (Ontario Ministry of Natural Resources, 1981).

Smith-Meyer (1995) developed a hierarchical channel typology for a nationwide classification of Norwegian rivers for use in a GIS. The scheme enables the identification of a wide range of river types examined at different geographical scales and using remote sensing data, and can incorporate site-specific detailed information where appropriate. The method is best used for large-scale classification of channel type, but the hierarchical structure may be useful in evaluation schemes on whole river systems.

The potential contribution of such approaches to the development of the geomorphological content of river evaluation schemes is thus limited. Both the New Zealand and Canadian earth science evaluations have concentrated on cataloguing sites with little attention to the scientific framework that can be used to establish both the relevance and quality of landforms for geomorphological or ecological interests.

23.3.1.2 The Geological Conservation Review

The Geological Conservation Review (GCR) was developed in the UK as one of the most thorough systematic programmes of evaluation of earth science heritage (Ellis, in press). A system of over 40 site networks subdivide the GCR, with one network, Fluvial Geomorphology, devoted to the evaluation of landforms and landforming environments of rivers. The GCR is distinctive from other earth science conservation evaluations in that it requires that all successfully selected sites are at least of national scientific significance in Britain. The principal criteria for site assessment are international importance, the presence of exceptional features, and representativeness of British earth history (Ellis, in press). More specific guidelines were then developed for particular subject areas such as fluvial geomorphology (McEwen, 1994a; Werritty and McEwen, in press).

All selected sites are of high quality in terms of their earth science conservation value. Several definitions of 'quality' are implicit, in evaluating 'uniqueness', in assessing the best examples of 'typical' sites and in terms of 'naturalness'. Significantly disturbed river reaches, such as on the Tulla Water (Bluck, 1976) where major dredging had been undertaken, were excluded. Thus the absence of particular rivers from the GCR does not necessarily imply an absence of 'high quality' geomorphology; it could equally reflect significant modification by human activity or the duplication of the interest at other sites.

Specific site selection categories were determined for river systems. These were used to identify and classify the range of river system types in terms of channel planform and the typology of bedrock channels and alluvial channels, with the latter classified by both sinuosity and channel division (Table 23.2). Although these categories provide a comprehensive list of fluvial environments in Scotland, different cells within the classification vary in the extent to which they are typical or unique in a Scottish context. For example, truly braided systems are relatively rare, whereas irregular meanders with no bars and sinuous channels with frequent bars are relatively common.

The classification extends evaluation further to address the principal charac-

Table 23.2 GCR site selection criteria for fluvial geomorphology (Scotland): channel and landform typology (modified from Kellerhals *et al.*, 1976).

Channel and landform typology. Column groupings: **Bedrock rivers** (Slot gorge, Wide bedrock reach, Waterfall); **Alluvial rivers** (Straight, Straight-sinuous, Irregular/irregularly meandering, Regular meanders, Tortuous meandering, Frequent bars, Split, Wandering, Braided, Anabranching, Reticulate); **Alluvial channels with high slopes** (Fluvially-modified debris cone, Alluvial cone, Alluvial fan: upland valley confluence, Alluvial fan: lowland valley confluence).

Site	Slot gorge	Wide bedrock reach	Waterfall	Straight	Straight-sinuous	Irregular/irregularly meandering	Regular meanders	Tortuous meandering	Frequent bars	Split	Wandering	Braided	Anabranching	Reticulate	Fluvially-modified debris cone	Alluvial cone	Alluvial fan: upland valley confluence	Alluvial fan: lowland valley confluence
Corrieshalloch Gorge	X																	
Falls of Clyde	X		X															
River Findhorn at Randolph's Leap	X																	
Falls of Dochart		X	X															
Grey Mare's Tail	X		X															
River Clyde meanders							X	X										
Strathglass							X											
Abhainn an t-Srath Chuileannaich						X	X	X		X								
River Endrick							X											
Derry Burn							X	X			X							
River Balvag delta				X														
Lower River Spey								X				X	X					
Glen Feshie composite site								X			X	X	X	X				X
Allt Dubhaig				X	X	X					X							
Dorback Burn											X							
Glen Coe composite site									X	X	X				X	X	X	
Luibeg Burn				X							X							
Allt Mor/River Nairn					X						X							
Allt Mor/River Druie											X						X	
Quoich Water fan											X		X					X
Allt a' Choire											X				X		X	
Eas na Broige															X			
Allt Coire Challein	X																X	
Oldhamstocks Gullies											X						X	

teristics which make selected Scottish river sites/catchments geomorphologically interesting for research (Table 23.3) (Werritty *et al.*, 1994; Werritty and McEwen, in press). This is based on an exhaustive review of past research publications and informal research interest (McEwen, 1994a). This comprehensive framework for

Table 23.3 Geomorphologically distinct characteristics of GCR sites selected for fluvial geomorphology (Scotland).

Site	Classic sedimentary structures	Downstream changes in fluvial controls	Integrated system	Discordant	Progressive	Interfaces between different types of geomorphic activity	Colluvial-fluvial	Lacustrine-fluvial	Geomorphic impact of floods	Immediate landforming capacity	Longer term geomorphic persistence	Fluvial adjustment over historic time	Changes in sinuosity	Changes in channel division	Evidence as to Lateglacial and Holocene fluvial adjustment	Fluvial terraces	Glacio fluvial	Outwash	Debris cones/alluvial fans
River Clyde meanders	X												X						
Strathglass													X						
Abhainn an t-Srath Chuileannaich	X			X									X						
River Endrick	X												X						
Derry Burn				X									X						
River Balvag delta	X							X											
Lower River Spey	X									X	X				X				
Glen Feshie composite site	X						X			X	X				X	X	X	X	
Allt Dubhaig				X															
Dorback Burn										X	X								
Glen Coe composite site							X	X											
Luibeg Burn										X	X								
Allt Mor/River Nairn			X		X														
Allt Coire Gabhail	X			X	X														
Allt Mor/River Druie		X			X					X	X								
Quoich Water fan										X	X	X							
Allt a' Choire		X			X														X
Allt Choire Challein	X	X			X														X
Eas na Broige fan					X														X
Oldhamstocks gullies										X	X								X
Findhorn terraces																X	X	X	
River North Esk palaeosandur																X	X	X	
Glen Roy composite site																X	X	X	X

classification and evaluation, applicable to widely differing river environments, defines the scope of the fluvial geomorphology GCR coverage of Scottish rivers.

Some attributes developed for evaluation in this exercise may be useful in the development of other evaluation schemes. However, the GCR scheme was designed for a particular purpose and scale—the identification of nationally important sites for scientific research and education. Transferability to a different context was not an objective. There are therefore several features of the GCR evaluation that limit its routine application to evaluating the quality of river geomorphology (Table 23.1).

- The GCR requires that sites must be at least nationally important for earth science conservation. The GCR is therefore an evaluation of a selection of *sites* that were already known by experts, not a systematic survey of all rivers to find the best catchments or landform assemblages, independent of previous research. The more remote river sites and western catchments are probably under-represented as their research interest is only now being identified. However, there are mechanisms in place for updating the site coverage as new information becomes available.
- There is generally a high requirement for scientific detail in assessing the scientific interest of sites that are significant for recent and historic developments in fluvial geomorphological research. Werritty and McEwen (in press) also identify other reaches of rivers throughout Scotland that could equally well qualify for GCR status, but are currently excluded primarily because of their lack of existing or published research.
- To be of practical use in other forms of evaluation, the criteria for geomorphic assessment need to be disaggregated further. For example, the important geomorphic characteristics of a lacustrine-fluvial system, such as the River Balvag/Loch Lubnaig delta (central Scotland), would require to be identified at different scales (from planform to bank composition and stability).
- To understand the development of sites like the River Balvag delta, the links between geomorphic characteristics and vegetation succession need to be established. Several of the GCR sites identified as unique geomorphologically were already Sites of Special Scientific Interest based on their ecological status. There was, however, no requirement for holistic assessment of the river landscape, although some of the geomorphological categories have significant relevance for the biological interests (e.g. Table 23.3 columns 4, 5 and 6).
- The GCR evaluation process was carried out by professional geomorphologists with considerable experience in Scottish fluvial geomorphology. It is not designed as a scheme for frequent and simple use.

The GCR is best summarized as rigorous, fit for purpose and a useful over-arching framework for other kinds of geomorphic evaluation. Sites with GCR status would be expected to score highly, at least in terms of naturalness, in other geomorphological evaluation schemes.

23.3.2 *Geomorphological evaluation: the experience of river restoration and rehabilitation*

Another area where geomorphological evaluation has been developed for more routine use is in river morphology surveys for river restoration and rehabilitation (Sear, 1994). 'Geomorphological assessments aim to establish the character of a river in terms of stability, morphology, sedimentary and hydraulic characteristics, vegetation and engineering features ... establish the relationship between different hydraulic processes, which control erosion, deposition and channel form' (RSPB *et al.*, 1994, p104). Such surveys potentially provide data for both pure research and applied evaluations of river form and process, particularly river stability (see Brookes, 1988, 1991; RSPB *et al.*, 1994). From a management perspective, geomorphological information is used to identify suitable means for either river restoration to some perceived former 'natural' state or river rehabilitation to some desired 'natural' state. This includes the maintenance and enhancement of existing sites with varying degrees of human intervention. Variations between different schemes for morphological evaluation include the size of reach to be assessed, the speed of the survey (detailed project-specific survey or rapid assessment of a number of reaches) and the detail of information collected (restricted qualitative assessment or precise topographic survey). However, Sear (1994) argues that the geomorphological contributions of such schemes are frequently superficial, with principal focus on instream features.

The River Channel Morphology Assessment, developed by Brookes for the National Rivers Authority (NRA) with particular reference to lowland rivers, is designed for quick survey by non-geomorphologists (RSPB *et al.*, 1994). It incorporates four elements: scope of survey (some environmental context prior to survey); general description (site details which include valley description, land use of valley floor and planform description); channel characteristics (channel description, bank characteristics, substrate character); and management interpretation. Elements 1–3 are essentially descriptive and ordered at reducing scales of resolution from the basic environmental setting downwards, but the restricted nature of the data collected makes it difficult to place the site in a catchment context. The level of potential synthesis of information is low but it does allow basic characterization of a reach. More detailed analyses might involve assessment of stability of channel bed and banks. Element 4 (management interpretation) involves some interpretation from field observation (e.g. evidence of recovery from impact). Little attention, however, is paid to the relationship of the reach to its corridor and the evidence for past channel adjustment.

An example of more detailed site-based morphological evaluation is the Thorne's Stream Reconnaissance Survey. The purpose of this evaluation is primarily for river restoration and was developed from good practice in the USA (US Army Engineer Waterways Experiment Station; Thorne and Easton, 1994). The main details, strengths and limitations of the scheme are outlined in Table 23.1. Key contrasts with Brookes' scheme are the detail of the data collected, the mix of qualitative and quantitative assessment and the balance between description and interpretation.

Assessing or at least recording basic geomorphological attributes is widely accepted as a necessary part of conservation, restoration and resource management of river channels (e.g. Jaeggi, 1992; Wolfert, 1992; RRP, 1993; RSPB *et al.*, 1994). It is less well recognized as an important part of similar evaluation and management strategies for river corridors, floodplains, standing waters and whole catchments (Brookes, 1991; Newson, 1992; Van Velzen, 1992).

23.3.3 *Geomorphological evaluation: as part of habitat and ecological evaluation*

It is easiest to understand the role of geomorphology in shaping habitat structure, when the focus is the vitality, maintenance and/or restoration potential of the river channel itself. There are various objectives in including geomorphological assessment in ecological evaluations of rivers. Habitat foundation, structure, diversity and stability are partly or wholly determined by the nature and rate of geomorphological processes. However, it is the overall objectives of the different evaluation schemes that have determined the quantity and degree of geomorphological information required by each evaluation procedure. The three schemes reviewed here (River Corridor Survey, River Habitat Survey and SER-CON) can be used on their own or in combination, depending on the objectives of the survey.

23.3.3.1   River Corridor Survey

The classification and evaluation of river corridors is an important current research theme (see Gurnell *et al.*, 1994). The River Corridor Survey (RCS) developed from a need to record rivers and their corridors as part of the planning process for any major works affecting rivers (NRA, 1992; RSPB *et al.,* 1994), and it forms part of catchment inventories for river and floodplain features and conservation assessments in the UK. A river corridor survey identifies four broad zones encompassing a river and its floodplain (NRA, 1992):

- Aquatic zone (flow and current features, substrate and physical features)
- Marginal bank (plant communities, substrate and physical features)
- Bank zone (tree species, other plant communities, physical features)
- Adjacent land zone (habitat types, land use)

In addition, critical areas that are sensitive to damage, and 'non-recreatable' habitats are highlighted (NRA, 1992).

A major strength of RCS is its visual form of representation so that spatial relationships between geomorphic features can be evaluated from the survey (as well as the links between geomorphic and ecological characteristics from the descriptive recording of features in the field). Various limitations can be seen, however, in the geomorphological content. RCS is not specifically designed for detailed annotation although increasing detail can be provided if the remit of the survey so requires. Unscaled sketch maps are used for recording. The lack of precision means it is impractical to map-check or re-survey, make effective comparisons between sites, and evaluate change at the same site over time. It is also difficult to visualize the sketch map as part of the larger reach or river system, particularly in dynamic environments with regular channel switching. For example, in a recent RCS, the alluvial fan reach of the River Feshie (see Plate 4b) was described inadequately as an 'upland river with braiding and new channels' with few threats to the conservation interest of the area (Cobham Resource Consultants, 1994). The physical attributes noted during the survey are purely descriptive, and no framework is given for grouping or classifying features beyond the simple but robust sets of standard symbols. The ability to detect evidence for geomorphic change depends on the expertise of the assessor; field evidence may not be meaningful to the untrained eye.

23.3.3.2 River Habitat Survey

River Habitat Survey (RHS) is a system to classify rivers based on habitats of value to wildlife (NRA, 1995; Raven *et al.*, this volume) (Table 23.1). It provides an assessment of the physical structure of watercourses based on a 500m sample unit and as such incorporates most of the physical features assessment within SERCON (Section 23.3.3.3; Boon *et al.*, this volume). It is designed to be based on objective and robust field data. Currently a reference site network is being established particularly to provide a baseline to underpin the river typology. By 1996, there will be three reference sites per 10km × 10km square in England and Wales; one per 10km × 10km square in Scotland and Northern Ireland. Ten spot checks allow assessment of flow types and physical features as well as vegetation structure, land-use and vegetation type, channel dimensions, influences and special features. The strengths of this approach include consistency and objectivity in recording. Background map-based information (altitude, slope, predominant valley form) provides a basic, albeit simple, environmental context for the reach.

Limitations include the lack of ordering of, for example, the extent of channel features, which might assist interpretation and categorization as to type of river environment. Features typical of alluvial and bedrock channels are lumped together. There is also a lack of spatial ordering in the geomorphic assessment, other than the number of pools, riffles and points bars being noted. There is limited assessment of the river corridor (land use within 50m) or the transverse relationship between the channel and floodplain. Little evidence is noted of past channel adjustment (descriptive notation provided under Features of Special Interest) and how that relates to the diversity of habitat sites. There is no assessment of the role of vegetation in relation to geomorphic features or channel stability. The emphasis is therefore on descriptive recording rather than interpretative analysis (due in part to the nature of the recorder; see Table 23.1).

23.3.3.3 SERCON

SERCON, or 'System for Evaluating Rivers for Conservation', combines a database with a simple scoring system. In its initial form, it is designed primarily for ecological assessment and was developed alongside the NRA's scheme for River Habitat Survey. The objectives of SERCON (Boon *et al.*, this volume) were developed to ensure greater uniformity and rigour in data collection and evaluation, to provide a simpler way to communicate technical information to planners, developers and policy makers, and to enable assessments of rivers within a wide range of environmental quality. (Here 'quality' encompasses all three definitions in Section 23.2.2.) SERCON also aims in the longer term to incorporate other environmental characteristics, including the geomorphological interest and land-scape value of rivers.

SERCON is structured around the following principles:

(a) There is an identifiable set of attributes which cumulatively determine the nature and quality of river character. The different assessment criteria are physical diversity, naturalness, representativeness, rarity, species richness and special features.

(b) It is possible to assign scores to different attributes with a recognized level of confidence.

(c) The scoring is repeatable by different individuals.

(d) Scores and criterion indices can be interpreted to provide an assessment of environmental quality.

Field survey sheet headings include some geomorphological attributes: channel substrates (e.g. bedrock, gravel, artificial), fluvial/habitat features, channel and bank naturalness (percentage realignment, recovery), number of artificial structures (e.g. weirs, groynes), impacts (e.g. channelization) and special features (e.g. gorges). Where appropriate, some of these are scored with reference to a DAFOR index (dominant, abundant, frequent, occasional, rare). Nevertheless, the focus is on describing and interpreting the character of the channel and banks/riparian zone (the river corridor and floodplain). The listings of fluvial/habitat features are not grouped and include a variety of different features associated with different sorts of river environments at different scales (e.g. backwaters/connected cut-offs, riffles, submerged woody debris) without differentiation.

SERCON's conservation criteria and attributes developed for ecological assessment (e.g. physical diversity, naturalness, representativeness, rarity) are equally applicable to geomorphological assessment and could be re-evaluated in the development of a geomorphological module for SERCON (McEwen, 1994b). For example, the concept of naturalness is equally important in geomorphological evaluation. Increasing naturalness, as well as the ability of a geomorphological system to return quickly to pre-disruption form, enhances river value for earth science conservation, river rehabilitation, and in more general assessments of environmental quality. The capacity to describe and evaluate geomorphological elements systematically through a geomorphological module for SERCON would benefit routine assessment of river sites. It would also help in standardizing information collected and in establishing a national database of river channel characteristics. Moreover, it would facilitate better integration of ecological and geomorphological criteria as part of a more holistic approach to evaluating rivers. It would also have benefits in allowing more objective assessment of the deterioration to earth science conservation value associated with alternative river management strategies.

There are, however, some issues that would need to be addressed if a geomorphological module were to be developed for SERCON. For example, it is arguable whether geomorphological features can be weighted objectively and unambiguously in terms of value. On the one hand, increased diversity of landforms and processes at a site may increase geomorphological value. Alternatively, a restricted range of features tied to a specific set of controls may be of equally high value. In addition, the value of the whole geomorphological system may be greater than the sum of itemized or scored parts and it is important that SERCON is able to aggregate geomorphic features of value at different scales into an overall picture of geomorphological 'quality' at site and catchment levels. Similarly, there is a requirement to be able to aggregate evidence for change at different levels to get an overall picture of sensitivity at a site. SERCON also needs to incorporate change over time (both through repeat surveys and field evidence of change) and so be sensitive to both stable and transient features of river geomorphology. Finally, the aesthetic value of different sorts of riverscape is also notoriously difficult to quantify (see Leopold, 1969; Morisawa, 1971; Moseley, 1989), but is incorporated as an integral part of RIGS (Regionally Important Geological/ Geomorphological Sites) site assessment schemes.

23.4 Discussion

23.4.1 Lessons from existing methods

All the different evaluation methods include important elements of characterization, description, quantification and evaluation. Most evaluations give an indication of diversity of features but there is a frequent lack of attention to structure and spatial ordering of geomorphological elements. If geomorphological quality is to be evaluated, the properties represented must provide the means to assess uniqueness, rarity and representativeness (both from a pure geomorphological perspective and integrated in terms of habitat). Few evaluation schemes give explicit indication of change over time (at different temporal scales), or collect information that would provide insight into threshold behaviour and sensitivity to change. Degree of naturalness is frequently assessed with particular reference to degradation or improvement.

A number of lessons can be learned from the review of existing methods.

(a) It is important to identify elements of 'quality', in terms of all three definitions. Degree of degradation of different parts of the channel and floodplain is an important part of geomorphological evaluation.

(b) Surveys need to be standardized and comprehensive in their coverage of the essential elements of the geomorphological system being assessed, as well as focused and structured to the remit of the scheme.

(c) A solely site-based approach has inherent problems due to the interconnected nature of drainage basin controls.

(d) Key indicators of change need to be identified and systematically assessed. It is important to establish the ability or limitations of each evaluative scheme to incorporate system change.

(e) Surveys need to have well-defined objectives but, where possible, there should be compatibility in the structure and format of evaluation schemes to allow exchange and coordination of data.

(f) The need for specialist skills must be minimized (in all but special interest surveys). It is important to provide basic geomorphological training for ecological assessors and vice versa.

(g) There are variations in the degree to which geomorphological elements can be easily quantified (with meaning) in the field.

(h) It is essential that evaluation surveys possess accuracy and replicability.

23.4.2   *Recommendations for geomorphological evaluations*

In the light of the above review, the following recommendations are made to enhance the future use of geomorphological evaluations.

(a) There is a need for an integrated and well-structured assessment scheme which both accurately records and interprets morphological characteristics, and reinforces the inter-relationships between geomorphology and ecology in river system evaluation (e.g. in terms of channel, bank and floodplain stability). The schemes evaluated above display different strengths which can form the basis of good practice.

(b) Evaluation surveys must include the basis for comparison and therefore be nested at a hierarchy of scales. This involves setting the range of river channel form (at cross-section and extended reach scales) at a given site in a catchment context and in an appropriate environmental setting, standardizing information for repeat surveys at intervals, and building up an inventory of data on channel form and channel change. Information collected can then be used for comparison between reaches in the same and different catchments.

(c) Any evaluation needs to consider the spatial organization of landforms in channel, corridor and floodplain (e.g. spacing of pools and riffles; spacing of transverse ribs in coarse-grained channels; relative location of floodplain units of different ages; location of cut-offs and avulsions).

(d) Any assessment must incorporate evidence for change (over recent and historical timespans) and hence provide insight into system sensitivity. First, it is important to determine effective indicators of recent change in channel adjustment. This involves interpreting available evidence (field, aerial photograph) for the river's response to flows of different magnitudes and frequencies (e.g. identify landforms clearly formed by extreme events). Second, evaluation of sensitivity is difficult without monitoring. It is essential to understand present and past relationships between channel, area of recent reworking, corridor and floodplain when interpreting landform evidence.

This includes not only sensitivity to human intervention but also impact of changing climatic patterns or flood frequency on river systems.

(e) As geomorphological assessment moves from description and morphometric measurement in the field to interpretation and evaluation, statements about the level of confidence of that interpretation are essential. Some of the skills required to assess, for example, the propensity for channel change and the relationship between a channel, its river corridor and floodplain are in part intuitive, based on prior experience, and in part gained through understanding the scientific relationships and models of river system development. The required skills and knowledge base are more difficult for the non-geomorphologist to acquire, although significant advances may potentially be made by geomorphologists and ecologists working together on pilot site evaluations.

(f) It is important to recognize the needs, in terms of geomorphic information, of different sorts of surveys. This does not mean that routine proformas cannot be used as part of a more specialist analysis. A possible solution is to standardize and nest the proformas used for different purposes and different agencies dealing with river conservation and management. An example of nesting of geomorphological evaluations would be the quick morphological survey, the detailed morphological survey, and special interest site survey. The first two are distinguished by increasing detail in the resolution of the data collected and a shift in emphasis from description to evaluation. The last focuses on certain features of potential special interest while building on the descriptive and interpretative detail of the detailed morphological survey.

(g) It would be appropriate to have integrated geo-ecological assessment where ecology and geomorphology are clearly inter-related (e.g. floodplain successions, bank stability).

The value of systematic field-based 'bottom-up' approaches of river evaluation, such as SERCON, is as significant for earth science evaluation as it is for ecological evaluation. In addition, the incorporation of the principles of SERCON into the Scandinavian evaluation System Aqua (Willén *et al.*, this volume) provides the potential for consistent evaluation schemes across Europe (and the ability to set conservation value in different contexts). With the development of a geomorphological module for SERCON, there is an unrivalled opportunity to redress the imbalance in our knowledge of our fluvial geomorphological heritage, which has through necessity tended to rely heavily on a 'top-down' approach to site evaluation.

23.5   Conclusions

Effective geomorphological evaluation is a key issue in earth science conservation, assessments for river management and ecological habitat surveys. It is important to learn from the positive aspects and good practice identified in the comparisons between different evaluation schemes. Any ecological assessment which omits the geomorphological context at a reach and catchment level will be deficient at the interpretation stage in situations where the ecological habitat is closely underpinned by geomorphological processes. Similarly, any geomorphological survey which omits the environmental context allows incomplete interpretation of river regime. The structure of any evaluation scheme also needs to make sense from a geomorphological perspective, so that the links between system elements are highlighted and it is clear where the river fits in a classification of river type. Ideally, a coordinated system for geomorphological and ecological evaluations at a national/international level would be the most efficient use of expertise and data collecting resources. Specialist requirements can be nested within the hierarchy of evaluation schemes. Given the interdisciplinary nature of the issues associated with river resource management, it is essential that there is communication between experts in the development and use of evaluation schemes. Data collection at different scales of resolution can then be efficiently coordinated so as to be meaningful for both geomorphological and ecological assessment. Only then can there be an effective national database and interpretative resource through which to evaluate the quality of freshwater geomorphology and provide the necessary physical underpinning for river conservation and management strategies.

References

Björklund, G. (1987). Geovetenskaplig naturvärdering i internationellt perspektiv. *Uppsala University UNGI Report*, No. 67.

Bluck, B. (1976). Sedimentation in some Scottish rivers of low sinuosity. *Transactions of the Royal Society of Edinburgh*, **69**, 425–456.

Boon, P. J., Holmes, N. T. H., Maitland, P. S., Rowell, T. A. and Davies, J. (This volume). A system for evaluating rivers for conservation (SERCON): development, structure and function.

Brookes, A. (1988). *Channelized Rivers: Perspectives for Environmental Management*. John Wiley, Chichester.

Brookes, A. (1991). Geomorphology/geology. In: Gardiner, J. L. (Ed.), *River Projects and Conservation*. John Wiley, Chichester, 57–66.

Brunsden, D. and Thornes, J. B. (1979). Landscape sensitivity and change. *Transactions of the Institute of British Geographers*, **NS4**, 463–484.

Cobham Resource Consultants (1994). 'River Corridor Survey. River Feshie: Site Descriptions and Field Maps'. Report to Scottish Natural Heritage, Edinburgh.

Davidson, R. J. (1988). *A Strategy for the Conservation of Ontario's Earth Science Heritage*. Parks and Recreational Areas Branch, Ontario Ministry of Natural Resources, Toronto.

Ellis, N. V. (Ed.) (in press). *An Introduction to the Geological Conservation Review*. Joint Nature Conservation Committee, Peterborough.

Erikstad, L. (1994). Kvartærgeologisk verneverdige områder I Norge. Evaluering av et landsomfattende registreringsmateriale. *NINA Utredning*, **57**, 95–128.

Gordon, J. E. (1994). Conservation of geomorphology and Quaternary sites in Great Britain: an overview of site assessment. In: Stevens, C., Gordon, J. E., Green, C. P. and Macklin, M. G. (Eds), *Conserving Our Landscape. Proceedings of the Conference on Conserving our Landscape: Evolving Landforms and Ice-age Heritage*. English Nature, Peterborough, 11–21.

Gurnell, A. M., Angold, P. and Gregory, K. J. (1994). Classification of river corridors: issues to be addressed in developing an operational methodology. *Aquatic Conservation: Marine and Freshwater Ecosystems*, **4**, 219–231.

Hoey, T. and Ferguson, R. I. (1994). Numerical simulation of downstream fining by selective transport in gravel bed rivers: model development and illustration. *Water Resources Research*, **30**, 2251–2260.

Jaeggi, M. N. R. (1992). Sediment regime and river restoration. In: *Ecological Rehabilitation of Floodplains. Contributions to the European Workshop, Arnhem, The Netherlands 22–24 September 1992.* Report No 11-6 Internationale Kommission für die Hydrologie des Rheingebietes (CHR/KHR), The Hague, 147–155.

Kellerhals, R., Church, M. and Bray, D. I. (1976). Classification and analysis of river processes. *Journal of the Hydrological Division of Civil Engineers,* **102,** Proceedings Paper 12232, 813–829.

Knighton, A. (1987). River channel adjustment—the downstream dimension. In: Richards, K. S. (Ed.), *River Channels: Environment and Process.* Blackwell, Oxford, 95–128.

Leopold. L. B. (1969). Quantitative comparison of some aesthetic factors among rivers. *U.S. Geological Survey Circular,* **620.**

Lewin, J. and Weir, M. J. C. (1977). Morphology and recent history of the lower Spey. *Scottish Geographical Magazine,* **93,** 45–51.

McEwen, L. J. (1994a). Site assessment criteria for the conservation of fluvial systems: the Scottish experience. In: Stevens, C., Gordon, J. E., Green, C. P. and Macklin, M. G. (Eds), *Conserving Our Landscape. Proceedings of the Conference on Conserving our Landscape: Evolving Landforms and Ice-age Heritage.* English Nature, Peterborough, 131–136.

McEwen, L. J. (1994b). *A Feasibility Study on the Extension of SERCON to the Assessment of Fluvio-geomorphological Features of Nature Conservation Interest.* Report to Scottish Natural Heritage, Edinburgh.

Morisawa, M. E. (1971). Evaluating riverscapes. In: Coates, D. R. (Ed.), *Environmental Geomorphology.* Publications in Geomorphology, State University of New York, Binghampton, 91–106.

Mosely, M. P. (1989). Perceptions of New Zealand river scenery. *New Zealand Geographer,* **45,** 2–13.

Newson, M. (1992). *Land, Water and Development: River Basin Systems and their Sustainable Management.* Routledge, London.

Newson, M. and Sear, D. (1994). River conservation, river dynamics, river maintenance: contradictions? In: Stevens, C., Gordon, J. E., Green, C. P. and Macklin. M. G. (Eds), *Conserving Our Landscape. Proceedings of the Conference on Conserving our Landscape: Evolving Landforms and Ice-age Heritage.* English Nature, Peterborough, 125–130.

NRA (1992). *River Corridor Surveys: Methods and Procedures.* Conservation Technical Handbook No. 1, Bristol.

NRA (1995). *River Habitat Survey Field Methodology Guidance Manual.* Bristol.

Ontario Ministry of Natural Resources (1981). *A Framework for the Conservation of Ontario's Earth Science Features.* Ontario Ministry of Natural Resources, Toronto.

Petts, G. E., Gilvear, D. J. and Large, A. R. G. (1990). *Water Level Variations Along the River Spey Between Loch Insh and the Feshie Confluence.* Report by Freshwater Environments Research Group, Loughborough University, to the Nature Conservancy Council, Peterborough.

Petts, G. E., Large, A. R. G., Greenwood, M. T. and Bickerton, M. A. (1992). Floodplain assessment for restoration and conservation: linking hydrogeomorphology and ecology. In: Carling, P. A. and Petts, G. E. (Eds), *Lowland Floodplain Rivers: Geomorphological Perspectives.* John Wiley, Chichester, 217–234.

Priestley, R. and Crozier, M. (1990). *New Zealand Landform Inventory.* 2nd approximation. Occasional Paper No. 4, Physical Geography, Research School of Earth Sciences, Victoria University of Wellington, NZ, Parks and Recreational Areas Branch, Wellington.

Ratcliffe, D. (Ed.) (1977). *A Nature Conservation Review.* Cambridge University Press, Cambridge.

Raven, P. J., Fox, P., Everard, M., Holmes, N. T. H. and Dawson, F. H. (This volume). River Habitat Survey: a new system for classifying rivers according to their habitat quality.

RRP (1993). The River Restoration Project Phase 1: The feasibility study report for the River Restoration Project. Unpublished report, Ecological Consultancy, Biological Sciences, University of East Anglia, Norwich.

RSPB/NRA/RSNC. (1994). *The New Rivers and Wildlife Handbook.* RSPB, Sandy.

Sear, D. (1994). River restoration and geomorphology. *Aquatic Conservation: Marine and Freshwater Ecosystems,* **1,** 169–177.

Smith-Meyer, S. (1995). Geogaglig klassifisering av norske vassdrag. *NVE Norges Vassdrags og Energiverk Publikasjon,* Nr **10.**

Schumm, S. A. (1977). *The Fluvial System.* Wiley-Interscience, New York.

Thomas, D. S. G. and Allison, R. J. (1993). *Landscape Sensitivity.* John Wiley, Chichester.

Thorne, C. R. and Easton, K. (1994). Geomorphological reconnaissance of the River Sence, Leicestershire for river restoration. *East Midlands Geographer,* **17,** 40–50.

Van Velzen, E. H. (1992). Hydraulic roughness of floodplain forest. In: *Ecological Rehabilitation of Floodplains. Contributions to the European Workshop, Arnhem, The Netherlands 22–24 September 1992.* Report No 11–6 Internationale Kommission für die Hydrologie des Rheingebietes (CHR/KHR), The Hague, 131–136.

Warren, A. (1993). Naturalness: a geomorphological approach. In: Goldsmith, F. B. and Warren, A. (Eds), *Conservation in Progress.* John Wiley, Chichester, 15–24.

Werritty, A. and Brazier, V. (1991). Geomorphological aspects of the proposed Strathspey flood alleviation scheme. In: Johnson, R. C., Piper, B. S., Acreman, M. C. and Gilman, K. (Eds), *Flood Alleviation in Upper Strathspey. Modelling and Environment Study* Vol II. Supporting Report 7. Institute of Hydrology, Wallingford. Report for the Nature Conservancy Council for Scotland, Edinburgh.

Werritty, A. and Brazier, V. (1994). Geomorphic sensitivity and the conservation of fluvial geomorphology SSSIs. In: Stevens, C., Gordon, J. E., Green, C. P. and Macklin, M. G. (Eds), *Conserving Our Landscape. Proceedings of the Conference on Conserving our Landscape: Evolving Landforms and Ice-age Heritage.* English Nature, Peterborough, 100–109.

Werritty, A., Brazier, V., Gordon, J. E. and McManus, J. (1994). Geomorphology. In: Maitland, P. S., Boon, P. J. and McLusky, D. S. (Eds), *The Fresh Waters of Scotland: a National Resource of International Significance.* John Wiley, Chichester, 65–88.

Werritty, A. and Ferguson, R. I. (1983). Bar development and channel changes in the gravelly River Feshie, Scotland. *Special Publication International Association of Sedimentologists,* **6,** 181–193.

Werritty, A. and McEwen, L. J. (in press). Fluvial geomorphology sites in Scotland. In: *Fluvial Geomorphology. Geological Conservation Review.* Chapman and Hall, London.

Willén, E., Andersson, B. and Söderbäck, B. (This volume). System Aqua: a biological assessment tool for Swedish lakes and watercourses.

Wolfert, H. P. (1992). Geomorphological differences between river reaches: differences in nature rehabilitation potentials. In: *Ecological Rehabilitation of Floodplains. Contributions to the European Workshop, Arnhem, The Netherlands 22–24 September 1992.* Report No 11-6 Internationale Kommission für die Hydrologie des Rheingebietes (CHR/KHR), The Hague, 137–144.

24 WATERWAYS BIRD SURVEY: EVALUATION OF POPULATION MONITORING AND APPRAISAL OF FUTURE REQUIREMENTS

R. H. W. Langston, J. H. Marchant and R. D. Gregory

Summary

1. The Waterways Bird Survey is an effective monitor of riparian breeding birds in the UK. However, it is labour intensive and, consequently, limited in geographical representation.

2. The new Breeding Bird Survey addresses the problems of the effort required, sampling strategy and the geographical coverage in providing a national bird population monitoring scheme. However, as rivers are under-represented, several river specialist species are not effectively monitored.

3. The River Habitat Survey measures the physical features of rivers, but there is a need for a complementary, biological measurement. This can be provided by a modified form of Waterways Bird Survey which can be used for river catchment management, in particular to assess the effects of operational works.

24.1   Introduction

The Waterways Bird Survey (WBS) is a national bird census scheme, started in 1974, which uses a linear territory mapping method to monitor population change and habitat usage by a suite of bird species associated with river corridors (Table 24.1). The WBS is undertaken by volunteers, coordinated by the British Trust for Ornithology (BTO). Indices of year-to-year change can be calculated for 19 bird species. Additional species are recorded, but their frequency of occurrence is too low to permit indexing.

Since 1994, a new scheme has taken on the role of national population monitoring. This is the Breeding Bird Survey (BBS), which is funded jointly by the BTO, Joint Nature Conservation Committee (JNCC) and the Royal Society for the Protection of Birds (RSPB). The BBS adopts a transect method in a stratified, random sample of 1 km squares, involves two census visits in each breeding

Table 24.1 Bird species monitored by WBS, with an indication of their population trends from 1974 (commencement of WBS) to 1993 (after Marchant and Balmer, 1994).

Mallard	++
Coot	+
Oystercatcher	+
Curlew	+
Mute swan	+
Little grebe	s
Tufted duck	s
Moorhen	s
Dipper	s
Pied wagtail	c
Kingfisher	c
Grey wagtail	c
Sedge warbler	m
Whitethroat	m
Lapwing	—
Redshank	—
Common sandpiper	—
Reed bunting	—
Yellow wagtail	— —

Key: +, Some increase; ++, Steady increase; s, Stable; c, Cold weather fluctuations; —, Some decrease; — —, Steady decrease; m, Fluctuating migrants.

season, and covers all habitats and a wider geographical spread than the detailed mapping censuses of WBS and the Common Birds Census (CBC). This development in national population monitoring has prompted the evaluation of WBS to determine whether it has a continuing role to play, potentially in a modified form (Marchant *et al.*, 1995). The first step in this process has been to identify who needs WBS-type data, and why.

24.2 Why Monitor Bird Populations Along Waterways

The assessment of the conservation importance of freshwater habitats requires (among other things) information on species diversity, frequency of occurrence, and habitat use by different taxa. Birds are highly visual indicators of river habitat quality (e.g. Marchant and Hyde, 1980; Tyler and Ormerod, 1992) and so are very suitable subjects for biological monitoring. This is particularly true because national population statistics are available to provide the context for site-based and regional trends, whilst also contributing to the overview of the status of bird populations in the UK.

The impact of operational works can be more fully assessed by monitoring biological as well as physical parameters. There are several published studies of impacts on birds of river management operations (e.g. Williamson, 1971; Williams,

1980) which have contributed to the development of management advice for furthering wildlife conservation on rivers (RSPB *et al.*, 1994).

24.3 Who Uses (or Could Potentially Use) a Waterways Bird Monitoring Scheme?

There are several key sectors which currently use, or could be using, waterways birds monitoring results and/or methodology:

(a) *Statutory conservation agencies.* JNCC and the country agencies have a statutory responsibility to conserve and, where practicable, to enhance wild species and wildlife habitats (e.g. UK Biodiversity Action Plan: Department of the Environment *et al.*, 1994).

(b) Other conservation bodies, such as RSPB, the Wildlife Trusts Partnership.

(c) The Environment Agency (EA) has a duty to assess and monitor the conservation status of inland and coastal waters and associated lands.

(d) *Environmental consultancies.* The WBS provides baseline data for individual sites and contextual data at larger spatial scales. A nationally recognized scheme provides a methodological standard for widespread application in site assessment.

24.4 Objectives of the Evaluation of WBS

Having established the *why* and the *who* of waterbird monitoring, the evaluation had the following objectives:

(a) Interrogation of the WBS database to determine its effectiveness for measuring changes in waterbird populations, notably in relation to the EA's catchment management plans.

(b) Review methodologies of WBS, BBS, River Corridor Survey (RCS) and River Habitat Survey (RHS) (Raven *et al.*, this volume) to identify potential links for development, in collaboration with the EA.

24.5 Methods of Evaluation

The methodologies of WBS, BBS, RHS and RCS are summarized in Table 24.2 and indicate that recording units and survey season for waterbird and river habitat surveys are broadly similar. Further investigations concentrated on: (a) the selection, distribution and type of sample sites, (b) the frequency and duration of visits, and (c) the effectiveness of WBS and BBS in monitoring bird species associated with rivers. In order to assess (c), data from WBS and BBS for 1994 were compared, making allowance for the differences in variability between the two schemes (Gregory *et al.*, 1994).

24.6 How Effective is WBS?

Population indices can be calculated for different geographical areas, for example EA regions, but not all EA regions are well represented. WBS plots are chosen by observers, rather than being randomly selected—hence the paucity of sites in

Table 24.2 General comparisons of survey methods for rivers and for waterbirds in the UK.

Method	Coverage	Recording units	Survey season	Visits	Fieldworker status
River Corridor Survey	England and Wales; physical features; complete river corridors	500m; features mapped precisely	End April to early October	1	Professional (EA)
River Habitat Survey	UK; physical features; random river sites	500m; 50m spot checks	May to June	1	Professional (EA)
Rivers Environmental Database: Linear Bird Survey	EA Anglian Region; all bird species; complete river corridors	500m for birds; habitat features mapped precisely	April to June	3	Professional
Waterways bird survey: standard mapping census	UK; waterbirds only; habitats mapped; observer-selected sites	River or canal; lengths mostly 3–5km; bird territories mapped precisely; 500m stretches for habitat data	Late March to early July	Normally 9; each of 1–2 hours	Volunteer (BTO)
Waterways bird survey: mapping visits treated as transects	(see above)	River or canal; mostly 3–5km for birds; 500m stretches for habitat data	Variable within late March to early July	Variable in range 1–9; each of 1–2 hours	Volunteer (BTO)
Breeding bird survey	UK; all bird species; all habitats; habitats coded; random sites	1km squares of National Grid; 10×200m transects	April to June	2; each about $1\frac{1}{2}$ hours	Volunteer (BTO)

parts of the UK. The WBS is labour-intensive, in terms of both the number of visits and data preparation, and this has limited the sample size. WBS is a territory mapping survey in which the survey plots are linear. This fact permitted a comparison of results derived from territory mapping and transect methodologies on the same sample of plots. Observers were asked to record all birds seen on each mapping visit as well as submitting territory maps in 1992 and 1993. These two years of data were used to assess the precision of estimates of population change by running simulations of different numbers of visits.

The precision of estimates of year-to-year change is greater with increased number of survey visits in a season, but acceptable levels of precision in estimates of population change could be achieved with 3–5 visits (Figure 24.1). The recommendation of five visits for WBS is based on a combination of improved precision and the ability to monitor particular species of river specialists for which more than three visits are necessary, as these are considered to be (conservation) priority species on rivers. There is a trade-off between reducing the number of visits and, hence, observer effort, whilst retaining the ability to detect population changes in these specialists, since they are the species most likely to be affected by changes to the river environment.

Figure 24.2 shows that WBS is better than BBS at monitoring river specialists (e.g. kingfisher, grey wagtail, goosander and common sandpiper), because it targets

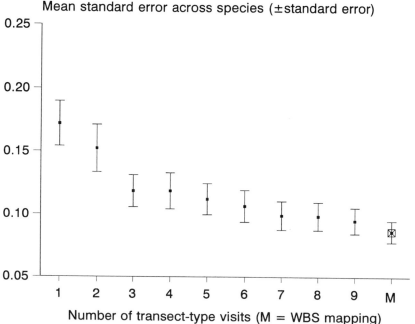

Figure 24.1   Standard errors of estimation of population changes between 1992 and 1993, using WBS visits as transects, in relation to the number of visits made and in relation to standard WBS mapping (M). To simulate different numbers of transects, visits were selected from the standard 9 per survey according to a regular pattern.

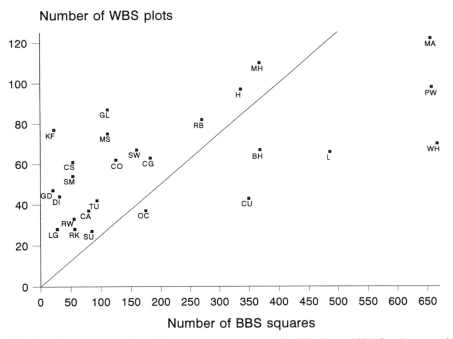

Figure 24.2   Incidence of waterside bird species on WBS plots and BBS plots in 1994. Species appearing on fewer than 25 WBS plots are omitted.

Key: Standard BTO two-letter codes have been used for species: (BH) Black-headed Gull; (CA) Cormorant; (CG) Canada Goose; (CO) Coot; (CS) Common Sandpiper; (CU) Curlew; (DI) Dipper; (GD) Goosander; (GL) Grey Wagtail; (H) Grey Heron; (KF) Kingfisher; (L) Lapwing; (LG) Little Grebe; (MA) Mallard; (MH) Moorhen; (MS) Mute Swan; (OC) Oystercatcher; (PW) Pied Wagtail; (RB) Reed Bunting; (RK) Redshank; (RW) Reed Warbler; (SM) Sand Martin; (SU) Shelduck; (SW) Sedge Warbler; (TU) Tufted Duck; (WH) Whitethroat.

river habitats. Figure 24.2 shows the line x = 4y. Species occurring on fewer than four times as many BBS as WBS plots lie between this line and the WBS axis and would be monitored more precisely by that scheme. The sampling regime for BBS is designed to cover a wide spectrum of habitat types, but tends to under-represent rivers as a result of transect orientation.

WBS territory mapping has the advantage, for site appraisal, of enabling detailed temporal and spatial assessment of the effects on birds of changes in physical features (e.g. Marchant and Hyde, 1980; Taylor, 1982). These studies were limited by the inadequacies of habitat recording, which is overcome by the development of RHS (Raven *et al.*, this volume). Monitoring habitat structure and biological features in a complementary way will assist in assessing the impacts of change to the river habitat.

A single-season study along the River Wye in 1977 enabled a comparison to be made of a managed stretch with an adjacent stretch of unmanaged river (Williams, 1980). On 10.5 km of managed river there were 11 breeding species and (excluding sand martin) an overall density of 43 territories per 10 km, compared with 25 species and 146 territories per 10 km along the unmanaged stretch. These examples have helped inform published advice on management practices which further wildlife conservation on rivers (Lewis and Williams, 1984; RSPB *et al.,* 1994).

24.7 How Can Waterways Bird Monitoring Complement the EA's Work?

(a) Monitoring enables the EA to quantify its effectiveness in furthering conservation.

(b) RHS classifies rivers on the basis of physical features. Waterways bird monitoring can complement RHS by providing a biological measure of habitat quality (akin to similar measures available for invertebrates, for example) and enable the performance of catchment management plans to be monitored.

(c) Waterways bird monitoring before and after operational works by the EA can provide biological data relating to impacts and recovery time. Distinctions can be made between EA management effects and other effects.

24.8 Conclusions

The best attributes of existing monitoring schemes should be modified to develop a new waterways bird monitoring scheme. Such a scheme must complement other, similar schemes, and allow population monitoring at different spatial scales, from individual river sections to country level.

Acknowledgements

The authors thank the Environment Agency (then the NRA) for funding the evaluation of the Waterways Bird Survey. The WBS received funding (until recently) from JNCC, on behalf of the Countryside Council for Wales, English Nature, Scottish Natural Heritage, and the Department of the Environment (Northern Ireland).

References

Department of the Environment *et al.* (1994). *Biodiversity: the UK Action Plan.* Command 2428. HMSO, London.

Gregory, R. D., Marchant, J. H., Baillie, S. R. and Greenwood, J. J. D. (1994). A comparison of population changes among British breeding birds using territory mapping and point count data. In: Hagemeijer, E. J. M. and Verstrael, T. J. (Eds), *Bird Numbers 1992. Distribution, Monitoring and Ecological Aspects.* Proceedings of the 12th International Conference of IBCC and EOAC, Noordwijkerhout, The Netherlands. Statistics Netherlands, Voorburg/Heerlen and SOVON, Beek-Ubbergen, 503–512.

Lewis, G. and Williams, G. (1984). *Rivers and Wildlife Handbook.* RSPB/RSNC, Sandy.

Marchant, J. H. and Balmer, D. E. (1994). Waterways bird survey 1992–1993 population changes. *BTO News* **191,** 8–10.

Marchant, J. H. and Hyde, P. A. (1980). Aspects of the distribution of riparian birds on waterways in Britain and Ireland. *Bird Study, 27,* 183–202.

Marchant, J. H., Langston, R. and Gregory, R. D. (1995). *An Evaluation of the Waterways Bird Survey as a Monitor of Regional and National Populations of Waterbirds, and an Appraisal of its Future Role.* BTO Research Report No. 155 to the National Rivers Authority. British Trust for Ornithology, Thetford.

Raven, P. J., Fox, P., Everard, M., Holmes, N. T. H. and Dawson, F. H. (This volume). River Habitat Survey: a new system for classifying rivers according to their habitat quality.

RSPB/NRA/RSNC (1994). *The New Rivers and Wildlife Handbook*. RSPB, Sandy.

Taylor, K. (1982). *BTO Waterways Bird Survey Instructions*. British Trust for Ornithology, Tring.

Tyler, S. J. and Ormerod, S. J. (1992). A review of the likely causal pathways relating the reduced density of breeding Dippers *Cinclus cinclus* to the acidification of upland streams. *Environmental Pollution,* **78,** 49–56.

Williams, G. (1980). Swifter flows the river. *Birds,* **8,** 19–22.

Williamson, K. (1971). A bird census study of a Dorset dairy farm. *Bird Study,* **18,** 80–96.

25 ASSESSING THE CONSERVATION VALUE OF A MEDITERRANEAN RIVER BASIN (SADO, PORTUGAL)

I. Moreira, M. G. Saraiva and P. Pinto

Summary

1. This chapter describes a comprehensive approach, developed by a multi-disciplinary research team, assessing some biotic and abiotic parameters of the Sado river basin in the south west of Portugal. The main purpose of the project is criteria formulation for river basin planning, and management for nature conservation and water quality improvement.

2. An initial survey of climate, lithology, geomorphology and soil characteristics allowed the definition of seven large landscape units. A grid of about 60 sampling sites was established, where a set of field observations were made on flora (aquatic and riparian), fauna (macroinvertebrates, fishes and birds) and landscape. For each one, an index of quality was assessed and computed for the surveyed sites.

3. Some low values for the biotic indices related to the water environment were explained by the high variability of the hydrological features in a Mediterranean context, aggravated by severe conditions of drought during recent years. The indices related to river corridor features showed better conservation values.

25.1 Introduction

Freshwater quality assessment is an important task in river basin or catchment planning, regulation of water and river corridor uses, and the establishment of policy and management guidelines. In general, it requires the integration of several multi-disciplinary approaches and different criteria to address the complexity and diversity of a river system subjected to a wide array of biophysical and anthropic influences.

This chapter describes a comprehensive approach, developed by a multi-disciplinary research team for assessing the physical, chemical, biological, scenic and cultural features of the Sado river basin. The main aim of this project is the formulation of criteria for environmentally sound catchment planning and management for nature conservation and water quality improvement.

25.2 Basin Characteristics

The Sado river basin (7,000 km²) in the south west of Portugal (Figures 25.1, 25.2) was chosen as a case study. This basin, influenced by a typical Mediterranean climate producing a marked seasonality in the tributary streams, has been little studied from a biological point of view. The basin may be divided into seven large landscape units (Figure 25.3), each one relatively homogeneous in terms of lithology, geomorphology and soils (Table 25.1). The estuarine zone (unit 1)— comprising marshland, industrial and tourist areas—was not included in this study. The typically Mediterranean climate, with a very dry and hot summer and rainfall concentrated in winter, induces marked intermittent river flows. Therefore, the large drainage basin has little correspondence in flow magnitude, owing to the drier characteristics of the climate and lower altitude in southern Portugal. This seasonality of flow coupled with the need of water for agriculture led the administration to implement several dam projects, both for irrigation and for water supply. Under pristine conditions, only the reach furthest downstream has permanent flow, and headwaters can experience no flow for up to 5 months each year (Figure 25.4).

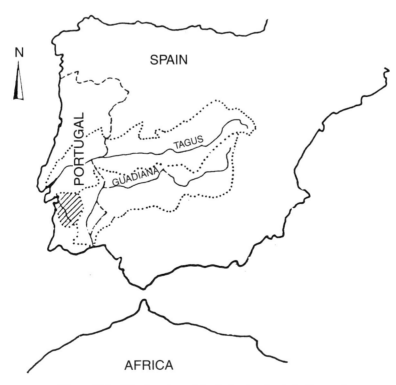

Figure 25.1 The location of the Sado river basin in Portugal.

Figure 25.2   A watercourse in the Sado River basin, Portugal. (Photo: P. J. Boon)

Table 25.1   Geomorphological, lithological and soil characteristics of the landscape units.

Unit	Geomorphology	Lithology	Soil
1	Low and level land	Detritic rocks	Arenosols, solonchaks
2	Sloping (altitude 50–100 m)	Detritic rocks; deep alluvial deposits	Fluvisols along the valleys; arenosols, gleyic and cambisols
3	Idem 2	Detritic rocks; gravel plateaux	Fluvisols along valleys, arenosols, luvisols and planosols
4 and 5	Rolling (altitude 50–300 m)	Schist-grauwacke rocks and metamorphic series	Leptosols and some cambisols; intensive erosion
6	Level and gently sloping (100–200 m)	Idem 4 and 5; basic and ultrabasic rocks	Planosols, vertisols and vertic soils
7	Undulating and rolling	Idem 4 and 6; granite and quartzodiorite	N–leptosols; NW–vertisols and vertic soils

The typical natural vegetation in the catchment is the *Quercus* evergreen forest dominated by cork oak, *Q. suber* (units 2, 3, 5 and part of 4) and in the poorest soils and dryer climate, the holm oak, *Q. rotundifolia* (unit 6), or both (unit 7). The Portuguese oak *Q. faginea* is the dominant tree in the higher altitudes of unit 4. The exploitation of those oak stands is associated with extensive cattle raising and cereal crop rotations. Units 2 and 3 are dominated by large irrigated areas of rice,

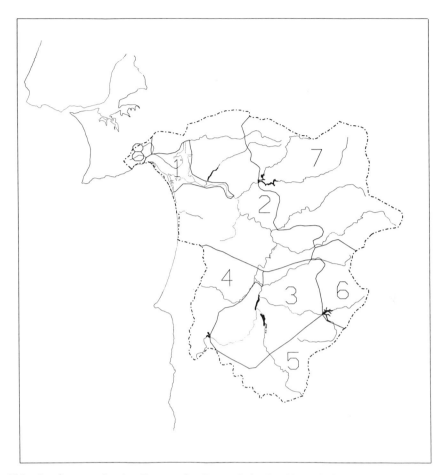

Figure 25.3   Landscape units: 1—Estuary; 2—Lower Sado; 3—Upper Sado; 4—West Headwaters; 5—
South Headwaters; 6—East Headwaters; 7—North Headwaters.

maize, sunflower and tomato. In unit 2, pine and eucalyptus exploitation are important.

In most areas population density is very low (less than 50 inhabitants per km^2), with the exception of the urban areas of Setúbal, Évora and Beja.

25.3   Methods

A grid of about 60 sampling sites, covering the seven landscape units, was established in the watercourses of the Sado basin. At each site, a set of examples was taken or field observations were made to obtain information on six aspects: riparian flora, aquatic flora, macroinvertebrates, fish, birds and aesthetic quality. For each one, an index of quality, scored in five classes and ranging from bad quality (class I) to good quality (class V), was assessed and computed for the surveyed sites. Flow regime and other physical and chemical characteristics were evaluated to complement the previous information surveyed. Water quality sampling refers only to spring data (April) because of the severe drought conditions in this region.

Phytosociological observations of the riparian vegetation were undertaken in a standard minimal area according to Braun-Blanquet (1979). A conservation index of the riparian vegetation was assessed based on the density of typical trees and shrubs and the herbaceous coverage. Aquatic plants were also surveyed in 100 m reaches to determine a macrophyte conservation index (Ferreira, 1994), computed using the mean percentage cover of the different types of plants, the total richness of lotic species, and the number of limnetic habitats.

The aquatic and riverside breeding birds were surveyed using the I.P.A. point count method (Blondel *et al.*, 1970) with a counting period of 10 minutes. An index of ornithological importance was computed based on the total richness, the number of aquatic and riverside species, and the number of classified species according to the Portuguese Vertebrate Red Data Book (Cabral *et al.*, 1990). The macroinvertebrate communities were sampled with a hand net operated for 5 minutes in all the major habitat types present (Hellawell, 1978). Macroinvertebrate diversity and the degree of species tolerance were used to compute the Alba Biotic Index (Alba-Tercedor *et al.*, 1983). Fish were sampled by electrofishing, and a fish biotic index developed to evaluate the degree of stress to which these communities are subjected. The index is based on the number of species, number of Iberian endemic species, and the dominance of the pollution-tolerant species.

The aesthetic value of the river corridor was also assessed through a public preference survey on river landscape quality. This technique was developed as part of a larger research project on the aesthetic quality of river landscapes, using a set of photographs taken in the Sado river basin for which aesthetic appreciation scores have been assigned (Saraiva, 1995).

As well as these specific surveys, a detailed biophysical characterization of the basin was undertaken, collecting and producing cartographic information about climate, geology and lithology, land morphology, soils and other physical features. All data produced are organized and stored using a digital database and a Geographical Information System based on ARC/INFO software. The integration of cartographic and alphanumerical data is performed by the GIS, allowing also the development of spatial and quantitative analysis required for conservation and management purposes.

25.4 Results

Results obtained during the first two years of research are shown in Figure 25.5 which summarizes the computed scores assigned, based on a five-class scale from highest to lowest conservation value.

The assessment of riparian and aquatic vegetation recorded 354 taxa in 79 families, of which 132 (37%) were associated with lotic habitats. Eleven phytosociological associations were described (Costa *et al.*, in press). The best conserved riparian forest communities are characterized by ash (*Fraxinus angustifolia*), poplar (*Populus nigra*), alder (*Alnus glutinosa*) and, in temporarily inundated places,

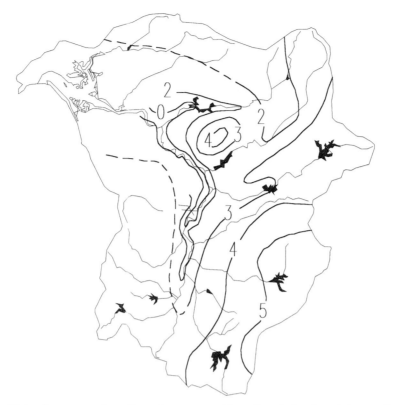

Figure 25.4   Average number of months per year with no flow during the pristine condition.

willow (*Salix atrocinerea*). A new thermo-mediterranean community of the south-west Iberian Peninsula was proposed—*Salicetum atrocinereo-australis* association. This community, associated with willow (*Salix salvifolia* ssp. *australis*), is typical of torrential rivers. The three successive degraded communities are associated with bramble thicket (*Rubus ulmifolius*), the sedges of *Juncus effusus* and *Scirpus holoscenus* (*Holoschoenus romanus* ssp. *australis*). The index for riparian vegetation (Figure 25.5A) shows a reasonable conservation status; the macrophyte conservation index, connected with aquatic vegetation (Figure 25.5B), shows lower values, related to the reduced number of limnetic habitats and cover values for each species.

Most of the recorded breeding birds are passerine species associated with riverside habitats. The few aquatic bird species included widespread residents such as mallard *Anas platyrhynchos*, moorhen *Gallinula chloropus* and kingfisher *Alcedo atthis*. The little bittern *Ixobrychus minutus*, a summer visitor usually inhabiting large reedbeds, was also found in several watercourses—even in sites with only small curtains of reeds. Fish assemblages in the Sado basin are very poor both in numbers of individuals and in numbers of endemic species, resulting in lower scores for the fish biotic index (Figure 25.5D), compared with the more important nearest basins (Tejo and Guadiana). *Lepomis gibbosus* (the most abundant), *Rutilus alburnoides, Barbus bocagei* and *Leuciscus pyrenaicus* are the more important species.

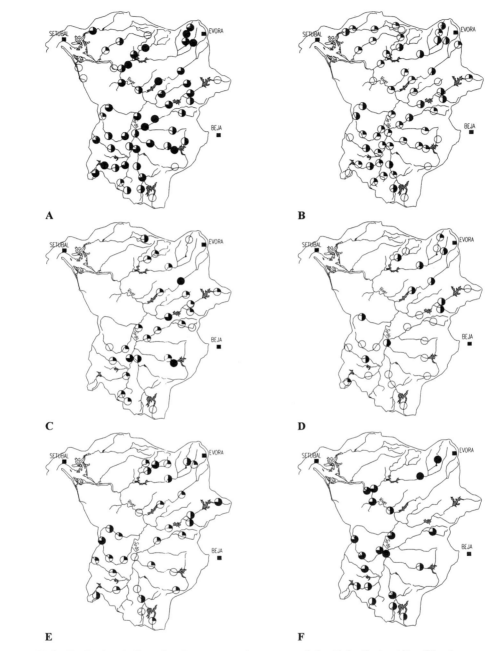

Fig. 25.5 Evaluation indices for the conservation status of the Sado Basin: (A)—Riparian vegetation conservation index; (B)—Macrophyte conservation index; (C)—Birds biotic index; (D)—Fish biotic index; (E)—Alba Biotic Index; (F)—Aesthetic quality of river corridor index. ●, Very high; ◕, High; ◑, Medium; ◔, Low; ○, Very low to nil.

The macroinvertebrate communities are dominated by taxa tolerant of poor water quality (Oligochaeta and Chironomidae), with the more sensitive taxa (Plecoptera) present in only a few sites.

The results from the first samples collected in spring for water quality analysis indicate that most sites surveyed were polluted, probably due to agro-industrial effluents, domestic sewage, fertilizers and, in particular cases, abandoned pyrite mines. The results are in accordance with the low values of the Alba Biotic Index (Figure 25.5E).

Aesthetic quality assessment showed some variation where the highest scores were related to a greater diversity of slope, contrast and vegetation cover (Figure 25.5F). Reaches with undisturbed riparian vegetation and with boulders and gravel present were scored higher, associated with more variety and naturalness (Saraiva, 1995).

25.5   Final Comments and Further Development

The high variability in hydrological features of Mediterranean rivers is a key to understanding the structure and the organization of these systems (Boulton and Suter, 1986; Williams, 1987). The Sado basin has experienced severe drought during the last three years, which may explain some of the low values for biotic indices. Two main trends can be identified—one is the relative concordance between indices related to the water environment, such as the Alba index on biological water quality, the fish biotic index and the macrophyte conservation index; the second is the relative harmony between the indices related to the terrestrial part of the river corridor—the riparian vegetation conservation index, birds biotic index, and aesthetic quality index. These trends will be assessed in future annual surveys, and their results will be confirmed through quantitative analysis. The combination and aggregation of these indices with physical and chemical water parameters is also under way. However, to create an integrated index for all aspects is very difficult, owing to the heterogeneity and complexity of lotic ecosystems and to the marked differences between the aquatic and terrestrial components. Integrated studies for Mediterranean rivers are scarce particularly in southern Portugal (Morais, 1995; Saraiva *et al.*, 1995).

The following steps will be needed to achieve the project goals:

- Identification of reaches of highest interest for conservation.
- Detailed study of a catchment or sub-basin that shows highest conservation interest, (Alcáçovas river basin) with the aim of producing management guidelines and recommendations for water authorities, farmers and other users.
- Assessment of human impacts (especially agricultural practices) on rivers.
- Promotion of buffer zones and buffer strips through planting riparian areas, coupled with new approaches to irrigation and with environmental education guidelines for farmers.

River basin plans have been implemented recently in Portugal and their output is expected over the next two years. The development of methods for assessing features contributing to river 'quality' should prove valuable in promoting strategies for integrated river management in a Mediterranean context.

Acknowledgements

To Direcção Geral do Ambiente and Junta Nacional de Investigação Científica e Tecnológica, for the financial support of this project under the Programme for the Environment 1995/97. To the research team for relevant comments and data input: Dr J. Bernardo, Dr A. Cancela d'Abreu, Dr J. C. Costa, Dr M. T. Ferreira, Dr M. Lousã, Dr F. Nunes Correia, Dr R. Rodrigues, F. Aguiar, H. Alves, F. Bernardo, H. Botelho, O. Freire, I. Freitas, J. P. Martins, J. Rabaça, A. Ramos, I. Ramos, M. Serra, P. Simões. To Centro Nacional de Informação Geográfica, Instituto Geográfico do Exército, and Instituto Superior Técnico, for institutional facilities. To Dr P. Boon and Dr John Gardiner, for the revision of the manuscript and relevant suggestions.

References

Alba-Tercedor, J., Sanchez Ortega, A. and Guisasola, A. (1983). *Caracterizacion de los cursos permanentes de agua de la cuenca del rio Adrta: factores fisicoquimicos, macroinvertebrados acquaticos y calidad de las aguas*. Facultad de Ciencias, Universitad de Granada.

Blondel, J., Ferry, C. and Frochot, B. (1970). La méthode des Indices Ponctuels d'Abondance (I.P.A.) ou des relevés d'avifaune par stations d'écoute. *Alauda*, **41**, 55–71.

Boulton, A. J. and Suter, W. D. (1986). Ecology of temporary streams—an Australian perspective. In: Decker, P. and Williams, W. D. (Eds), *Limnology in Australia*. CSIRO/Junk Publ., Melbourne, 313–327.

Braun-Blanquet, J. (1979). *Fitosociologia. Bases para el estudio de las comunidades vegetales*. Ed. H. Blume, Madrid.

Cabral, M. J. M., Magalhães, C. P., Oliveira, M. E. and Romão, C. (1990). *Livro Vermelho dos Vertebrados de Portugal, Volume I—Mamíferos, aves, répteis e anfíbios*. Serviço Nacional de Parques, Reservas e Conservação da Natureza, Lisboa.

Costa, J. C., Lousã, M. and Paes, A. P. (in press). As comunidades ribeirinhas da bacia hidrográfica do rio Sado (Alentejo, Portugal). *Actas I. Colóquio Internacional de Ecologia da Vegetação*, Universidade de Évora.

Ferreira, M. T. (1994). Criação de um índice de avaliação do valor conservacionista de locais dulciaquícolas com base em características habitacionais e macrófitos aquáticos. *Actas 4ª Conferência Nacional do Ambiente*, Lisboa.

Hellawell, J. M. (1978). *Biological Surveillance of Rivers: A Biological Monitoring Handbook*. Water Research Centre, Stevenage.

Morais, M. M. (1995). *Organização espacial e temporal de um rio temporário mediterrânico (rio Degebe, Bacia hidrográfica do Guadiana). Descritores fisico-químicos e produtores primários, comunidade bentónica de invertebrados*. Dissertação de Doutoramento, Universidade de Évora.

Saraiva, M. G. (1995). *O Rio como Paisagem. Gestão de Corredores Fluviais no Quadro do Ordenamento do Território*. Dissertação de Doutoramento, Instituto Superior de Agronomia, Universidade Técnica de Lisboa, Lisboa.

Saraiva, M. G., Pinto, P., Rabaça, J. E., Ramos, A. and Revez, M. (1995). Protection, reclamation and improvement of small urban streams in Portugal. In: Harper, D. M. and Ferguson, A. J. D. (Eds), *The Ecological Basis for River Management*. John Wiley, Chichester. 275–287.

Williams, D. D. (1987). Movements of benthos during the recolonization of temporary streams. *Oikos*, **27**, 265–272.

26 A System for Evaluating Rivers for Conservation (SERCON): Development, Structure and Function

P. J. Boon, N. T. H. Holmes, P. S. Maitland, T. A. Rowell and J. Davies

Summary

1. SERCON (System for Evaluating Rivers for Conservation) is a broad-based technique for river evaluation, designed to be applied with greater consistency than present methods, and to provide a simple way of communicating technical information to decision makers. Its applications include the identification of important rivers for conservation and potentially the monitoring of river rehabilitation schemes.

2. SERCON has been developed for use within the whole of the UK. Rivers are evaluated as a series of contiguous stretches termed ECSs (Evaluated Catchment Sections). Although catchment characteristics are included in the assessment, the principal focus of SERCON is on the physical, chemical and biological features of river channels and banks, riparian zones, and associated floodplains.

3. SERCON evaluates data on 35 attributes, grouped within six conservation criteria: Physical Diversity, Naturalness, Representativeness, Rarity, Species Richness, and Special Features. Eleven human impacts are also assessed. Each attribute (or impact) is scored, then weighted and combined by SERCON to produce a composite index for each criterion. Users may also record 'Additional Features of Importance', although these do not form part of the scored data entry. Unscored background data on physical features, catchment characteristics, and water quality provide the context for each evaluation.

4. Guidance is provided on how scores and indices should be interpreted, and where they fit into a SERCON classification (A–E) of conservation quality.

5. SERCON may be used either in conjunction with a printed manual, or as a PC version in Microsoft Windows™. The latter incorporates an extensive photo gallery as part of the on-screen Help facility, and can provide a range of output reports, including both text and graphs.

26.1 Introduction

The concept of 'conservation quality' may be understood in a variety of ways. Society values rivers, as it does many other elements of the landscape, from several different perspectives. A river may be considered particularly important for its habitats and wildlife, for its recreational opportunities, its natural beauty, its contribution to the local economy or, in some cultures, its religious significance. Even though these values are not mutually exclusive, the factors which contribute to 'quality' in each case are often not closely related, so it is inappropriate to attempt to produce some total assessment of 'conservation quality' (Boon *et al.*, 1994; Boon and Howell, this volume). This chapter considers the term only in the restricted sense of nature conservation value and its assessment.

A simple model describing the broad relationship between the conservation value of a given river and the appropriate management regime was proposed by Boon (1992) (Figure 26.1). In this, as conservation value decreases, so management regimes change from 'preservation' where the river is still essentially 'natural', to 'dereliction' (where rivers have become so degraded that in the short or medium term it is not cost-effective to consider any form of rehabilitation). Between these two extremes are 'limitation' (of catchment development), 'mitigation' (of damaging activities), and 'restoration' of lost or degraded habitats. Evaluation is needed, therefore, both in the selection of high quality sites for protection, and in the full range of activities which fall under the general heading of 'management'.

In the UK, the main agencies with direct or indirect responsibilities for river conservation and management are the Environment Agency (EA) in England and Wales, the Scottish Environment Protection Agency (SEPA) in Scotland, the successor bodies to the Nature Conservancy Council (NCC)—English Nature (EN), Countryside Council for Wales (CCW), Scottish Natural Heritage (SNH), and the Joint Nature Conservation Committee (JNCC)—and the Environment and Heritage Service of the Department of the Environment in Northern Ireland. The EA needs to utilize river conservation evaluations when carrying out its statutory duty to 'further', and its free-standing duty to 'promote', nature conservation; it also utilizes such outputs when carrying out its other functions (e.g. land drainage, water resource management), when producing catchment management plans, and in its role in consenting activities affecting rivers but which are carried out by others. For the statutory conservation agencies, river evaluation has been focused chiefly on the selection of Sites of Special Scientific Interest (SSSIs) (Boon, 1991, 1995; English Nature, 1992) and more recently

NATURAL/
SEMI-NATURAL

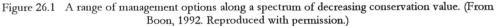

DEGRADED

Preservation   Limitation   Mitigation   Restoration   Dereliction

Figure 26.1 A range of management options along a spectrum of decreasing conservation value. (From Boon, 1992. Reproduced with permission.)

potential Special Areas of Conservation (SACs) under the EC Habitats Directive. Selection of the former has been carried out with reference to the *Guidelines for Selection of Biological SSSIs* (Nature Conservancy Council, 1989), which draw on the principles set out in *A Nature Conservation Review* (NCR) (Ratcliffe, 1977).

The NCR was the first comprehensive attempt in Britain to produce an evaluation of nationally important nature conservation areas. It contains descriptions of 816 sites, of which 99 are fresh water, 18 being exclusively or mainly riverine. They were evaluated using 10 principal criteria: representativeness, naturalness, diversity, rarity, potential value, size, fragility, recorded history, position in an ecological/geographical unit, and intrinsic appeal. These criteria have achieved a broad level of acceptance, and they have continued to influence conservation evaluations, including those of rivers.

One of the fundamental problems with this approach is the inherent subjectivity of many of the criteria (see Usher, this volume). While it is recognized that subjectivity will always be an element of conservation evaluation, such a process becomes effectively unworkable if values are left undefined. Unless an evaluation procedure can be used that is rigorous and repeatable it is also extremely difficult both to describe the value of rivers in anything other than vague terms, and to compare the relative merits of different rivers. For example, descriptions of five rivers or streams in the NCR contain the following phrases:

> ...a good example of a torrential, upland, limestone stream (Cowside Beck)
> ...a good example of a short, west-coast, spating, oligotrophic river (R. Strontian)
> ...the best example of a lowland, base-poor stream (Oberwater)
> ...the river ... is fairly intact (R. Lathkill)
> ...probably representative (Knock Ore Gill)

The rationale for developing SERCON (System for Evaluating Rivers for Conservation) was the perceived need for a more rigorous method which, for example, would provide evidence using evaluated data for a wide range of clearly defined features to support descriptions such as those in the NCR.

The SERCON project has been guided from its inception by a series of clearly stated objectives:

(a) To encourage greater rigour and repeatability in data collection and evaluation.
(b) To identify gaps in the scientific knowledge of specific rivers.
(c) To enable the assessment of rivers within a wide range of environmental quality (i.e. not only those that qualify for selection as SSSIs).
(d) To provide a simpler way of communicating technical information to planners, developers and policy makers.
(e) To aid in the assessment of the rehabilitation potential of degraded rivers.
(f) To construct a tool to assist in predicting the impact of different development options on river conservation value.

(g) To establish a framework for extending the principles of SERCON to the evaluation of other attributes of rivers (e.g. important geomorphological, landscape, or recreational features), as well as those related to fauna, flora and habitats.

An introduction to SERCON has been given by Boon *et al.* (1994). This chapter sets out the stages in the design of the project, and describes the structure and functioning of the system. Full details are contained in the manual to SERCON Version I (Boon *et al.*, 1996).

26.2   Preliminary Work

The need for some better system for assessing the conservation value of rivers, and a possible methodology, began to come together during 1991 with some exploratory studies on the 'River Conservation System' (RCS). This is a computer-based system designed for evaluating rivers in South Africa (O'Keeffe *et al.*, 1987). The RCS requires the user to enter scores for a wide range of attributes considered important for river evaluation, such as 'percentage natural vegetation in catchment', 'bank stability', 'number of indigenous fish species', and 'naturalness of physical features'. These scores are weighted by the RCS to indicate the relative importance of each attribute, with the output consisting of three composite conservation scores—for the river, the biota and the catchment.

Early in 1992 the RCS software was applied to the evaluation of 10 Scottish rivers, chosen to represent a spectrum of perceived conservation value. Despite many gaps in the data, a lack of precision in much of the information, and the inappropriateness of parts of the system for evaluating Scottish rivers, the results were broadly in line with expectations. Although SERCON gained impetus from the RCS, SERCON evolved rapidly to become quite distinct.

Work on SERCON began in May 1992. System design was the responsibility of a Project Development Group (PDG) comprising the first four authors of this chapter, assisted for part of the time by a Project Officer (the fifth author). The PDG was guided by a Steering Group, composed of one member of each of the statutory conservation bodies (SNH, EN, CCW, JNCC), together with a representative of the National Rivers Authority (NRA), the Association of Directors and River Inspectors of Scotland (ADRIS), and the Industrial Research and Technology Unit (IRTU, a government agency sponsored by the Department of Economic Development in Northern Ireland) to ensure that the project was applicable to the whole of the UK.

The RCS had been developed in South Africa with the assistance of an 'expert group'—freshwater ecologists throughout the country whose views were sought at various stages of the work. This principle was retained for SERCON, and a 'Specialist Group' was set up, comprising more than 150 individuals and 25 organizations (both statutory and voluntary) spanning a wide range of expertise relevant to conservation (Table 26.1).

Table 26.1   Composition of the SERCON Specialist Group.

Principal specialisms of individuals consulted	Numbers of individuals
Mammals	4
Birds	2
Amphibia	1
Fish	16
Invertebrates	35
Macrophytes	11
Algae	13
Fungi	2
Protozoa	2
Bacteria	1
Wetlands	6
Hydrology	10
Water quality	11
Geomorphology	3
Landscape	2
Catchment planning	1
Environmental assessment	1
Public perception	3
General	37
TOTAL	161

Organizations consulted

Botanical Society of the British Isles	National Rivers Authority
Biological Records Centre	National Trust
British Dragonfly Society	National Trust for Scotland
British Trust for Ornithology	River Purification Boards
Countryside Council for Wales	Royal Society for Nature Conservation
English Nature	Royal Society for the Protection of Birds
Fisheries Society of the British Isles	Scottish Natural Heritage
Friends of the Earth	Scottish Wildlife Trust
Institute of Biology	Vincent Wildlife Trust
Institute of Ecology and Environmental Management	Water PLCs
Institute of Fisheries Management	Wildfowl and Wetlands Trust
Keep Scotland Beautiful	Water Research Centre

26.3   Designing the System

26.3.1   The early stages

The first task was to decide which characteristics of rivers should be included within the evaluation scheme. Following lengthy discussions, the PDG circulated a provisional list of proposed attributes to the Specialist Group, accompanied by a brief definition of each, a statement of why they were considered to be important, and an indication of how they should be measured. At this stage, no attempt was made to structure the system or to link attributes in any way. Members of the Specialist Group were asked to register their acceptance or rejection of each attribute and, if they wished, to propose others for inclusion. The results of this first round of consultation indicated a broad degree of approval (Table 26.2) although a number of amendments and refinements were introduced directly as a result of the exercise.

26.3.2 Spatial scope of SERCON

SERCON has been designed for use within the UK as a whole although it is recognized that information on some aspects may not be available yet for Northern Ireland. The *principles* of SERCON could also be applied outside the UK, but the system requires for each country custom-built databases (e.g. checklists of native and alien riverine species), an ability to define what might be expected in terms of

Table 26.2 The percentage of Specialist Group respondents (n = 123) agreeing with the inclusion of a given attribute in SERCON ('Yes'), compared with those disagreeing ('No') or those undecided.

Attribute		% Yes	% No	% Undecided
A: Physical Descriptors				
A1:	Mean daily flow in lower reaches of ECS	81	6	13
A2:	Stream flow stability	86	3	11
A3:	River length	86	3	11
A4:	Stream order	78	11	11
A5:	Catchment size	85	2	13
A6:	Channel profile—gradient and sinuosity	87	2	11
A7:	Altitude at source	72	12	16
A8:	Altitudinal range in catchment	82	2	16
A9:	Solid geology of catchment	88	2	10
A10:	Drift geology of catchment	88	2	10
B: Catchment Characteristics				
B1:	Extent of conifer plantation	88	2	10
B2:	Extent of arable farming	89	0	11
B3:	Extent of open water	75	9	16
B4:	Extent of urban development	86	4	10
B5:	Population density	75	11	14
C: Physical and Chemical Characteristics of Channel and Floodplain				
C1:	Channel naturalness and substrate diversity	84	1	15
C2:	Diversity of fluvial features	83	5	12
C3:	Variety of marginal features	82	5	13
C4:	Importance of on-line natural lakes	72	9	19
C5:	Naturalness of banks	84	2	14
C6:	Trophic status of lower reaches of ECS	82	2	16
C7:	Floodplain: unrecreatable water-dependent habitats	88	2	10
C8:	Floodplain: recreatable water-dependent habitats	81	3	16
C9:	Gorge habitats	76	10	14
C10:	Riparian strip	85	3	12

continued

Table 26.2   *Continued.*

Attribute		% Yes	% No	% Undecided
D: Biotic Characteristics				
D1:	Native fish: species richness	89	1	10
D2:	Aquatic invertebrates: range of communities/species richness	91	0	9
D3:	Invertebrates of river margins and banks	82	6	12
D4:	Aquatic macrophytes: range of communities/species richness	90	0	10
D5:	Amphibia in channel and floodplain habitats	81	3	16
D6:	Breeding birds: species richness	89	1	10
D7:	Mammals: species richness	86	1	13
D8:	Red Data Book species: international	86	3	11
D9:	Red Data Book species: national	89	1	10
D10:	Protected or scheduled species	87	2	11
D11:	Regionally important macrophytes and wetland plants	84	2	14
E: Aquatic Impacts				
E1:	Water abstraction: groundwater	89	0	11
E2:	Water abstraction: surface water	90	0	10
E3:	Sewage effluent	89	1	10
E4:	Toxic/industrial effluent	89	1	10
E5:	Flow regulation by dams	85	2	13
E6:	Inter-river transfers	83	3	14
E7:	Man-made structures in rivers	79	3	18
E8:	Channel impoundment for navigation	76	6	18
E9:	Channelization	83	2	15
E10:	Acidification	84	2	14
E11:	Angling	84	2	14
E12:	Other recreational pressures	85	3	12
E13:	River-based fish farms	87	2	11
E14:	Slurry, silage, mine drainage, etc.	82	3	15
E15:	Introduced fish species	84	2	14
E16:	Introduced invertebrate species	80	4	16
E17:	Introduced macrophyte species	81	3	16
E18:	Introduced mammal species	77	6	17

physical and biotic features, and an understanding of the particular pressures and impacts on that country's river systems.

SERCON has been developed principally for use at the scale of the catchment and subcatchment. In most cases, it is considered inappropriate to use SERCON to evaluate rivers as units from source to mouth because of the characteristic downstream continuum of change in their physical and biological properties. Instead, a river is divided into a series of shorter Evaluated Catchment Sections (ECSs) and each one evaluated separately. This procedure allows a more manageable approach to data collection, and permits comparisons of conservation value along the river and between similar sections on other rivers.

ECS boundaries can be located using data derived from maps on features such as change in slope or the point at which major tributaries enter the main river. An example of ECS division is shown in Figure 26.2 for the River Teith (Central Scotland). The Teith (Figure 26.3) rises as a series of steep gradient, high altitude headwaters. It has a middle section of very low gradient, separated from those sections upstream and downstream by two large lakes (Loch Voil and Loch Lubnaig), and a lowland reach where the gradient increases again. These characteristics are obvious markers for dividing the river into three ECSs.

Each ECS constitutes a single river (including subsidiary channels) and will often be the main stem; if associated tributaries are to be evaluated this is done separately. The length of an ECS is usually between 10 km and 30 km, unless the ECS is (a) the whole of a short river or tributary, (b) a short length of river separated from other ECSs by major physical features such as lakes or large waterfalls, (c) a short river which should be divided into ECSs on the basis of natural divisions, but this results in one or more of the ECSs being shorter than 10 km. There are two exceptions which may be used with caution: where an ECS contains a continuous length of at least 5 km that contrasts in perceived quality to the remainder of the ECS and is thus deemed to merit separate evaluation; and in pre- and post-project appraisals of rehabilitation schemes where a continuous length of at least 1 km of grossly modified river is situated in a much longer and uniform ECS.

The principal focus of SERCON assessments is the river channel and its banks, together with the adjacent floodplain habitats such as wet meadows and marshlands. Although SERCON also includes background data on catchment land use, less emphasis is placed in the assessment on catchment characteristics than on those of the river and its floodplain. This is not intended to undervalue the importance of the catchment as the fundamental unit in river conservation, but rather because of the complexity of designing a system for evaluating entire catchments, and the difficulty of correlating river conditions downstream with events that may be occurring in the catchment far upstream.

26.3.3   Structure of SERCON

A preliminary study by the PDG of the South African RCS (O'Keeffe *et al.*, 1987) highlighted three problems. First, the RCS is comparatively structureless, providing information on only three basic facets: the river, the biota, and the catchment. Second, the output scores are an amalgamation of attributes considered valuable and thus given a positive score (e.g. number of endemic fish species), and those that detract from conservation value and assigned a negative score (e.g. impact of toxic industrial waste). Third, the RCS functions rather like a 'black box' system, and is therefore relatively impenetrable to the user. Each of these difficulties has been resolved during the development of SERCON.

SERCON comprises a combination of scored and unscored elements (Figure 26.4). Those that are scored relate to a suite of conservation criteria and a range of human impacts; those that are unscored are included either as background data to set the context in which evaluations are made, or so that important features can be highlighted which cannot be evaluated using the scored criteria. The outputs

1: River Profile

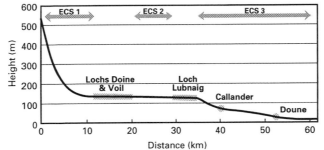

2: Catchment Geology

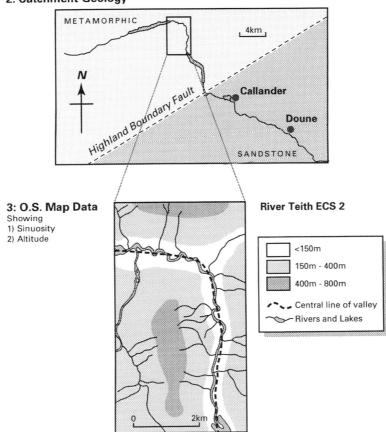

Figure 26.2 The use of data on river profiles, catchment geology, sinuosity and altitude to assist in determining ECS boundaries for the River Teith (Central Scotland).

Figure 26.3   River Teith, Central Scotland (Photo: Ian Fozzard).

from both parts of SERCON are essential to a balanced interpretation of the conservation value of an ECS.

The design of SERCON has taken place in parallel with the development of the EA's River Habitat Survey (RHS) (Raven *et al.*, this volume). RHS provides a consistent approach to creating inventories of river corridor features, and enables stretches of river to be classified according to their habitat quality. It is intended that the data gathered on physical features by RHS should also provide most of the physical information components in SERCON, and work is continuing to ensure that both systems are fully integrated.

26.3.3.1   Conservation criteria

SERCON has been designed so that evaluations can be related readily to the wider field of nature conservation assessment. This has been achieved by fitting each attribute into a framework of generally accepted conservation criteria—a slightly modified subset of those used in *A Nature Conservation Review* (Ratcliffe, 1977). In all, there are 35 attributes grouped to contribute to the overall assessment of six criteria: Physical Diversity, Naturalness, Representativeness, Rarity, Species Richness, and Special Features. However, in practice the 35 attributes require data from only 15 principal areas, as for some attributes (especially those relating to species) the data may be manipulated in different ways to throw light on different aspects of conservation value. For example, a list of fish species present can be used to evaluate the naturalness, representativeness, rarity and species richness of the fish assemblages in the ECS. Table 26.3 lists the attributes used in SERCON

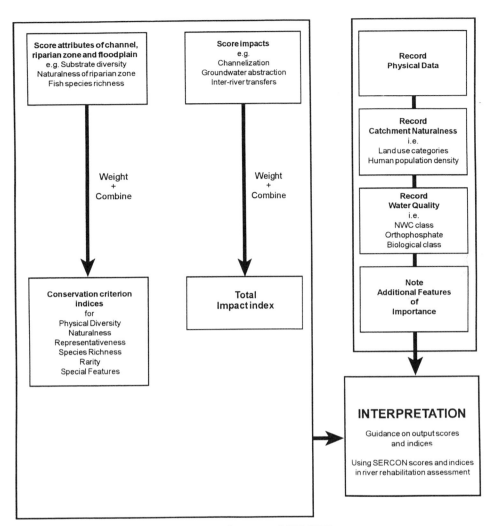

Figure 26.4   Structure of SERCON.

(together with their codes, e.g. NA 1, RE 2, etc.) and shows how they are grouped under the six conservation criteria.

One important feature of the SERCON project has been a detailed critique of the use of terms such as 'naturalness' and 'representativeness'. Although these have been used widely in conservation evaluation (e.g. Margules and Usher, 1981), their interpretation in the context of river systems has rarely been discussed. The following paragraphs provide a broad definition of each of the six conservation criteria as used in SERCON.

Physical Diversity. The physical diversity of rivers and their corridors is an important criterion in conservation assessment—not least because the riverine substrates, fluvial features and vegetation structure have a profound impact on biotic diversity. In SERCON, the term 'physical diversity' refers both to the variety of physical features present and their relative proportions, and is considered (deliberately) without reference to the size or nature of the ECS. However, some river systems have a natural limitation to their range of physical features, while others have an artificially wide range owing to disturbance. These situations are

Table 26.3 The final suite of attributes selected for SERCON grouped under six conservation criteria and under 'Impacts'. Weights allocated to criteria and attributes are also given.

Conservation criteria		Weight
PDY:	Physical Diversity	3
NA:	Naturalness (NA 1–4: NA 'A')	5
	Naturalness (NA 5–8: NA 'B')	1.5
RE:	Representativeness	3
RA:	Rarity	2
SR:	Species Richness	2.5
SF:	Special Features	1
Physical Diversity		
PDY 1:	Substrates	4
PDY 2:	Fluvial Features	5
PDY 3:	Structure of Aquatic Vegetation	1
Naturalness		
NA 1:	Channel Naturalness	5
NA 2:	Physical Features of the Bank	3.5
NA 3:	Plant Assemblages on the Bank	2
NA 4:	Riparian Zone	2
NA 5:	Aquatic and Marginal Macrophytes	4
NA 6:	Aquatic Invertebrates	3.5
NA 7:	Fish	2.5
NA 8:	Breeding Birds	1
Representativeness		
RE 1:	Substrate Diversity	3
RE 2:	Fluvial Features	5
RE 3:	Aquatic Macrophytes	4
RE 4:	Aquatic Invertebrates	4
RE 5:	Fish	2.5
RE 6:	Breeding Birds	1
Rarity		
RA 1:	EC Habitats Directive/Bern Convention Species (+rare in UK)	4.5
RA 2:	Scheduled Species	4
RA 3:	EC Habitats Directive Species (but not rare in UK)	3.5
RA 4:	Red Data Book/Nationally Scarce Macrophyte Species	2
RA 5:	Red Data Book/Nationally Scarce Invertebrate Species	2
RA 6:	Regionally Rare Macrophyte Species	1
Species Richness		
SR 1:	Aquatic and Marginal Macrophytes	4.5
SR 2:	Aquatic Invertebrates	4.5[1], 3[2]
SR 3:	Fish	2
SR 4:	Breeding Birds	1

continued

Table 26.3 *Continued.*

Conservation criteria		Weight
Special Features		
SF 1:	Influence of Natural On-line Lakes	3.5
SF 2:	Extent and Character of Riparian Zone	4.5
SF 3:	Floodplain: Recreatable Water-dependent Habitats	2
SF 4:	Floodplain: Unrecreatable Water-dependent Habitats	4.5
SF 5:	Invertebrates of River Margins and Banks	2.5
SF 6:	Amphibians	1.5
SF 7:	Wintering Birds on Floodplain of ECS	1.5
SF 8:	Mammals	2.5
Impacts		
IM 1:	Acidification	3
IM 2:	Toxic/Industrial/Agricultural Effluent	4
IM 3:	Sewage Effluent	4.5
IM 4:	Groundwater Abstraction	3
IM 5:	Surface Water Abstraction	2
IM 6:	Inter-river Transfers	1
IM 7:	Channelization	4.5
IM 8:	Management for Flood Defence	2.5
IM 9:	Man-made Structures	2.5
IM 10:	Recreational Pressures	2
IM 11:	Introduced Species	2

[1]Weighting used for species data.
[2]Weighting used for BMWP family data.

addressed in other parts of SERCON such as Naturalness, Representativeness and Impacts.

Naturalness. A natural habitat in the UK is a rare commodity because so much has been changed profoundly from its original state by human activities. Naturalness is a criterion which is virtually impossible to define objectively, yet is highly prized in conservation assessment (Ratcliffe, 1977; Margules and Usher, 1981), and attempting to 'specify and sustain what is natural' is one of the commonest goals of ecologists (Shrader-Frechette and McCoy, 1993).

The distinction between 'natural', 'semi-natural' and 'artificial' cannot be rigidly defined and arbitrary separations are required. Because of this, determining 'naturalness' requires considerable knowledge of habitats and their response to human intervention and natural processes over time, and requires an element of professional judgement. The apparent overlap between questions relating to community naturalness, as opposed to community representativeness, is removed by posing questions such as: 'What proportion of the total flora or fauna is native?' In this way, a semi-objective indication of species naturalness can be derived, but a more subjective approach is required for assessing the naturalness of fluvial and morphological features.

In SERCON, eight separate assessments of naturalness are made. In structural terms, the criterion is assessed by considering how close the river's physical features and vegetation are to the perceived pristine state. At the level of plant and animal communities, a more radical approach is adopted based upon the degree to which the native aquatic and riparian communities have been infiltrated by non-native (alien) species. However, during tests on SERCON it became clear that some degraded rivers had their Naturalness index raised simply by virtue of a lack of alien species. For this reason, SERCON indices for Naturalness are given as two separate outputs: Naturalness 'A' (NA 1–4) refers to the physical features and vegetation characteristics of the channel, banks and floodplain; Naturalness 'B' (NA 5–8) refers to the presence of alien species.

To obtain a more complete picture of the true naturalness of plant and animal communities, the user must also take into account the indices for Species Richness, Representativeness, and Naturalness. A high value for the Naturalness 'B' index alone might be obtained where there are no aliens, but where communities are impoverished due to pollution or habitat destruction. Low values for Species Richness and Representativeness indices would indicate an ECS in a very unnatural state. On the other hand, high values for all three indices would suggest an ECS in a more natural state, lacking aliens.

Species of amphibians and mammals are not sufficiently numerous in the UK to evaluate using the Naturalness assessment procedure. Instead, both are considered under the criterion of Special Features.

Representativeness. In SERCON, 'Representativeness' is taken to be synonymous with 'typicalness' as used in *A Nature Conservation Review* (Ratcliffe, 1977), and refers to how representative the attributes are for an ECS in relation to its location, catchment geology, etc. When assessing a river's conservation value it is important to take account of 'typical' or 'representative' features as well as atypical or unusual ones. Moreover, representativeness also impinges on the value attributed to other features. For example, 'richness' (expressed as numbers of features or species) may detract from conservation value if not representative for the type of river being assessed.

A prerequisite for assessing representativeness is a classification system into which any ECS can be fitted, and from which an expected range of attributes can be predicted. In some cases, SERCON uses the botanical classification of British rivers based on 10 River Community Types (Holmes, 1983; NCC, 1989; Holmes and Rowell, in press). However, for the assessment of substrate diversity and fluvial features, the use of this classification is likely to be an interim measure until a new system is available.

Rarity. While conservation assessments should not overvalue the presence of particular species, the occurrence of rare or protected species should certainly be included in an evaluation. Of course, the size and distribution of populations may change with time, new information may come to light, criteria for assessing rarity may alter, and so the status of individual species may change. The reference tables accompanying this particular section of SERCON have been compiled from several sources: e.g. Schedules 1, 5 and 8 of the Wildlife and Countryside Act 1981, the annexes of the EC Habitats Directive, etc.

The categories within Rarity (Table 26.3) are listed in a hierarchy; species shown in a higher category are not listed again in a lower one and thus will only contribute once to the Rarity index. For example, freshwater pearl mussel (*Margaritifera margaritifera*) is only evaluated under RA 1: 'Riverine species (native to the UK) listed in Annexes II and IV of the EC Habitats Directive or Appendices I and II of the Bern Convention and considered rare in the UK' and not in RA 2: 'Riverine species protected under Schedules 1, 5 and 8 of the Wildlife and Countryside Act 1981, and the Wildlife (Northern Ireland) Order 1985.

Species Richness. The terms 'species richness' and 'species diversity' are sometimes used as if they were synonymous. In SERCON, Species Richness refers solely to the number of native species (sometimes taxa) known to occur within an ECS. Species diversity (usually described by one of several diversity indices) is an expression that takes into account both the numbers of species and their relative abundance. Species diversity is not assessed in SERCON because of the difficulty in obtaining quantitative as well as qualitative data for assessment, and because of the widespread use of species richness in conservation evaluation. A species-rich ECS is not necessarily considered to have a higher conservation value than one with fewer species, unless the ECSs are of a comparable nature. For example, oligotrophic streams in the Scottish Highlands are naturally poor in rooted aquatic macrophytes but rich in bryophyte species, compared with lowland systems which have more rooted macrophytes but few bryophytes. Thus, caution is needed when interpreting Species Richness indices.

Special Features. The category of Special Features represents a suite of attributes which may contribute greatly to the overall conservation value of an ECS but which are not commonly encountered, or are not appropriately assessed using descriptors such as Naturalness, Representativeness, Species Richness, etc. For example, the presence of water shrew (*Neomys fodiens*) or water vole (*Arvicola terrestris*) on a river is unquestionably an important conservation feature, but their comparative rarity prevents their inclusion within any of the other SERCON conservation criteria. Similarly, as there are very few mammal species associated with rivers in the UK, it is inappropriate to evaluate mammals in terms of criteria such as Species Richness. Of the eight attributes listed as Special Features, four relate to structural or habitat characteristics, and four to species groups.

26.3.3.2. Additional Features of Importance (AFIs)

Within some ECSs there may be river or floodplain features (either physical or biological) which are important regionally or nationally, but which cannot be assessed adequately in the routine scoring system. By noting (not scoring) AFIs, the user is alerted to their presence and can assess this information together with the various SERCON scores and indices. Table 26.4 reproduces the checklist of AFIs, but there is also the facility to record other AFIs not listed in the table and considered worthy of note. AFIs are subdivided into 'unique features', 'other

Table 26.4   Additional Features of Importance.

'Unique' features

The particular features noted under (a) to (d) are to be specified. If the same features are listed in the next section ('Other positive features') they are only recorded once under 'Unique' features.

(a)   The presence of a feature or features 'unique' at a regional level

(b)   The presence of a feature or features 'unique' at a country level (England, Scotland, Wales, Northern Ireland)

(c)   The presence of a feature or features 'unique' at a national level (GB or UK)

(d)   The presence of a feature or features 'unique' at an international level

Other positive features

(e)   Gorges or waterfalls of ecological significance (e.g. acting as barriers to fish migration)

(f)   Floodplain with ancient mosaics of dykes and reeds/fen/marsh/wet grassland (such as the Ouse Washes, Pevensey Levels, Tregaron Bog, Loch Insh marshes)

(g)   Important populations of breeding wildfowl or waders using floodplains

(h)   Exceptionally large populations of rare or characteristic plants or animals (e.g. otter, kingfisher, twaite shad, freshwater pearl mussel, floating water-plantain)

(i)   Features which might normally indicate impoverishment but which have positive attributes in specific ECSs—e.g. native pinewoods vs conifer plantations; river rehabilitated or recovering well from previous major degradation

(j)   Long history of extensive research; knowledge of how ECS has been managed and changed over time

(k)   Notable islands within the ECS river channel which add greatly to diversity and act as a haven for river birds and mammals

(l)   The presence of a notable population of plant or animal which is rare but not yet recognized in legislation or elsewhere (e.g. *Bathynella natans* in the Altquhur Burn)

(m)   The occurrence, within the ECS, of a population of plant or animal (rare or common) which is believed to be distinct genetically

(n)   Presence of algae and lichens of conservation value

(o)   Birds of conservation value associated with the ECS but not included in SERCON scoring system (e.g. Cetti's warbler)

(p)   Presence of lacustrine plants and animals in the ECS but not included in SERCON scoring system

(q)   Presence of a designated river or wetland site within the catchment (e.g. SSSI, Ramsar Site, SPA)

(r)   A positive trend, observed over a period of years, in physical, chemical or biological features (e.g. improving water quality, increasing population of an important species)

(s)   Presence of subterranean waters

(t)   Presence of nationally or internationally rare wetland plants within the corridor

Negative features

(u)   *Potential* for human impact to ECS (e.g. proposed fish farms, disused mines, catchment development, etc.)

(v)   Presence of alien species with the *potential* for causing significant ecological damage (e.g. signal crayfish)

(w)   Introduction of a native species to a catchment from which it was previously absent, and where it is thought to be having a deleterious effect

(x)   A negative trend, observed over a period of years, in physical, chemical or biological features (e.g. deteriorating water quality, decreasing population of an important species)

(y)   Large quantities of litter, discarded household waste, etc., in the channel or on the banks

Other, as yet undefined, features of importance

positive features' and 'negative features'. Whilst 'uniqueness' is linguistically a rather unsatisfactory term, the concept has been considered useful in conservation evaluation (e.g. Gehlbach, 1975; van der Ploeg and Vlijm, 1978). In SERCON an ECS or some species population within it would be described as 'unique' if, for example, it were the most southerly or northerly of its type, or the only one regionally, nationally or internationally.

26.3.3.3   Impacts

Impact scores are *not* used in SERCON for computing indices of conservation value. Data are gathered on 11 impacts (Table 26.3) to provide a context for both high and low scores and indices, to compare pressures on ECSs having similar conservation criterion indices, and to help develop appropriate management strategies for rivers. At present, precise guidance on scoring impacts is frequently impossible and, in most cases, only some points on the score bands are defined. Within these limits, the user can allocate scores depending on the nature of the impacts in the ECS in question.

When allocating scores for impacts, it is important to take account of the *context* of the impact. For example, in some rivers sewage effluent may provide the primary source of flowing water during periods of low flow. Thus, an impact that would normally be considered severe (input of sewage effluent) may be considered less severe when its ameliorating effect on the environment (providing adequate flow) is taken into account. Similarly, the negative impact of large amounts of Canadian pondweed (*Elodea canadensis*) (preventing the establishment of native plant communities) may be counter-balanced by its positive effect in providing habitat and cover for fish and invertebrates in structurally impoverished rivers.

Some activities (e.g. fish farming, hydro-power generation) may have several impacts; these are dealt with separately. However, where activities such as fish farming constitute an important threat to an ECS this can be highlighted in Additional Features of Importance.

26.3.3.4   Background data

It is important that the conservation criteria forming the central core of SERCON are set alongside other information, both to establish context and to aid interpretation (Figure 26.3). Background data for SERCON fall into three distinct categories: physical data; catchment land types and human population densities; and data on water quality. By complementing SERCON scores and indices with a tabulation of background data, the parameters of the ECS to which these scores and indices apply can be defined. When cross-referenced to data on catchment land use and water quality, the interpretation of SERCON outputs for river conservation value can be refined further.

Physical data entered for each ECS are: location of ECS, length of ECS, channel gradient, channel sinuosity, stream order at lowest point of ECS, stream flow stability, mean daily flow at lowest point of ECS, altitudinal range of ECS catchment, catchment size at lowest point of ECS, soil types in ECS catchment, and solid geology of ECS catchment. Not only does this ensure that evaluations of different ECSs take full account of their context, but as data on specific ECSs are collected and stored, so further analysis and refinement of SERCON can be carried out (e.g. by investigating possible correlations between the physical features of rivers and particular aspects of conservation value).

SERCON utilizes most of the ITE land classes derived from satellite imagery (Barr *et al.*, 1993) to provide information on the extent of semi-natural vegetation, degree of urban development and other features which characterize the catchment. Those classes which are omitted are coastal and will not be found in an ECS catchment. In SERCON, the land classes are amalgamated into eight categories ('Land Types') and used as indicators of the extent of semi-natural habitats within the catchment. An estimate of human population density is also included as a good indication of the potentially wide range of human impacts on rivers.

Background information on water quality is an important component of the overall interpretation of conservation scores and indices, and is also highly relevant when considering rehabilitation of a degraded river. In England and Wales, a new system of Statutory Water Quality Objectives is being planned, but until this is finalized SERCON relies on the existing UK schemes. In addition to the water quality class, a score for ortho-phosphate levels is assigned in SERCON, based on recommendations by EN and CCW, but modified to take account of rivers in which higher phosphate levels are encountered. The 'biological class' for an ECS is recorded using the system developed for use during the 1990 quinquennial survey of water quality in the UK. This classification was based on the comparison of field-generated aquatic macroinvertebrate data with predictions derived from RIVPACS (Wright *et al.*, 1989).

Usually, water quality data in SERCON refer to the point furthest downstream in the ECS, but if there are wide variations along the length of the ECS, a separate record is made for the point furthest upstream.

26.4 Data Manipulation

26.4.1 *Weighting attributes and criteria*

Most conservation assessment methods do not ascribe equal value to all attributes. For example, the conservation value of a relatively natural river channel may well be considered greater than the presence of one rare invertebrate species. In SERCON, weights were set by the PDG after consultation with the Specialist Group and the Steering Group. Attribute weights are used in the process of combining attribute scores to calculate criterion indices. On the other hand, while criterion weights form part of the output report so that users know the relative importance each is considered to have, they are not used in calculations as criterion indices are not combined into one overall SERCON conservation index.

Weights were assigned by issuing a questionnaire to all members of the specialist group who were asked to rank in order of importance (1 = most important) the attributes in each conservation criterion and in the Impacts section, and to rank the six conservation criteria. They were then instructed to assign weights to each attribute (and criterion) with a value of 1.0 for the attribute ranked the lowest and with the remaining weights allocated according to the perceived importance of each attribute (i.e. in line with the rank order). No weight greater than 5.0 was permitted. The same exercise was also carried out by the Steering Group and the PDG. The PDG then applied this information to devise a series of rules for allocating both the extremes and the intermediate points of each weighting scale. These protocols were then used to set weights for each attribute and each criterion. The results are given in Table 26.3.

26.4.2 The problem of 'double scoring'

The attributes evaluated by SERCON are not separate, unrelated entities. Rather, the complex ecosystems formed by rivers and their catchments are the expression of interacting physical, chemical and biological features. Evaluating attributes individually and then combining them into groups (conservation criteria) could lead, therefore, to 'double scoring' in which an ECS might appear to rate more highly than it should. For example, species richness in rivers is partly correlated with physical habitat diversity: if the latter scores highly, the former is more likely to as well. This need not constitute a problem as the final indices for the main nature conservation criteria (such as Species Richness and Physical Diversity) are kept separate for interrogation by the user.

Within some criteria, however, there may be a tendency for evaluations of some partially related attributes to reinforce each other. For example, it could be argued that 'substrates' and 'fluvial features' are linked within the criterion 'Physical Diversity', and high scores for both could be misleading. However, even these attributes are not completely correlated, and the principle in SERCON of comparing like with like should minimize this problem.

Finally, it should not be assumed that simply because the score for one attribute is high or low, others within the same criterion will be also. Assessing each one separately enables a statement to be made concerning the value of each element, and increases the degree of confidence in the final assessment.

26.5 Using SERCON

26.5.1 Data collection

The principal task in completing any SERCON evaluation is to assemble the required environmental information from a wide variety of sources; the process of evaluation itself is far less time consuming.

Data sources include both statutory and voluntary organizations (e.g. EA, SEPA, conservation agencies, wildlife trusts), as well as research institutes (e.g. Institute of Hydrology, Institute of Freshwater Ecology) and published literature. Some parts of SERCON also rely on the expert views of those who are the most familiar with the ECS—often staff in some of the organizations listed above. Attributes within the criterion of Physical Diversity, as well as some in Naturalness,

Representativeness, and Special Features, require field survey to assess physical habitat features. Much of this information should be available from EA River Habitat Survey forms and, to a lesser extent, from river corridor survey maps, but some additional survey will usually be necessary.

Once data on each attribute have been assembled they are then used to derive attribute scores (on a scale of 0–5) with guidance from the SERCON manual or on-screen help (for the PC version). The unscored data are entered (Background Data, Additional Features of Importance) and brief notes written to highlight any especially important points (e.g. listing rare species that provided the basis for the rarity scores).

26.5.2 Derivation of conservation criterion indices

Calculation of the SERCON criterion indices is simple. The basic operation involves the weighting (through multiplication) of the attribute scores, followed by summation of the weighted attribute scores. This summed valued is then expressed as a percentage of the maximum possible summed weighted score. For example, the Physical Diversity (PDY) criterion comprises three attributes (Table 26.3): PDY 1–Substrates, PDY 2–Fluvial Features, and PDY 3–Structure of Aquatic Vegetation. Clear guidance is given on how scores are to be allocated. Thus, for PDY 1, the user refers to a table of nine substrate types occurring naturally in rivers, and assigns scores as follows:

0: Only 1 natural substrate type present.
1: 2–3 natural substrate types present.
2: 4–5 natural substrate types present.
3: 6–7 natural substrate types present.
4: 8–9 natural substrate types present.

For this attribute, and for some others in SERCON, the basic score may be increased or reduced if other conditions are met, although final scores must always lie within the range of 0–5. In the present version of PDY 1, for example, the score is raised by 1 if 5–6 natural substrate types are recorded in $\geqslant 5\%$ of RHS (River Habitat Survey) transects in the ECS, thus providing a better indication of substrate *diversity* (number of substrate types and their relative proportions) as opposed to substrate *richness*. The scores are manipulated as follows to produce the Physical Diversity criterion index:

Attribute	Score	Weight	Weighted score	Max possible score	Max possible weighted score
PDY 1	5	4	20	5	20
PDY 2	3	5	15	5	25
PDY 3	4	1	4	5	5
Sum			39		50

The criterion index is 39 expressed as a percentage of 50: that is, 78.

The calculation operates in exactly this way in all cases where data are available for *all* attributes of a particular criterion. Sometimes, however, data are missing for one or more attributes. In these cases, it would clearly be misleading to calculate the criterion index using the maximum possible summed weighted score. Thus, the calculation is made by expressing the summed weighted scores as a percentage of the sum of the maximum possible weighted scores *of those attributes for which data are available*. For instance, if the above example were lacking in data for PDY 2:

Attribute	Score	Weight	Weighted score	Max possible score	Max possible weighted score
PDY 1	5	4	20	5	20
PDY 2	?	5	—	—	—
PDY 3	4	1	4	5	5
Sum			24		25

The criterion index is 24 expressed as a percentage of 25: that is, 96.

To interpret these criterion indices, the user needs some indication of how complete the data set is. SERCON therefore assigns a suffix to indices to indicate the proportion of the maximum possible weighted score for a full data set that is represented by the actual data set, using a–e to indicate 20% bands from 0–100. In the example above, SERCON would assign a c-suffix based on 25 as a percentage of 50; i.e., the index would be 96c. If the data set is complete, an a*-suffix is assigned: i.e. 78a* for the example above.

If these two indices represented two ECSs, any comparison would conclude that an index of 96c, although high, is derived from an extremely incomplete data set. Caution should be exercised in rating this ECS above the ECS with an index of 78a* without first filling some or all of the gaps in the data set.

SERCON also addresses the problem of evaluations based on data of limited reliability, by asking users to enter a 'level of confidence' ('A', 'B', or 'C') for each attribute score.

SERCON indices can be presented in the form of a simple A–E classification (Table 26.5), where 'A' represents the highest quality band. This classification has

Table 26.5   The allocation of SERCON index values (for the six conservation criteria and for Impacts) to five quality bands (A–E).

Criterion	A	B	C	D	E
Physical Diversity	>80–100	>60–80	>40–60	>20–40	0–20
Naturalness (NA 'A' and NA 'B')	>80–100	>60–80	>40–60	>20–40	0–20
Representativeness	>90–100	>75–90	>60–75	>30–60	0–30
Rarity	>60–100	>45–60	>30–45	>15–30	0–15
Species Richness	>80–100	>60–80	>40–60	>20–40	0–20
Special Features	>60–100	>45–60	>30–45	>15–30	0–15
Impacts	0–15	>15–30	>30–45	>45–60	>60–100

been derived from the rather limited set of data from test rivers, and future revisions of SERCON may need to incorporate changes to the system of quality bands. For most categories, high values for SERCON indices are considered indicative of high conservation quality. However, for Impacts the bands are reversed such that an ECS with the highest level of impact is placed in the lowest quality band 'E'. Moreover, as noted previously, high values for the Species Richness index may not necessarily imply high conservation value, but for the sake of convenience this criterion is also included in the same quality banding system.

26.5.3 Interpreting SERCON scores and indices

SERCON scores and indices can be used in several ways: for comparing ECSs down the length of one river, for comparing ECSs of a similar type but in different rivers, and for comparing the same ECS over a period of time. Although some comparisons can be made without recourse to a large database of evaluations, the more comprehensive the SERCON coverage of UK rivers the easier it will be to interpret the results. During 1995, work commenced on evaluating 21 rivers in England, Wales and Scotland using SERCON Version 1. However, two programmes to test prototype versions of SERCON have already been completed as part of project development. In the first, indices were derived for 18 rivers (39 ECSs) in all four countries of the UK, representing a range of perceived conservation 'quality'. Modifications were made to the system and tests repeated on 12 rivers (21 ECSs) 10 of which had been included in the first test programme.

Table 26.6 gives the SERCON indices and quality bands for two of the rivers tested—the Teith in Central Scotland (Figure 26.3), and the Quaggy (Figure 26.5) in south-east London—to illustrate the difference in conservation criterion indices for two rivers of contrasting quality. (Note that the data on physical features of rivers in the test programme were not derived from SERCON field surveys, so the results should only be considered as indicative.) The Teith flows through a wide range of geological environments from source to mouth, giving rise to a

Table 26.6   SERCON indices (weighted) and quality bands for the River Teith and the River Quaggy, derived from the prototype test programme. PDY = Physical Diversity, NA = Naturalness, RE = Representativeness, RA = Rarity, SR = Species Richness, SF = Special Features, IM = Impacts, I = weighted index value (0–100 scale), Q = quality band (A–E scale).

River	Length (km)	PDY I	PDY Q	NA 1–4 I	NA 1–4 Q	NA 5–8 I	NA 5–8 Q	RE I	RE Q	RA I	RA Q	SR I	SR Q	SF I	SF Q	IM I	IM Q
Teith																	
ECS 1	12	66a*	B	94a*	A	100a*	A	84b	B	43a	C	35b	D	48a*	B	7a*	A
ECS 2	9	30a*	D	44a*	C	93a*	A	67a	C	53a	B	76b	B	57a*	B	16a*	B
ECS 3	27	78a*	B	71a*	B	93a*	A	84a	B	67a*	A	88b	A	74a*	A	25a*	B
Quaggy																	
ECS 1	6	2a*	E	17a*	E	69a*	B	14b	E	5a*	E	0a*	E	19b	D	57a	D

Figure 26.5   River Quaggy, south-east England (Photo: Alastair Driver).

diverse range of aquatic habitats and communities. At its source ($>500\,$m), nutrient-poor water flows over boulder-strewn channels where the sparse vegetation is dominated by aquatic mosses. Further downstream plant diversity and abundance increases as the river flows across richer, sandstone rocks. In contrast, the Quaggy is an urban river, predominantly culverted, or deepened and re-aligned within a strait-jacket of revetments. The floodplain has been extensively developed although some old paddocks remain containing pools of local interest.

SERCON outputs clearly reflect the large differences in quality between the two rivers. Indices for Physical Diversity, Naturalness (A and B), and Representativeness are high for the Teith (ECSs 1 and 3), and extremely low for the Quaggy (with the exception of Naturalness B, owing to the presence of relatively few alien species) whilst the Impact index is far higher for the Quaggy than for the Teith. As well as large differences between rivers, there are also marked differences between the middle ECS and the other two ECSs on the Teith. Thus, for ECS 2 the lower levels for Physical Diversity, Naturalness A and Representativeness indices are a reflection of some channelization in this section.

26.5.4 *Assessing the potential for river rehabilitation*

At present, there is no systematic approach for determining which sections of river most deserve rehabilitation at the reach or catchment scale, and certainly not at a regional or national level. River rehabilitation works should lead to an increase in river corridor 'values': higher scores for at least some of the attributes assessed by SERCON, as well as the overall criterion indices for Naturalness, Representativeness, etc. Conversely, rehabilitation works should bring about lower scores for at least some of the impacts evaluated by SERCON. If SERCON is a useful tool for measuring the improvement brought about by rehabilitation, it should also have a role to play in the early stages of planning rehabilitation programmes.

At a general level, SERCON scores and indices for conservation criteria and Impacts, coupled with data on water quality, can be used to give a preliminary assessment of rehabilitation priority. The recommended procedure comprises four steps. First, the quintile values (A–E) for all the conservation criterion indices for an ECS are listed to give a general impression of 'conservation value'. Second, any low values for these indices are assessed against impact scores and relevant background data to indicate any general relationship and to identify areas of cause and effect. Third, individual low-scoring conservation attributes are assessed against high scoring impacts. An approach that may be helpful is to consider the four main areas of impact for which rehabilitation is theoretically an option. These are: degraded physical environments, modified flow regimes, reduced water quality, and the influence of aliens on native biota. Suites of conservation attributes associated with each of these four areas can then be compared with appropriate data on impacts and water quality to see whether there may be a causal relationship. The fourth step in the process is a consideration of the technical feasibility and cost of reversing impacts within the ECS and its catchment.

For SERCON to be used effectively for setting rehabilitation priorities, scores and indices for individual ECSs must be compared with those for other ECSs on the same river and with those for ECSs of a similar type in other rivers locally, regionally and nationally. SERCON can also help in determining the appropriateness of any given rehabilitation proposal. It does this by enabling the identification of key conservation elements that have been lost in places where they should be expected, based on a comparison with SERCON scores and indices from other rivers of a similar type and in a similar geographical location, and on outputs from species and habitat surveys.

The value of SERCON in rehabilitation assessment goes beyond establishing appropriateness, and setting priorities and objectives. It can also be used in measuring the effectiveness of the rehabilitation work through pre- and post-project appraisal by comparing specific conservation scores before and after rehabilitation is undertaken, and for a specified period after the work is completed. In this case, it is important to compare the scores for those attributes where improvement was a specific objective.

26.6   SERCON on PC

The computer version of SERCON operates essentially as an aid to the user in completing the calculation of indices for conservation criteria and Impacts. However, this relatively simple calculating function is backed by the full body of explanatory text in hypertext format, supported by on-screen diagrams and colour photographs of certain riverine and riparian features. In addition, attribute scores (not raw data) can be stored in a database from which they can be recalled for modification, or for comparisons between ECSs. Presentation of scores and indices is enhanced by a series of text and graphical reports which can be displayed on screen or as hard copy.

SERCON is implemented on PC as a Microsoft Windows™ application that presents a familiar interface to most users. Experience suggests that learning to use SERCON takes only a few minutes for an occasional Windows user who has seen a demonstration. Data are stored in Microsoft Access™ files which means they can be accessed and queried from other software, if desired. Graphical output can be pasted into the user's own documents, thus enhancing the output possibilities. The use of the Windows Help system to drive the hypertext means that it can be used both to supply context help at the SERCON input screens, and can also be accessed independently. To reduce the disk storage requirements, photographs in SERCON have been compressed using fractal compression software so that they take up a relatively insignificant amount of space.

26.7   Future Developments

The first priority for future SERCON development must be to ensure that the system operates efficiently and produces results that are reliable and repeatable. It is hoped that a wide range of rivers will be evaluated in the first three years following completion of SERCON Version 1 (1995–1998) thereby enabling refinements to be made to the guidance on interpreting outputs, and any short-comings to be modified for Version 2.

Several other areas require examination during the first phase of implementation. For example, further work may be needed to ensure the compatibility of SERCON with the EA's River Habitat Survey methodology, the robustness of

SERCON might be tested by asking different users to evaluate ECSs from the same sources of raw data; and recent developments relevant to SERCON will need to be assessed. These developments include the new river classification scheme being produced by the EA, and new sources of reference data such as the soil distribution maps in preparation in Northern Ireland.

In the longer term, the approach used in SERCON for assessing river habitats and biota could be applied in other areas. For example, the statutory conservation agencies in Britain are concerned with river conservation not only from a biological but also from a geomorphological perspective. A system which could evaluate fluvial geomorphological features in a systematic way (i.e. a new module for SERCON) might represent a useful advance in conservation assessment. A feasibility study on this has already been completed with encouraging results (McEwen, 1994; McEwen *et al.*, this volume). Other 'values' of rivers—recreational, economic, fisheries, or landscape and amenity—might also be considered for any future extension of SERCON. The SERCON approach clearly has potential, too, in other countries, and need not be restricted to running waters. For example, recent work in Sweden on developing an evaluation system for Swedish rivers and lakes has relied heavily on the framework provided by SERCON (Willén *et al.*, this volume).

The need for a broad-based system for assessing river 'quality' has been brought into sharp focus by the anticipated EC framework Directive on water policy. This is likely to contain measures previously proposed for inclusion within a Directive on the Ecological Quality of Water (Commission of the European Communities, 1994) in which member states would be required to monitor rivers and lakes in terms of their 'ecological quality', which is defined in far broader terms than merely 'water pollution' or 'chemical water quality'. Whilst the scope of monitoring is not yet clear, the elements considered to contribute to ecological quality include physical habitat structure, the diversity and naturalness of plant, invertebrate, amphibian, fish, bird and mammal communities, and the status of the riparian zone, as well as 'traditional' water quality characteristics. It remains to be seen whether SERCON itself is eventually used as a monitoring tool with respect to the framework Directive. However, the principles governing the development of SERCON should certainly be taken into account when monitoring protocols are established.

Acknowledgements

The SERCON project was funded principally by SNH, with contributions from EN and CCW.

We are indebted to the many individuals and organizations for their co-operation, time and effort in providing information and advice. In particular we extend our thanks to the statutory conservation agencies, the EA, SEPA, IRTU, and Ove Arup. We acknowledge the valuable role that past and present members of the Steering Group have played in the evolution of SERCON: David Howell (SNH), John Hellawell, Patrick Denny and Chris Newbold (EN), Catherine Duigan

(CCW), Margaret Palmer (JNCC), Paul Raven (EA), Peter Hale (IRTU), and Ian Fozzard (SEPA). SERCON benefited greatly from the views of Specialist Group members, both in the questionnaire and at demonstrations. Additional administrative assistance was provided by Jenny Lowe and Tessa Harding (SNH). We are grateful to Jay O'Keeffe (Rhodes University, South Africa) for making available the software for the River Conservation System, and to John Wright (Institute of Freshwater Ecology) for providing the check-list of invertebrate taxa comprising RIVPACS III. Figures 26.2 and 26.3 were drawn by Robert Burns (Drawing Attention, Herts). Richard Howell (EA) provided helpful comments on an earlier version of this chapter.

References

Barr, C. J., Bunce, R. G. H., Clarke, R. T., Fuller, R. M., Furse, M. T., Gillespie, M. K., Groom, G. B., Hallam, C. J., Hornung, M., Howard, D. C. and Ness, M. J. (1993). *Countryside Survey 1990: Main Report*. Department of the Environment, London.

Boon, P. J. (1991). The role of Sites of Special Scientific Interest (SSSIs) in the conservation of British rivers. *Freshwater Forum,* **1,** 95–108.

Boon, P. J. (1992). Essential elements in the case for river conservation. In: Boon, P. J., Calow, P. and Petts, G. E. (Eds), *River Conservation and Management*. John Wiley, Chichester, 11–33.

Boon, P. J. (1995). The relevance of ecology to the statutory protection of British rivers. In: Harper, D. M. and Ferguson, A. J. D. (Eds), *The Ecological Basis for River Management*. John Wiley, Chichester, 239–250.

Boon, P. J. and Howell, D. L. (This volume). Defining the quality of fresh waters: theme and variations.

Boon, P. J., Holmes, N. T. H., Maitland, P. S. and Rowell, T. A. (1994). A system for evaluating rivers for conservation ('SERCON'): An outline of the underlying principles. *Verhandlungen der Internationalen Vereinigung für theoretische und angewandte Limnologie,* **25,** 1510–1514.

Boon, P. J., Holmes, N. T. H., Maitland, P. S. and Rowell, T. A. (1996). SERCON: System for Evaluating Rivers for Conservation. Version 1 Manual. *Scottish Natural Heritage Research Survey and Monitoring Report* No. 61. Scottish Natural Heritage, Edinburgh.

Commission of the European Communities (1994). *Proposal for a Council Directive on the Ecological Quality of Water*, COM (93) 680 final, Brussels, 15.06.1994. Office for Official Publications of the European Communities, Luxembourg.

English Nature. (1992). *SSSIs*. Peterborough.

Gehlbach, F. R. (1975). Investigation, evaluation, and priority ranking of natural areas. *Biological Conservation,* **8,** 79–88.

Holmes, N. T. H. (1983). Typing British rivers according to their flora. *Focus on Nature Conservation,* **4**. Nature Conservancy Council, Peterborough.

Holmes, N. T. H. and Rowell, T. A. (in press). *Vegetation Classification of British Rivers*. Joint Nature Conservation Committee, Peterborough.

Margules, C. R. and Usher, M. B. (1981). Criteria used in assessing wildlife conservation potential. *Biological Conservation,* **21,** 79–109.

McEwen, L. J. (1994). 'A Feasibility Study on the Extension of SERCON to the Assessment of Fluvio-geomorphological Features of Nature Conservation Interest'. Unpublished report to Scottish Natural Heritage, Edinburgh.

McEwen, L. J., Brazier, V. and Gordon, J. E. (This volume). Evaluating the geomorphology of fresh waters: an assessment of approaches.

Nature Conservancy Council (1989). *Guidelines for Selection of Biological SSSIs*. Peterborough.

O'Keeffe, J. H., Danilewitz, D. B. and Bradshaw, J. A. (1987). An 'expert system' approach to the assessment of the conservation status of rivers. *Biological Conservation,* **40,** 69–84.

Ratcliffe, D. A. (Ed.) (1977). *A Nature Conservation Review*. Cambridge University Press, Cambridge.

Raven, P. J., Fox, P., Everard, M., Holmes, N. T. H. and Dawson, F. H. (This volume). River Habitat Survey: a new system for classifying rivers according to their habitat quality.

Shrader-Frechette, K. S. and McCoy, E. D. (1993). *Method in Ecology: Strategies in Conservation.* Cambridge University Press, Cambridge.

Usher, M. B. (This volume). Principles of nature conservation evaluation.

Van der Ploeg, S. W. F. and Vlijm, L. (1978). Ecological evaluation, nature conservation and land use planning with particular reference to methods used in the Netherlands. *Biological Conservation,* **14,** 197–221.

Willén, E., Andersson, B. and Söderbäck, B. (This volume). System Aqua: a biological assessment tool for Swedish lakes and watercourses.

Wright, J. F., Armitage, P. D., Furse, M. T. and Moss, D. (1989). Prediction of invertebrate communities using stream measurements. *Regulated Rivers: Research and Management,* **4,** 147–155.

27 SYSTEM AQUA: A BIOLOGICAL ASSESSMENT TOOL FOR SWEDISH LAKES AND WATERCOURSES

E. Willén, B. Andersson and B. Söderbäck

Summary

1. System Aqua has been designed to meet the growing need for an objective, reproducible and comprehensive tool for assessing the conservation value of lakes and watercourses in Sweden. The system may be used to provide an integrated assessment of whole catchments as well as their component waters. Emphasis is placed on biological qualities, with biodiversity as a focal concept.

2. Biodiversity is evaluated by five criteria characterized by indicators, varying in number from three to five. The criteria are structural diversity, naturalness, rarity, species richness and representativeness, and the biotic groups evaluated consist of riparian vegetation, macrophytes, algae, macroinvertebrates, fish and nesting birds.

3. Indicators are scored from 0 to 5, where 5 reflects the highest biodiversity or the highest natural value, and 0 an extremely uniform or highly impacted habitat.

4. A numerical index value, based on weighted scores of assessed indicators, is obtained for each criterion. The indices are presented in an easily understandable criteria profile, where the proportion of indicators used reflects the confidence of the assessment.

27.1   Introduction

Sweden has a large abundance and diversity of inland freshwater habitats. Indeed, some 9% of Sweden's surface is covered by lakes with a surface area ≥ 1 ha (c. 92,400 lakes), and there are more than 300,000 km of watercourses. This diversity of freshwater habitat types is distributed across 117 main catchment areas (with an area > 200 km^2) and 27 ecoregions, from the nemoral to the alpine and arctic vegetation zones.

At the beginning of this century the degradation of natural resources attracted public attention, and the first national parks were established in 1909, with an effort to preserve larger, relatively pristine areas (Götmark and Nilsson, 1992). Since then, a number of selected terrestrial and aquatic ecosystems have been legally protected as national parks, nature reserves and nature management areas. Of these, about 12% (by area) are covered by freshwater habitats. In addition, there are some 400 separate lakes and watercourse stretches that are protected as areas of special natural interest (SEPA, 1991a).

Discussions and evaluations of criteria used in assessing water quality have attracted a special interest in Sweden since the mid-1960s following the eutrophication debate. A number of methods and procedures have been proposed for characterizing waters, directed towards either impact assessment or towards evaluating conservation status (e.g. Berntell *et al.*, 1984; SEPA, 1989; Ståhl, 1992). Guidelines of a more official nature were also worked out for classifying lakes and running waters using water-chemical variables, and for calculating the degree of perturbation compared with a background value (SEPA, 1991b).

Though some national surveys of freshwater habitats have provided information on the large-scale spatial variability of aquatic biodiversity (Rosén, 1981), there is a growing demand for an official and standardized approach to catchment- and site-specific characterization. This chapter describes System Aqua, designed to meet this need as an objective, reproducible and comprehensive tool to be used in a country-wide assessment of lakes and watercourses planned to take place in the next few years. The system, which is funded by the Swedish Environmental Protection Agency (SEPA), has been inspired by several international contributions (Ratcliffe, 1977; Rabe and Savage, 1979; O'Keeffe *et al.*, 1987; Ten Brink *et al.*, 1991; Dynelius and Nilsson, 1994), and especially those presented in the UK SERCON system (Boon *et al.*, 1994; this volume), which has served as a model for the scoring technique and some of the indicators for river assessment.

27.2   Description of System Aqua

Emphasis in System Aqua is placed on biological qualities, with biodiversity as a focal concept, here interpreted as the variation among organisms, habitats and ecosystems. The overall objective is to obtain an integrated assessment of whole catchments as well as their component lakes and watercourses.

Some advantages of System Aqua are as follows:

- Standard methods are proposed for inventories, data handling and analyses, resulting in a more objective and reproducible assessment of fresh waters at regional and national scales.
- Rivers and lakes deserving special consideration regarding their conservation value or their need for restoration are easily assessed.
- The system is easy for non-experts to use and understand.
- The use of scores, weighted summary criteria indices and a final criteria profile gives comprehensible and easily accessible information.
- The system is constructed for use in several ways: in Tier I whole catchments

are rapidly evaluated using maps, statistics, and other printed sources; in Tier II lakes or watercourses nested in their respective catchments are comprehensively assessed, and in Tier III individual lakes or river stretches are evaluated.

27.2.1 Criteria

The five criteria being evaluated are *structural diversity, naturalness, rarity, species richness* and *representativeness* (Table 27.1). There is a broad international consensus about the special importance of these five criteria, and they are frequently used in assessments of ecosystem quality (Ratcliffe, 1977; Margules and Usher, 1981; Smith and Theberge, 1986). In System Aqua these criteria provide information on overall diversity—from landscape to individual (e.g. rare) taxa.

Three to five indicators are assessed for each criterion (Table 27.1). In addition,

Table 27.1   An outline of System Aqua with criteria and indicators used in the scoring procedure, and special features for subjective assessment of other important values.

I. Catchment area
Background data

Assessment criteria scores for:

Structural diversity	Naturalness
Average score (0–5) for:	*Lowest score (0–5) for:*
● Number of lakes and lake area	● Physical manipulations
● Diversity of vegetation types/land use	● Degree of perturbation
● Topographic relief	● Land use

II. Lake or watercourse
Background data

Assessment criteria scores for:

Structural diversity	Naturalness	Rarity	Species richness	Representativeness
Average score (0–5) for:	*Lowest score (0–5) for:*	*Weighted average score (0–5) for:*	*Average score (0–5) for:*	*Average score (0–5) for:*
● Riparian land-use categories	● Long-lasting physical encroachment	● Endangered species	● Macrophytes	● Macrophytes
● Bottom substrates	● Flood control	● Vulnerable species	● Phytoplankton	● Phytoplankton
● Shore developmental/fluvial features	● River corridor vegetation	● Rare species	● Macro-invertebrates	● Macro-invertebrates
● Structure of aquatic vegetation	● Biotic changes	● Care demanding species	● Fish	● Fish
	● Water quality	● Regionally threatened species	● Nesting birds	● Nesting birds

Special features, e.g. amenity value, recreation value, other special characteristics.

the system incorporates physical and chemical water quality criteria and an indication of the degree of human perturbation (SEPA, 1991b).

Definitions of the criteria used in System Aqua are as follows.

Structural diversity assumes that a prerequisite for high biological diversity is high structural or habitat diversity. System Aqua scores the structural diversity of catchments, rivers and lakes in terms of shoreline habitat structure, bed morphology, macrophyte structure, and so on. For example, a varied catchment area, with a mosaic of different habitats should result in a potentially higher biodiversity than a homogeneous coniferous forested or flat agricultural landscape.

Naturalness is defined as the degree of human impact or perturbation. Assessment is made along a continuous gradient from a natural or near-natural state to a completely non-natural state. For example, sites are scored according to the degree of physical and chemical impact (e.g. water regulation, nutrient enrichment, acidification) and biological impacts (e.g. nuisance algal blooms).

Rarity is a criterion frequently used in nature conservation assessments (Smith and Theberge, 1986), and may be considered both in terms of species and habitats, at local, regional, national or international scales. In System Aqua, rarity is scored using the IUCN threat categories: endangered, vulnerable, rare, care demanding, and an additional category of regionally threatened species (Ahlén and Tjernberg, 1992; Ehnström *et al.*, 1993; Aronsson *et al.*, 1995).

Species richness is scored as the number of species or taxa of macrophytes, algae, macroinvertebrates, fish, and nesting birds in six abundance classes. As high latitude/altitude may influence these estimates, it is recommended that comparisons of observations are made specific to ecoregions.

Representativeness is assessed by comparing the observed and predicted species occurrence for macrophytes, algae, macroinvertebrates, fish, and nesting birds. This criterion is still in preparation. It will be completed within an additional project funded by SEPA over the next few years. Several multivariate techniques will be tested in this project. One available method used for macroinvertebrates in British waters is presented in Moss *et al.* (1987), and for Swedish running waters in Söderbäck and Lingdell (in press).

In addition to the five criteria scores used in site assessment, System Aqua contains *background information*, such as geographical and morphological character as well as the raw data used in assessment. Examples of background information are: site location and size, human population density in the catchment, height above sea level, length of the main watercourse, bathymetric information, land use characteristics in catchment areas and close to rivers and lakes, regulation measures, chemical water quality, mitigation or restoration, etc. An additional category known as 'special features' assesses the value of attributes which may be important but less amenable to scoring, such as the degree of uniqueness, aesthetic value, recreational use, etc.

27.2.2   Scoring

Each indicator is scored from 0 to 5, where 5 reflects the highest biodiversity or the highest natural value, whereas in contrast extremely uniform or highly impacted

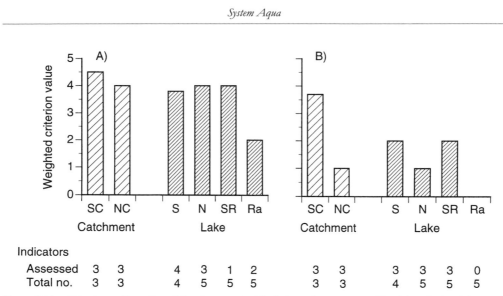

Figure 27.1   Criteria profiles of two lakes integrated with their catchment areas: (A) a lake of a special natural interest; (B) a very acidified lake with a catchment much influenced by acid deposition. Weighted summary criterion value for SC (structural diversity in catchment), NC (naturalness in catchment), S (structural diversity), N (naturalness), SR (species richness), Ra (rarity). Representativeness is not yet included.

habitats are scored as 0. Indicator scores form the basis for criteria indices by using average scores for the indicators of structural diversity and species richness, the lowest indicator scores for naturalness, or a strength given to a single indicator for rarity. The indices can be plotted graphically, revealing special criteria profiles (Figure 27.1). The number or proportion of indicators used in criterion assessment is presented and reflects the degree of confidence in the evaluation.

27.3   Implementation of System Aqua

System Aqua is used to evaluate the biodiversity of whole catchments and their mosaic of habitat types as well as individual lakes or stream stretches. The system can be applied at three operative levels or tiers: Tier I is used to obtain a superficial or rapid assessment of a catchment's structural and natural diversity, by using maps and printed information. Tier II, on the other hand, consists of a careful assessment of a lake or reaches of a watercourse integrated with its catchment. In Tier II assessment, it is recommended that all criteria and as many as possible of the indicators are used in the final evaluation. Tier III is used for the careful assessment of lakes or watercourses without their catchment areas.

27.4   Discussion

The increasing demand for an assessment tool, based on quantifiable, biological variables has been accomplished with the development of System Aqua. In the next few years when a large-scale inventory of Swedish lakes and watercourses will be performed, System Aqua is the tool which will be used. The scoring system of indicators and the resulting summary criteria profiles are easy to use and facilitate intra- and inter-regional comparisons of rivers and lakes and their catchment areas.

System Aqua includes both rivers and lakes in its appraisal while many of the internationally presented systems are exclusively directed towards river assessment. In the Swedish system the number of criteria are minimized and the indicators are selected to facilitate practical use while still maintaining high efficiency in the assessments. System Aqua has profited from earlier Swedish works for characterization of waters, but the subjective features of those have been specifically avoided. Characteristics which are unsuitable for quantification and scoring are registered instead as 'special features'.

A further development of System Aqua is a computer-based version with the aim of giving definitions, showing help-files and illustrating habitats, and in general simplifying selection processes and assessment procedures. A present task is to adapt System Aqua to knowledge-based and analyser systems.

References

Ahlén, I. and Tjernberg, M. (1992). *Sweden's Threatened and Rare Vertebrates* (in Swedish). Swedish Threatened Species Unit, SLU, Uppsala.

Aronsson, M., Hallingbäck, T. and Mattsson, J.-E. (Eds) (1995). *Swedish Red Data Book of Plants*. Swedish Threatened Species Unit, SLU, Uppsala.

Berntell, A., Wenblad, A., Henriksson, L., Nyman, H. and Oskarsson, H. (1984). *Criteria for Evaluation of Lakes for Conservation*. (In Swedish). County Board of Älvsborg, 1983: 3, Vänersborg.

Boon, P. J., Holmes, N. T. H., Maitland, P. S. and Rowell, T. A. (1994). A system for evaluating rivers for conservation ('SERCON'): an outline of the underlying principles. *Verhandlungen der Internationalen Vereinigung für theoretische und angewandte Limnologie,* **25,** 1510–1514.

Boon, P. J., Holmes, N. T. H., Maitland, P. S., Rowell, T. A. and Davies, J. (This volume). A system for evaluating rivers for conservation (SERCON): development, structure and function.

Dynelius, M. and Nilsson, C. (1994). Fragmentation and flow regulation of river systems in the northern third of the world. *Science,* **266,** 753–761.

Ehnström, B., Gärdenfors, U. and Lindelöw, Å. (1993). *Red-listed Terrestrial and Limnetic Vertebrates*. (In Swedish with an English summary). Swedish Threatened Species Unit, SLU, Uppsala.

Götmark, F. and Nilsson, C. (1992). Criteria used for protection of natural areas in Sweden 1909–1986. *Conservation Biology,* **6,** 220–231.

Margules, C. and Usher, M. B. (1981). Criteria used in assessing wildlife conservation potential: a review. *Biological Conservation,* **21,** 79–109.

Moss, D., Furse, M. T., Wright, J. F. and Armitage, P. D. (1987). The prediction of the macroinvertebrate fauna of unpolluted running-water sites in Great Britain using environmental data. *Freshwater Biology,* **17,** 41–52.

O'Keeffe, J. H., Danilewitz, D. B. and Bradshaw, J. A. (1987). An expert system approach to the assessment of the conservation status of rivers. *Biological Conservation,* **40,** 69–84.

Rabe, F. W. and Savage, N. (1979). A methodology for the selection of aquatic natural areas. *Biological Conservation,* **15,** 291–300.

Ratcliffe, D. (Ed.) (1977). *A Nature Conservation Review*, Cambridge University Press, Cambridge.

Rosén, G. (1981). Phytoplankton indicators and their relations to certain chemical and physical factors. *Limnologica,* **13,** 263–290.

SEPA (1989). *Surveys of Lakes and Watercourses. Manual*. Swedish Environmental Protection Agency, Information, Stockholm.

SEPA (1991a). *Areas of Special Natural Interest and Open Air Activities*. (In Swedish). Swedish Environmental Protection Agency, Report, 3771, Stockholm.

SEPA (1991b). *Water Quality Criteria for Lakes and Watercourses. A System for Classification of Water Chemistry and Sediment and Organisms' Metal Concentration.* Swedish Environmental Protection Agency, Information, Stockholm.

Smith, P. and Theberge, J. (1986). A review of criteria for evaluating natural areas. *Environmental Management,* **10,** 715–734.

Söderbäck, B. and Lingdell, P.-E. (in press). Prediction of macroinvertebrate communities from environmental factors in north Swedish streams. *Proceedings of the International Association of Theoretical and Applied Limnology,* **26**.

Ståhl, P. (1992). *Selection and Assessment of Watercourses for Conservation.* (In Swedish). County Board of Gävleborg, No. 8, Gävle.

Ten Brink, B. J. E., Hosper, S. H. and Colijn, F. (1991). A quantitative method for description and assessment of ecosystems: the AMOEBA-approach. *Marine Pollution Bulletin,* **23,** 265–270.

28 ASSESSING THE CONSERVATION VALUE OF STANDING WATERS

O. L. Lassière and W. M. Duncan

Summary

1. This chapter examines ways in which the conservation value of standing waters can be assessed, using as an example the standing water resource of Scotland.

2. In the UK, conservation involves (in part) the designation of a network of statutorily protected sites. Evaluating the quality of a range of physically and biologically diverse lakes to enable site selection requires appropriate classification schemes. Such schemes may be based either on the present condition of the lake (spatial state schemes) or on retrospective information giving an indication of the lake's status at some point in its history (state changed schemes).

3. The lake classification scheme used in Britain for nature conservation purposes is based on macrophyte flora, and subdivides lakes into one of 10 Types, chiefly reflecting trophic status. This scheme has been applied to lakes in Scotland and a scoring system for regional evaluation has been developed.

4. Classification schemes based on single biotic groups (e.g. macrophytes, zooplankton) can lead to problems when a lake has a number of conservation interests. For example, in Loch Eye (north-east Scotland) eutrophication caused partly by protected wildfowl populations has already had adverse effects on the aquatic vegetation.

5. New developments in conservation biology favour an integrated approach to habitat classification and evaluation; a natural corollary is to develop an integrated catchment approach to lake conservation as a whole.

28.1 Wetlands: Definition and Values

Within the last 30 years it has been recognized that wetlands, which are found in every climate from the tropics to the frozen tundra (Richardson, 1995), are under serious threat of destruction (Fisher, 1993; Navid, 1994a). It has been estimated that, as a result of development processes which did not take their functions and values adequately into account, two thirds of Europe's wetlands have disappeared since the beginning of the twentieth century (Commission of the European Communities, 1995). Although the term 'wetland' has over 50 separate definitions (Dugan, 1990), it is the definition of the Ramsar Convention which has been adopted for the purposes of this chapter.

> Areas of marsh, fen, peatland or water, whether natural or artificial, permanent or temporary, with water that is static or flowing, fresh, brackish or salt, including areas of marine water the depth of which at low tide does not exceed six metres.

The convention on Wetlands of International Importance was adopted in 1971 at Ramsar, Iran to provide a coordinated international approach for the conservation and wise use of wetlands (Navid, 1994a). This was a pioneering move and apart from the Antarctic continent, wetlands are the only major ecosystems forming the subject of an international treaty (Commission of the European Communities, 1995). The Convention, although global in coverage, was created very much as a European initiative and in recent years the Convention has become increasingly active, with European countries playing their part in its application (Navid, 1994a). By 1994, 81 states were contracting parties to the Convention and 654 Ramsar wetlands had been designated covering an area of more than 43×10^6 ha (Navid, 1994b).

It is clear that European wetland ecosystems are highly valued, not only because they perform very important environmental functions, but also as they provide resources for a large number of human activities and comprise a valuable cultural and natural heritage (Commission of the European Communities, 1995). These diverse functions and values have been fully summarized by Richardson (1995) and the US Fish and Wildlife Service (1984). This chapter examines a subset of these wetland habitats—namely standing waters—and the ways in which an assessment of their value and quality for nature conservation purposes can be achieved. The following sections deal primarily with the assessment of quantity and the methods for defining and evaluating quality of standing waters in Britain. Although the scope of this chapter is limited to these habitats it is important to bear in mind that standing waters are not merely isolated islands in a sea of land, but form an integral part of the catchment.

28.2 Quantity

The first consideration in an assessment of a resource is some form of 'stock take'. The World Conservation Union (Dugan, 1990) has identified that a necessary prerequisite to the conservation of wetlands is an improvement of the information base. Accordingly, they describe the value of a wetland directory and classification for each nation or region. The British government has also recognized the need for comprehensive data when devising national environmental policy (Department of the Environment, 1992). This may be illustrated with reference to the standing waters in Scotland. Most lakes in Scotland are known as lochs, with their smaller counterparts known as lochans, and this terminology will be adopted throughout. A complementary chapter (Boon *et al.*, this volume) examines one approach to river evaluation and conservation in Britain.

28.2.1 *Scotland's standing water resource*

It has been estimated that there are at least 31460 freshwater lochs in Scotland (Lyle and Smith, 1994). These range in size from the small peaty mountain lochans <1ha in area to the expanse of Loch Lomond (7110ha). In Scotland, 1.9% of the land surface is covered by fresh waters (Macaulay Land Use Research Institute, 1993). The distribution has a marked north-west to south-east gradient with the highest concentration of lochs occurring in the Western Isles (over 7500 lochs) (Plate 5d). In terms of volume, the water contained in Loch Ness (7,452,000,000m³) is nearly twice that found in the standing waters of England and Wales combined (Lyle and Smith, 1994).

28.3 Defining Quality

The next stage in the assessment of a wetland resource is the identification of important attributes which confer its value. The Scottish lochs provide a good example of the process which is currently used in Britain to assess the nature conservation value of standing water bodies.

28.3.1 *Nature conservation in Britain*

The primary objective of nature conservation (as described by the Nature Conservancy Council (NCC)) is to ensure that the national heritage of wild flora and fauna and geological and physiographic features remains as large and diverse as possible so that society may use and appreciate its value to the fullest extent (NCC, 1984). These goals arose in Victorian times when the study of natural history became a fashionable scientific, intellectual and recreational pursuit (NCC, 1989). The interests of these early natural historians led to an awareness of the best sites to find rare and local species. As a logical progression, the protection and management of the most important areas for wild flora and fauna and their habitat became the cornerstone of conservation practice. Early attempts to identify important sites were based on the soundness of judgement and expertise of those concerned. As the demands upon natural resources increased it became necessary to have a reasoned and coherent rationale for the process of site evaluation.

The first attempt at standardizing conservation evaluation criteria in the UK came with the publication of the Nature Conservation Review (NCR) (Ratcliffe, 1977) which provided a retrospective quality assessment of the designations that had been made up until that time. It identified six primary criteria: diversity, naturalness, size, rarity, fragility and typicalness/representativeness, and four secondary criteria: recorded history, position in an ecological/geographical unit, potential value, and intrinsic appeal, that should be used in assessing conservation value. These 10 criteria have been widely adopted throughout the world (Usher, 1986). With respect to open waters, Ratcliffe (1977) listed the increasing threats to the nature conservation interest of these habitats, stressing the urgency of survey and description of intact open waters in Britain and the selection of a series of sites to represent adequately the range of variation.

To complement the recognition of valued sites for conservation, statutory protection is provided by the National Parks and Access to the Countryside Act 1949 and the Wildlife and Countryside Act 1981, under which legislation areas may be designated as Sites of Special Scientific Interest (SSSIs). At an international level, designations may currently be made under the Ramsar Convention on Wetlands of International Importance. By 2004, under the EC Directive on the conservation of natural habitats and of wild flora and fauna (the 'Habitats Directive'), a network of Special Areas of Conservation (SACs), called Natura 2000, will be established.

Some species of flora and fauna found in freshwater habitats are also afforded legal protection under the Wildlife and Countryside Act 1981 and under international designations provided by the Bern Convention and the Habitats Directive (Annexes IV and V). This protection is primarily aimed at rarer species and those at the limit of their geographical distribution.

28.3.1.1 The Scottish perspective

In Scotland, nature conservation is dealt with by a range of organizations including government departments, statutory agencies and voluntary bodies. The main government agency charged with nature conservation in Scotland is Scottish Natural Heritage (SNH) which was set up under the Natural Heritage (Scotland) Act 1991 to secure the conservation and enhancement of the natural heritage of Scotland, and to foster its enjoyment and understanding.

The conservation of flora and fauna in Scotland is achieved through a range of complementary activities including site designation for species and habitat protection (as described in the previous section), species recovery programmes, the control of species introductions and the promotion of best management practice in land and water management in the wider countryside (Boon, 1994).

28.4 Evaluating Quality

It is not appropriate, for the purpose of nature conservation, to compare lakes of differing physical and biological characteristics. One solution to this problem is to subdivide the resource into a series of classes so that lakes with similar characteristics can be compared with each other. Elster (1974) succinctly described the virtues of this approach as a means to (a) gain an overall view (b) to simplify understanding of complex systems by characterizing a few common factors, and (c) to predict properties or relationships of parts of systems from other measured properties.

28.4.1 Classification schemes

This approach is not new in limnology and many workers have attempted to classify lakes on the basis of various criteria for a range of purposes. Schemes fall into two categories: state changed and spatial state. The former involves an appraisal of the present conditions which exist in a lake and how these differ from some point in its history; the latter schemes take account only of the present condition of the lakes. Leach and Herron (1992) thoroughly reviewed lake habitat classification systems (all spatial state types) and described numerous approaches ranging from those using single variables such as lake surface area or total phosphorus concentration to complex multivariate models. Almost all abiotic and biotic factors that influence lake metabolism have been used in classification schemes. Of the 32 categories reviewed, 24 were trophic classifications, reflecting the recent interest in quantifying the eutrophication process. The classification schemes fell into five broad groups: origin, shape and location; physical; chemical; trophic status (single parameter and composite indices); biological indicators (including bacteria, phytoplankton, macrophytes, zooplankton, fish, benthos, birds).

State-changed schemes for the assessment and monitoring of water and ecological quality in standing waters have recently been developed in England and Wales (Moss *et al.*, this volume) and in Scotland (Fozzard *et al.*, this volume). Most schemes such as these are orientated towards an assessment of water quality and are less applicable for conservation evaluation, although Duigan (1995) recognized the relevance of state-changed schemes in several aspects of conservation assessment including ecosystem representativeness, naturalness and stability. She cites the example of the critical loads approach which has been used in the assessment of the acidification status of freshwater SSSIs throughout Britain.

28.4.2 *Classification schemes for lake conservation*

Over the last 20 years classification schemes have been developed on the basis of species and/or habitat characteristics of lakes. One of the early attempts was by Ratcliffe (1977) who, as part of the Nature Conservation Review, described six broad lake types on the basis of their water chemistry, and provided extensive descriptions of the flora and fauna associated with each type. He was careful to emphasize that the divisions between each type were arbitrary, and recognized that the ideal basis for the selection of sites, including lakes, for nature conservation would be an appraisal of the ecosystem as a whole. In reality the lack of suitable data, and the means of describing them, led to the use only of the vegetational component. He considered the flora to be a suitable choice since it reflected the environmental influences at a site and is a major determinant of associated animal communities.

Following the impetus of the NCR, the Nature Conservancy Council began a major programme of survey work leading to the development of a classification scheme, both to describe the botanical resource of British lakes and to contribute to their conservation assessment (Palmer, 1989; Palmer *et al.*, 1992). Sites were classified by analysing macrophyte species data collected between 1975 and 1988 from 1,124 sites in England, Scotland and Wales. These water bodies included lakes, meres, reservoirs, ponds, pools, gravel pits and canals of which over half were in Scotland. For each site a species list of all the floating and submerged plants was drawn up and these data were subjected to TWINSPAN (Two Way Indicator Species Analysis) (Hill, 1979). This analysis produced an ordered matrix of sites by species and a series of 10 end-groups of sites with similar vegetational characteristics. These groups or Types follow a general trend of increasing nutrient status from dystrophic Type 1 sites to mesotrophic Type 5 sites and eutrophic Type 10 sites. A simple dichotomous key is used to assign a loch type to a new site on the basis of its floating and submerged flora (NCC, 1989).

28.4.2.1 The application of the lake macrophyte classification scheme in Scotland

Since 1983, 2350 lochs have been surveyed and classified on the basis of their macrophyte flora according to the Palmer *et al.* (1992) scheme (Figure 28.1, Table 28.1). A continuing programme of summer survey work should result in the completion of the survey by the year 2000. The classification scheme has allowed the resource to be summarized in a manageable form and has revealed those types which are rare in Scotland (Table 28.2), although some difficulties have been encountered if there are limited numbers of indicator species or if a loch is seasonally dry (note the number of unclassified lochs in Table 28.2). On a wide geographical scale, the well documented difference between the steep, flood-prone catchments in the west of Scotland and the low-lying, slow-flowing catchments to the east, is mirrored by the range of loch Types. As an example, data are presented for Wester and Easter Ross (Table 28.2) (see Figure 28.1 for location of these areas). Wester Ross is dominated by lochs of low nutrient status whilst those in Easter Ross cover the entire fertility spectrum.

28.4.3 *Evaluation of lakes classified on the basis of macrophyte flora*

The evaluation methods and criteria for assessing lake conservation value are described in the *Guidelines for Selection of Biological SSSIs* (NCC, 1989). These guidelines still provide the basis for the evaluation of lakes for conservation purposes and more specifically for the identification of sites worthy of SSSI status by the statutory conservation agencies. Occasionally, freshwater SSSIs may be selected to protect particular rare species or species assemblages. More usually, a broader evaluation is made on the basis of three groups—standing waters, lowland ditch systems, and flowing waters—with each habitat type classified according to its macrophyte flora.

28.4.3.1 Habitat criteria used in evaluation

The guidelines for the selection of standing freshwater SSSIs (NCC, 1989) have been summarized in Table 28.3. Some of these summary points have been expanded in the following sections which should be read in conjunction with Table 28.3.

Numbers of species. When selecting sites it is important to ensure that unusual features are not confused with those which are considered to be natural and/or

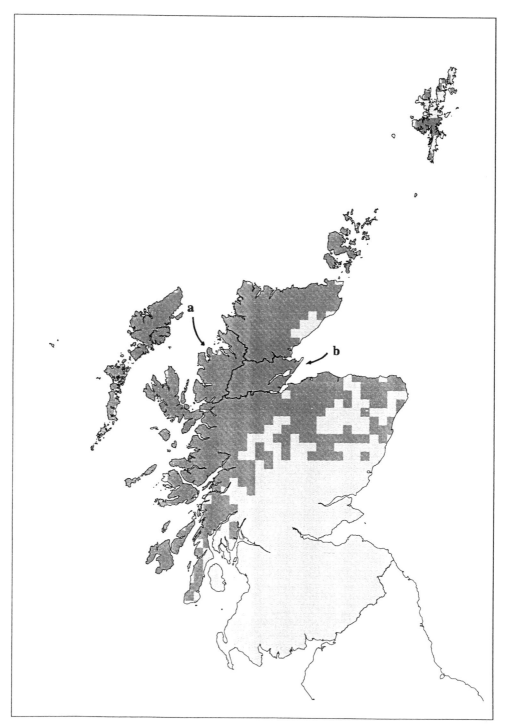

Figure 28.1   Map of loch survey coverage in Scotland by 10 × 10km square (■ = surveyed area); (a) =
Wester Ross; (b) = Easter Ross (Scale 1:3,000,000).

Table 28.1   Numbers of lochs surveyed by area and year.

Year	Survey area	No. of lochs
1983/4	South Uist	38
1985	Spey valley	53
	Loch Eye	1
1986	Orkney	166
	Shetland	31
	Ross-shire	18
1986/7	Caithness	69
1987	Moray and Nairn	4
1987/8	Sutherland	546
1988	Inverness District	130
	Deeside	25
1989	Skye and Lochalsh	340
	South Argyll	68
1990	Wester Ross and Cromarty	189
	Loch Eck	1
	Loch Enich	1
	North Argyll	24
1993	Lochaber	229
	Loch Awe	1
	Islay	12
1994	Easter Ross	63
	Inner Hebrides	124
1995	Grampian and Strathspey	64
	Outer Hebrides	166
	Total	2,350*

*The total for Scotland is not the sum of totals for each area because there is some overlap of sites between years.

Table 28.2   Percentage frequency of loch Types in Scotland.

Area	Percentage frequency by loch Type										
	U	1	2	3	4	5	6	7	8	9	10
Scotland	4.2	10.3	31.3	40.8	2.9	3.1	0.8	4.3	1.4	0.2	0.6
(2,227)	(93)	(230)	(696)	(909)	(65)	(70)	(18)	(95)	(32)	(5)	(14)
Wester Ross	0.5	3.2	25.9	70.4	0	0	0	0	0	0	0
(189)	(1)	(6)	(49)	(133)							
Easter Ross	12.7	17.5	11.1	34.9	1.6	12.7	0	0	6.3	1.6	1.6
(63)	(8)	(11)	(7)	(22)	(1)	(8)			(4)	(1)	(1)

Numbers of lochs given in parentheses. U = sites which could not be classified using the Palmer *et al.* (1992) scheme.

Table 28.3   Selection criteria for lake Sites of Special Scientific Interest based on habitat criteria (adapted from NCC, 1989).

(a)	Select one example of each loch Type
(b)	Preference given to those sites with high species numbers or numbers of National Vegetation Classification communities within Type
(c)	A rich assemblage of *Potamogeton* species (≥ 8) should be considered as long as at least one of these species is nationally rare or uncommon within the relevant water authority area
(d)	Diversity of physical features including shoreline, pH, substrate, depth, fresh to salt, nutrient poor to rich, altitude
(e)	Unusual site Types within an Area of Search and nationally rare site Types e.g. Type 4, Type 5, Type 6, Type 7. Marl water bodies, high altitude sites, temporally dry sites should be given special consideration
(f)	Artificial features should have a negative influence on the choice of a site (includes alien species e.g. *Elodea nuttallii*)
(g)	Natural sites are preferred to artificial, although there may be exceptions e.g. canals
(h)	Palaeolimnological and geological features should be taken into account
(i)	A site should form part of an ecological series
(j)	Range of sizes of loch should be selected
(k)	Catchment naturalness. Successional vegetation should be included to 'complete the ecological unit'
(l)	50 m boundaries around the water are recommended and should include some of the outflow

representative (Table 28.3 (b, f)). High levels of diversity should be considered carefully since in some cases this may indicate recent perturbation or environmental stress e.g. the increase in invertebrate diversity below sewage treatment works (Hynes, 1960) and the recent increase in fish diversity in Loch Lomond through the introduction of non-native species (Adams, 1994). In terms of valuing natural sites, it is worth bearing in mind a recent reappraisal of anthropic systems in the USA. In this, Luken (1994) put forward a rather different view by considering that those plant communities with high numbers of non-native plants maintained in a state of equilibrium by human activities should also be considered for natural area designation.

Pondweed assemblages. A high diversity of *Potamogeton* (pondweed) species (eight or more, including at least one nationally uncommon or rare species within the relevant water authority area (Palmer and Newbold, 1983)) is considered to impart high botanical quality to a site (Table 28.3 (c)). There are 21 *Potamogeton* species and 26 hybrids in Britain and Ireland. Some species are widely distributed and tolerate a range of ecological conditions and others occupy specialized niches (Seddon, 1972; Palmer *et al.*, 1992; Preston, 1995). Clearly there is scope for using these species to identify standing waters with specific ecological conditions.

Although a large number of *Potamogeton* species is judged to impart botanical quality to a site, data for 197 lochs in two areas of Scotland (Easter Ross and Orkney) show that there is only a weak relationship between the number of *Potamogeton* species and the diversity of other aquatic macrophyte species (Figure

28.2). In this example, *Potamogeton* species diversity would not be an appropriate surrogate for overall diversity; further work would be needed to determine whether stronger relationships exist for lakes in other areas of Scotland.

Artificial sites. Reservoirs, which have widely fluctuating water levels, are generally of low conservation interest for macrophytes. However, they can be valuable refugia for some bird species and for the establishment of 'safeguard' populations of rare fish (Table 28.3 (f)). Canals can also provide conservation opportunities, e.g. sections of the disused Forth and Clyde canal have been designated as an SSSI for their wildlife interest.

Recent plans to reopen it and to include its footpath in SNH's 'Paths for All' initiative will provide an interesting challenge for the conservation bodies, planners and developers concerned: how to maintain the wildlife interest whilst developing the canal as a recreational resource.

Size. The importance of size varies from site to site (Table 28.3 (j)). Generally, the ability of a site to withstand change increases with size and therefore larger water bodies are preferred (Probert, 1989). It must be borne in mind that further increases may result in negative influences being included in the catchment. Small sites may still be of high conservation value, usually in areas where the habitat type represents a diminishing resource e.g. ponds in the lowlands.

Catchment naturalness. Undisturbed sites in natural or semi-natural (Tansley, 1939)

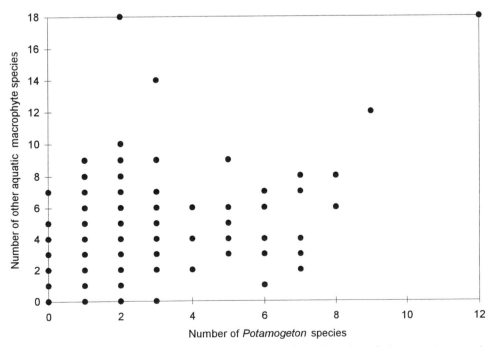

Figure 28.2   Relationship between number of *Potamogeton* species and number of other aquatic macrophyte species in lochs from two areas of Scotland (*n* = 197).

catchments are preferred to those which lie in areas where large tracts of land are devoted to forestry, agriculture or urban development as they are less likely to suffer human impacts (Table 28.3 (k)). One exception to this approach is atmospheric pollution from which no direct form of protection is possible. Evidence of this has been found from the composition of the sediments of high Cairngorm lochs which have shown slight signs of acidification resulting from atmospheric contamination (Jones *et al.*, 1993).

28.4.3.2 Refinements of the Nature Conservancy Council (1989) evaluation scheme

Bell and Butterfield (in preparation) extended the NCC (1989) evaluation methodology to identify the best examples of each loch Type at a regional level in Scotland. Two forms of assessment are used: an objective estimate of the number and rarity of species at a site (primary criteria) and a subjective assessment of other factors influencing the diversity and vulnerability of the habitats of a loch (secondary criteria).

The primary criteria include the number of open water species, the total number of species, and species rarity. Species rarity is calculated by allocating points for Red Data Book species or nationally scarce species (3 points), species in need of special protection within the relevant River Purification Board area (2 points) and species described as rare in a local flora (1 point). Up to date information on the distribution of aquatic species is obtained from the atlas of aquatic plant distribution (Croft *et al.*, 1991). For each site these ranks are summed to give a total rank.

The secondary criteria deal with the habitat diversity and naturalness of a site. Rather than assigning an absolute value to these features which are difficult to quantify, positive and negative points are awarded. The features are largely those identified as important in the *Guidelines for Selection of Biological SSSIs* (NCC, 1989) and include substrate variety, number of National Vegetation Classification (NVC) emergent sub-communities, presence of stands of tall reed swamp, presence of adjacent wetland, naturalness, and number of *Potamogeton* species.

A number of problems arise from Bell and Butterfield's approach. The addition of values for different features of a site to obtain an overall site score has been criticized by Goldsmith (1991):

> The addition of various parameters to make a composite value for a site is not recommended as the parameters are not equivalent to each other and therefore are not additive.

An improved technique would be to rank sites in order for each of several criteria, and then to rearrange the list of sites so that those with the highest values for criteria are moved to the top (Goldsmith, 1991). As a result, the best sites can be seen at a glance. Only two rules are needed: (a) the higher the ranking for any criterion, the better the site; and (b) the more criteria with a higher ranking, the better the site. This method is quite flexible and other criteria (e.g. educational, heritage or cultural value) could be added to the scheme if necessary. It would clearly be of value to examine the results of such an approach in future analysis of Scottish freshwater loch survey data.

28.4.3.3 Northern Ireland lake survey

A similar approach to the classification and evaluation of lakes was adopted in Northern Ireland by the Countryside and Wildlife Branch of the Department of the Environment. Following surveys of 338 randomly selected lakes in 1988 and 1989, three separate classifications were developed on the basis of the assemblages of aquatic macrophytes, lake shore vegetation and water chemistry (Wolfe-Murphy *et al.*, 1992). The macrophyte flora was used to assess conservation importance and to identify Areas of Special Scientific Interest (ASSIs). Their evaluation methodology was similar to that developed by the NCC (Palmer *et al.*, 1992) with a few modifications. It included both primary criteria (species rarity, species richness and typicality) and secondary criteria (number of *Potamogeton* species, open water area, total phosphorus, naturalness, structure of lake and lake vegetation, geographical position). The assessment recognized the difficulties associated with considering the relative conservation criteria as equal. In addition, they indicated that some features which were not measured may have been useful for assessing conservation value of sites e.g. catchment area, catchment naturalness, sediment diversity and diversity of vegetation structure.

28.4.3.4 National Vegetation Classification scheme

The National Vegetation Classification (NVC) also utilizes lake macrophytes to produce a lake classification scheme. The NVC was commissioned in 1974 following the recognition of a lack of any comprehensive classification of British vegetation types on which to base a systematic selection of habitats for conservation (Rodwell, 1995). The scheme describes communities of plants which are associated with particular habitat types. Of these, 28 swamp and fen, 24 aquatic and some mire communities are found in association with lake habitats. This scheme allows for the description of vegetation stands at a site but does not provide an overall site classification.

28.4.4 *Non-macrophyte lake classification and evaluation schemes*

Although there has been a considerable investment in the use of macrophytes in lake classification and evaluation schemes, other approaches have been developed in recent years. This is because macrophytes have been considered an unreliable means of selecting a representative range of sites for the conservation of other biotic groups, e.g invertebrates (Duigan and Kovach, 1994). Although fraught with the difficulties associated with sorting and identification (Premazzi and Chiaudani, 1992), a number of classification schemes for conservation based on standing water invertebrates have recently been developed in the UK.

28.4.4.1   Zooplankton

Duigan and Kovach (1994) examined the distribution of 33 littoral micro-crustacean (Ctenopoda, Anomopoda, Onchyopoda) taxa and aquatic macro-phyte communities in 51 freshwater lochs on the Isle of Skye, Scotland. Canonical Correspondence Analysis (CCA) was used to provide an overview of the relationships between the microcrustacean assemblages, the environmental data and the aquatic macrophyte community types used for floristic classification of standing waters. Cluster analysis was used to classify lochs based on their microcrustacean assemblages. The major trends in microcrustacean distributions were related to pH, catchment area, macrophyte diversity and distance from the sea, but there was little correlation between the plant community types and microcrustacean assemblages. This result led the authors to favour the development of an integrated approach to lake surveys so that correlations could be made between environmental variables and the distribution and abundance patterns of the plant and animal taxa of conservation interest.

28.4.4.2   Water beetles

Aquatic Coleoptera have been used to classify and assess the conservation value of wetland sites in Britain and Ireland (Eyre *et al.*, 1986, 1990; Foster *et al.*, 1990). The suitability of this group for such assessments is discussed by Foster (1987). The method involves allocating a score for the beetle species occurring at a site and using multivariate statistical analysis (TWINSPAN, Detrended Correspondence Analysis (DECORANA)) of species lists in order to rank and group them. A point scoring system has been developed on the basis of the distribution and ease of capture and identification of the beetle species (Foster, 1987). The species scores (SSs) are on a geometric scale from 1 for the most common species to 32 for the rarest. SS scores are also given to those species listed in the *Red Data Book* (Shirt, 1987) and those which are nationally notable (Ball, 1986). Species scores have been produced on a regional basis to allow for fine tuning in the assessment of conservation value of sites (Foster and Eyre, 1992).

For any one site, the SSs for all the beetle species recorded are added together and divided by the total number of beetle species found in order to produce a Species Quality Score (SQS). SQSs > 2 are considered to be 'good' beetle sites (Foster and Eyre, 1992). Additionally a WETland Site Coleoptera Record Evaluation (WETSCORE) can be calculated for each site as the product of the SQS and the number of species found. Values > 100 are considered to be 'top sites'.

Foster *et al.* (1992) made a limited attempt to find correlations between Irish water beetle assemblages and the vegetation classification of lakes in Northern Ireland. They noticed that certain beetle assemblages were found with equal frequency in all the vegetation classes, and it was suggested that a more detailed comparison between assemblages with an uneven frequency of occurrence, using a larger data set, could be more instructive. By contrast, Palmer (1981) found a positive correlation between the numbers of macrophyte species and the numbers of species of Coleoptera and Hemiptera, or Coleoptera alone in Breckland ponds.

Clearly, further work is required if these faunal groups are to be used in a nation-wide scheme.

28.4.5 *Classification and evaluation schemes for pond habitats*

An important subset of standing water habitats are ponds, which include waters from $1 m^2$ to 2ha in area (Pond Conservation Group, 1993). Since 1880 the number of ponds in Britain has fallen from 1.3×10^6 to 375×10^3 (a 75% loss) (Oldham and Swan, 1993). In the light of these losses and the known importance of ponds as wildlife habitats '*A Future for Britain's Ponds: An Agenda for Action*' has been produced (Pond Conservation Group, 1993). In the last two decades, a number of holistic assessments of pond quality have been developed. Pond Action (1991) surveyed the water chemistry, flora and fauna of 111 pond sites throughout Britain and following multivariate analysis (DECORANA, TWINSPAN) of the macroinvertebrate assemblages, produced a classification scheme which identified 16 groups of sites with similar macroinvertebrate communities. There was a high degree of overlap between groups and many sites were mis-classified in this scheme. It was the authors' hope that analysis of data from other sites would lead to the prediction of animal and plant communities of a pond using environmental data alone. They suggested that

> If survey results show there to be less animals or plants than predicted, then we will know that something is 'going wrong' with the site. The difference between predicted and actual flora and fauna might be due, for example, to water pollution or some other form of damage... The National Pond Survey results will provide us with a means of assessing whether or not a site is reaching its full potential for wildlife (Pond Action, 1991).

These were ambitious claims and the finalized scheme has not yet been published. Given the wide variety of biotic and abiotic factors (e.g. age, area, predation, water regime, colonization stochasticity) which determine pond plant and animal community structure, it seems unlikely that a simple classification will be possible on the basis of the macroinvertebrates. Similar difficulties arose in the use of multivariate statistics (DECORANA, TWINSPAN, CANOCO) to classify the biota of 30 lochs and ponds in Central Region, Scotland (Lassière, 1993). The preferred approach was to rank sites on the basis of 16 biotic and abiotic criteria, a technique which was developed for the selection of forest nature reserves in Nova Scotia, Canada (Goldsmith, 1987). Interestingly there was limited overlap between the sites with the highest diversity and number of rare plants and animals and those sites considered to have the most suitable habitat characteristics for wildlife.

28.5 Conflicting Situations Arising from Evaluations Based on Specific Biotic Groups

Most of the classification and evaluation schemes described above are based on single biotic groups (e.g. macrophytes, zooplankton). This approach has led to difficulties at sites where there are a number of conservation features of competing interest, or the management of one aspect may have a detrimental impact on another. A good example is Loch Eye (195 ha), a shallow inland loch in the Moray Firth lowlands of north-east Scotland. The spatial variation in the chemistry of water draining the catchment has resulted in the establishment of plant communities characteristic of both nutrient-rich and nutrient-poor conditions, resulting in high species diversity. This floral diversity had a strong bearing on its designation as an SSSI. It is also the second largest greylag goose (*Anser anser*) roost in the UK holding up to 30 000 at any one time. Large numbers of other bird species have been recorded, some of which reach national significance. Consequently, Loch Eye was designated under the Ramsar Convention as a wetland site of international importance and as a Special Protection Area under the terms of European Community Directive 79/409/EEC on the Conservation of Wild Birds in 1986.

Increasing numbers of roosting geese at Loch Eye, along with changes in land use in the catchment, have contributed to the development of extensive algal blooms at Loch Eye (Bailey-Watts and Kirika, 1991). These algal blooms, exacerbated by the loch's naturally low turnover rate, have become a public health problem and have also disrupted the popular brown trout fishery (Duncan, unpublished data). The eutrophication process may also have increased populations of epiphytic algae on the macrophyte beds which could explain their observed dieback in the summer months (Phillips *et al.*, 1978). It is likely that the nutrient enrichment will also result in diminished populations of macrophyte species which are typically found in nutrient-poor waters. It must be borne in mind that some dystrophic or oligotrophic species have a wide tolerance and are thought to be excluded from sites of higher trophic status by competition rather than physiological limitation (Seddon, 1972).

Loch Eye is a good example of how decisions restricted to the conservation of specific biotic groups can have a cascade effect on the integrity of the whole site, and illustrates that a more holistic approach to loch management in the past may have avoided current problems.

28.6   An Integrated Approach

It is clear how conservation classification and evaluation schemes based on specific biotic groups can lead to management problems. As a result, the value of these methods has been criticized and the broad ecosystem approach to this branch of environmental management and assessment has been endorsed (Whitman, 1995). Interestingly, the freshwater chapter of the NCC (1989) SSSI selection guidelines predicted the use of the entire biota in site evaluation. Developments in this direction have occurred for flowing fresh waters and have resulted in an integrated system for evaluating British rivers for conservation (SERCON) (Boon *et al.*, this volume). Lake assessments based on single biotic groups, such as the Palmer *et al.* (1992) macrophyte scheme, have been called into question because they assume that broad environmental gradients or individual vegetation communities can be used as surrogates for ecosystem variation (Duigan, 1995).

As far as lakes are concerned, it appears to be a logical step to follow one of two alternatives: either to incorporate standing waters into the broad-based SERCON scheme for flowing waters, or to develop a scheme for standing waters alone which adopts the integrated approach to both classification and evaluation.

The latter path has been followed by Duigan (1995) who attempted to classify five Welsh lakes according to their physical and chemical features, algae, aquatic macrophytes, zooplankton and macroinvertebrate communities. Using multi-variate analysis, lakes were divided into two groups on the basis of a restricted number of biotic and abiotic variables. Duigan (1995) predicted that it should be possible to identify key variables which summarize important gradients of eco-system variation. These in turn could be used in an integrated scheme without losing effective representation of total ecosystem variation.

Duigan's (1995) integrated approach is commendable in principle but in reality the availability of funds often dictates a more pragmatic approach. Conservation managers constantly face the challenge of trying to balance survey requirements with available money. In Scotland, where the freshwater resource is extensive it would be impossible in the short or medium term to collect the breadth of information for individual sites required for integrated classification schemes, except in a limited number of special cases e.g. the International Biological Programme study of Loch Leven (Morgan, 1974).

SNH's current extensive survey of Scottish freshwater macrophytes has resulted in a first attempt to classify and evaluate the standing water resource of Scotland. As macrophytes were the target group for survey only limited information is available for other biotic groups e.g. algae and invertebrates. SNH has identified ecological research and survey of these neglected groups as one of the main themes of a conservation strategy for Scotland's fresh waters (Boon, 1994) but it can only be achieved if it is seen as a major requirement for future conservation policy.

The logical development from an integrated lake classification and evaluation scheme would be an integrated catchment approach. The development of Geo-graphical Information Systems for whole catchments (e.g. work at present under way at the Macaulay Land Use Research Institute) will provide a useful medium for the manipulation of data relating to fresh waters. The challenge for the twenty-first century will be to convince those concerned with conservation of fresh waters to allocate the resources to realize this goal.

Acknowledgements

We would like to thank the Environmental Audit Branch of Scottish Natural Heritage for help in the production of the Scottish map.

References

Adams, C. E. (1994). The fish community of Loch Lomond, Scotland: its history and rapidly changing status. *Hydrobiologia*, **390**, 91–102.

Bailey-Watts, A. E. and Kirika, A. (1991). *Loch Eye, Easter Ross—A Case Study in Eutrophication.* Final report to the Nature Conservancy Council (March 1991). Institute of Freshwater Ecology, Edinburgh.

Ball, S. G. (1986). *Invertebrate Site Register.* Nature Conservancy Council Contract Report No. 637, Peterborough.

Bell, S. L. and Butterfield, I. (in preparation). *A Standard Method for Surveying Scottish Freshwater Lochs.* Scottish Natural Heritage Research, Survey and Monitoring Report.

Boon, P. J. (1994). Nature conservation. In: Maitland, P. S., Boon, P. J. and McLusky, D. S. (Eds), *The Fresh Waters of Scotland: a National Resource of International Significance.* John Wiley, Chichester, 555–576.

Boon, P. J., Holmes, N. T. H., Maitland, P. S., Rowell, T. A. and Davies, J. (This volume). A system for evaluating rivers for conservation (SERCON): development, structure and function.

Commission of the European Communities (1995). *Wise Use and Conservation of Wetlands.* Communication from the Commission to the Council and the European Parliament COM (95) 189 final, 29.05.95, Brussels.

Croft, J. M., Preston, C. D. and Forrest, W. A. (1991). *Database of Aquatic Plants in the British Isles. Phase I (Submerged and Floating Plants).* Project Report F028/1/N, National Rivers Authority, London.

Department of the Environment (1992). *This Common Inheritance. The Second Year Report: Summary Booklet.* Department of the Environment, London.

Dugan, P. J. (Ed.) (1990). *Wetland Conservation: a Review of Current Issues and Required Action.* International Union for Conservation of Nature and Natural Resources, Gland.

Duigan, C. A. (1995). *Integrated Classification and Assessment of Lakes in Wales: Phase 1.* Countryside Council for Wales Contract Science Report No. 85, Bangor.

Duigan, C. A. and Kovach, W. I. (1994). Relationships between littoral microcrustacea and aquatic macrophyte communities on the Isle of Skye (Scotland), with implications for the conservation of standing waters. *Aquatic Conservation: Marine and Freshwater Ecosystems, 4,* 307–331.

Elster, H. J. (1974). History of limnology. *Mitteilungen der Internationalen Vereinigung für theoretische und angewandte Limnologie, 20,* 7–30.

Eyre, M. D., Ball, S. G. and Foster, G. N. 1986. An initial classification of the habitats of aquatic Coleoptera in north-east England. *Journal of Applied Ecology, 23,* 841–852.

Eyre, M. D., Foster, G. N. and Foster, A. P. (1990). Factors affecting the distribution of water beetle assemblages in drains of Eastern England. *Journal of Applied Entomology, 109,* 217–225.

Fisher, R. (1993). Biological aspects of the conservation of wetlands. In: Goldsmith, F. B. and Warren, A. (Eds), *Conservation in Progress.* John Wiley, Chichester, 97–113.

Foster, G. N. (1987). The use of Coleoptera records in assessing the conservation status of wetlands. In: Luff, M. L. (Ed.), *The Use of Invertebrate Community Data in Environmental Assessment.* Agricultural Environment Research Group, University of Newcastle, Newcastle upon Tyne, 8–17.

Foster, G. N. and Eyre, M. D. (1992). *Classification and Ranking of Water Beetle Communities.* U.K. Nature Conservation No. 1, Joint Nature Conservation Committee, Peterborough.

Foster, G. N., Foster, A. P., Eyre, M. D. and Bilton, D. T. (1990). Classification of water beetle assemblages in arable fenland and ranking of sites in relation to conservation value. *Freshwater Biology, 22,* 343–354.

Foster, G. N., Nelson, B. H., Bilton, D. T., Lott, D. A., Merritt, R., Weyl, R. S. and Eyre, M. D. (1992). A classification and evaluation of Irish water beetle assemblages. *Aquatic Conservation: Marine and Freshwater Ecosystems, 2,* 185–208.

Fozzard, I. R., Doughty, C. R. and Leatherland, T. M. (This volume). Defining the quality of Scottish freshwater lochs.

Goldsmith, F. B. (1987). Selection procedures for forest nature reserves in Nova Scotia, Canada. *Biological Conservation, 41,* 185–201.

Goldsmith, F. B. (1991). The selection of protected areas. In: Spellerberg, I. F., Goldsmith, F. B. and Morris, M. G. (Eds), *The Scientific Management of Temperate Communities for Conservation.* Blackwell, Oxford, 273–291.

Hill, M. O. (1979). TWINSPAN—a FORTRAN Program for arranging multivariate data in an ordered two-way table by classification of the individuals and attributes. *Ecology and Systematics,* Cornell University, Ithaca, New York.

Hynes, H. B. N. (1960). *The Biology of Polluted Waters.* Liverpool University Press, Liverpool.

Jones, V. J., Flower, R. J., Appleby, P. G., Natkanski, J., Richardson, N., Rippey, B., Stevenson, A. C. and Battarbee, R. W. (1993). Palaeolimnological evidence for acidification and atmospheric contamination of lochs in the Cairngorm and Lochnagar areas of Scotland. *Journal of Ecology,* **81,** 3–24.

Lassière, O. L. (1993). 'Central Region Lochs and Ponds: the Operation Brightwater Survey of their Status; Past, Present and Future.' Unpublished report from the University of Stirling and Scottish Conservation Projects.

Leach, J. H. and Herron, R. C. (1992). A review of lake habitat classification. In: Busch, W.-Dieter, N. and Sly, P. G. (Eds), *The Development of an Aquatic Habitat Classification System for Lakes.* CRC Press, Inc., Boca Raton, 27–57.

Luken, J. O. (1994). Valuing plants in natural areas. *Natural Areas Journal,* **14,** 295–299.

Lyle, A. A. and Smith, I. R. (1994). Standing waters. In: Maitland, P. S., Boon, P. J. and McLusky, D. S. (Eds), *The Fresh Waters of Scotland: A National Resource of International Significance.* John Wiley, Chichester, 35–50.

Macaulay Land Use Research Institute (1993). *The Land Cover of Scotland, 1988, Final Report.* The Macaulay Land Use Research Institute, Aberdeen.

Morgan, N. C. (1974). Historical background to the International Biological Programme project at Loch Leven, Kinross. *Proceedings of the Royal Society of Edinburgh B,* **74,** 45–56.

Moss, B., Johnes, P. and Phillips, G. (This volume). New approaches to monitoring and classifying standing waters.

Navid, D. (1994a). A threatened habitat: wetlands. In: Bennett, G. (Ed.), *Conserving Europe's Natural Heritage. Towards a European Ecological Network.* Proceedings of the international conference held in Maastricht, 9–12 November 1993. International Environment Law and Policy Series. Graham and Trotman/Martinus Nijhoff, London, 55–59.

Navid, D. (1994b). The legal development of the Convention on Wetlands: getting it right, or the importance of proper legal drafting. *Ramsar Newsletter Special Issue,* April.

NCC (1984). *Nature Conservation in Britain.* Shrewsbury.

NCC (1989). *Guidelines for Selection of Biological SSSIs.* Peterborough.

Oldham, R. and Swan, M. (1993). Pond loss—the present position. In: Aistrop, C. and Biggs, J. (Eds), *Protecting Britain's Ponds.* Wildfowl and Wetlands Trust and Pond Action, Oxford, 8–25.

Palmer, M. A. (1981). Relationship between species richness of macrophytes in insects in some water bodies in the Norfolk Breckland. *Entomologist's Monthly Magazine,* **117,** 35–46.

Palmer, M. A. (1989). *A Botanical Classification of Standing Waters in Great Britain and a Method for the Use of Macrophyte Flora in Assessing Changes in Water Quality.* Research and Survey in Nature Conservation No. 19. Nature Conservancy Council, Peterborough.

Palmer, M. A., Bell, S. L. and Butterfield, I. (1992). A botanical classification of standing waters in Great Britain: applications for conservation and monitoring. *Aquatic Conservation: Marine and Freshwater Ecosystems,* **2,** 125–143.

Palmer, M. A. and Newbold, C. (1983). *Wetland Plants in Great Britain.* Focus on Nature Conservation, No. 1. Nature Conservancy Council, Peterborough.

Phillips, G. L., Eminson, D. and Moss, B. (1978). A mechanism to account for macrophyte decline in progressively eutrophicated freshwaters. *Aquatic Botany,* **4,** 103–126.

Pond Action (1991). 'Preliminary Results from the National Pond Survey: Single Season Analysis of Macroinvertebrate Samples from 111 National Pond Survey Sites'. Unpublished report from Pond Action, Oxford.

Pond Conservation Group (1993). *A Future for Britain's Ponds: An Agenda for Action.* Pond Conservation Group, Oxford.

Premazzi, G. and Chiaudani, G. (1992). *EUR 14563—Ecological Quality of Surface Waters: Quality Assessment Schemes for European Community Lakes.* Environmental Quality of Life Series. European Communities Commission, Brussels.

Preston, C. D. (1995). *Pondweeds of Great Britain and Ireland.* BSBI Handbook No. 8. Botanical Society of the British Isles, London.

Probert, C. (1989). *Pearls in the Landscape.* Farming Press, Ipswich.

Ratcliffe, D. R. (Ed.) (1977). *A Nature Conservation Review.* Cambridge University Press, Cambridge.

Richardson, C. J. (1995). Wetlands ecology. In: Nierenberg, W. A. (Ed.), *Encyclopedia of Environmental Biology*. Academic Press, London, 535–550.

Rodwell, J. S. (1995). *British Plant Communities, Volume 4. Aquatic Communities, Swamps and Tall-herb Fens*. Cambridge University Press, Cambridge.

Seddon, B. (1972). Aquatic macrophytes as limnological indicators. *Freshwater Biology,* **2,** 107–130.

Shirt, D. B. (Ed.) (1987). *British Red Data Books. 2. Insects*. Nature Conservancy Council, Peterborough.

Tansley, A. G. (1939). *The British Islands and their Vegetation*. Cambridge University Press, London.

US Fish and Wildlife Service (1984). *Wetlands of the United States: Current Status and Recent Trends*. Washington DC.

Usher, M. B. (Ed.) (1986). *Wildlife Conservation Evaluation*. Chapman and Hall, London.

Whitman, R. L. (1995). Introduction: Assessment of aquatic ecosystems. *Natural Areas Journal,* **15,** 215.

Wolfe-Murphy, S. A., Lawrie, E. W., Smith, S. J. and Gibson, C. E. (1992). *Section 1. Introduction to the Classification of Lakes in Northern Ireland and Section 6. Site Evaluation: the Assessment of Conservation Importance*. Report from the Northern Ireland Lakes Survey. Countryside and Wildlife Branch of the Department of the Environment, Northern Ireland, Belfast.

29 ASSESSING THE NATURE CONSERVATION VALUE OF FRESH WATERS: A SCANDINAVIAN VIEW

T. Wiederholm

Summary

1. There is a growing recognition in Scandinavia that nature conservation is vital to sustainable development, and that environmental considerations must be given equal weight to social and economic ones in the development of society. This increases the requirement for relevance and reproducibility of methods used in assessing nature conservation values.

2. Historically, traditional conservation criteria, e.g. diversity, naturalness, representativeness, rarity, etc. have been used to describe conservation value. National parks, nature reserves, areas of national interest, and reference watercourses have been established on the basis of such criteria. Methods and value judgments have changed over time, however, and the available information is difficult to use in spatial and temporal comparisons and for management purposes. Parallel to the traditional conservation criteria, water quality criteria have been developed and used in both Norway and Sweden.

3. The recent development is toward integration of habitat characteristics and information on organisms into systems that enable numerical descriptions and comparisons between sites and ecosystems. Furthermore, environmental objectives are increasingly being used to define direction and ambition of the environmental policies. Many of these objectives are formulated by use of criteria and numerical values that have been derived for assessment of conservation value.

4. Monitoring and surveillance are increasingly being recognized as fundamental to nature conservation, with the dual purpose of providing baseline values for nature conservation criteria and to provide a basis for assessing compliance with environmental standards.

29.1   Introduction

The International Union for Conservation of Nature and Natural Resources (IUCN) (1980) has described nature conservation as being:

> The management of human use of the biosphere so that it may yield the greatest sustainable benefit to present generations while maintaining its potential to meet the needs and aspirations of future generations. Thus, conservation is positive, embracing preservation, maintenance, sustainable utilization, restoration, and enhancement of the natural environment.

From the above it follows that nature conservation involves:

- Definition of scope—what is to be preserved and protected?
- Development of measures/indicators of conservation value.
- Identification of areas/sites with particular conservation values, through surveys and inventories.
- Analysis of the vulnerability of, and threats to, conservation values.
- Establishment of measurable goals/objectives.
- Development of strategies and programmes to meet the goals, aimed at different sectors of society and appropriate geographic levels—international, national or regional.
- Development of monitoring systems.
- Establishment of appropriate legal and administrative procedures.
- Communication—between scientists, administrators, politicians and the general public.

This chapter reviews how the conservation value of fresh waters has been assessed in Scandinavia and how vulnerability analyses, environmental objectives and monitoring may be applied in nature conservation.

29.2   The Scandinavian Environment

A large share of the natural fresh waters of Europe is located in Scandinavia (Norway and Sweden), Finland and the Karelo-Kola part of the Russian Federation (Kristensen and Hansen, 1994). Approximately 240,000 lakes larger than 1 ha occur on the Scandinavian peninsula, among which are the five deepest and two of the five largest lakes of Europe (The Swedish Lake Register maintained by the Swedish Meteorological and Hydrological Institute; Bernes, 1993; Henriksen *et al.*, 1996).

Within the 48 ecoregions that have been recognized within Scandinavia (Nordic Council of Ministers, 1984) a range of widely different lake and stream types occur, from the nutrient-poor waters of the mountain areas, over the humic waters of the boreal forest regions, to the eutrophic waters of the more fertile lowland areas in the south and central parts of Scandinavia.

Owing to the history of glaciation, the species richness of the aquatic ecosystems in Scandinavia is expected to be lower than in non-glaciated parts of Europe and other parts of the world with similar climatic and edaphic conditions. Species inventories are far from complete, but more than 2,600 species of freshwater animals from 16 phyla are recorded from Norway (Aagaard and Dolmen, 1996).

Given the abundance of waters and the low population density of Scandinavia compared with most other parts of Europe (2100 inhabitants ha^{-1} compared with 10,100 in Europe not including the former Soviet Union and 23,800 in the British Isles), lakes and watercourses in Scandinavia are probably in a better state than those in many other parts of Europe. Yet, substantial parts of the natural fresh water resources have been lost, degraded or threatened by agricultural and industrial development, urban development and the long-range transport of atmospheric pollutants (Swedish Environmental Protection Agency—SEPA, 1990; Bernes, 1993, 1994). For example, nearly 17,000 projects to lower or drain water bodies took place in southern and central Sweden between 1880 and 1930, many with financial support from the state, the aim being to increase the amount of agricultural land. Few watercourses within the agricultural landscape have retained their natural shape. Two-thirds of the potential resources for electric power production have been exploited, including nearly all major rivers in Sweden. More than half of the total lake surface area is affected by water regulation. Eutrophication of surface waters is common in areas with high population densities or intensive agriculture. Acid rain has reduced the productivity and biodiversity of numerous lakes and watercourses in sensitive areas of southern Scandinavia. Heavy metals and organic pollutants occur in high concentrations in several locations.

29.3 Assessment of Conservation Value

29.3.1 *National parks and nature reserves*

Sweden was the first country in Europe to establish national parks, when nine areas were set aside in 1909 (see Plate 4c). Until now, 42 national parks have been established in Scandinavia—18 in Norway and 24 in Sweden—representing 4.2% and 1.3% of the countries' land areas, respectively. In addition, a large number of nature reserves have been established. In many of the protected areas aquatic habitats are important components of the conservation value—in Sweden 17% of the protected area is covered by water. However, rather few areas have been established with limnological values as a primary reason (1–2%, nature conservation areas included) (SEPA, 1991a; Statistics Sweden and SEPA, 1995).

Criteria for national parks and other protected natural areas have been established by the IUCN and other international organizations. These criteria have formed the basis for the Swedish Environmental Protection Agency's set of rules, shown in Table 29.1. As seen, representativeness, naturalness, uniqueness and size are considered as essential criteria. In the procedure of designating protected areas these criteria are applied subjectively, based on surveys of geology, vegetation, species inventories, and so on.

Table 29.1   Criteria for national parks according to the Swedish Environmental Protection Agency (SEPA, 1989a)

National parks should meet the following standards:
- Consist of areas with representative or unique types of Swedish landscape in a system covering the whole country
- Consist of untouched natural or nearly natural landscape
- Contain landscape formations, features or natural environments that are magnificent or highly unusual and which have high scientific value
- Cover a large area, normally at least 1000 ha
- Can be used within reasonable limits for outdoor recreational pursuits and research without natural values being threatened

29.3.2   Sweden's areas of national interest to nature conservation

In the process of physical planning, and later in response to the nature resources law, SEPA has decided on areas of national interest to nature conservation. Altogether, 1366 sites, covering 10^6 ha, have been designated as areas of national interest. This is about 20% of the total land and water area of Sweden. Areas of national interest to nature conservation are loosely protected under the Natural Resources Act, according to which they shall be protected against measures that may substantially damage the natural or cultural environment. The provisions of the law are primarily implemented by the Planning and Building Act in the process of physical planning, and by the Nature Conservation Act, which regulates the management of the natural environment and offers protection through designation as national parks, nature reserves, natural monuments or nature conservation areas (Johansson and Gull, in preparation).

Criteria used to select areas of national interest for nature conservation were developed by SEPA in cooperation with the National Board of Fisheries, county authorities, universities and other organizations (Table 29.2). Based on these criteria and the available information, the counties selected their most important areas. These were reviewed by SEPA, which later decided that areas which were to be accepted as being of national interest were those unique in the ecoregion, in the country or internationally. The ecoregions used were those previously established for the Nordic countries (Nordic Council of Ministers, 1984). Parallel work was done to select areas of national interest to outdoor life.

The criteria and procedure for selection of areas of national interest were later expanded somewhat and published as a general handbook for the inventory and assessment of conservation value of lakes and watercourses (SEPA, 1989b). The procedure included nearly 100 indicators of the criteria mentioned above. Based on the available evidence for each indicator, the user was expected to arrive at a classification for each criterion as being high, average or low, and to a summarizing judgement on each water body. The guidelines have not been widely used or implemented, possibly because much work had already been put into selecting areas important to conservation, possibly also because of a certain ambiguity

Table 29.2   Criteria used for assessing conservation value in Norway's watercourse protection plan (Anonymous, 1983, 1991) and the selection of areas of national interest to nature conservation in Sweden (SEPA, 1986, 1991b).

	Norway	*Sweden*
Size	•	•
Diversity	•	•
Naturalness		•
Continuity		•
Representativeness	•	•
Rarity	•	•
Importance to research or education	•	•
Uniqueness	•	•
Ecological function (gene bank, productivity, etc.)	•	•
Vulnerability	•	•
Possibility of retaining natural values		•
Documentation of historical conditions	•	
Documentation of recent processes	•	
Productivity	•	
Usefulness as reference area	•	
Well-studied area	•	

concerning the requirements for supporting data and the deduction of conservation value.

Somewhat simplified methods have been used by county authorities for regional planning and evaluation purposes (e.g. Berntell *et al.*, 1988). These methods have also involved a certain degree of subjective judgement by the user. Development of new national guidelines is currently under way (see the discussion on System Aqua below and elsewhere in this volume).

29.3.3   Norway's watercourse protection plan

An extensive national plan for the protection of natural watercourses was adopted by the Norwegian parliament in successive steps taken in 1973, 1980, 1986 and 1993. The national plan is concerned primarily with hydropower exploitation by banning licensing for any such schemes within the protected river systems. 340 river systems have been included in the national plan. These represent a total energy resource of $35 \, \text{TWh yr}^{-1}$, or 20% of Norway's total amount of commercially exploitable hydroelectric power (NWEA, 1994).

The evaluation of watercourses included scientific, cultural and recreational aspects. Watercourses were placed in one of four value classes (small, moderate, large, very large) based on information on their geomorphology and the occurrence of plants and animals, and with the use of a large number of 'traditional' conservation criteria (Table 29.2) (Anonymous, 1983, 1991; Faugli, 1994). The classification was based on expert judgment, with several university institutions being involved in the process of collecting and analysing information. It was explicitly stated that criteria could not be weighted or summarized, but had to be judged against the specific goal of the watercourse protection plan (Anonymous, 1983; see also Anonymous, 1991, and Faugli, 1994).

For management purposes, the following grouping was suggested, with increasing demand for protection (Anonymous, 1991):

- Watercourses near large population concentrations or in the cultural landscape.
- Type watercourses, defined as: 'Watercourses that may represent a large number of watercourses in the region or part of the country where they belong and that contain as many as possible of the region's nature types and nature forms with their plant and animal life'.
- Watercourses with high botanical/zoological/geological value.
- Reference watercourses, defined as: '... untouched watercourses where the natural processes are allowed to develop unaffected by human influence as much as possible'.

A number of reference watercourses have recently been proposed based on a smaller number of criteria: (a) the 'degree of impact', (b) whether the area is or can be protected, and (c) scientific values (geomorphological, botanical, freshwater and terrestrial fauna) (Øvstedal, 1995). The degree of impact (i.e. naturalness) was given the highest priority. Several of the proposed watercourses are located in existing or planned national parks, which may have to be expanded to include the reference watercourses.

29.3.4   The Swedish Watercourses Commission

A similar classification of watercourses as in the Norwegian watercourse protection plan was recently suggested by The Watercourses Commission (1994) of Sweden. The Commission had been given the task by the government to suggest which further valuable water areas and watercourse stretches should be protected from hydropower development. Four categories were recognized: (a) natural (in as much as possible) reference watercourses, (b) type watercourses, (c) watercourses with significant cultural value, and (d) watercourses with special nature value. The Commission had been preceded by a number of studies with similar aims, resulting in several watercourses being exempted from hydropower development through decisions by Parliament. However, objective or quantifiable criteria (enabling comparisons to be made) for conservation values in protected watercourses have been lacking. Furthermore, methods and value judgements have changed over time, which means that the information available at present on conservation values is incomplete and based on variable criteria (Brandel, in The Watercourses Commission, 1994).

The Commission received more than 1000 suggestions from county authorities in response to its questionnaire on areas that were deemed valuable to nature conservation. It suggested some 20 areas as possible type watercourses but concluded that more work was needed to identify criteria and undertake inventories before further areas could be selected. The Commission was given the task by the Department of Environment and Natural Resources to continue its work, and to suggest criteria and methods for inventories that could be completed within a few years and result in a uniform judgement of conservation values for watercourses in the whole of Sweden. The future work of the Commission is based on the assumption that a stepwise approach has to be used, in which possible areas may be identified by simple criteria and data sources, permitting large areas to be examined relatively quickly.

Representativeness and naturalness are considered to be important criteria. To assess the former, watercourse regions will be defined, based on existing ecoregions and the distribution of fish and macrophytes (southern Sweden), or the precipitation pattern and the distribution of cultivated land (northern Sweden). The latter criterion will initially be assessed as the degree of fragmentation, measured as the occurrence of regulation dams on the watercourse, and based on information in the dam register of the Swedish Meteorological and Hydrological Institute.

In the subsequent analysis remote sensing may be used for a further assessment of naturalness. Based on the analysis of black and white high-level images (1:50,000–1:60,000), watercourse stretches with a minimum length of 200 m will be classified as unaffected, slightly affected or strongly affected, depending on the occurrence of different land types in the nearest 50–100 m from the watercourse. The results may be reported as the amount and distribution of the various classes of naturalness and as indices of fragmentation and diversity (Granath, 1995).

A number of additional criteria may be used if the image analysis does not give relevant information:

- Occurrence of lakes, rapids, meanders, deltas, wetlands
- Occurrence of fish, top carnivores, bottom fauna
- Social aspects, sectoral values, local conservation values
- Degree of regulation, eutrophication, acidification, occurrence of toxic substances

The Watercourse Commission will report its findings in October 1996 to the Department of Environment and Natural Resources.

29.3.5 *Water quality criteria and indices*

National guidelines for classifying water bodies using mostly physical and chemical indicators exist in both Norway and Sweden (NPCA, 1989; SEPA, 1991c; Holtan and Ibrekk, 1993). The Norwegian guidelines enable water bodies to be classified both with respect to the degree of pollution and suitability for different uses, whereas the Swedish guidelines may be used to classify status and degree of human impact (Table 29.3). Both systems use natural background values as a basis for the evaluation of pollution/human impact, either by comparison with historical data, unpolluted reference areas, or background values predicted from physical or chemical conditions in the water bodies under consideration.

In the Norwegian guidelines, nature conservation is one among several areas

Table 29.3   Overview of national water quality criteria variables in Norway and Sweden (NPCA, 1989; SEPA, 1991c).

	Norway	Sweden
Status and degree of perturbation/pollution (1)		
Nutrients		
Total P	X	X
Total N	X	X
Chlorophyll	X	
Primary education	X	
Secchi depth	X	
Organic matter		
COD	X	X
TOC	X	
Secchi depth	X	
Oxygen	X	X
Light and particulate materials		
Colour		X
Turbidity	X	X
Secchi depth	X	X
Suspended solids	X	X
pH and alkalinity		
pH	X	X
Alkalinity	X	X
Toxic substances		
Heavy metals	X	X
Microbiological conditions		
E. coli	X	
Suitability for water resource use		
Municipal water supply	X	
Irrigation	X	
Bathing	X	
Boating	X	
Aquaculture/fish farming	X	
Fishing	X	
Nature conservation	X	
Preservation of ancient monuments related to water resources	X	

Notes: Norway. Four pollution classes; calculated as present status relative to background conditions. *Sweden.* Five classes (present conditions) and four degrees of human impact (present status relative to background conditions).

of water resource use. The criteria of the Norwegian watercourse protection plan (see above) are said to be too extensive and demanding with respect to information need and scientific basis to be generally useful in municipal planning. Instead, a simplified evaluation scheme is suggested, consisting of six criteria (naturalness, recreational and aesthetic value, biological function, diversity, rarity, and value for research and education) and the classification of water bodies (by judgement) into one of the four classes for each criterion. A concluding summary recommends whether or not the water should be protected in municipal planning.

In many European countries, biological indices and scoring methods have been standardized and/or officially endorsed for water quality assessments at a national or regional level (De Pauw *et al.*, 1992). Various indices are also used more or less widely in Scandinavia (Johnson *et al.*, 1993), but none has been recognized as a national standard by the authorities. The Nordic Council of Ministers is currently sponsoring a project to investigate the possibility of reporting the biological water quality in all the Nordic countries using monitoring methods based on macroinvertebrates (Friberg and Johnson, 1995).

29.3.6 *System Aqua*

The need for an expanded system—beyond the current water quality criteria—for assessing the environmental quality of lakes and watercourses has resulted in SEPA sponsoring the development of System Aqua (see Willén *et al.*, this volume). The system is to be used both for identifying waters with particular nature conservation value, and also for impact assessment and evaluating restoration requirements. System Aqua is being developed and modelled after SERCON (System for Evaluating Rivers for Conservation) (see Boon *et al.*, this volume), having general and specific features in common with it, but also several characteristics that are unique.

System Aqua places particular emphasis on biological qualities, and evaluates both the water bodies and their catchment areas. Evaluation is based on habitat characteristics and indirect measures of the biological communities. The catchment area is evaluated using two criteria and the water body by six, each one characterized by a number of indicators (Table 27.1 in Willén *et al.*, this volume) scored from 0 to 5. Results are weighted and may be presented graphically to show the specific criteria profile for a site and its catchment area. Supplementary background information on each site and its catchment is also provided. An important feature of System Aqua is that it can be used in a stepwise manner. In the first step, a preliminary or limited assessment can be made using information from maps, statistics on land use and/or the analysis of aerial photographs. This may be followed by broader assessment, involving the remaining indicators or criteria. The methods that are to be used for field inventories are the same ones being prescribed by SEPA for national and regional environmental monitoring.

29.4 Vulnerability Analyses

In the long run, the usefulness of techniques for assessing the conservation value of fresh water is limited unless the likelihood of retaining conservation value can also be assessed. Concepts such as diversity, rarity and naturalness have received considerable attention in the ecological literature and much work has been put into developing measures of these properties (cf. the abundant literature on diversity indices). However, much less has been done to develop tools for determining the sensitivity of specific values and bringing this into the management process in an orderly way. Two such examples may be mentioned here: the prediction of how lakes respond to eutrophication, and the calculation of critical load of sulphur and nitrogen to surface waters.

The sensitivity of lakes to eutrophication has been calculated by different types of Vollenweider models, where the critical state was originally defined as that where the lake might change from a mesotrophic to a eutrophic state (Vollenweider, 1976). These models enabled the user to estimate critical levels for phosphorus loading and, based on source apportionment, to devise management plans for catchment areas. An advanced application of this approach was used on Norway's largest lake, Lake Mjøsa (Ibrekk *et al.*, 1993), where the project 'Locally Adapted Regulatory Impact Analysis' (LARIA) developed a methodology involving: (a) identification and weighting of user interest, (b) modelling the effect of pollution loading on water quality, (c) modelling the benefits to society from improvements in water quality, and (d) identification and ranking of abatement measures and the performance of a cost analysis for each measure. Nature conservation was included here among user interests and was given the highest weighting among these (55%). Other user interests were identified as drinking water supply (14%), 'interests downstream' (12%), bathing (5%), sports fishing, other recreational activities, boating, irrigation and industrial water supply (each less than 5%).

The Swedish Environmental Protection Agency is currently sponsoring a 'tool box' project to develop catchment analysis and loading estimates, in parallel with the System Aqua project mentioned above. The approach is similar to that of LARIA, but the scope is somewhat narrower.

Critical load is defined as 'a quantitative estimate of the loading of one or more pollutants below which significant harmful effects on specified sensitive elements of the environment are not likely to occur according to our present knowledge' (Nilsson and Grennfelt, 1988). The concept has been widely used in dealing with the effects of airborne pollutants (sulphur and nitrogen) on Scandinavian fresh waters (Henriksen *et al.*, 1992). Observations on the occurrence of sensitive species of fish (salmon, brown trout, roach) have been used to establish numerically-based chemical criteria. Simple steady-state models have then been applied to estimate the loading levels that will meet these criteria. Based on national inventories of lakes, the critical loading within the Nordic countries has been mapped and compared with the measured and/or calculated loading. The approach has been expanded to other areas and has formed the basis for international agreements on the reduction of air pollution (Hettelingh *et al.*, 1991).

At the species level the need for better data on the environmental requirements and vulnerability of endangered and sensitive species as well as indicator species for various biotopes has been stressed (Larsson *et al.*, 1992; SEPA, 1995), but little work has been done so far.

29.5   Environmental Objectives

Assessing nature conservation value also involves environmental objectives, either as a basis for, or as a result of, the assessment procedure. SEPA (1993) recognized four types of environmental objectives.

- Overall environmental objectives: describe the desirable environmental situation in general terms for different ecosystems.
- Environmental quality objectives (EQOs): define the status to be achieved by a given time in terms of quantifiable biological, chemical or physical units.
- Objectives related to pollution loads or physical impact: express the greatest acceptable impact that will meet the quality objectives.
- Objectives related to abatement: stipulate the results (e.g. emission reductions, protected areas) that a set of measures are to produce within a given period of time.

A number of EQOs are currently being considered by the environmental authorities in Sweden and Norway in which biological, chemical and physical variables are used (Table 29.4). Among the Swedish EQOs, the ones describing the desirable water quality in chemical terms—alkalinity, nutrients and toxic substances—have been introduced already in earlier action programmes, whereas the biological objectives are new and related to the proposed EC Directive on the Ecological Quality of Water (see Preface). The objectives for fresh waters in mountain areas, based on indicator species, are also new, with few similarities elsewhere (see Reynoldson, 1993). Regarding the EQOs for habitats and species it may be noted that the reference level is set at the beginning of the 1990s. This may seem rather late in view of the losses of species and habitats that have already taken place, but a more ambitious level would probably be difficult to attain. A general problem here is the availability of reference data on aquatic habitats and species from the beginning of the 1990s, since inventories of aquatic habitats and species have not been undertaken on any broader scale.

The objective on red-listed species implies not only the preservation of these species and their habitats, but also active measures to restore habitats and populations. So far, the most extensive work aimed at restoring habitats and species has been the Swedish liming programme (Henrikson and Brodin, 1995). Other habitats that have been restored are wetlands (Larsson, 1992), hypereutrophic lakes and watercourses, and a few water bodies polluted by heavy metals or PCBs (SEPA, 1982). Plans are currently under way for restoring habitat and/or populations of European catfish (*Silurus glanis*) (Nathanson, National Board of Fisheries, personal communication), otter (*Lutra lutra*), and several other red-listed species of fish (Torsten Larsson, SEPA, personal communication). Several local or regional projects concerning birds and amphibians are sponsored by WWF (Lennart Nyman, World Wide Fund for Nature, Sweden, personal communication).

Table 29.4   Environmental objectives relating to the freshwater environment, proposed or considered by environmental authorities in Sweden (SEPA, 1995) and Norway (see text).

Sweden

Overall objective for surface waters:

Lakes, watercourses, and seas must support viable, balanced populations of naturally occurring species. Pollution is not to limit the use of fresh waters for the production of drinking water.

Environmental quality objectives (EQOs) for lakes and watercourses:

Biological diversity as in areas without significant human impact. Key taxa associated with undisturbed conditions should be present.

N and P $\leqslant 2 \times$ natural background (may need modification in agricultural areas). No indication of excessive development of macrophytes or algae due to human influence.

Oxygen levels that permit survival and reproduction of native biota.

Alkalinity $\geqslant 0.75 \times$ natural background, but not < 0.05 meq L^{-1} unless natural.

Toxic substances below known effect levels. Background levels of metals not higher than at present.

Natural water regime in unexploited watercourses.

EQOs for mountain areas

pH and alkalinity permitting the following species to occur: *Acentrella lapponicum* (Ephemeroptera) in small watercourses, *Gammarus lacustris* (watercourses, small water bodies and larger lakes), and *Polyarcinicta forsipata* and *Branchinecta polydosa* (Crustacea) in temporary waters.

EQOs for habitats and species

Habitat diversity shall be maintained at least at the same level as at the beginning of the 1990s.

All native species that are not red-listed shall occur in viable populations in all regions where they have their natural area of distribution.

Rare and care-demanding species shall occur in viable populations at least to the same extent as at the beginning of the 1990s.

Red-listed species, species in the EU's Habitats and Birds Directives, and other acutely threatened or vulnerable species shall occur in viable populations at least to the same extent as at the beginning of the 1990s, and be given the opportunity to increase their area of distribution.

Norway

Conservation of biological diversity and nature

Water quality

Particles $< 1.3 \times$ natural background

Phosphorus $< 1.3 \times$ natural background

Algae $< 1.3 \times$ natural background

Natural quality	*(1)*	*(2)*
Water flow	90–110%	$<70/>130\%$
Regulation	<1m	>3m
Channelization	none	>200m
Development of shore line	<100m	>300m
Lake lowering	<0.5m	>1m
Remaining riparian zone, length	$>90\%$	$<70\%$
Remaining riparian zone, width	$>50\%$	$<25\%$
Unaffected by gravel extraction	$>95\%$	$<70\%$
	(1) Suitable, (2) Less suitable.	

PLATE 5: SCOTTISH FRESHWATER LANDSCAPES

5a(right) – Rannoch Moor (Photo: L Gill).

5b(top) – Loch Laggan (Photo: L Gill).

5c(middle) – River Dee (Photo: L Gill).

5d(bottom) – South Uist
(Copyright NERC 1996).

PLATE 6: RECREATION AND ENJOYMENT

6a(main picture) – Salmon fishing, River Tay (Scotland) (Photo: L Gill).

6b(right) – Picnicking, Loch Lubnaig (Scotland) (Photo: L Gill).

6c(below) – Canoeing, River Tay (Photo: L Gill).

In Norway, EQOs are being developed at present by the Norwegian Pollution Control Authority and the Directorate for Nature Management. Within the area 'conservation of biological diversity and nature', a number of EQOs relating to habitat quality are being considered (Table 29.4). National water quality criteria are being used to set water quality objectives in terms of particle, phosphorus and algal concentrations relative to natural conditions. It is notable that neither pH nor alkalinity are among the water quality objectives considered for conservation of biological diversity. Instead they appear in a section on sports fisheries. Besides the water quality variables, a number of EQOs describing physical habitat are being considered—water flow, regulation and channelization, development of shore line and riparian zone. The objectives are generally expressed as the maximum deviation from a natural state that may be accepted with respect to biological diversity.

29.6   Development of Monitoring Systems

Surveillance and monitoring programmes may seem essential to any meaningful assessment of the status and development of natural resources, yet this area has been rather neglected in Scandinavia as elsewhere.

As the focus of environmental policy changes there is, however, an increasing awareness of the need for improved access to both spatial and temporal data on the state of the environment (see Wiederholm, 1993). Sweden is currently revising the entire area of environmental monitoring to meet these needs. New or revised programmes are being developed and implemented for air, seas, lakes and watercourses, groundwaters, wetlands, mountain areas, forest areas, agricultural land, landscapes, and health and urban areas (SEPA, 1993). Monitoring lakes and watercourses will be implemented by a set of sub-programmes at national and/or regional levels (Table 29.5). Some of these already exist—the oldest time series

---

Table 29.5   Structure of the proposed Swedish freshwater monitoring programme (SEPA, 1993) (see text).

National level
- River transport network (water chemistry)
- National lake and stream surveys (water chemistry, macroinvertebrates)
- Temporal reference sites (water/sediment chemistry, macroinvertebrates, phytoplankton, palaeoindicators)
- Integrated temporal reference sites (water/sediment chemistry, phytoplankton/periphyton, zooplankton, macroinvertebrates, fish, palaeoindicators, palaeoreconstruction)

Regional level
- Biotopes
- Species
- Areas of national interest
- Water supplies
- Bathing waters
- Effects of liming
- Effluent impact monitoring

---

date back to the mid-1960s—while others have not yet begun. Quality assurance and continuous evaluation, resulting in yearly State of the Environment Reports, improved official statistics, and dissemination of results to the general public, are considered to be important.

A similar development of monitoring programmes is taking place in Norway, with recurring synoptic lake surveys and a set of temporal reference sites in freshwater habitats (NPCA, 1995; Øvstedal, 1995; Henriksen *et al.*, 1996).

29.7   Conclusions

With an abundance of waters and a low population density, Scandinavia would seem to be in a better position than many other parts of Europe to protect and preserve the quality of fresh waters. Yet, many natural values have been lost and much of what remains is threatened—by eutrophication, airborne pollutants, and by exploitation and fragmentation for urban development, traffic and energy production.

To preserve what is left, and where possible restore what has been lost, requires considerable changes in the lifestyle of individuals and in the development of society. Nature conservation and environmental protection must be integrated in all sectors of society and environmental costs (and benefits) must be included in economic considerations at all levels. These changes will require economic sacrifices by individuals, industry and society at large, and will place increasing demands on professionals in nature conservation to describe and quantify conservation values in a reproducible way, to assess and monitor impacts, and to make information available and understandable to administrators, politicians and the general public. This poses a great challenge but also provides a stimulus to research and development.

Acknowledgements

Per Faugli (Norwegian Water and Energy Administration), Gunnar Fredriksson (The Watercourses Commission), Erik Hauan (Norwegian Pollution Control Authority) and Carl-Erik Johansson (Swedish Environmental Protection Agency) provided background material and checked relevant parts of the manuscript. Richard Johnson, Department of Environmental Assessment, read the English text.

References

Aagaard, K. and Dolmen, D. (Eds) (1996). *Limnofauna norvegica-Katalog over norsk ferskvannsfauna.* (A catalogue of Norwegian freshwater fauna). Tapir, Trondheim. (In Norwegian).

Anonymous (1983). *Naturfagliga verdier og vassdragsvern.* (Nature conservation values and watercourse protection). NOU 1983:42, Universitetsforlaget, Oslo-Bergen-Tromsø. (In Norwegian).

Anonymous (1991). *Verneplan for vassdrag* IV. (Protection Plan for Watercourses IV). NOU 1991:12A, Adademika as, Oslo. (In Norwegian).

Bernes, C. (Ed.) (1993). The Nordic environment—present state, trends and threats, *Nord,* **93**: 12. Fritzes, Stockholm.

Bernes, C. (Ed.) (1994). Biological diversity in Sweden. A country study. *Monitor,* **14**. Swedish Environmental Protection Agency, Stockholm.

Berntell, A., Henriksson, L., Nyman, H., Oskarsson, H. and Wenblad, A. (1988). Criteria for the biological evaluation of lakes from a nature conservation viewpoint. *Verhandlungen der Internationalen Vereinigung für theoretische und angewandte Limnologie,* **23**, 1500–1504.

Boon, P. J., Holmes, N. T. H., Maitland, P. S., Rowell, T. A. and Davies J. (This volume). A system for evaluating rivers for conservation (SERCON): development, structure and function.

De Pauw, N., Ghetti, P. F., Manzini, D. P. and Spaggiari, D. R. (1992). Biological assessment methods for running water. In: Newman, P. J., Piavaux, M. A. and Sweeting, R. A. (Eds), *River Water Quality, Ecological Assessment and Control.* Commission of the European Communities, EUR 14606 En-Fr, 217–248.

Faugli, P. E. (1994). Watercourse management in Norway. *Norsk geografisk Tidskrift,* **48**, 75–79.

Friberg, N. and Johnson, R. K. (Eds) (1995). Biological monitoring of streams. Methods used in the Nordic countries based on macroinvertebrates. *TemaNord* 640. Nordic Council of Ministers, Copenhagen.

Granath, L. (1995). 'Flygbildstolkning av strandstatus'. Preliminär rapport, etapp 1 till Vattendragsutredningen, mars 1995. (Image analysis of shoreline status. Preliminary report to the Watercourses Commission, March 1995). Stockholm. (In Swedish).

Henriksen, A., Kämäri, J., Posch, M. and Wilander, A. (1992). Critical loads of acidity: Nordic surface waters. *Ambio,* **21**, 356–363.

Henriksen, A., Skjelvåle, B. L., Lien, L., Traaen, T. S., Mannio, J., Forsius, J., Kämäri, J., Mäkinen, I., Berntell, A., Wiederholm, T., Wilander, A., Moisenko, T., Harriman, R. and Jensen, J. P. (1996). *Regional Lake Surveys in Finland—Norway—Sweden—Northern Kola—Russian Karelia—Scotland—Wales—1995. Coordination and Design.* Norwegian Institute for Water Research, Report 40/1996, Oslo.

Henrikson, L. and Brodin, Y.-W. (1995). Liming of surface waters in Sweden—a synthesis. In: Henrikson, L. and Brodin, Y.-W. (Eds), *Liming of Acidified Surface Waters. A Swedish Synthesis.* Springer-Verlag, Berlin, Heidelberg, 1–44.

Hettelingh, J.-P., Downing, R. J. and de Smet, P. A. M. (Eds) (1991). *Mapping Critical Loads for Europe.* CCE Technical Report No. 1. RIVM Report No. 259101001, Bilthoven.

Holtan, H. and Ibrekk, H. O. (1993). Norwegian water quality criteria—ecosystems approach. *Journal of Aquatic Ecosystem Health,* **2**, 73–79.

Ibrekk, H. O., Børset, E. and Hauan, E. (1993). An approach for water pollution abatement. *Journal of Aquatic Ecosystem Health,* **2**, 45–53.

International Union for Conservation of Nature and Natural Resources (1980). *An Introduction to the World Conservation Strategy.* International Union for Conservation of Nature and Natural Resources, Gland.

Johansson, C.-E. and Gull. I. (In preparation). Protection of geosites in Sweden. In: Karis, L. (Ed.), *Aspects of European Geosite Protection.* Proceedings from the Symposium at the 1st ProGEO General Assembly. SGU (Swedish Geological Survey).

Johnson, R. K., Wiederholm, T. and Rosenberg, D. M. (1993). Freshwater biomonitoring using individual organisms, populations, and species assemblages of benthic macroinvertebrates. In: Rosenberg, D. M. and Resh, V. H. (Eds), *Freshwater Biomonitoring and Benthic Macroinvertebrates.* Chapman and Hall, New York, 40–158.

Kristensen, P. and Hansen, H. O. (Eds) (1994). *European Rivers and Lakes. Assessment of their Environmental State.* EEA Environmental Monographs 1. European Environment Agency, Copenhagen.

Larsson, T. (1992). *Wetland Restoration in the Fennoscandian Region.* Proceedings of IWRB Symposium, St. Peterburg, Florida, USA, IWRB Publication No. 26: 195–200.

Larsson, T.-B., Ebenhard, T., Sjögren, P., Andrén, H., Angelstam, P. and Widén, P. (1992). Recommendations on how measurable objectives for nature conservation shall be formulated. In: Larsson, T.-B. (Ed.), *Objectives for Nature Conservation. A Strategy for the Preservation of Biological Diversity.* Swedish Environmental Protection Agency Report 3986, Stockholm, 92–106. (In Swedish).

Nilsson, J. and Grennfelt, P. (Eds) (1988). *Critical Loads for Sulphur and Nitrogen.* Nordic Council of Ministers, Miljørapport 1988:15. Copenhagen.

Nordic Council of Ministers (1984). *Naturgeografisk regionindelning av Norden.* (Nordic ecoregions). Copenhagen. (In Danish, Norwegian and Swedish).

NPCA (1989). *Vannkvalitetskriterier for ferskvann.* (Water quality criteria for fresh water). Norwegian Pollution Control Authority, Oslo. (In Norwegian).

NPCA (1995). *Statlig program for forurensningsovervåking. Projektkatalog 1995.* (National programme for pollution monitoring. Project catalogue 1995). Norwegian Pollution Control Authority Rapport 95:14, Oslo. (In Norwegian).

NWEA (1994). *The Norwegian Protection Plan for River Systems.* Norwegian Water and Energy Administration, Oslo.

Øvstedal, J. (1995). *Förslag till referansevassdrag.* (Proposal on reference watercourses). Norwegian Water Resources and Energy Administration Publ. Nr. 12/95, Oslo. (In Norwegian with abstract in English).

Reynoldson, T. B. (1993). The development of ecosystem objectives for the Laurentian Great Lakes. *Journal of Aquatic Ecosystem Health,* **2,** 81–85.

SEPA (1982). *Restaurering av förorenade vattenområden. Erfarenheter från restaureringsprojekt 1969–81.* (Restoration of polluted water areas. Experiences from restoration projects 1969–1981). Swedish Environmental Protection Agency PM 1596, Stockholm. (In Swedish).

SEPA (1986). *Översyn av områden av riksintresse för naturvård och friluftsliv. Allmänna råd. Statens naturvårdsverk promemoria 1985-09-23. Reviderad 1986-01-24.* Bilaga till Statens planverks meddelande Dnr 407/85, Stockholm. (In Swedish).

SEPA (1989a). *Nationalparksplan för Sverige.* (National Park plan for Sweden). Swedish Environmental Protection Agency, Stockholm. (In Swedish with summary in English).

SEPA (1989b). *Naturinventering av sjöar och vattendrag. Handbok.* (Nature inventory of lakes and watercourses. A handbook). Swedish Environmental Protection Agency, Stockholm. (In Swedish).

SEPA (1990). *Fresh Water '90. Strategy for Good Water Quality in Lakes, Watercourses and Groundwater.* Swedish Environmental Protection Agency, Stockholm. (In Swedish).

SEPA (1991a). *A Nature Conservation Plan for Sweden.* Swedish Environmental Protection Agency, Stockholm. (In Swedish with summary in English).

SEPA (1991b). *Areas of National Interest for Nature Conservation and Outdoor Life.* Swedish Environmental Protection Agency, Stockholm. (In Swedish).

SEPA (1991c). *Quality Criteria for Lakes and Watercourses.* Swedish Environmental Protection Agency, Stockholm.

SEPA (1993). *Svensk nationell miljöövervakning.* (Swedish national environmental monitoring). Swedish Environmental Protection Agency, Stockholm. (In Swedish).

SEPA (1995). *Aktionsplan för biologisk mångfald.* (Action plan for biological diversity). Swedish Environmental Protection Agency Report 4463, Stockholm. (In Swedish).

Statistics Sweden and SEPA (1995). *Skyddad natur 30 juni 1995.* (Protected nature 30 June 1995). Statistics Sweden SCB Na 41 SM 9501. (In Swedish with summary in English).

The Watercourses Commission (1994). *Vilka vattendrag skall skyddas? 1. Principer och förslag.* (Which watercourses shall be protected? 1. Principles and suggestions). SOU 1994: 59, Norstedts Tryckeri AB, Stockholm. (In Swedish).

Vollenweider, R. A. (1976). Advances in defining critical loading levels for phosphorus in lake eutrophication. *Memorie dell' Istituto Italiano di Idrobiologia,* **3,** 53–83.

Wiederholm, T. (1993). A living environment. Objectives and measures in the Swedish Government Bill on Environmental Policy 1990/91, pertaining to waters and the seas. *Journal of Aquatic Ecosystem Health,* **2,** 21–27.

Willén, E., Andersson, B. and Söderbäck, B. (This volume). System Aqua: a biological assessment tool for Swedish lakes and watercourses.

30 METHODS OF ASSESSING CONSERVATION STATUS FOR NATURAL FRESH WATERS IN THE SOUTHERN HEMISPHERE

J. O'Keeffe

Summary

1. In the past few years a number of different methods have been developed for the assessment of the conservation status of rivers in South Africa, Australia and New Zealand. This chapter gives an overview of these methods, and suggests a sequence of actions which will result in a coherent conservation plan for a river.

2. This sequence is described in a series of questions: 'What do we want the river to be like (defined as the desired state)? What is it like now? What needs to be done to achieve its desired state? How important is it to achieve the desired state?'

3. Definitions are suggested for the terms 'desired state', 'conservation status', and 'conservation importance'. A number of confusing and nebulous terms for aspects of conservation status have become entrenched in the literature (and in legislation) in northern hemisphere countries, and have caused problems for the managers who are charged with achieving unquantifiable environmental targets. It is suggested that South Africa would do well to adopt the simplest terminology for conservation assessment, leading to quantifiable goals that are comprehensible to managers and planners.

4. Climatic, geomorphological and developmental differences between typical north temperate and southern semi-arid rivers are described, and the consequences for conservation management evaluated. The importance of defining specific environmental objectives for each river is emphasized.

30.1 Introduction

The question posed in the title of this book asks whether it is possible to define 'freshwater quality'. To answer this question: Conservationists and environmental scientists *have to be able* to define 'freshwater quality', because, as Boon *et al.* (1994) point out, definition is one of the fundamental prerequisites for the implementation of nature conservation strategies. In other words, if conservationists are unable to do it, then those responsible for managing water resources will do it in whatever way suits them. Whether it can be defined precisely or scientifically is more open to question, because many of the components of freshwater quality are subjective, others are extremely complex to measure accurately, almost all are interactive, and many are synergistic.

The interpretation of 'freshwater quality' used in this chapter is much broader than water chemistry and associated variables, and includes all aspects of natural freshwater ecosystems that affect their acceptability for human use and appreciation. This chapter has a strong bias towards rivers, because they comprise practically the only kind of natural fresh water in South Africa, and the author's research experience has largely been confined to rivers. Although the title of the paper speaks of the southern hemisphere, this review is mainly concerned with southern Africa, Australia and New Zealand, because the research in these three regions has concentrated on similar issues, and rivers of similar size. The scale of rivers which have been the focus of research in the southern hemisphere tropics and South America in particular, is generally far larger than those which are the focus of this chapter. Almost all the rivers in South Africa can be forded on foot for most of the time, in fact many of them can be traversed dry-shod, and the perspectives in this chapter are very much influenced by these arid and semi-arid conditions.

The variability and unpredictability which characterize the hydrology of much of South Africa and Australia has fundamental implications for the conservation of the rivers (Davies *et al.*, 1995). Rivers are characterized by a seasonality, flash floods, and prolonged droughts, and the biota appears to be hardy, resilient and opportunistic in response to these conditions. The conservation of natural biodiversity is dependent on the maintenance of the full range of the natural disturbance regime of the rivers, and it is extremely difficult to predict the consequences for the biota of a switch from a naturally highly disturbed system to one which is artificially stabilized, by impoundment, inter-basin transfer or other management. Developing the ability to predict these consequences, and to evaluate them in terms of changes in the conservation status of rivers, is the major challenge facing river ecologists in arid regions.

Although the hydrology of much of South Africa and Australia is similar, there are major differences in the socio-economic conditions of the two regions, and these have fundamental consequences for conservation policies. Australia, like most of the north temperate countries, is a relatively affluent country in which most problems can be solved if they are given a high enough priority. Australia has the added advantage of a low population density. South Africa, although rich in most resources, has a growing population, many of whom lack even the most basic amenities. Out of a total population of over forty million, twelve million people do not have access to an adequate supply of potable water, and nearly twenty-one million lack basic sanitation (Department of Water Affairs and Forestry, 1994a). The recently elected government has put a high priority on the provision of these amenities, and conservation policy is very strongly directed at sustainable development rather than preservation. In a recent speech, President Mandela emphasized that conservation efforts would have to contribute directly to the welfare of the people, if they were to receive government support. From this policy emphasis, a number of challenges emerge for South African conservationists. These include the following:

- Motivations for conservation issues in the face of urgent needs to exploit natural resources.
- The need for direct, simple expressions of conservation priorities, comprehensible to non-specialists.
- The provision of basic resources in the short term, while sustaining the long-term viability of natural systems.

The development of methods for conservation assessment of South African rivers described in this chapter have to be seen in the light of these challenges, and the contrasts with methods from other parts of the world arise largely from the differences in emphasis described above. Apart from providing a brief overview of some of the methods that have been and are being developed to assess the conservation status (*sensu lato*) of rivers, the aims of this chapter are to define more clearly the steps that need to be followed to form a plan for the conservation of rivers; to distinguish between the status and importance of any river, since this has been a source of confusion in river conservation, at least in South Africa and Australia; and to describe some methods that are currently being developed and used, particularly in South Africa, to achieve assessments of rivers and their conservation requirements, which find consensus amongst different disciplines and can be understood and implemented by managers.

In order to understand the sequence of actions that has evolved in South Africa to develop a coherent plan for the long-term conservation or sustainable use of a river system, it may be useful to reduce the process to a few simple questions. (Although the questions may be simple, the answers seldom are.) 'What do the stakeholders want the river to be like?' This requires the definition of a 'desired state' for the river. 'What is it like now?' This requires an assessment of the conservation status or biotic integrity of the river. 'What needs to be done to achieve its desired state?' The differences between the desired state and the present conservation status will indicate whether the condition of the river is acceptable, and, if not, what action needs to be taken to achieve the desired state. 'How important is it to achieve the desired state?' This requires some measure of the conservation importance of the river, from which maintenance, remedial or rehabilitation priorities can be decided upon. A question which has to be answered where further developments are planned for a river is: 'How will the conditions and biota of the river change in response to a planned development?' To answer this question requires a multidisciplinary predictive capability in hydrology, hydraulics, geomorphology, and ecology, and is the ultimate test of the usefulness of environmental scientists in the process of river management. To address this question in detail is beyond the scope of this chapter, but it forms the background to much of the applied ecological research in South Africa.

Many of these questions immediately pose others such as: 'Who are the stake-holders who define the desired state?' 'What is the baseline against which to compare the present condition?' 'Important to whom?' These are questions which are currently being debated in South Africa in order to develop coherent methods for incorporating environmental issues into water resource planning and river management policy. The next three sections of this chapter discuss some of the concepts arising from these questions.

30.2 Desired State

Before any environmental management plan for a river can be drafted, there has to be an objective towards which the plan is aimed. Without explicit environmental objectives, planning is likely to be arbitrary and reactive, attempting to prevent or remedy developments which are planned with other aims in mind, such as maximum water supply or effluent disposal. The objective may be river-specific, or river-zone-specific, and has come to be referred to in South Africa as the desired state of the river.

Methods for defining ecological desired states of rivers in South Africa are not yet well developed, and at present there is a reliance on the opinions of groups of 'experts' to set an objective. Such groups will typically include ecologists, nature conservation officers, water managers, hydrologists, engineers, and one or two representatives of the residents in the catchment. Such a method has been used to set the desired state for a number of South African rivers, including the Luvuvhu, Letaba, and Komati in the eastern Transvaal, the Mooi in Natal, the Great Kei in the eastern Cape, the Keurbooms in the southern Cape, and the Olifants in the western Cape (Figure 30.1). These exercises have all been the starting point for instream flow requirement workshops using the ' building-block methodology' of King *et al.* (1994). These three-day workshops, preceded by about three months of planning and field work, have become the preferred method applied by the South African Department of Water Affairs for the setting of initial flow regimes to meet the environmental requirements of rivers.

30.2.1 Example: The Luvuvhu River

The following example of the definition of the desired state for a particular river is taken from the final report of the instream flow requirement workshop on the Luvuvhu River (Department of Water Affairs and Forestry, 1995).

> The Luvuvhu River is seen as the second most pristine river in the Kruger National Park after the Sabie River and has some special attributes. The river flows through a unique area in the Kruger National Park which is not duplicated elsewhere. The river forms the lifeline through this area of exceptionally high aesthetic value and biotic

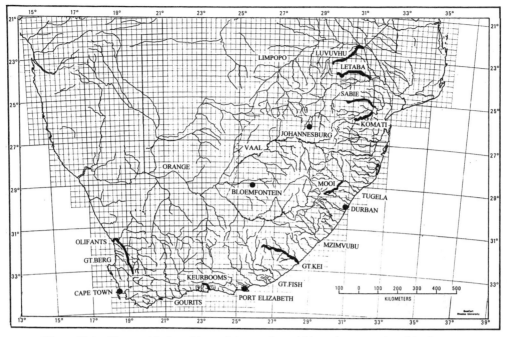

Figure 30.1   Geographical positions of the southern African rivers mentioned in the text.

diversity, and includes various Red Data Species and other important species, the existence of which are all dependent on the river.

The Luvuvhu flows through a rural area and local communities are dependent on the riverine ecosystem for various aspects of their daily lives.

The objective ... [is] the following:

To manage flows in the Luvuvhu River system from the Mutoti Dam site to the confluence with the Limpopo River in order to ensure the long-term conservation and maintenance of the riparian vegetation in the lower reaches in pre-drought, 1991/1992, condition; reinstate a perennial flow regime; ensure the long-term conservation of the aquatic biota, particularly through the maintenance of habitats during low flow months; ensure the sustainable resource utilization of stream flow, aquatic communities and riparian communities by the rural population; ensure that flows are provided to maintain the unique natural character of the Luvuvhu River in the Kruger National Park.

The desired state for the Luvuvhu is therefore to retain as many of the natural ecosystem communities and processes as possible, and to restore others through the reinstatement of perennial flow.

30.2.2   Example: The Great Kei River

A more modest objective was defined for the Instream Flow Requirements Workshop on the upper Great Kei River, a substantially modified river system in the eastern Cape Province (Department of Water Affairs and Forestry, 1994b).

To determine flow requirements downstream of proposed developments, to a point just downstream of the confluence of the Black and White Kei, in order to ensure the maintenance of the habitat for aquatic biota and riparian vegetation presently occurring in the system. The predominantly perennial nature of the river should be maintained downstream of the proposed Stichel dam site. The potential for sustained use of the river by rural communities must be maintained.

A number of subsidiary objectives followed on from these main ones, dealing with aspects such as water quality, introduced alien and translocated fish species, and the need for freshwater flows to the Great Kei estuary, but the overall desired state remains one of retaining the surviving natural characteristics of the river, and is summed up in the report as: 'The main requirement is that the river should not be allowed to degrade further, and with integrated catchment management practices, such as removal of exotics, could improve'.

30.2.3   Summary of desired state

The characteristics of these definitions of desired state are that they are river-specific, subjective value judgements which define a set of desired conditions in the rivers, in relation to present and future uses and the present extent of naturalness/degradation of the rivers. The shortcomings of the present method are that the process is not inclusive of all the interests within the catchment, and the definitions are not very detailed or precise, and therefore may not be translated easily into specific management options.

Few other assessment methods incorporate river-specific objectives in their methodologies, and most are restricted to global objectives such as diversity, rarity, naturalness, area, and representativeness (Macmillan and Kunert, 1990). Swales and Harris (1995) propose an expert panel method for the assessment of environmental flows in Australian regulated rivers, and they use general criteria including fish survival and abundance, productivity of aquatic and riparian macroinvertebrates, river morphology, bank erosion, and substrate stability. Such general criteria are appropriate for the objective classification of large numbers of rivers, but are not specific enough to be very useful for assessments or value judgements for individual rivers, leading to specific management recommendations. One example of a method for deciding on a river-zone-specific desired state is the Receiving Water Quality Objectives (RWQO) method, developed in the USA for the setting of waste load allocations for rivers. This has now been adopted for South Africa (van der Merwe and Grobler, 1989), and essentially relies on the users of the water (including the natural biota) to define limits for each water quality variable according to their uses or tolerances. This method results in very specific objectives for the water quality manager to aim at, or for planners to compare with other catchment objectives. It points the way for the development of methods for the definition of more inclusive desired states in South African rivers. The result will be a more unwieldy method requiring more time and resources to achieve, but will be inclusive and specific.

30.3   Conservation Status/Biological Integrity

The conservation status of a river should be a reflection of its condition in comparison to some standard baseline, and should be as objective a measure as possible. It should be comparable between different rivers, between different parts of the same river, and between the same river/part of a river at different times. It should provide an integrated measure of as many as possible of the diverse aspects of the river that contribute to its ecological functioning, and should be comprehensible to non-ecological specialists, who should be able to use it to decide on management options for the river.

The terminology and meanings attached to the concepts of conservation status, biological integrity and associated terms have proliferated in the past 10 years (Table 30.1) and have done little to assist non-specialists in coming to an understanding of the concepts. This is serious because the purpose of conservation status, etc., is to provide methods of communicating environmental concerns to planners and managers who may not have a specialist knowledge of the field. The following sections explain two of the main causes of confusion, and suggest the simplest practical solution.

30.3.1   *The difference between status and importance*

Admittedly, previous publications by this author (e.g. O'Keeffe *et al.*, 1987) have contributed to the above confusion in the past by including the separate concept of conservation importance under the heading of conservation status. This mistake is still being perpetuated in the development of assessment methods in other parts of the world, and needs to be clarified as a priority. O'Keeffe *et al.* (1987) defined conservation status as 'a measure of the relative importance of the river for conservation, and the extent to which it has been disturbed from its natural state'.

Kleynhans (1994) has pointed out that a river may be highly degraded yet very important—perhaps because of the survival of endemic fish species, or it may be in pristine condition but low in biodiversity and rarity, and therefore perhaps not as important as the former example. Both examples might score equally in an assessment that attempts to quantify both of these concepts in one term, despite the great differences in the rivers. Thus, the term conservation status (of a river) could be simplified to mean 'a measure of the extent to which a river has been modified from its natural state'. This will enable a comparable assessment between and within rivers, as far as such a baseline can be defined. There are obvious difficulties with the definition of 'natural state', since rivers are dynamic, historical data are often sparse, and many rivers are so modified that their natural state may be a matter of guesswork. However, the great majority of rivers in the southern hemisphere still retain sufficient of their 'pre-industrial man' condition, or are near enough to a comparable, less modified river from which to infer a reasonable natural state.

The confusion between status and importance is evident in assessment methods still being developed and used. Criteria suggested by Ratcliffe (1977) such as

Table 30.1   Terms used to describe the environmental condition and value of rivers.

Conservation status As proposed in this chapter	For definition, see text
Conservation importance As proposed in this chapter	For definition, see text
Conservation values (MacMillan and Kunert, 1990)	Generally include both intrinsic values and non-material utility values, including scientific (ecological and cultural), aesthetic, social and historic values.
Conservation significance (Macmillan and Kunert, 1990)	Can only be established in the context of a regional, state, or national evaluation of the resource. For example, state significance: the area contains the only, or otherwise significant, population(s) of a species in the state.
Conservation potential (Naiman *et al.*, 1992)	The ecological potential of a stream and its sensitivity to natural and human disturbance. Kleynhans (1994) points out that ecological potential is undefined, but can be interpreted as referring to the current potential of the riverine habitat to support aquatic biological communities. Implicit in this is the potential for the improvement of existing habitat conditions in order that they can support a more diverse biota.
Natural value (Collier, 1993)	The survival of all indigenous species of flora and fauna, both rare and commonplace, in their natural communities and habitats, and the preservation of representative samples of all classes of natural ecosystems and landscapes which in the aggregate originally gave New Zealand its own recognizable character.
Ecological health (Karr, 1993)	The condition when a system's inherent potential is realized, its condition is stable, its capacity for self repair, when perturbed, is preserved, and minimal external support for management is needed.
Ecological integrity (Regier, 1993)	A living system exhibits integrity if, when subjected to disturbance, it sustains an organizing, self-correcting capability to recover toward an end-state that is 'normal' or 'good' for that system. End states other than pristine or naturally whole may be taken to be 'normal and good'.
Biological integrity (Karr and Dudley, 1981)	The ability to support and maintain a balanced, integrated, adaptive community of organisms having a species composition, diversity and functional organization comparable to that of natural habitats of the region.
Habitat integrity (Kleynhans, in press)	The maintenance of a balanced, integrated composition of physico-chemical and habitat characteristics on a temporal and spatial scale comparable to the characteristics of natural habitats of the region.

naturalness, diversity, representativeness, and rarity include elements of both status and importance: naturalness and diversity (partly) are components of conservation status as defined above, but representativeness, rarity and other aspects of diversity are irrelevant to the state of modification of the river, but are certainly criteria for assessing its importance. Blyth (1983) used diversity, naturalness, and rarity (amongst other criteria) to assess Australian streams, and MacMillan and Kunert (1990) used diversity, rarity, naturalness, area, and representativeness to assess the conservation value and status of rivers in Victoria, Australia.

Two recently developed systems have largely avoided the confusion of status and importance by dividing the assessment into distinct sections: SERCON—a system for evaluating rivers for conservation being developed in the UK by Boon *et al.* (1994, this volume); and a protocol for assessing the value of New Zealand rivers, by Collier (1993). Both systems were originally based on the River Conservation System (RCS) of O'Keeffe *et al.* (1987), but focus on separate conservation criteria rather than components of the river (channel, catchment, and biota), and no attempt is made to integrate the criterion scores into one overall score. SERCON assesses value (equivalent to importance) separately from impacts and modification (equivalent to status), while Collier's protocol uses separate assessments for degree of modification; diversity and pattern; rarity and unique features or species; and fragility.

30.3.2 *Status vs. integrity*

Alternative concepts to conservation status, such as 'biological integrity' (Karr and Dudley, 1981), 'ecological integrity' (Regier, 1993), and 'ecological health' (Karr, 1993), developed in the USA are obscure to non-specialists (e.g. Polls, 1994), and the baseline against which the assessment is made is neither consistent nor comparable, and confuses present status with desired status. For example, Regier (1993) uses as a baseline for the measurement of ecological integrity: 'An organizing, self-correcting capability to recover toward an end-state that is normal or 'good' for that system'.

Apart from the difficulty of defining 'organizing' and 'self-correcting' in coherent ecological terms, 'normal' and 'good' are completely subjective judgements which belong in the desired state category rather than in the assessment of condition, which should be as objective as possible. In their definition of biological integrity, Karr and Dudley (1981) use as a baseline: '... a species composition, diversity, and functional organisation comparable to that of *natural* habitat of the region'. Similarly Kleynhans (in press) defines a baseline for 'habitat integrity' as: '... a balanced, integrated composition of physico-chemical and habitat characteristics on a temporal and spatial scale that are comparable to the characteristics of *natural* habitats of the region'.

In both these cases, the baseline is natural conditions (this author's italics in the quotations), which are assumed to be balanced, integrated and so on, and the methods of measuring them, in the examples given, are simply a comparison of present conditions with hypothetical natural conditions. There appears to be no practical difference between these terms and the modified definition of conservation status.

In the USA, the term biological integrity became entrenched in legislation in 1972 (the Water Pollution Control Act Amendments, Public Law 92-500) before there was a measurable definition, and the authorities and companies charged with evaluating, restoring and maintaining the chemical, physical and biological integrity of the nation's waters are struggling to find methods of measuring whether they have achieved this requirement (e.g. Jackson and Davis, 1994; Polls, 1994; Steedman, 1994). Other countries should certainly beware of saddling themselves with complex concepts leading to unattainable water quality requirements.

30.3.3 *Summary of conservation status*

Terms such as 'biological integrity', 'ecological integrity', 'habitat integrity', and 'ecological health' are proliferating in the literature, and are confusing to non-specialists. In South Africa, it would be sensible to revert to the simpler term 'conservation status', differentiated from 'conservation importance'. It may be that, in countries where rivers are often so severely physically modified that the original state cannot be inferred, there is a need for a baseline other than natural conditions, against which to assess rivers, but it is hard to envisage any consistent baseline which would be any simpler to define than the natural state.

30.4 Conservation Importance

Few rivers anywhere have escaped some kind of degradation, and this is certainly true in South Africa, where there are plans for the further exploitation of many of the rivers. As Kleynhans (in press) points out, the scale of the problem is such that not all rivers can be conserved, and priorities need to be assigned, hence the need for some way of assessing the relative importance of rivers from an environmental perspective. Conservation importance is a term that has gained currency among researchers on South African rivers over the past few years (e.g. Breen *et al.*, 1994; Kleynhans, 1994), although there is as yet no formal way of assessing it. The following definition is an expansion of that suggested by Kleynhans (1994): Essentially, 'conservation importance is a measure of the value of a river for conservation, and should include natural, socio-economic and cultural aspects'.

Natural aspects. An assessment of the rarity or uniqueness of the river, its biodiversity, levels of endemism, geographical position and size, special features, and fragility, as well as the degree of modification, or conservation status. Having differentiated between status and importance in the previous section, it may seem odd to include status as a criterion for importance, but it should be clear that the degree of modification of a river will often influence its conservation value, whereas the reverse is not true.

Socio-economic aspects. An assessment of the number of people directly dependent for water supplies, sanitation, subsistence, or recreation, and the economic value of agriculture and industry dependent on the river.

Cultural aspects. An assessment of the historical and archaeological value of the river; its importance in rituals and rites of passage; the use of riparian plants for such diverse purposes as building or traditional medicines; and the intrinsic and aesthetic value of the river for those who live within the catchment, or even for those who only visit it.

Some of these aspects, and particularly the economic ones, are easy to quantify, but others, such as the cultural aspects, are very difficult, and it may be for this reason that little progress has been made to turn this concept into a usable method.

Although the distinction between status and importance is not formally recognized in the present methods of conservation assessment, most systems have made use of many of the aspects of importance. The protocol for assessing the natural value of New Zealand rivers (Collier, 1993) includes separate sections on diversity and pattern, rarity and unique features or species, and fragility, as well as the status section on degree of modification. In describing methods for assessing conservation values and status of Victorian rivers in Australia, Macmillan and Kunert (1990) define intrinsic, scientific, aesthetic, social and historic values. An analysis of the expert-system based River Conservation System of O'Keeffe *et al.* (1987), revealed that 20 of the 58 questions posed by the program could be classified as evaluating the importance of a river, while the remaining 38 referred to the status of a river. Perhaps the clearest way of illustrating how to distinguish between status and importance is to present modifications of the same question. 'How many endemic fish species are there in this river?' This would be a question on the conservation importance of the river, because the presence of endemics is of value to conservation. 'How many of the original endemic fish species still survive in this river?' This would refer to the conservation status of the river, since it solicits information about modifications to the natural state of the river.

30.5   Methods of Conservation Assessment

This section describes the methods that have been developed in the southern hemisphere to make conservation assessments of rivers. No attempt is made to distinguish between conservation status and importance, or any of the other terms used (see Table 30.1), since almost all the systems described assess aspects of both, and the distinction has been made at length in the previous sections.

A number of different assessment methods have been proposed in the past 12 years in the rivers of Australia, New Zealand, and South Africa. Blyth (1983) describes a rapid stream survey to assess conservation value and habitats available for invertebrates. The method is based on physical and botanical features of streams recorded by volunteers walking the length of the rivers and recording, in a consistent manner, riparian vegetation, canopy cover, water temperature, gradient, structure and shape of the stream bed. Richness of habitat type, diversity, rarity, naturalness, representativeness and aesthetic qualities were evaluated in a semi-quantitative manner that resulted in comparative scores for different streams. The method is essentially a preliminary assessment, providing valuable low-resolution information for low investment of resources.

A series of 'filters', including natural catchment vegetation, number of impoundments, mining activities, logging, road crossings, grazing and the presence of exotic species was used by Macmillan (1983) to screen out Australian streams in terms of their conservation status. The system is chiefly interesting because it does not attempt to score each river, but simply identifies those of highest status/ importance by a process of elimination.

The River Conservation System (RCS) of O'Keeffe *et al.* (1987) has already been mentioned. This is a fairly sophisticated and labour intensive semi-quantitative computer model for the assessment of conservation status/importance, requiring extensive knowledge of the river channel, its catchment and biota. Expert system techniques provide flexibility in the scoring system, and the results offer a range of scores from one overall score to partial scores for different components of the river. The program also provides confidence limits reflecting the user's knowledge of the river. The major advantage of this method has been its use as a predictive model to assess the effects of future developments on a river, and it provided an initial starting point for the development of the SERCON system in the UK (Boon *et al.*, 1994, this volume), and Collier's (1993) protocol for assessing the natural value of New Zealand rivers.

Collier's protocol is based on the criteria of ecological representativeness or rare type of ecosystem, degree of modification, diversity and pattern, rarity and unique features or species, and long-term viability. A number of descriptors in each category were defined, and a weighting and scoring system similar to that in the RCS was developed, but without the flexibility provided by the expert system model. The main advance has been the use of separate sections based on the criteria rather than the components of the river, which has distinguished between status and value (or importance), although the distinction is not formalized.

A methodology for the assessment of the conservation value and status of rivers in Victoria, Australia, is described by Macmillan and Kunert (1990). They make a strong case for the need for a comprehensive classification of rivers (on the basis of physiography and climate) as a prerequisite for conservation assessment, since it is necessary to compare like with like. Such a classification does not yet exist for the whole of Australia, but Macmillan and Kunert (1990) describe 14 river types in Victoria, based on drainage system, drainage type, and physiography. Their assessment of conservation values includes both intrinsic and non-material utility values (Table 30.1), but only methods for assessing the scientific/ecological value are described in their report. The assessment procedure is based on the criteria of naturalness, diversity, rarity, area, and representativeness, and separate values are calculated for the catchment, instream features, and riparian features. The scoring system is largely qualitative, with categories such as 'essentially unmodified', 'slightly modified', 'moderately modified', 'heavily modified', and 'severely degraded', and features such as 'percentage catchment cleared' and 'intensive agriculture'. If 10% of the catchment were cleared this would qualify as 'slightly modified', as would 'parallel roads of slight impact'. The system is detailed but subjective and flexible, and appears to provide a useful assessment for low resource input.

A method for evaluating the habitat integrity of a river (Table 30.1) has been developed by Kleynhans (in press) for South Africa. The assessment is survey-based, ideally from a helicopter, using a qualitative rating of the impacts of major disturbance factors such as water abstraction, flow regulation, and channel modification. Separate assessments are made for the riparian zone and the channel, and the survey information is supplemented with existing data from hydrological databases, catchment studies, and surveys of the biota. Severity of impact is allocated to one of six classes ranging from 'no impact' to 'critical impact'. Criteria have been weighted by expert consensus, and scores are allocated according to the severity of impact. The river to be assessed is divided into 5 km segments, and scores are calculated for each segment, providing a detailed view of changes in condition down the river (e.g. Figure 30.2). This method has been used frequently to provide background information for the instream flow requirement workshops which have become a standard part of the assessment of environmental impacts of planned water resource developments on South African rivers.

A project to integrate a regional classification system, a rapid bioassessment

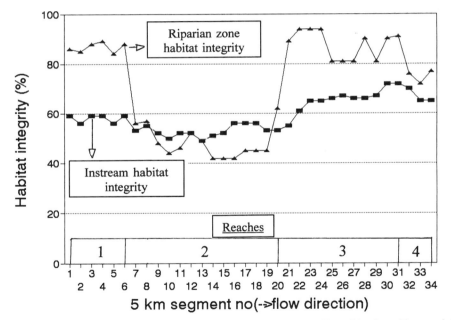

Figure 30.2 Habitat integrity scores for 5 km segments of the Luvuvhu River, Northern Transvaal, South Africa. Percentage scores have the following significance: 100%—unmodified, natural; 80–99%—largely natural with few modifications. A small change in natural habitats and biota may have taken place but the ecosystems functions are essentially unchanged; 60–79%—moderately modified. A loss and change of natural habitat and biota have occurred but the basic ecosystem functions are still predominantly unchanged; 40–59%—largely modified. A large loss of natural habitat, biota and basic ecosystem functions has occurred; 20–39%—the losses of natural habitat, biota and basic ecosystem functions are extensive; 0–19%—modifications have reached a critical level and the lotic system has been modified completely with an almost complete loss of habitat and biota. In the worst instances the basic ecosystem functions have been destroyed and the changes are irreversible (from Kleynhans, 1994).

protocol, and a habitat assessment matrix into a procedure for assessing biotic integrity in South African rivers is described by Roux *et al* (1994). The study made use of the South African Scoring System (SASS), a biological index based on benthic invertebrates (Chutter, 1994), and a habitat assessment matrix based on the index used by the US Environmental Protection Agency (Plafkin *et al.*, 1989), which initially focuses on the instream habitat, followed by channel morphology, and finally bank and riparian vegetation. The classification by physiographic regions is still being developed for South Africa as a whole, and is based on the integration of four environmental variables: potential natural vegetation; geology; rainfall; and altitude (Everett and Quibell, 1994). Reference sites where impacts were minimal were chosen for each physiographic region (Roux *et al.*, 1994). Conditions at sampling sites were characterized in terms of the biological index and the habitat matrix and compared with the reference sites to provide an integrated index expressed as a percentage of the reference site (Figure 30.3). This method was tested on some of the rivers of the eastern Transvaal, and it is planned to extend its use as a long-term national method. It seems to have the right combination of classification, accepted and relatively manageable sampling methods, and understandable results, to become a standard monitoring tool.

A number of methods for evaluating the ecological health of rivers (Arthington and Pusey, 1994; Hart and Campbell, 1994), and their conservation status

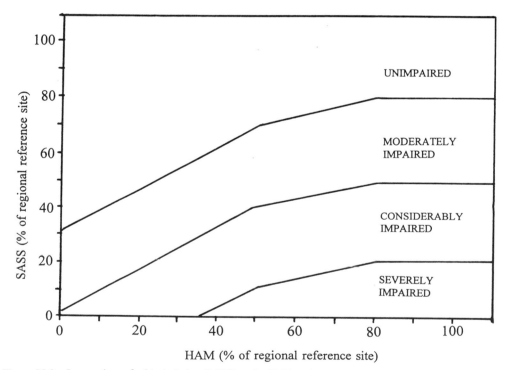

Figure 30.3 Integration of a biotic index (SASS) and a Habitat Assessment Matrix (HAM) to evaluate the extent of impairment of river sites in comparison with least impacted reference sites (from Roux *et al.*, 1994).

(Kleynhans, 1994) are being developed and tested in South Africa and Australia, and are described in Uys (1994). Since they have yet to be finalized, a review of their methods would be inappropriate at present.

30.6 Conclusions

The preceding review has ranged fairly widely over the field of conservation assessment, and the purpose of this section is to try to pull the threads together. Despite the diversity of terminology and methods, there are clear trends that emerge repeatedly:

- A regional or similarity classification of like parts of rivers is a prerequisite for effective conservation assessment.
- Conservation assessment is not an exact science, and attempts to develop the perfect method are doomed to over-elaboration and obscurity. The key requirements are for the methods to be achievable within the available skills and resources, and comprehensible to the end users, often planners and managers, who may not be ecological experts. This is especially true if the concepts and methods are to be incorporated into legislation.
- It is important to recognize the different steps involved in assessing ecosystems/natural resources and planning their management. These steps can be summarized, following the questions in the introduction, as defining the desired state, assessing the conservation status, defining the actions required to achieve the desired state, and assessing the conservation importance. This is a multidisciplinary sequence, in which all the steps involve ecologists and other environmental scientists. Following this sequence, a clear set of priorities and their motivation should emerge. Although there are rudimentary methods for the first and last of the above steps, there is an urgent need for more inclusive and generally accepted methods to be developed. There are many methods already available for the assessment of conservation status.

There has been an explosion of terms invented for various aspects of conservation assessment over the past two decades, and they have done nothing to simplify the concepts or methods, especially for the non-ecologists who have to implement the resulting plans. A concept such as 'ecological health', while initially seductive, is obscure and ecologically meaningless. Definitions (see Table 30.1) of 'inherent potential' are uncertain and unmeasurable; the condition of most rivers (and certainly those in semi-arid regions such as South Africa) is only fleetingly stable; and the external support needed for management depends on the human requirements of the river. A river heavily polluted with organic effluent will be a 'healthy' home to an enormous biomass of dipteran larvae, oligochaete worms, and sewage fungus, which remove nutrients from the water far more efficiently than the fauna of a pristine stream (Wurhmann *et al.*, 1967). While 'ecosystem health' may be an effective public relations catch-phrase, it is unhelpful and misleading in practical applications.

30.6.1 Differences between different parts of the world

With a large number of methods available, the question arises as to which is the best one to use. The answer will depend on the objectives and scale of the assessment, and the country or region where the river is located. While it would be ideal to have worldwide standard methods, this is probably not feasible, and the aim should be to standardize in particular countries. Even so, different applications require different solutions, and several methods may be needed for each country. In South Africa, the method of Kleynhans (in press) has proved effective in providing background information for instream flow assessments, and has the virtue of confining its attention to the level of modification of the river (its conservation status). For long-term monitoring, the procedure tested by Roux *et al.* (1994) has the benefits of simplicity, standard techniques, classification and reference sites, although it is primarily aimed at water quality (*sensu stricto*).

In the more developed parts of the world, the application of simple concepts such as conservation status may present difficulties, especially where rivers have been so modified from their natural state that the definition of natural conditions is not possible. In these cases, finding a standard baseline against which to measure conservation status may be impractical, and the solution may be to define a theoretical baseline against which to measure the status of a river. River rehabilitation is often a matter of engineering the structures of a river channel and its riparian zone so as to create habitats and diversity that no longer exist in the modified river. In South Africa, such solutions have been tried at a small scale, in canalized urban rivers, but these remain a minor part of the conservation effort. The major challenge in South Africa, and in many other semi-arid and less-developed parts of the world, is to promote the sustainable use of natural water resources in the face of urgent priorities to increase the supply of basic necessities to a growing population.

Acknowledgements

Many of the ideas and developments in this paper are the result of cooperative multidisciplinary efforts between researchers and managers within South Africa and Australia. In particular the members of the Kruger National Park Rivers Research Programme (Breen *et al.*, 1994, King *et al.*, 1994, Kleynhans, 1994) have been central to the developments described here. The opinions expressed here are, however, those of the author alone.

References

Arthington, A. H. and Pusey, B. J. (1994). River health assessment and classification based on relationships of flow regime, habitat and fish assemblage structure. In: Uys, M. C. (Ed.), *Classification of Rivers and Environmental Health Indicators. Proceedings of a Joint South African/Australian Workshop*, 191–204.

Blyth, J. D. (1983). Rapid stream survey to assess conservation value and habitats available for invertebrates. In: Myers, K., Margules, C. and Mustoe, I. (Eds), *Proceedings of a Workshop on Survey Methods for Nature Conservation*. CSIRO, Adelaide, 343–375.

Boon, P. J., Holmes, N. T. H., Maitland, P. S. and Rowell, T. A. (1994). A system for evaluating rivers for conservation ('SERCON'): an outline of the underlying principles. *Verhandlungen der Internationalen Vereinigung für theoretische und angewandte Limnologie* **25,** 1510–1514.

Boon, P. J., Holmes, N. T. H., Maitland, P. S., Rowell, T. A. and Davies, J. (This volume). A system for evaluating rivers for conservation (SERCON): development, structure and function.

Breen, C., Quinn, N. and Deacon, A. (1994). *A Description of the Kruger Park Rivers Research Programme (Second Phase)*. Collaborative Report from Foundation for Research and Development, Pretoria, South Africa.

Chutter, F. M. (1994). The rapid biological assessment of stream and river water quality by means of the macroinvertebrate community in South Africa. In: Uys, M. C. (Ed.), *Classification of Rivers and Environmental Health Indicators. Proceedings of a Joint South African/Australian Workshop*, 217–234.

Collier, K. (1983). Towards a protocol for assessing the value of New Zealand rivers. *Science and Research Series* **58**. National Institute of Water and Atmosphere Research Ltd., New Zealand.

Davies, B. R., O'Keeffe, J. H. and Snaddon, C. D. (1995). River and stream ecosystems in southern Africa: Predictably unpredictable. In: Cushing, C. E., Cummins, K. W. and Minshall, G. W. (Eds), *Ecosystems of the World, 22: River and Stream Ecosystems*. Elsevier, Amsterdam, 537–599.

Department of Water Affairs and Forestry (1994a). 'Water Supply and Sanitation Policy'. White Paper, Republic of South Africa.

Department of Water Affairs and Forestry (1994b). 'Proceedings of the Instream Flow Requirements Worksession (Draft). Queenstown Regional Water Supply Feasibility Study, Initial Environmental Assessment'. Unpublished report.

Department of Water Affairs and Forestry (1995). 'Instream Flow Requirements. Annexure F, Pre-Feasibility Study. Luvuvhu River Dam Feasibility Study'. Unpublished Report.

Everett, M. J. and Quibell, G. (1994). *Towards Regional Reference Site Selection and Bioguideline Development: An Ecoregional Approach*. IWQS Report No N-0000/00/REQ/0794. Department of Water Affairs and Forestry, Pretoria, South Africa.

Hart, B. T. and Campbell, I. C. (1994). Assessment of river 'health' in Australia. In: Uys, M. C. (Ed.), *Classification of Rivers and Environmental Health Indicators. Proceedings of a Joint South African/Australian Workshop*, 177–190.

Jackson, S. and Davis, W. (1994). Meeting the goal of biological integrity in water-resource programs in the US Environmental Protection Agency. *Journal of the North American Benthological Society*, **13,** 592–597.

Karr, J. R. (1993). Defining and assessing ecological integrity: beyond water quality. *Environmental Toxicology and Chemistry*, **12,** 1521–1531.

Karr, J. R. and Dudley, D. R. (1981). Ecological perspectives on water quality goals. *Environmental Management*, **5,** 55–68.

King, J., Bruwer, C., Louw, D., Rowlston, W. and Tharme, R. (1994). The Building Block Methodology II. Appendix 15 in *Proceedings of the Driekoppies Dam IFR Worksession* prepared by Ninham Shand Consulting Engineers, Pretoria.

Kleynhans, C. J. (1994). The assessment of conservation status for rivers. In: Uys, C. (Ed.), *Classification of Rivers and Environmental Health Indicators. Proceedings of a Joint South African/Australian Workshop*, 255–270.

Kleynhans, C. J. (in press). A qualitative procedure for the assessment of the habitat integrity status of the Luvuvhu River (Limpopo system, South Africa). *Journal of Aquatic Ecosystem Health*.

MacMillan, L. (1983). A method for identifying small streams of high conservation status. In: Myers, K., Margules, C. and Mustoe, I. (Eds), *Proceedings of a Workshop on Survey Methods for Nature Conservation*. CSIRO, Adelaide, 139–342.

MacMillan, L. and Kunert, C. (1990). 'Conservation Value and Status of Victorian Rivers. Part I. Methodology: Classification, Nature Conservation Evaluation and Strategies for Protection'. Faculty of Environmental Design and Construction Research, Royal Melbourne Institute of Technology, Melbourne, Victoria.

Naiman, R. J., Lonzarich, D. G., Beechie, T. J. and Ralph, S. C. (1992). General principles of classification and the assessment of conservation potential in rivers. In: Boon, P. J., Calow, P. and Petts, G. E. (Eds), *River Conservation and Management*. John Wiley, Chichester, 93–123.

O'Keeffe, J. H., Danilewitz, D. B. and Bradshaw, J. A. (1987). An 'expert system' approach to the assessment of the conservation status of rivers. *Biological Conservation*, **40,** 69–84.

Plafkin, J. L., Barbour, M. T., Porter, K. D., Gross, S. K. and Hughes, R. M. (1989). *Rapid Bioassessment*

Protocols for Use in Streams and Rivers: Benthic Macroinvertebrates and Fish. US Environmental Protection Agency Report No. EPA/440/4-89-001. Assessment and Watershed Division, Washington, DC.

Polls, I. (1994). How people in the regulated community view biological integrity. *Journal of the North American Benthological Society,* **13,** 598–604.

Ratcliffe, D. A. (Ed.) (1977). *A Nature Conservation Review.* Cambridge University Press, Cambridge.

Regier, H. A. (1993). The notion of natural and cultural integrity. In: Woodley, S., Kay, J. and Francis, G. (Eds), *Ecological Integrity and the Management of Ecosystems.* St. Lucie Press, Delray Beach, Florida.

Roux, D. J., Thirion, C., Smidt, M. and Everett, M. J. (1994). *A Procedure for Assessing Biotic Integrity in Rivers— Application to Three River Systems Flowing through the Kruger National Park, South Africa.* IWQS Report No N-0000/00/REQ/0894. Department Water Affairs and Forestry, Pretoria, South Africa.

Steedman, R. J. (1994). Ecosystem health as a management goal. *Journal of the North American Benthological Society,* **13,** 605–610.

Swales, S. and Harris, J. H. (1995). The Expert Panel Assessment Method (EPAM): A new tool for determining environmental flows in regulated rivers. In: Harper, D. M. and Ferguson, A. J. D. (Eds), *The Ecological Basis for River Management.* John Wiley, Chichester, 125–134.

Uys, M. C. (Ed.) (1994). *Classification of Rivers and Environmental Health Indicators. Proceedings of a Joint South African/Australian Workshop.*

Van der Merwe, W. and Grobler, D. C. (1989). Water quality management in the RSA: Preparing for the future. *Water SA,* **16,** 49–54.

Wurhmann, K., Ruchti, J. and Eichenberger, E. (1967). Quantitative experiments on self purification with pure organic compounds. In: Jaag, O. and Liebmann, H. (Eds), *Advances in Water Pollution Research* Vol 1. International Conference on Water Pollution Research, Munich, 229–251.

PART FOUR
BROADER ASPECTS OF FRESHWATER QUALITY ASSESSMENT

31 ASSESSING THE RECREATION VALUE OF FRESH WATERS: THE UK EXPERIENCE

C. J. Spray

Summary

1. In recent years there has been increasing conflict in the UK between recreational use of fresh waters and other demands for water space. The conflict has been fuelled by increasing leisure time, the lack of a single methodology for assessing the recreation value of fresh waters, and the absence of any effective legal basis to the protection or enhancement of fresh waters for their recreation value.

2. The few approaches to assessing recreation value which have been developed have largely reflected only the particular reason for which the assessment has been carried out. As a result different approaches have been adopted by users, planners and owners/developers. Most are not quantitative, not transferable and concentrate on classification rather than evaluation.

3. With the exception of the strategic planning approach, most assessments have been based on single issues. The new statutory Water Quality Objectives proposed by the Environment Agency are seen as one way to move towards a broader-based approach.

4. There is a major difference between the potential value of any fresh water for recreation and the actual value society may wish to give it. Value is influenced by access, location, ownership, conservation status and physical characteristics. The absence of a single body with a statutory responsibility for recreational development leads to further practical and empirical difficulties and restricts severely the usefulness of methodologies that have been proposed for assessing recreation value.

31.1 Introduction

In recent years there has been an increasing awareness of the value and importance of recreation and leisure activities to the general welfare, culture and local economy of many parts of the UK (Council for the Protection of Rural England (CPRE), 1994). At the same time, the environmental impact of the attendant growth in recreational activity has become a cause for concern (House of Commons Environment Committee, 1995) and there is increasing pressure for changes in the way we plan and assess the challenges and conflicts inherent in this development. In particular, the CPRE (1994) report stresses the need for a more systematic public and political approach to these issues. It calls for new mechanisms to understand ways of integrating recreational activities with the wider environment and cultural conditions, and highlights the extent to which the countryside is becoming an area for conflicting values and priorities.

Water-based recreation is not isolated from these changes and conflicts. When in 1992 the Lake District Special Planning Board decided to introduce a 10 mph speed limit on Lake Windermere (effectively halting water-skiing and speedboats), the whole question of the value society places on the need for recreation was thrust into the limelight. Much of the debate in the resultant Public Inquiry revolved around the intrusive nature of noisy water sports and the precise *raison d'être* for the designation of National Parks. Their role in conservation, landscape appreciation and public recreation (of a quiet nature, or not) only served to open up the issue of conflicting values. The Public Inquiry ended in 1994, and upheld the imposition of the speed limit. This recommendation was overturned by the Government in 1996, a ruling which is itself likely to be subject to judicial review. This long process emphasizes the problems of resolving the value of even a single resource to different sectors of society.

The situation in the UK is further compounded by the number and variety of organizations that are involved at the policy level in sport and recreation in the countryside. At the European level sport in the European Union is under the remit of Directorate General X which deals with information, communication and culture. Separate directorates deal with environmental policy and with tourism. At the UK level, sport and recreation is split between the Department of National Heritage, the Department of the Environment, and the Welsh, Scottish and Northern Ireland Offices. The Department of National Heritage has general responsibility for sport and for tourism, but the Department of the Environment, particularly through its oversight of planning, rural affairs and water, and its local government divisions, is of direct relevance to sport and recreation provision in the countryside (Sports Council, 1994).

The Sports Council is the government's adviser on sport and active recreation and the primary body associated with recreation on fresh waters, receiving grant-in-aid from the Department of National Heritage. It also coordinates the Sports Councils for Wales, Scotland and Northern Ireland with the English and British positions. Countryside and water recreation has been identified as a key area in the Council's strategy document for the 1990s (Sports Council, 1993) and its position in this area was set out in *A Countryside for Sport* (Sports Council, 1992). This document stresses the need for a strategic approach towards planning and management of countryside activities, with partnerships seen as a key way forward. The English Tourist Board also answers to the Department of National Heritage, acting to stimulate the improvement of tourism facilities, many of which form key wetland recreation resources.

A number of other relevant public bodies are responsible to the Department of the Environment. The Countryside Commission, English Nature, the Rural Development Commission, British Waterways and the Environment Agency (EA) all have remits covering aspects of recreation in the countryside (for details see Sports Council, 1994). The position in Wales and Scotland is different, with the conservation duties of English Nature merged with the countryside, landscape and access duties of the Countryside Commission into one single body—the Countryside Council for Wales (CCW) and Scottish Natural Heritage (SNH). A similar merger of the two English agencies was proposed in 1994 but ultimately rejected. Thus the inherent conflicts between conservation and recreation which so often surface in matters relating to water recreation have been approached differently. Howell (1994) gives an account of the role of the various environmental agencies in Scotland. Of particular relevance to this chapter is the requirement of recently created organizations (e.g. SNH, the Scottish Environment Protection Agency and the EA) to take into account issues of sustainable development in their approach to water management and the increasing promotion of catchment planning as a holistic approach to such issues (Newson, 1992; Werritty, this volume).

31.2 Whose Values?

With this plethora of bodies involved in recreation, perhaps the best starting point for an examination of the recreation values of fresh waters has to be the question 'for whom is the evaluation being undertaken?' Whereas it might be possible to suggest and even agree common standards and methodologies for individual conservation aspects in order to protect the water environment from deterioration, the subjectivity involved in assessing recreation value is perhaps even more complex. Leaving aside the question of public perception of freshwater quality (see Tunstall *et al.,* this volume), and without entering into the debate on economics and methodologies for cost assessment (see Hanley, this volume), one is still left with three very different approaches: those of the user, the planner and the owner (or developer).

Even within the three broad classifications, there are many subgroups, and recreation value will have a different meaning and different thresholds to each of these. Thus, within the user groups different perspectives can be expected from the active and the passive participant, the individual or the club, the expert or the recreational sportsperson, and those involved in different sports. The individual recreational angler can be expected to have a very different view of the value of fresh waters to that of (e.g.) a competition water-skier.

Similarly, within the planning group different approaches could be expected from, for instance, a local authority planning department on the one hand and the regional council for sport and recreation on the other. The former might perhaps adopt more of a precautionary approach to avoid conflict and minimize environmental impact whilst attempting to meet local demands; the latter perhaps being more proactive in promoting new resources, attempting to increase usage levels and demand. Within the third category, recreation value to the owner could be related to investment priorities, visitor numbers or some measure of customer satisfaction.

Implicit within this split of approaches is also the question 'why attempt to assess the recreation value of fresh waters?' To the individual user it may be a simple question of minimizing a health risk or a personal choice between sites related to access, distance, landscape or aesthetic pleasure. To the planner it may be a requirement to integrate recreation into a wider planning framework as part of regional structure plans. To the owner there may be values associated with a potential commercial return. The nature of the reason will in many ways dictate the methodology used in assessment.

31.3 Approaches to Assessing Recreation Value

A range of approaches to assessing recreation value—many somewhat rudimentary and not quantitative—have evolved in response to the different motivating forces discussed above. In some instances it has been more a case of classification rather than evaluation, and there is a need to move from the former to the latter. This is especially true when comparisons have to be made between competing claims for resource allocation—whether from other recreational activities, conservation interests, housing, transport or other sources.

There are perhaps five broad elements that could be considered in assessing and managing the recreation value of fresh waters:

- Safety—risk assessment
- Water quality—health and aesthetics
- Specific recreation requirement—individual sport definitions
- Resource and demand—regional priority studies
- Strategic plans—development and control

These elements are not mutually exclusive, and indeed the strategic planning approach attempts to incorporate aspects of all the others in reaching a balanced arrangement of recreation quality. There is also great variation in the extent to which each element has been formally proposed or documented, and in the quality of information available with which to make value judgements. Finally there is often considerable disparity between the potential value of any particular fresh water and its actual value for recreation. Access, location, ownership and other factors may completely alter the situation.

Perhaps the simplest expressions of recreation values are those pertaining to the aesthetic value of individual sites, rather than any specific attributes such as water quality that could be measured directly. Although studies of perception of freshwater quality have revealed the nature of people's likes and dislikes (see for instance House and Sangster, 1991) they have not transferred such descriptive values into a method of ranking or value classification *per se*. Thus they were able to show that the public had a strong preference for natural-looking river banks and channels with good quality water, bankside trees and meandering channels.

Close relationships also existed between perceived water and river-corridor quality, but this was not explored further.

31.3.1 Safety assessment

It is worth remembering that the most basic assessment of all relates to risks to human safety, and in particular drowning. In the UK in 1994 there were 448 reported drownings, of which 17% were recorded in lakes and reservoirs, 6% in canals and 37% in rivers and streams (Royal Society for the Prevention of Accidents, 1995). By activity, 17% of those drowning were swimming, 12% were taking part in angling, 5% canoeing and 12% in other forms of boating. These figures far outweigh any reported deaths from illnesses associated with water recreation, and remain a major factor in any assessment of the value of fresh waters for recreation, be it from the user's perspective or that of the owner (Department of National Heritage, 1993).

The most common technique for evaluating safety is a safety audit, concentrating on a site-by-site appraisal of the potential physical dangers and risks to users (e.g. Royal Society for the Prevention of Accidents, 1993). Reservoirs in particular may be steep-sided, concrete bowls with deep, cold water and their value as a recreation site may be severely restricted by these features. Safety concerns, rather than risks of illness or pollution, have led most water companies to ban swimming from many of their reservoirs.

Sports associations as well as individual participants also make value judgements based on safety issues. For example, the British Canoe Union (BCU, 1993) has graded the ease of navigability of rivers from I (not difficult) to IV (limit of practicability). The vast majority of use (over 80%) occurs in classes II and III, with a recognition that the higher classes require more specialized skills and techniques to enable them to be utilized. This is primarily a subjective system and changes in flood conditions may drastically alter these gradings. The British Canoe Union also notes that performance of canoeists and boat designs have improved radically over the last 20 years and consequently such judgements are not static measures of recreation value.

31.3.2 Water quality

For many people, water quality for recreation is perceived primarily as a public health issue. More specifically it relates to the risk of contracting various illnesses associated with fresh waters, by bathing in or having contact with polluted water. It is an area where increasing attention is being paid to efforts to define meaningful standards for water quality assessment in order to counter public concern (e.g. Royal Commission on Environmental Pollution, 1992; Kay and Hanbury, 1993). In addition, the debate on the exact criteria to be used in assessing recreational quality has moved to the proposed definitions of watersports and amenity classes within the new statutory Water Quality Objectives (WQOs) being promoted for rivers and canals in England and Wales by the Environment Agency (formerly the National Rivers Authority) (NRA, 1991).

Within the European Union, the legal framework behind recreational water quality is the EC Bathing Waters Directive (76/160/EEC). However, this only applies to freshwater or marine beaches that have been designated as bathing beaches, and focuses on the use of indicators of faecal contamination as microbiological standards. In addition, it lists a number of other physical and chemical standards, but the main emphasis has been on the attainment of compliance with the mandatory standards for total and faecal coliforms.

A fundamental problem with this approach is that the standards are not based on epidemiological studies and do not recognize that different recreational activities will have different degrees of immersion and different frequency of contact with water (Stanwell-Smith, 1993). Where research has been conducted on the relationship between individual sporting activities and diseases, the results have not been consistent (Fewtrell, 1991). Neither have they produced any consistent results as to the most appropriate indicators of health risks, or reliable evidence of the magnitude of risk based on the levels of indicator organisms.

Fewtrell *et al.* (1993) have provided evidence from epidemiological studies that it may be possible to construct dose-response curves for slalom canoeists using a range of investigations across a wide range of water qualities. However, even within this one sport, it was apparent that users of white (turbulent) water and placid water sites had different exposures to water and hence different risks of water ingestion and the chance of illness. Within the UK, the EC Bathing Waters Directive was transposed into law by the Bathing Waters (Classification) Regulations 1991. However, the UK remains the only country within the European Union not to have designated any freshwater sites as bathing waters, alongside the coastal ones. This remains the position, despite the fact that the potential risk to human health when bathing is probably higher in fresh waters, due to the relatively lower degree of dilution and dispersion, and because many viruses and bacteria have a longer life in fresh water (Chamberlain and Mitchell, 1978).

A number of other European Union states have adopted stricter standards for one or more parameters, whilst others do not comply with some of the mandatory requirements. Further afield, in North America there is a similar diversity in standards, techniques, sampling regimes and conflicting evidence from the studies on which they are based (see for instance Saliba, 1993).

The proposed statutory WQOs being considered by the Environment Agency represent the most likely prospect in the UK for reaching any degree of standardization in this particular area. They form the basis of a system of classification which relates to the range of uses for which waters are expected to be suitable. Appropriate standards are defined for each of 11 use classes, the purpose of which is to help monitor and improve the quality of the water, provide a means by which consent limits can be set for discharges into rivers and canals, and pollution from diffuse sources can be addressed. The use classes for (1) Basic Amenity and (9) Water Contact Activity remain to be articulated, though the nature of the criteria to be considered has been proposed (NRA, 1991) and eight pilot study areas identified.

The Basic Amenity class refers to general aesthetic aspects so as to prevent public nuisance from visual and smell problems akin to some of the physical and chemical parameters in the EC Bathing Waters Directive. These include colour, transparency, odour, oil, litter, foam, biological growth and dissolved oxygen. Many of these are known to be important influences on public perceptions of river quality (House and Sangster, 1991). The Watersport use class aims to address those activities such as water-skiing, bathing and diving where there is frequent intimate contact with fresh water, so as to protect participants from health risks. It thus lists the parameters to be considered as measures of faecal coliforms, faecal streptococci, staphylococci and bacteriophages.

31.3.3 *Specific recreation requirements*

Individual participants and the governing bodies of sport have attempted to define their own requirements as to the characteristics of fresh waters that make them of intrinsic value. These have largely been in the form of physical parameters, with often the minimum size and shape of water recommended for different activities being the prime category. However, length (rowing), depth (angling), clarity (sub-aqua) or other features such as bankside cover or slope (sailing) may be of equal or greater importance for specific sports. In addition, the relative ease with which the sports concerned can coexist on a multi-purpose site without danger or disruption to, or from, other users will also affect the potential recreation value of the site.

The production of standard requirements for each sport has been promoted by the Sports Council and this has certainly aided the planning of sport provision. A useful, though incomplete, compendium has been included in the Minerals Planning Guidance Note 7 (Department of Environment, 1989) (Table 31.1) covering a range of sports that might be considered as after-use for reclamation of wet mineral workings. However, Monnington and Tanner (1992) in a review of guidance notes for preferred areas, have shown that the figures recommended for individual sports vary dramatically between different sources. These recommendations apparently take little account of differences required when a sport is practised at different levels of proficiency or in different forms. Furthermore, their examination of the size of waters used by sports showed further disparities. Many were smaller, reflecting in part the shortage of better waters, the satisfaction of many recreational users with less than that needed by enthusiasts, and the willingness of some sports (e.g. angling, jet skiing) to take almost any water 'as found'. It appears that recreational users cannot afford to be choosy in case they lose a potential resource entirely, so their judgements can be easily influenced.

31.3.4 *Resource and demand*

The relative imbalance between the available resource and some measure of latent demand for any particular sport could be used (at least on a regional basis) as one method of assessing the recreation value of fresh water. However, assessment of demand in this context is beset with methodological problems and a lack of

Table 31.1 Guidance notes on operational requirements for water-based recreational uses. (From: Department of the Environment, 1989)

Sport	Type of bank	Minimum depth of water	Preferred shape of water	Approximate minimum size of water	Bankside facilities
Canoeing	No special banking needed. Provision for easy launching and beaching of canoes.	1.5 m	Rectangular. Competitive canoeing requires length of 1200 m.	7 ha	Space for canoe storage and repair. Clubhouse.
Power Boating	Well protected banks, preferably strengthened against wash. Norfolk reed or reed mace planted adjacent to the bank to limit erosion from bank wash.	2 m	Triangular. Each leg of triangle course should be at least 400 m.	15 ha	Concrete hardstanding for launching boats. Space for storage and repair of boats. Clubhouse. Good access. Mounds around site to protect from noise.
Rowing	No special banking needed. Should have a launching platform.	1.5 m.	Rectangular. Minimum length for competitions: 1200 m.	7 ha	Boathouse for storage and repair of boats.
Sailing	No special banking required. If possible, angled earth banks should be provided. No trees should be planted on the bank nearest the direction of the prevailing wind. Launch platform required.	2 m		20+ ha	Jetties and/or concrete ramps for launching boats. Clubhouse. Good access. Boat storage.
Water ski-ing	Banks strengthened against problems of wash. The provision of a shallow water area shelving rapidly at the launch platform is recommended.	2 m	Rectangular.	15 ha	Jetties, launching, ramps. Boathouse. Clubhouse. Good access.
Windsurfing	No special banking needed. Provision for easy launching and beaching of sail boards. No trees to be planted on the bank in the direction of the prevailing wind.	1.5 m		11 ha	Clubhouse. Good access. Space for sail board storage.
Angling	Fishing position more than 1 m from water surface. Banks preferably reinforced against erosion; and permanently installed positions.	2 m	Diverse with embayments.	2 ha	Clubhouse preferable.

Plate 7: Education, Research and Policy Formulation

7a(below) – Learning to sample
(Photo: L Gill).

7b(right) – Sampling to learn
(Photo: S Ormerod)   (see Chapter 21).

7c(bottom) – Priorities for river restoration in Flanders
(Belgium) (see Chapter 41).

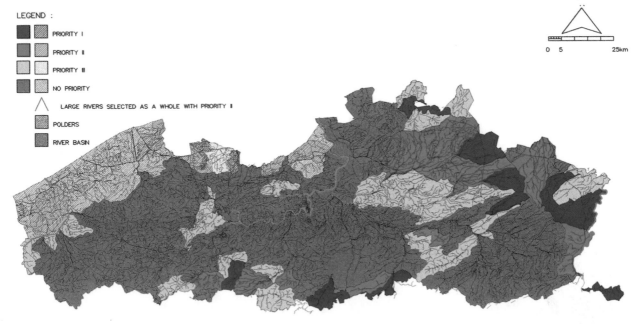

PLATE 8: REMOTE SENSING

8a(top left) – The predicted pattern of Secchi disk transparency in Loch Lomond (Scotland). Dark areas indicate regions of low transparency, lighter areas high transparency (Photo: T Malthus) (see Chapter 16).

8b(bottom left) – The predicted pattern of phytoplankton biomass (as chlorophyll-*a* concentration) in Loch Leven (Scotland). High chlorophyll concentrations (in yellow) are shown in the west of the loch (Photo: T Malthus) (see Chapter 16).

8c(right) – A stretch of the River Tay (Scotland) with a supervised classification of 50m buffer zones indicating different vegetation types. The river itself has been colour coded for approximate depth, as determined from an unsupervised classification (Photo: T Malthus) (see Chapter 16).

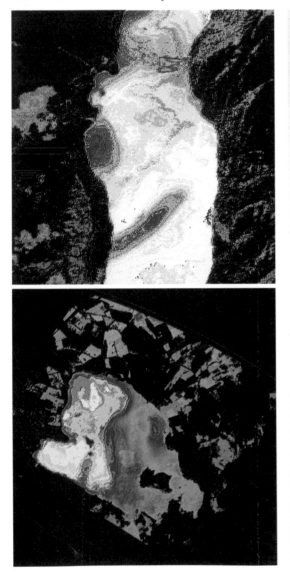

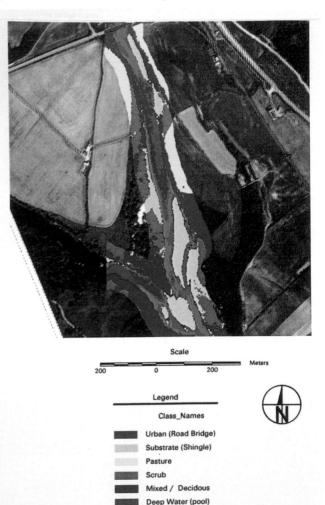

Scale

200   0   200   Meters

Legend

Class_Names

Urban (Road Bridge)
Substrate (Shingle)
Pasture
Scrub
Mixed / Decidous
Deep Water (pool)

intermediate

Shallow water (riffle)

adequate data. This is particularly true for informal sports and recreational activities, where the majority of participants do not belong to a club and are not affiliated to either regional or national governing bodies. Data on membership numbers, growth in participation rates or waiting lists are all difficult to interpret, as are the wide variations reported in national surveys of participation levels (Monnington and Tanner, 1992).

The various Regional Councils for Sport and Recreation in England and Wales have each produced a regional strategy for water recreation, and the Eastern Council recently produced a report on the supply and demand for watersports on enclosed waters in their area (Eastern Council for Sport and Recreation, 1993.) This attempts to meet earlier criticism of regional strategies by identifying both the existing demand and supply, and then examining the deficiencies in provision. From this has come a series of recommendations to address the shortfall for particular sports—rowing, sub-aqua, windsurfing and water-skiing—and to ease the greatest pressures for access to fresh water experienced in Essex and Hertfordshire as a result of limited resources and excessive demand from Greater London.

Like many other studies, the above report relied heavily on questionnaires to obtain details of demand. A similar approach was taken by the Northern Council and the NRA in a joint study of watersports in the North of England (Ash Consulting Group, 1994). Both, however, stop short of attempting to provide any hierarchy of value of sites to the region, or determining priorities for future opportunities. Thus, although they provide a baseline survey and recommendation for action to meet expected demands, they do not extend this further to define the quality of recreational waters other than in very general terms relating to potential use by sports.

It is left up to the individual governing bodies of sport to promote development plans that target specific waters, ranking their priority as local, regional or national standard sites to meet regional demands (e.g. British Water Ski Federation, 1993).

31.3.5 *Strategic plans*

Where ownership or control of a group of waters, or length of river, is in the hands of one body, the opportunity arises to place recreation value in a much wider context, and at least in some *a priori* manner to create a strategic overview. In doing so, an implicit part of the process is to assign some form of value to the potential use of each water under consideration, in such a manner as to be able to make choices about its use. The catalyst for such an evaluation may be varied— for example the increasing conflict between alternative uses (e.g. conservation and recreation), new commercial opportunities, changes in political or cultural values, the production of planning guidelines, or growth in demand for a particular activity.

Two examples of an integrated strategic approach are provided by a private water company in the north-east of England and a former Regional Council in the east of Scotland. In each case issues of safety, water quality, specific recreation requirements and demands were combined, to be judged against the available resource (reservoirs in each case) owned and managed by the organizations concerned.

31.3.5.1 Northumbrian Water

Following privatization of the water industry in 1989, a review was undertaken of the 16 reservoirs owned by Northumbrian Water in order to develop a comprehensive recreation and conservation strategy. The process had several stages (Figure 31.1), beginning with a conservation evaluation and a recreation evaluation. The former involved habitat surveys of each site and then a major two-year study on the ornithological importance of the reservoirs in a local, regional and national context (Westerberg *et al.*, 1994). This latter project also included an assessment of the impacts of recreational activities on wildfowl, with particular reference to angling, the main active user sport (67,000 visits each year) and to water-skiing, seen as potentially the most likely sources of conflict.

The recreation evaluation involved building up a site status report (location *vis-à-vis* main population, catchment, safety and physical site constraints, visitor

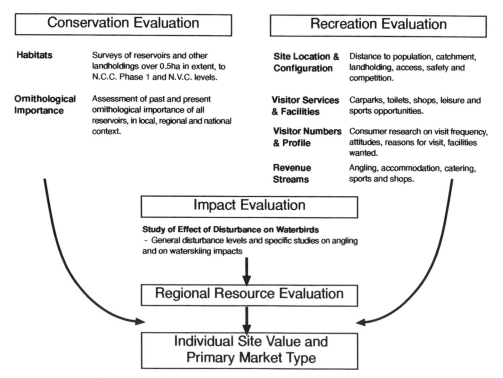

Figure 31.1 Methodology for strategic assessment of recreation and conservation value of fresh waters—Northumbrian Water's recreation and conservation evaluation. The Nature Conservancy Council (NCC) Phase 1 and National Vegetation Classification (NVC) are methods for standardised recording of vegetational diversity within surveyed areas (for details see NCC, 1990 and Rodwell, 1991).

numbers, existing sports facilities and recreational activities) and also identifying current income sources (from fishing, catering, accommodation). Together with the conservation data this allowed a review of current status for each site. Consumer research across the region was then used to assess the visitor habits, attitudes, reason for visiting and facilities they would wish to see at each site. The process of regional resource evaluation involved consultation with English Nature and the regional Sports Council and reference to published information on habitat and species rarity and recreational demands.

It was then possible to define a market type or primary value for each reservoir, reflecting both the visitor preferences and the conservation importance of each site (Figure 31.2). Whilst the position of each reservoir in this diagram reflects its primary recreation value, other uses are also recognized. For instance, Tunstall, Balderhead, Scaling Dam and Grassholme all have locally important conservation interests, which are protected by zoning within each reservoir's site development plan. Footpaths, picnic sites and viewpoints have also been developed around all but the two primary conservation sites. The individual and regional value of the recreational opportunity at each site is enhanced by the geographical spread of the resource allocation across the region (Figure 31.3).

A direct result of this approach was to give recreation a high priority at Kielder Water and to initiate a major investment programme to improve and extend visitor facilities there. With some 300,000 visitors each year it ranks as the most visited tourist site in Northumberland. By comparison, the other reservoirs attracted fewer visitors and the majority who visited were either anglers or passive visitors who enjoyed walking and other informal types of recreation. Both Cow Green (part of a National Nature Reserve) and Bakethin (a local County Trust Wildlife site) have been protected from recreational developments. Similarly, important breeding populations of wigeon *Anas penelope* on the Teesdale reservoirs have been afforded specific protection, though water-skiing and sailing occur at each site.

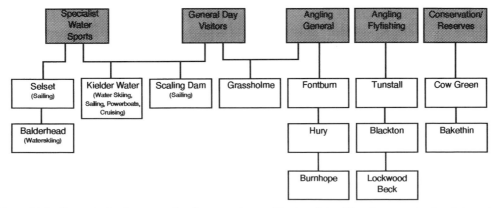

Figure 31.2   Strategic development plan for recreation on Northumbrian Water's reservoirs: breakdown by primary market type and recreation value.

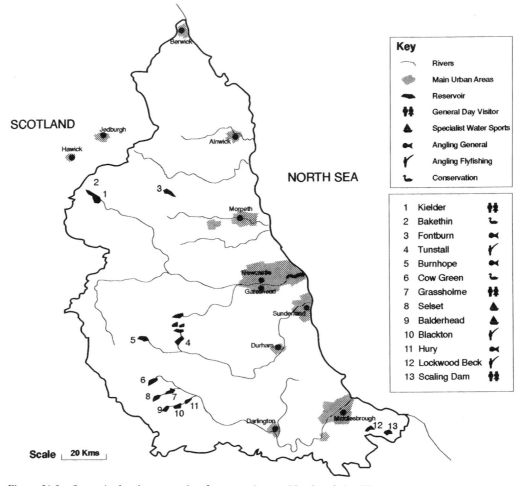

Figure 31.3 Strategic development plan for recreation on Northumbrian Water's reservoirs: site locations and primary recreational types.

Recognition of the primary value for each site also meant that certain activities were then relocated to take account of the overall strategy for recreation and conservation. Angling for instance was totally stopped on Bakethin Reservoir in 1994, as the research had shown the adverse impact of this activity on waterbirds at a site primarily designated for its conservation value. Similarly water-skiing was removed from Fontburn Reservoir as it clashed with the main angling interests. By contrast, water-skiing was expanded at Kielder and at Balderhead in line with the strategy provisions, with special reference at the latter site to also protect the breeding wigeon.

31.3.5.2 Lothian Regional Council

The Conservation and Recreation Strategy produced for the 23 reservoirs owned by Lothian Regional Council (1990) was more constrained: first, by concerns about water quality and second, by the seasonal presence of nationally and internationally important numbers of geese and other wildfowl. Thus, in order of priority, development of the potential for even quiet water-based recreation on the compensation reservoirs comes only fifth in the eight stated objectives of the strategy.

These can be summarized as:

1. Public water supply
2. Designated Sites of Special Scientific Interest
3. Areas of local wildlife importance
4. Natural fish populations of regional significance
5. Quiet water-based recreation
6. Creation of new wildlife areas
7. Development of angling
8. Improved water treatment to permit further recreation

The prospects for effective wildlife conservation are considered high, guided by the existence of recognized designations such as the Site of Special Scientific Interest at West Water and the local nature reserve designation at Gladhouse Reservoir. By comparison, the opportunity for recreational development appears much less positive, despite the potential value of integrating certain forms of recreation at particular sites.

A key point has been the constraints introduced by concerns about human contamination of the water supply. At certain direct supply reservoirs the treatment process is not sufficient to remove or inactivate potential contaminants that might be introduced into the water through recreational activities such as swimming, sailing or boating. In these cases, using the method suggested by North West Water Authority (Institution of Water Engineers and Scientists, 1981) reservoir managers have restricted or prohibited such recreational activities from these sites altogether.

Another key aspect to the value of the reservoirs for recreation has been that the sporting rights in many cases are still in private ownership. In particular this negates the potential recreation value of the three reservoirs in the Pentland Hills close to the main conurbation, Edinburgh, although in all other aspects these sites would be excellent for recreation. Within the constraints imposed upon the strategy, demand for recreation was assessed from published figures for general participation rates and from direct investigation, particularly of anglers utilizing the reservoirs. In addition a traffic survey was used to identify the destinations for outdoor recreation around the main conurbations of Edinburgh and West Lothian. No sites were deemed suitable for sports such as water-skiing, powerboating or rowing, but otherwise the strategy recommended working towards ensuring that a range of water-based recreation was available in each of the main separate population catchments across the region. Only when improved water treatment techniques were developed or when sites were no longer required for drinking supply could other opportunities for quiet activities also be promoted.

31.4   Discussion

Analysis of the various options for recreational assessment of fresh water reveals a number of common problems. Of these, the diversity of reasons for undertaking assessments ensures that no one method can ever be accepted by all. Indeed, nearly all suffer from a lack of an objective methodology and there is no comparable guide for standards to parallel that produced for the selection of biological SSSIs (NCC, 1989).

Within the UK, there is no effective legal basis to the protection or enhancement of sites for their recreation value, equivalent to the international (Special Protection Area) national (Site of Special Scientific Interest) or regional (Local Nature Reserve) designations for conservation. The Department of the Environment's Planning Policy Guidance on Sport and Recreation (DoE, 1991) represents the only recognition that countryside and water activities have a legitimate claim on natural resources, along with other land uses. It requires that Local Authorities plan for recreational activities at the regional, structural, unitary and local planning levels. However, although some sports such as water-skiing have defined their needs, standards and facilities at a local and regional level, this is not being coordinated and integrated into a cohesive comprehensive strategy (Sports Council, 1992).

Whereas there is stated recognition by the Sports Council of the need to adopt policies that are based on sustainable use of the natural resources of the countryside (Sports Council, 1992), it is clear that friction between watersports and nature conservation interests is of concern to both 'sides'. Partly this can be explained by the lack of any agreed methodology to weight recreation values and to compare them with conservation values. In addition many areas designated for conservation or landscape reasons are often also key areas for both informal and organized water-based recreation. In such circumstances there is a need for further research into the impact that recreational activities have upon conservation interests, in order to inform the debate on integration of activities.

This is a key area of growing concern to sports bodies at all levels. There is a feeling that prime sites for recreation are being lost because they have no statutory protection. The recent introduction of byelaws controlling recreation on such sites as Loch Lomond in Scotland is one such area of conflict. Indeed, where such sites are dominated by the more active and often noisy watersports, it increases pressure for quieter pursuits on other remaining sites. This raises more potential for conflict and concentrates particularly noisy sports at fewer and fewer locations, which themselves achieve greater recreation value in turn, as they become the only sites available. This however is obviously not a sustainable answer to the use of water by the various forms of recreational activity.

There is an increasing volume of literature on the impact of water recreation on conservation concerns (e.g. Hockin *et al.*, 1992; Land Use Consultants, 1995) and a growing number of case studies, codes of practice and planning manuals dealing with such issues (e.g. Sidaway, 1991; Elson *et al.*, 1995). However, whilst these and other studies deal with the various theoretical and practical issues associated both with conflict between recreational activities and between recreation and conservation issues, they do not assist in attempting to define recreation value, only in highlighting potential conflicts and methods of resolution.

The setting of statutory WQOs for recreational uses is seen by many to be a key step forward. The responsibility for setting WQOs lies with the Secretary of State, but it will be the EA who are in the forefront of the definition of standards in England and Wales. In the absence of unambiguous epidemiological data relating to water use and health, account must be taken of the degree of water contact experienced and there may be a need to recognize three classes of recreation: from total immersion, through incidental contact to non-contact. This may help to clarify the position, but varying frequency and length of time of exposure to the water is also important, as indeed will the type of sport being practised.

The nature of water recreation also ensures that there is no one single body with either a statutory responsibility or a natural lead in assessing the total variety of value judgements one might wish to apply to freshwater quality. The EA is not responsible for health-related matters associated with recreational water use, apart from legal obligations for monitoring under the Bathing Waters (Classification) Regulations 1991. It falls to the Local Authorities to assess and take whatever action necessary to ensure that any potential public health risk is identified and notified to potential water users.

Beyond the value judgements directly associated with chemical and biological water quality, other organizations also have a role to play. The Sports Council, Local Authorities and the Countryside Commission in England and Wales all have remits to promote recreation and access in the countryside. Similarly the privatized Water Companies, British Waterways, mineral companies and individual riparian and lake owners must also be brought into the debate. The recreation value of fresh waters cannot be assessed in isolation from these and other controlling bodies and influences.

Where individual bodies have specific responsibilities relating to single recreation issues the potential for conflict with other uses of the water resource is likely to be enhanced. By comparison, a diverse number of public and private bodies such as the EA, SNH, the Water Companies and the Broads Authority have duties relating both to recreation and conservation. It has tended to be these organizations that have, at least implicitly, had to put a value on recreation for the water bodies under their influence or control, in order to assess planning priorities or target expenditure. The *Draft Broads Plan—No Easy Answers* (Broads Authority, 1994) is one such example of a consultation document which attempts to resolve the inherent conflicts associated with its three responsibilities towards management of the Norfolk Broads—those relating to conservation, recreation and navigation. The emphasis is on wide consultation with the local community, education of all parties involved and taking account of local concerns and individual site-based issues. Wherever possible, proposals are backed by scientific data to explain the options, but every attempt is made to reach solutions without resort to legal or statutory designations. Emphasis is placed particularly on local feelings of the importance of a site for its recreation value.

The final problem to address in defining the recreation quality of fresh waters is that the potential value of any given location (however measured) will rarely equate to the actual value society might wish to give it. A quick look at the freshwater resource in the UK shows that there is no apparent shortage of water for recreation enthusiasts. Walker (1994) has estimated that inland waters in Scotland, for instance, cover about 2% of the total area; on the face of it a more than adequate resource to meet all types of recreation demand. The variation between areas of the country, however, can be very marked and many centres of population are poorly served by accessible water for recreation. Ash Consulting Group (1994) showed that the area of enclosed fresh water available to the populations of the northern counties of England varied between 13.7 ha (Cumbria) and 0.05 ha (Tyne and Wear) per thousand population.

This apparent excess of supply in certain areas hides barriers associated with location *vis-à-vis* the main centres of population, and access difficulties. The North of England Watersports Study (Ash Consulting Group, 1994) found that shortage of time was the most significant factor constraining participation in watersports, whilst Tivy (1990), in her study of lochs and reservoirs in Scotland, assumed that those water bodies beyond easy reach by car would not have significant recreational use. Participation in a range of watersports has been shown to be strongly influenced by distance from the recreation site (Central Water Planning Unit, 1976).

Physical characteristics, such as drawdown on water supply reservoirs (which may regularly exceed 20 m in summer), can leave launching ramps and landings high and dry and also expose areas of dangerous soft mud. Other aspects relating to the nature of the water body—size, shape, exposure to winds, depth and bank profile—have already been mentioned and will influence the type of activity that could potentially be accommodated on any particular site.

Management regimes such as multiple use zoning, and the ownership and control of the surrounding land and sporting rights may also dictate what recreational activities are permitted (Walker, 1994). Finally, nature conservation concerns (taking precedence over recreation demands) and planning conditions may restrict or prohibit recreational activities. Thus even if a value, or range of values defining recreation quality of fresh waters could be proposed, their usefulness will be severely restricted by practical and empirical difficulties associated with their application.

Acknowledgements

The views expressed in this chapter are those of the author and do not necessarily represent the views of Northumbrian Water. I am grateful to Barbara Pike and Craig McGarvey (Environment Agency), Lee Cousins and Marsailidh Chisholm (Scottish Sports Council), Geoff Hughes and Dacre Dunlop (Sports Council—Northern Region), Drew Jamieson (East of Scotland Water Authority), Graham

Newman (British Waterways) and colleagues at Northumbrian Water for discussions on this topic. Table 31.1 is Crown copyright and is reproduced with permission.

References

Ash Consulting Group (1994). *North of England Water Sports Study—A Consultation Document*. Report to the National Rivers Authority, Northern Council for Sport and Recreation and the Sports Council Northern Region. Edinburgh.

British Canoe Union (1993). *River Grading*. S662Feb93. Nottingham.

British Water Ski Federation (1993). 'Northern Region Development Plan'. Unpublished report.

Broads Authority (1994). *The Draft Broads Plan—No Easy Answers*. Norwich.

Central Water Planning Unit (1976). *Some Empirical Information on Demands for Water-based Recreation Activities*. Technical Note No 13. Reading.

Chamberlin, C. E. and Mitchell, R. (1978). A decay model for enteric bacteria in natural waters. In: Mitchell, R. (Ed.), *Water Pollution Microbiology*. John Wiley, New York, 325–348.

CPRE (1994). *Leisure Landscapes. Leisure Culture and the English Countryside: Challenges and Conflicts*. London.

Department of National Heritage (1993). *Report of the Water Sports Safety Working Group*. London.

Department of the Environment (1989). *The Reclamation of Mineral Workings*. Minerals Planning Policy Guidance Note 7. London.

Department of the Environment (1991). *Sport and Recreation*. Planning Policy Guidance Note 17. London.

Eastern Council for Sport and Recreation (1993). *The Supply and Demand for Water Sports on Water Bodies within the Eastern Region*. Bedford.

Elson, M. J., Lloyd, J. and Thorpe, I. (1995). *Good Practice in the Planning and Management of Sport and Active Recreation in the Countryside*. Sports Council, London and Countryside Commission, Cheltenham.

Fewtrell, L. (1991). Freshwater recreation: a cause for concern. *Applied Geography*, **11**, 215–226.

Fewtrell, L., Kay, D., Newman, G., Salmon, R. and Wyer, M. (1993). Results of epidemiological pilot studies. In: Kay, D. and Hanbury, R. (Eds), *Recreational Water Quality Management. Vol. II, Fresh Waters*. Ellis Horwood, Chichester, 75–108.

Hanley, N. (This volume). Assessing the economic value of fresh waters.

Hockin, D., Ounsted, M., Gorman, M., Hill, D., Keller, V. and Barker, M. A. (1992). Examination of the effects of disturbance on birds with reference to its importance in ecological assessments. *Journal of Environmental Management*, **36**, 253–286.

House of Commons Environment Committee (1995). *The Environmental Impact of Leisure Activities*. HMSO, London.

House, M. A. and Sangster, E. K. (1991). Public perception of river corridor management. *Journal of the Institution of Water and Environmental Management*, **5**, 312–317.

Howell, D. L. (1994). Role of environmental agencies. In: Maitland, P. S., Boon, P. J. and McLusky, D. S. (Eds), *The Fresh Waters of Scotland: A National Resource of International Significance*. John Wiley, Chichester, 577–611.

Institution of Water Engineers and Scientists (1981). *Recreation—Water and Land, a Water Practice Manual*. London.

Kay, D. and Hanbury, R. (Eds) (1993). *Recreational Water Quality Management. Vol. II, Fresh Waters*. Ellis Horwood, Chichester.

Land Use Consultants (1995). *Impact of Recreation on Wildlife*. National Rivers Authority, Marlow.

Lothian Regional Council (1990). *Strategy for Conservation and Recreation on the Reservoirs owned by Lothian Regional Council*. Department of Planning, Edinburgh.

Monnington, T. and Tanner, M. (1992). *The Potential of Wet Mineral Workings in the West Midlands for Sport and Recreation*. Report to the Sports Council West Midlands Region.

National Rivers Authority (1991). *Proposals for Statutory Water Quality Objectives*. Water Quality Series No 5, Bristol.

NCC (1989). *Guidelines for Selection of Biological SSSIs*. Peterborough.

NCC (1990). *Handbook for Phase 1 Habitat Survey*. Peterborough.

Newson, M. (1992). *Land, Water and Development: River Basins and their Sustainable Management*. Routledge, London.

Rodwell, J. S. (Ed.) (1991). *British Plant Communities*. Cambridge University Press, Cambridge.

Royal Commission on Environmental Pollution (1992). *Freshwater Quality*. HMSO, London.

Royal Society for the Prevention of Accidents (1993). 'Water safety—reservoirs, rationale and site recommendations.' Unpublished audit report to Northumbrian Water.

Royal Society for the Prevention of Accidents (1995). *Drownings in the UK*. Birmingham.

Saliba, R. (1993). Legal and economic implications in developing criteria and standards. In: Kay, D. and Hanbury, R. (Eds), *Recreational Water Quality Management. Vol. II, Fresh Waters*. Ellis Horwood, Chichester, 57–73.

Sidaway, R. (1991). *Good Conservation Practice for Sport and Recreation*. Sports Council, London.

Sports Council (1992). *A Countryside for Sport. A Policy for Sport and Recreation*. London.

Sports Council (1993). *Sports in the Nineties: New Horizons*. London.

Sports Council (1994). *Who's Who in Countryside Sport and Active Recreation*. Sports Council Facilities Factfile 3, CWR 19, London.

Stanwell-Smith, R. (1993). Public health and epidemiological aspects. In: Kay, D. and Hanbury, R. (Eds), *Recreational Water Quality Management. Vol. II, Fresh Waters*. Ellis Horwood, Chichester, 25–32.

Tivy, J. (1980). *The Effects of Recreation on Freshwater Lochs and Reservoirs in Scotland*. Countryside Commission for Scotland, Battleby.

Tunstall, S., Fordham, M., Green, C. and House, M. (This volume). Public perception of freshwater quality with particular reference to rivers in England and Wales.

Walker, S. E. (1994). Tourism and Recreation. In: Maitland, P. S., Boon, P. J. and McLusky, D. S. (Eds), *The Fresh Waters of Scotland: a National Resource of International Significance*. John Wiley, Chichester, 333–343.

Werritty, A. (This volume). Enhancing the quality of freshwater resources: the role of Integrated Catchment Management.

Westerberg, A. E., Muirhead, L. B., Donnison, A. and Bell, M. C. (1994). 'An Assessment of the Past and Present Ornithological Importance of Northumbrian Water Limited's Reservoirs, and the Effects of Disturbance on Waterbirds'. Unpublished report by the Wetlands Advisory Service to Northumbrian Water, Durham.

32 LANDSCAPE ASSESSMENT OF FRESH WATERS

C. Swanwick

Summary

1. Current approaches to landscape assessment make it clear that the emphasis has shifted away from thinking about *value* in landscape towards the concept of landscape *character*.

2. The concept of landscape character applies as much to rivers and other freshwater landscapes as it does to other 'drier' landscapes. Indeed many of the UK's most valued landscapes, including designated areas, are centred on freshwater environments.

3. Landscape assessment is increasingly being used as a key tool to help in understanding variations in landscape character, at national, regional and more local levels, and in progressing from that to decisions about conservation, management and enhancement.

4. This chapter focuses on the assessment of river landscapes in England and summarizes an approach which has been adopted by the Environment Agency. It particularly discusses issues relating to the progression from describing and classifying freshwater landscapes to decisions based on some form of evaluation. The method outlined is now contributing to many areas of activity relating to river landscapes and a case study of an urban river catchment is used to demonstrate its practical application.

5. It is concluded that the method fits well into the spectrum of approaches being used more generally to characterize environmental resources and is well suited to the integration which is being advocated as a new era of 'whole environment planning' approaches. It is argued that although the method has so far been applied only to rivers it should be equally applicable to other types of freshwater environment.

32.1   Introduction

This chapter addresses the topic of the landscape of fresh waters in Britain (see Plate 5), and specifically the issue of links between landscape classification and landscape value. It is necessary to begin by defining what is meant by the word 'landscape'. In its most common current usage the word refers to the visual appearance of the land, though it is increasingly recognized that we perceive our surroundings using our other senses as well. Essentially, landscape can be defined as the interaction of geology, topography, water, soils, vegetation and human activities as perceived by an observer. Perception of landscape is also, of course, influenced by many different cultural and aesthetic overlays.

The issue of landscape assessment in general and landscape evaluation in particular, has received a great deal of attention over the last 20 years. In the 1970s landscape evaluation, especially involving quantitative, supposedly objective scientific approaches, was very much the focus of work in this area (see, for example, University of Manchester, 1976). There appears, however, to have been a great reaction against this, not least because such approaches are seen by many to be far removed from the reality of what landscape actually means to many people—something which cannot easily be reduced to a scientific formula (Countryside Commission, 1988; Landscape Research Group, 1988). As a result, the methods which have evolved more recently, and especially over the last 10 years, for carrying out landscape assessment have attempted to draw a clear line between the processes of describing and classifying landscapes, and those of evaluating them. This distinction has crystallized into a division between the concepts of landscape character, on the one hand, and landscape quality, on the other. To quote someone asked about his preferences for the different landscapes around the city of Leeds: 'it's not that one's better than another, it's just that they are different'.

In current practical approaches to landscape assessment the emphasis has shifted away from the more conventional thinking about 'value' in landscape (perhaps best demonstrated by the traditional idea of landscape designation) towards the concept of landscape character. This may be summarized as a distinct pattern of elements which occur consistently in a particular type of landscape. Character is created by specific combinations of geology, water, soils, landform, vegetation, land use, field patterns and human settlement. In essence, therefore, landscape character is what makes one place different from another—it creates sense of place or distinctiveness in a locality.

32.2   The Importance of Freshwater Landscapes

Freshwater environments include lakes and other bodies of open water, rivers, canals and other watercourses. Such environments contribute significantly to the character and quality of the British landscape and there is a range of evidence demonstrating that people are often most attracted to landscapes which include water as a feature (see, for example, studies on landscape preferences summarized by the Landscape Research Group, 1988). Well-known designated areas like the Lake District and the Norfolk Broads owe much of their special landscape quality to the presence of large bodies of fresh water. Similarly, lochs are a key feature of many of the most well-known Scottish landscapes, including designated areas such as Loch Lomond and the Trossachs, and Loch Tummel.

Rivers and their surroundings also make a very important contribution to the character and quality of the landscape in both town and country. River valleys are often a highly distinctive type of landscape whose character frequently provides a marked contrast with the surrounding area. There are at present no special designations or measures aimed specifically at protecting these landscapes and ensuring their conservation. There are, however, a number of pointers to their importance:

(a) River valleys make an extremely important contribution to nearly all the English National Parks and Areas of Outstanding Natural Beauty (AONBs) such as, for example, the Yorkshire Dales, the North Pennines and Dedham Vale.

(b) A number of river valleys have been designated as Environmentally Sensitive Areas (ESAs) partly because of their landscape character, including the Test Valley in Hampshire, the Suffolk river valleys, the Cairngorm Straths, the Pennine Dales, and parts of the Norfolk Broads.

(c) Special areas of lowland river valley landscape have been recognized for their outstanding environmental qualities, notably the Broads, now recognized as equivalent to a National Park, and the Somerset Levels and Moors.

(d) In urban and urban fringe areas, local plans often give special attention to the protection of river valleys from development, and give them special status as 'green corridors', 'green wedges' or other such designations.

(e) The need to achieve appropriate management of river valley landscapes, for nature conservation and recreation as well as landscape conservation, has been recognized by the establishment (usually by partnerships of conservation agencies and local authorities) of countryside management schemes based on river valleys, notably the Medway Valley project, the Waverley Valley project, the various Manchester river valley schemes and projects on the River Clyde in Scotland.

The Countryside Commission has recognized the importance of river valleys, not only for their landscape qualities, but because of the opportunities they offer for recreation (Gilder, in press). A research study has been carried out (Countryside Commission, 1987) to show how river landscapes have changed since the Second World War; the Commission has jointly funded countryside management projects in river valleys; and guidance has been drafted to influence managers of river valleys and encourage them to think about wider aspects of landscape and amenity (Cobham Resource Consultants, 1986).

It is also important to note that the experimental 'Countryside Stewardship' scheme targets river and waterside landscapes, among others. This scheme, launched by the Countryside Commission and in 1996 taken over and expanded by the Ministry of Agriculture, aims to manage, enhance and recreate valued landscapes. This has proved to be of particular significance in areas such as the English Midlands where few of the other target landscape types occur, and as a result the 'waterside' option has proved popular among landowners and land managers.

The remainder of this chapter concentrates on rivers which have so far been the subject of more attention, at least in terms of landscape issues, than have lakes and other water bodies.

32.3   The Character of River Landscapes

> Any pond, any stream, and any river draws the instant response of a desire to paddle and peer into the mysterious depths. But that water has to be harmoniously connected with its setting.
>
> (Tony Soper, in a preface to *Taming the Flood*—Purseglove, 1988)

The concept of landscape character applies as much to rivers as it does to other 'drier' landscapes. Indeed it is apparent that river valleys, river corridors and the wider areas of river catchments have a distinctive character which makes them a key part of our landscape resource, even though few, with the exception of those referred to above, are rewarded with special designations.

The character of river landscapes is influenced by four main factors: first, river processes, especially the effects of erosion, sediment transfer and deposition; second, geology and soils which can have a profound effect on character at both the large and the small scale; third, particular landscape features, which create grain and incident and contribute significantly to distinctiveness in the landscape; and fourth, human activity, demonstrating the interactions, from time immemorial, between people and rivers and other freshwater environments, from reed cutting and willow pollarding, to culverting and drainage.

As a result of the interaction of these four main factors a wide range of features are now particularly characteristic of river landscapes. These include:

- Geomorphological features, especially the critical features of river channels and floodplains and special features like terraces and oxbows.
- Riverine and riparian vegetation which contributes much to landscape character (in particular trees and hedgerows which often define the limit of the floodplain and the course of the river), and also water-dependent habitats of many different types.
- Cultural landscape features which are many and varied and include constructed water features, designed water features (particularly in historic designed landscapes), water-related artefacts such as fish ladders, eel traps and fishing bothies, and riverside buildings from watermills to pubs.

All of these features continue to be modified by a number of forces for change which are influencing river landscapes. These include, among others: loss of natural river morphology; loss of continuity with the floodplain; lowering of groundwater levels; loss of floodplains to development; reductions in quantity of surface water; and reductions in water quality.

The end result of all these interactions is that the range of different types of river landscape is enormous. It includes degraded river corridors in predominantly urban areas, broad river floodplains in lowland agricultural areas, and dramatic river gorges and waterfalls in upland areas.

32.4   The General Approach to Landscape Assessment

'Landscape assessment' has come to be used, in recent years, as a broad term which embraces all the many different ways of looking at, describing, classifying and evaluating landscape. Variation in character is a particular feature of the British landscape and retaining this diversity is one of the main aims of landscape conservation and management. Landscape assessment is increasingly being used as a key tool to help in understanding this variation and in progressing from that to decisions about landscape conservation, management or enhancement (Countryside Commission, 1991, 1993; Countryside Commission for Scotland, 1992). The general approach which is now being widely used is well tried and tested. It is not so much a fixed 'recipe' to be followed but rather a 'toolkit' which can be used in different ways in different circumstances. In addition to its emphasis on landscape character the method has three other main distinguishing features.

First, it incorporates both objective and subjective approaches to assessment, but seeks to distinguish clearly between those parts which are objective, dealing with the intrinsic attributes of the landscape itself, and those which are subjective, dealing with perceptions of, and reactions to, the landscape. Second, it clearly distinguishes between three different products which may result from a landscape assessment.

(a) Landscape inventory/description. A generally objective documentation of the landscape, perhaps involving mapping or quantification of the various elements which contribute to it, together with descriptions of these elements and the way that they interact together to create character.

(b) Landscape classification. Classifying landscape into types which have distinct and homogeneous character. A landscape classification does not involve any judgements about quality or value, but is simply concerned with grouping areas of similar character together.

(c) Landscape evaluation. Making value judgements about the landscapes which have been described or classified, with the nature of the judgements depending upon the purpose of the assessment.

Third, it recognizes the need for the process of landscape assessment to be applied at several different levels within a hierarchy, depending on the particular purpose of the work. At the national/regional level the emphasis is on identifying *regional landscape types* which are recognizably distinct and homogeneous at this broad scale, based on general characteristics such as landform, geology, soils, land use, ecological patterns, and historical and cultural influences. Examples might include limestone uplands, chalk downlands, or gritstone moorlands. Some of these types may occur in more than one part of the country or region and the term *regional character areas* is used to describe the distinct geographical areas in which they occur. Some are well known and have a strong image and identity with easily recognizable names, such as Dartmoor, the Cotswolds, the Chilterns or the White Peak. Others are much less obvious and less easily named.

At the county/district level the emphasis is on *local landscape types* which are tracts of countryside which have a unity of character due to particular combinations of landform and land cover and a consistent and distinct pattern of constituent elements. Examples include river floodplains, wooded parklands, escarpments, plateau moorlands and ancient farmlands. The same landscape type may occur in different regional character areas, but will be distinguished by the broader regional influences. The same local landscape types will often occur in several different places in an area and in this case each discrete geographical area of a type is referred to as a *local character area* (or sometimes a landscape unit). These areas are often identified by giving them either a code, or an easily recognizable local name.

Ideally these different levels of landscape assessment should fit within a hierarchy. The broad regional types and areas would be defined first, then the local landscape types and character areas would be defined within them. More detailed site or area assessments can then easily be fitted within this hierarchical framework.

32.5   Assessment of River Landscapes

There has, perhaps surprisingly given the importance of freshwater environments, been little work on assessing the landscape of large bodies of fresh water. In contrast, perhaps because of the existence of the National Rivers Authority (NRA) and its regions in England and Wales, (now part of the new Environment Agency), river landscapes have received rather more attention in terms of approaches to their assessment and evaluation. In 1986 the Countryside Commission appointed Cobham Resource Consultants to develop an approach to river valley landscape survey and assessment. The aim was to produce a method for looking at river landscapes to complement the methods for surveying wildlife in river corridors, which were at that time quite well advanced. The work was undertaken in the context of the duty imposed on the Internal Drainage Boards and the Regional Water Authorities (RWAs) by the Wildlife and Countryside Act 1981 — to conserve flora, fauna and natural beauty and to have regard to the effect of proposed works on the natural beauty of an area.

The study set itself the main objective of developing and testing a 'practical and systematic approach for collecting 'base line' data on the visual importance of landscape components adjacent to the river, and relating these data to the river valley as a whole'. At that time the aim was to provide a practical method which could be applied by RWA staff without landscape backgrounds or training. Although the method was based on professional judgement, it therefore placed a great deal of emphasis on achieving consistency and standardization in recording information.

The method (see Cobham Resource Consultants, 1986) consisted of five stages, which can briefly be summarized as follows:

Stage 1. A desk exercise, for those not familiar with the study area, involving review of existing information and maps to build up a mental picture of the area.

Stage 2. A consultation stage aimed at gaining information about any areas of special significance.

Stage 3. Initial field survey involving the definition and description of character areas, plotting of views and viewpoints, and description of the part played by the area in the wider landscape.

Stage 4. Also field survey, involving recording on site, at 1:10,000 scale, the visual importance of landscape components in tracts viewed from the river and describing the character of each tract.

Stage 5. Data collection for areas likely to be affected by engineering works, involving completion of record cards for 1,000m stretches of river likely to be affected by such works. Each card summarized the averaged visual significance of different landscape components in this stretch and prediction of ways in which they might be affected by the works.

The proposed method was the subject of some discussion with RWA officers during its development, but was not apparently developed further for practical application. Informal comments from those involved suggest that whilst the approach had much to commend it, some may have been put off by its apparent, though not necessarily actual, complexity. This may have been partly due to the emphasis on standardized map recording techniques using a range of prescribed symbols.

In 1990, Land Use Consultants were asked to carry out a research project for the NRA to establish a method for undertaking landscape assessment of the water environment which would be applicable to a range of river corridor, estuary and coastal landscape types. The intention was to provide a method which could operate in parallel with the NRA's existing method for assessing the ecological character of river corridors and also be applicable to its work on catchment planning. The development of the method, and of a preferred approach, was described in a research report (Land Use Consultants, 1992a) which was adopted and published by the NRA (1993). The sections which follow draw on this research and describe the method of assessment derived from the more general approach to landscape assessment outlined above, but with modifications designed to tailor it specifically to the particular needs of river environments. There are four practical steps in carrying out such an assessment, each of which is described in turn below.

32.5.1 Step 1: Defining the purpose

As far as river landscapes are concerned the assessment process can contribute to many areas of activity. These might include: assessment of the environmental character and quality of rivers; catchment planning and integrated river corridor assessments; planning, design and environmental assessment of capital works; identification of opportunities for river landscape enhancement schemes; assessment of planning applications affecting rivers; and production of maintenance programmes for rivers, e.g. pollarding willows and bank maintenance.

It is essential to define the purpose of the landscape assessment at the outset, as different types of assessment are required for different uses. The list of applications above can be divided into two types, each of which requires a different level of detail in any assessment. A *strategic* assessment is appropriate to provide broad information about variations in the character and quality of river landscapes. This provides the high level overview needed for building up databases describing environmental character and environmental quality, and for contributing to integrated river corridor assessments, catchment planning, consultations on development and the establishment of performance indicators.

Landscape assessment of this strategic type falls within the hierarchical framework outlined above, but for work on river landscapes it is necessary to add additional levels as well. River valleys are only likely to emerge as regional landscapes in a limited number of cases; for example in areas such as the Somerset Levels and Moors, or the Norfolk Broads, as well as some of the larger river catchments like the Taw/Torridge lowlands in North Devon. More commonly they will form distinct landscape types within other regional character areas. So, for example, one river may pass in turn through an upland moorland regional character area, an industrial or urban fringe character area and a lowland agricultural character area. In each case it will create a local, river valley landscape type. Within each of these stretches of river landscape there will also be individual smaller-scale landscape types which can also be identified and described at a finer grain using the river landscape assessment method.

The term *'macro' river landscape* is used to describe the wider landscape of the river valley, defined by the limits of views from the river, or its 'visual envelope'. Depending on the nature of the river valley, its geology, landform, land cover, land-use history and settlement pattern, this wider area may include a number of different landscape sub-types of varying character. These can be identified and described through the process of landscape assessment.

By contrast, the term *'micro' river landscape* refers to the landscape of the river itself—that is the small-scale landscape created by the river channel and its immediate banks. The nature of this 'micro' river landscape depends on the form and character of the channel, the quality of the water, the presence and nature of the riverine vegetation, the nature of the river bank profile, bankside vegetation and land use, and hard features associated with the river.

These two types of small-scale landscape are, of course, closely related but they are likely to vary independently. So, for example, there may be a stretch of 'micro' river landscape of strong, positive character and high quality, which passes through a wider river valley where the 'macro' landscape is degraded. The character of the river does not therefore always mirror the character of the surrounding valley, although often it does. Both need to be assessed at the strategic level to give an overall picture of variation in the river landscape which covers the river and its banks, the floodplain and the wider river valley.

Detailed, as opposed to strategic, landscape assessment takes place where it is necessary to provide inputs to activities of a more practical, operational nature. Examples might include the planning, design and assessment of capital schemes; enhancement schemes; maintenance programmes; and the production of design guides. At this more detailed level the landscape assessment will be concerned with a smaller area which will be defined by the specific purpose of the work. It may be a particular stretch of river where maintenance work is to be carried out, or an area of river, river bank or floodplain which is to be the subject of an enhancement scheme, or an area of river valley within which a flood alleviation scheme or other major project is to be located, and where the environmental effects must be assessed. At this level of assessment the aim must be to collect specific information on important features to be conserved and, where relevant, comments on their need for management, as well as on opportunities to enhance the particular river landscape. Such a survey can also collect information on areas which could accept change without undue detriment, and on highly sensitive areas.

The distinction between the strategic and detailed levels of survey is a very important one since it has a major effect on the resources needed for such assessments. The strategic level of assessment can be applied to provide a general database of information on river landscape resources at the regional or national level. This may help in making decisions about where resources should be targeted and in what order of priority, as well as providing a context for more detailed assessments whenever these are needed. A detailed assessment will generally only be needed where specific works are proposed.

32.5.2   Step 2: Desk study

This is a relatively straightforward step and requires assembly of material from a variety of sources. These could include (depending on time and resources available) some or all of the following—aerial photographs, geological maps, floodplain maps, ecological surveys, Structure and Local Plans, maps of landscape designations/constraints, historic maps (e.g. first edition Ordnance Survey), and capital and maintenance programme details.

32.5.3   Step 3: Field survey

This is a central part of the process, not least because it is at this point that the surveyor begins to make judgements of various sorts, including assessments of value. The procedures involve first, driving around the defined survey area to gain an overall impression of the landscape and of variation within it, and of the contribution which the river corridor itself makes to the landscape; and second, walking the length of the river in the survey area and carrying out surveys of both the macro and the micro river landscape.

For the *'macro' level assessment* the first step is to plot the visual envelope which defines the extent of the river valley landscape, confirming or amending the rough boundary drawn during the desk exercise. Then, as far as is possible looking out from viewpoints along the river, the adjacent river valley landscape is divided into discernibly different types of landscape. For each identified type, a combination of written descriptions, checklists, sketches and photographs are used to provide a clear description of that type, evoking its overall character, quality and distinguishing features. An initial judgement is then made about the overall quality and conservation status of each type, and the features visible from the river which make a particular contribution to this are noted. This requires that both the positive features which add to landscape character and value, and the negative features which may detract from it should be noted. Moving away from the river itself, selected survey points in the wider river valley landscape are then visited. Each should give a clear view over the wider study area where the aim is to complete the 'macro' level assessment. At each point the procedures outlined above are repeated.

For the *'micro' level assessment* the river corridor (river channel and banks) is similarly divided into discernibly different types of river landscape and the divisions between adjacent types are plotted. A judgement of the overall quality and conservation status of each type is then made, as far as possible making mental comparisons between river landscapes of the same broad type, rather than between quite different types. Those features which make a particular contribution to the character and quality of each landscape type are noted (on maps and in writing), again including both the positive features which add to its value, and negative features which detract from it. If a detailed assessment is needed as well as the strategic one, it will usually be carried out at this stage by using a series of target notes which map and comment on individual features of the river landscape, particularly noting management needs and restoration or enhancement opportunities.

32.5.4   *Step 4: Analysis and reporting*

These field survey procedures already incorporate an element of decision making about value and quality. It is, however, in the final stage, of analysis and reporting, that aspects of evaluation become particularly prominent.

The initial product from the landscape assessment is a description and classification. This shows, in graphic and written form, the river in its context, a map of landscape types (both 'macro' and 'micro' as appropriate) and their boundaries, together with descriptions of these landscape types, focusing on particularly important and characteristic features. Information describing the character of the landscape can be provided graphically, in a variety of forms, and also in text which tries to evoke the distinctive character of the particular type of river landscape. The following examples are from a description of the Tanat Valley in Wales (Land Use Consultants, 1992a) and demonstrate that the aim is to provide a word picture of the landscape which captures its essential character and qualities:

> *Broad Upland Valley.* A varied, but rather fragmented pastoral landscape along the floor and

lower slopes of a broad, steep-sided, upland valley. The upper boundary of this landscape is often poorly defined by a zone of remnant oak woodlands, small conifer plantations and reverted pasture. The flat valley floor is characterized by rush-infested pasture, with a poorly defined field pattern, bounded by ditches and gappy hedgerows. Key linear elements in this landscape are the narrow, winding lanes bounded by tall hedges and the tree-lined river channel.

Middle Valley. A small-scale, pastoral landscape with a varied broken topography. For the most part there is a strong sense of enclosure created by the close association of landform, field pattern and tree cover. Fringing alders along the river are a particularly strong linear feature. The peaceful rural character of this landscape is emphasized by grazing animals and the sound of fast-flowing water.

Most applications of landscape assessment to river environments will also require some form of evaluation in this final stage. The nature of the evaluation depends primarily upon the original purpose of the assessment, but in all cases the approach to evaluation must assist in making decisions which will influence the future management of the river landscape. Evaluation issues are discussed further below.

32.6 Making Decisions Based on Evaluation of River Landscapes

In evaluating river landscapes, as in so many other areas of resource evaluation, professional judgement plays an important part. The need for this is now widely accepted, especially in the light of a much quoted statement in the Secretary of State for the Environment's decision letter following the public inquiry into the designation of the North Pennines Area of Outstanding Natural Beauty. This letter indicated a view that this type of evaluation 'necessarily involves a subjective assessment, within the consensus of informed opinion, allied with the trained eye and common sense'. Increasingly, however, the exercise of professional judgement must take place within the context of a more structured approach to landscape assessment, and also have regard to growing understanding of public perception of different landscapes and the changes which affect them.

For strategic assessments of river landscapes an evaluation can be presented in two ways, which can be viewed either as alternatives or as complementary approaches. The first method involves professional judgement about the *relative value* of each type of river landscape identified in the survey. Four value classes are often found to be most useful.

Class 1. Very strong, positive character, with many valued features which are of great importance and are essential to conserve.
Class 2. Strong, positive character and likely to be highly valued, though perhaps some evidence of degradation.
Class 3. Some positive character, but evidence that this has generally been eroded.
Class 4. Largely negative in character with few strong positive features.

The second approach is to make a professional judgement about what the general *management strategy* should be for each of the landscape types which are identified and described. This approach is commonly used in many different types of landscape assessment. The management strategies which are usually adopted in this approach are:

- *Conservation.* Appropriate for landscapes of strong and intact character which are highly valued for their special qualities and sense of place, often based on retention of traditional landscape features.
- *Enhancement.* Appropriate where landscape character is becoming weakened, individual features have suffered significant decline or damage, and positive improvement is needed. Enhancement strategies can take three forms:
  Restoration. To repair landscapes which still have reasonably intact character although there has been a decline in their condition.
  Reconstruction. To re-create an earlier landscape which has been lost.
  Creation. To construct a new and different landscape.

These are broad generalized strategies which should be used to indicate the overall needs of whole landscape types. This does not mean to say, for example, that in an area where the general strategy is enhancement, there will not be some features or areas which need conservation; or that in an area where the strategy is conservation, there may not be some need for restoration. Such decisions need to be based on more detailed assessment. The two ways of expressing the evaluation are clearly very closely linked. The advantage of using the 'management strategy' approach is that it avoids explicitly stating that some landscapes are 'better' or of higher quality than others, though this is still to some extent implicit in the decisions involved in identifying appropriate strategies.

For detailed assessments, such as those related to river enhancement schemes, evaluation is normally an integral part of the field survey and is recorded by means of 'target notes' relating to numbered locations on the survey map. These target notes may include observations about particularly important or distinguishing features of that particular stretch of river, notes about features which need to be conserved and which may be in need of particular management, and identification of specific opportunities to restore landscape character where it is being lost, or to enhance degraded river landscapes. They can also be used to describe the landscape of the river channel and banks, and any areas of the adjacent floodplain or valley which are closely linked to the river. These might, for example, include wet grazing meadows, willow plantations, and features like railway lines if they are close to the river. The notes can be grouped into types for later use, for example to identify all the features for conservation, all the opportunities for capital projects, and all the requirements for maintenance.

32.7 Practical Application of the Method

This overall approach to landscape assessment has now been applied to many different rivers, especially in the Thames and Severn Trent regions of the former

NRA where there has been particularly active involvement in landscape issues. It has been applied to a wide range of river landscape types, from highly modified urban rivers to rural, agricultural rivers, and for a variety of different purposes, from catchment planning, to integrated assessments involving ecological and recreation surveys, and to detailed identification of enhancement opportunities. The case study below gives a brief insight into one part of this range, showing how the method has been applied to an urban river system with particular emphasis on identifying enhancement schemes.

32.7.1   Case study: Ravensbourne catchment landscape assessment (Land Use Consultants, 1992b)

In January 1992 the Thames Region of the NRA commissioned Land Use Consultants to carry out a landscape assessment of the rivers in the catchment of the Ravensbourne, applying the NRA's method of river landscape assessment. The main purpose of this work was to provide a thorough understanding of the catchment and identify wide-ranging enhancement opportunities. It also had the additional purposes of allowing this catchment to be compared with others in the region, communicating a thorough understanding of the catchment to other members of the NRA's staff, and providing information on classification and evaluation of the river landscape to assist in comparative work on planning control and catchment planning issues.

The Ravensbourne catchment is in a heavily urbanized area in south-east London where many of the river floodplains have already been substantially developed. As a result of flood risk, engineering works have replaced many natural river courses with artificial concrete channels and much of the landscape character of the rivers has been dramatically altered. One of the underlying aims of the study was to identify opportunities to reverse this process and return some stretches of the river to a more natural state. Changes like this can bring landscape, recreation and nature conservation benefits and assist in the strategic process of developing rivers as 'green corridors' in urban areas.

The main rivers in the Ravensbourne catchment run from the North Downs to the Thames, originating on the chalk substrate of the Downs and flowing across the complex geological deposits of the Thames basin. The upper parts of the rivers are in more open landscapes of remnant areas of countryside on the edge of the urban area, but the middle and lower sections are predominantly urban (see Plate 1b, c). Out of the total length of 70 km of river in the catchment only 8 km (11%) are natural meandering rivers, while another 13 km (18%) are natural rivers in straightened sections. The remainder are either culverted, in artificial channels, or otherwise significantly modified.

By applying the method outlined above for river landscape assessment the study identified nine different 'micro' landscape types, largely reflecting the degree of naturalness or modification of the river channel, and eleven different 'macro' landscape types occurring alongside the rivers. Because of the highly urbanized nature of the catchment many of these are really land-use types including different types of residential development and different categories of open space and agricultural land. The combination of these two categories of channel type and adjacent landscape creates the landscape character of the catchment. The more natural combinations of channel types and rural landscapes only occur in the upper parts of the catchment.

The study also led to the identification of a wide range of significant opportunities for enhancement of river landscapes by returning them to a more natural form, especially where the river channel is surrounded by areas of open landscape of various types. A total of 70 enhancement schemes were identified, and priorities were assigned on the basis of the accessibility and visibility of the landscape. The proposed enhancements are mainly focused on the river channel and include a variety of channel modifications such as the creation of boggy areas or scrapes, introduction of fish spawning beds, channel improvements designed to create a more natural channel, introduction of meanders with associated planting, reduction of steep bank profiles, and introduction of two-stage flood relief channels where an additional channel allows for increased flood storage capacity but also allows natural colonization of the channel in times of low water flows. The enhancements identified added up to potential capital investment in landscape and environmental improvements of approximately £1.4 million. Assessments of the views of local people (Tunstall *et al.*, this volume; Plate 1) indicate that such enhancement proposals are likely to enjoy considerable public support.

32.8   Discussion and Conclusions

The Ravensbourne example demonstrates that the approach to landscape assessment outlined in this chapter is flexible enough to be applied to all sorts of rivers and for a wide range of different purposes. It is but one of a growing number of practical examples of the application of this approach and demonstrates that a structured approach to landscape has an important role to play in the conservation and enhancement of freshwater environments. The method fits well into the spectrum of approaches being used more generally to characterize environmental resources. It is also appropriate in the context of the growing emphasis on 'whole environment planning' (Swanwick, 1995) as its characterization of river landscapes dovetails well with methods for ecological assessment of river corridors, and with parallel approaches to appraisal of recreation use and potential—thus allowing for more integrated assessments.

The evaluation stage of the method relies on informed professional judgement in deciding upon either value classes or management strategies for different types of river landscape. This is comparable to some current thinking about decision-making processes for other more ecological aspects of river landscapes (e.g. Boon, 1992). Relatively little work has been done on the correlation between such professional judgements about river landscapes and public preferences. It is however quite reasonable to assume that the general public will prefer intact river landscapes of strong, positive character and support management strategies designed to conserve or restore such character or to recreate it by appropriate enhancement schemes (see Tunstall *et al.*, this volume). Further research on the matter of public preferences for river landscapes would allow such an assumption to be tested more widely.

It is noteworthy that most of the work on landscape issues for freshwater environments has focused on rivers to the exclusion of lakes and other water bodies. It has been suggested above (Section 32.5) that this may be largely a result of institutional frameworks and responsibilities. It is also possible that there are more fundamental differences in the nature of freshwater landscapes which might explain this discrepancy. Rivers and river valleys are quite readily recognized as landscape types in their own right. They can be distinguished at different levels in the assessment hierarchy, and the wider landscape of the river valley or floodplain can be easily recognized as having close links with the river itself. Equally, rivers themselves vary dramatically, both along their length and in different catchments, so that it is possible to distinguish different types of small scale 'micro' landscapes which vary independently from the wider landscape.

Large bodies of fresh water have a similar relationship with the wider landscape that surrounds them, but it is less easy to distinguish an equivalent 'micro' landscape for the water itself and its immediate shoreline. For this reason, any assessments of large water bodies tend to be subsumed within much broader 'terrestrial' landscape assessments. A study of Loch Lomond, for example (Land Use Consultants, 1993), identified eight different types of landscape which occurred around the immediate fringes of the loch and provided its immediate landscape setting, out of a total of 17 types in the whole of the Loch Lomond Regional Park. In this assessment there is no reference to smaller-scale variations in the landscape of the lake shore itself, although this is partly because the assessment was directed largely at developing guidelines for forestry.

There is every reason to believe that the basic principles of landscape assessment articulated in this chapter could be equally applicable to all types of freshwater environment, although the details of the method will need to be tailored both to the nature of the particular environment and to the purpose of the assessment. In order for the character and quality of freshwater landscapes to be maintained and enhanced, there seems little doubt that practical tools like this are essential, and that they need to be applied as widely as possible. The evidence from river landscapes is that this sort of approach can, and indeed does, work.

Acknowledgements

The author was a Principal of Land Use Consultants for 23 years prior to taking up her present post. This chapter draws on work carried out by Land Use Consultants for the National Rivers Authority.

References

Boon, P. J. (1992). Essential elements in the case for river conservation. In: Boon, P. J., Calow, P. and Petts, G. E. (Eds), *River Conservation and Management*. John Wiley, Chichester, 11–33.

Cobham Resource Consultants (1986). 'River Valley Landscape Survey and Assessment—Draft Method'. Unpublished report to the Countryside Commission. CCP 238. Cheltenham.

Countryside Commission (1987). *Changing River Landscapes*. CCP 238. Cheltenham.

Countryside Commission (1988). *Landscape Assessment—A Countryside Commission Approach*. CCD 18. Cheltenham.

Countryside Commission (1991). *Assessment and Conservation of Landscape Character—the Warwickshire Landscapes Project Approach*. CCP 332. Cheltenham.

Countryside Commission (1993). *Landscape Assessment Guidance*. CCP 423. Cheltenham.

Countryside Commission for Scotland (1992). *Landscape Assessment: Principles and Practice*. Battleby.

Gilder, P. (In press). Rivers in the countryside—an overview. In: *River Landscapes—Environmental Partnerships in Practice*. Proceedings of a Landscape Research Group Conference.

Land Use Consultants (1992a). *River Landscape Assessment Methodology*. Project Report 274/1/ST. National Rivers Authority, Bristol.

Land Use Consultants (1992b). *Ravensbourne Catchment Landscape Assessment Report*. National Rivers Authority, Reading.

Land Use Consultants (1993). 'Loch Lomond Regional Park Landscape Assessment'. Unpublished report to Loch Lomond Park Authority.

Landscape Research Group (1988). *A Review of Recent Practice and Research in Landscape Assessment*. CCD 25. Countryside Commission, Cheltenham.

National Rivers Authority (1993). *River Landscape Assessment—Methods and Procedures*. Conservation Technical Handbook Number 2. Bristol.

Purseglove, J. (1988). *Taming the Flood*. Oxford University Press, Oxford.

Swanwick, C. (1995). Integrated approaches to conservation issues in development plans. In: Southgate, M. (Ed.), *Whole Environment Planning*. Report of the 1995 Royal Society for the Protection of Birds Annual National Planners Conference. RSPB, Sandy, 95–102.

Tunstall, S., Fordham, M., Green C. and House, M. (This volume). Public perception of freshwater quality with particular reference to rivers in England and Wales.

University of Manchester (1976). 'Landscape Evaluation'. Unpublished report on the Landscape Evaluation Research Project, 1970–1975.

33   WATERSCAPE ARCHITECTURE

I. R. Smith

Summary

1. The application of design principles to ecological issues indicates that the quality of fresh waters cannot be defined solely by ecological requirements. Visual and other considerations must be taken into account.

2. The definition of 'quality' in this respect is a design problem rather than a purely scientific one and waterscape architecture provides a focus for cooperation between all the interests involved.

3. In developing the content of waterscape architecture, the pursuit of good design standards may be more rewarding than attempting to restore water bodies to their natural state.

33.1   The Function of Water Bodies

It has already been suggested that the application of the principles of design is not restricted to products and artificial systems (Smith, 1988) and that, in particular, the ideas of Papanek (1972) have direct relevance in applied ecology. Papanek lists seven interacting criteria that any design must meet.

Function	Is it clear what the design is expected to do?
Use	Does it work?
Need	Is it necessary?
Telesis	Is it appropriate to the society and conditions in which it has to function?
Association	Is it psychologically acceptable, are we comfortable with it?
Aesthetics	Is it visually exciting, a source of delight?
Method	How is it to be made?

The most important of these criteria is function—having a clear idea of what the design is expected to do. Ecological units, including water bodies, have to fulfil three functions.

(a) *Technical*. With water bodies, technical functions are primarily associated with hydraulic engineering requirements such as water supply, land drainage

423

and hydro-electric power. Also included are the specialist requirements of sport and recreation, e.g. boat launching and mooring facilities.

(b) *Ecological.* This includes not only the obvious absence of pollution and degradation but also the capacity to develop potential in terms of diversity and productivity.

(c) *Perceptual.* This reflects three of Papanek's criteria—aesthetics, association and telesis.

The theme of this book is, essentially, the recognition that it is not enough to define the quality of fresh waters in terms of ecological function alone. The perceptual function—individuals' reactions at the water's edge—must be considered. It is being increasingly recognized that appreciation of landscape in general owes as much to the cultural background of the visitor as to the physical features of the site. Rivers, especially, are linked to social systems as the focus of local and regional identity.

33.2   What is Waterscape Architecture?

Defining the quality of fresh waters is not, ultimately, a scientific question at all but a design issue concerned with creating water bodies that meet different requirements and functions. The cooperative activity of creating an appropriate design can be viewed as 'waterscape architecture'. The main areas of interest can be summarized as follows:

(a) The form of the water bodies themselves, including waterside vegetation and the land–water boundary.

(b) The specialist structures primarily associated with the technical function of water bodies, such as dams, weirs and jetties. The design of such structures must take into account not only their technical requirements but also their architectural properties and ecological impact.

(c) The features of the landscape in which water is dominant.

(d) The visual and other properties of the water itself.

All architecture involves combining the application of professional and technical skills to specific requirements, with the more elusive visual expression of the function and use of the design and how it relates to its surroundings. In waterscape architecture, the professional skills are drawn from hydraulic and structural engineering, various branches of environmental science, traditional architecture, as well as the 'softer' sciences concerned with human behaviour. If there is such an individual as a waterscape architect, then such a person is primarily a facilitator, coordinating the many different contributions. In many instances, it is less a matter of creating new skills than of recognizing the number of existing ones that have a part to play.

Yet effective and satisfying waterscape architecture means more than meeting a design specification, however broadly based that may be. This implies, in part, concern for the Papanek criteria related to perceptual function—is it visually exciting, are we comfortable with it and so on. It also involves expressing, in the final design, the characteristics inherent in the water itself—its fluidity, optical properties and varying moods.

A water level control weir has the potential to be as visually exciting as the cascades in an Italian garden. That the majority are not, is not simply because of the need to build the cheapest possible structure. The designer did not think of weirs in these terms. The additional cost may be quite small.

The value of cooperation between specialists is increasingly recognized. The challenge now is to develop what may be termed a 'water aesthetic', accepting that much that is satisfying in the public eye is not necessarily natural. Not all development is bad. To demand that the ultimate objective is to restore all waters to what is believed to be their natural state is equivalent to assuming that all history since hunter/gatherers turned to agriculture has been retrograde. The rest of the chapter is devoted to sketching out a few topics that contribute to the development of this aesthetic.

33.3   A Water Aesthetic

33.3.1.   *The land-water boundary*

The design of land-water boundaries is a major question covering topics ranging from how to ameliorate the scar created by reservoir drawdown to the nature of river banks near centres of population. It is, essentially, a matter of determining the appropriate edge geometry and materials given a number of requirements and constraints such as the following:

(a) Enhancing ecological interest; in particular, taking account of the factors controlling plant distribution, e.g. tolerance of desiccation and inundation, underwater light penetration, sediment and soil type (themselves affected by erosion), etc. Other factors, such as allowing animal movement in and out of the water, must also be considered.

(b) Water level fluctuation, both natural and as a result of the technical functions of the water body.

(c) Providing resistance to erosion that may be caused by flowing water, wave action, boat movement, and public access.

(d) Controlling public access, i.e. providing pathways while minimizing disturbance to wildlife.

Every situation generates its own solution and it is not always possible to satisfy conflicting demands. A wider view of 'quality' in fresh waters suggests that emphasizing ecological interest at the expense of good design may be mistaken. A stone wall may be the most appropriate form of river bank in a city. Who worries about the lack of ecological interest when strolling the banks of the Seine? Elsewhere, the ecological interest may be paramount and restrictions on public access, boat movement and the like perfectly acceptable.

A solution to the problem of reservoir drawdown was attempted in Kielder

Reservoir in Northern England. A small control dam near the upper end maintains a more or less constant level around the inflow delta, allowing the rest of the reservoir to be drawn down to meet storage requirements. The benefits have not been all that obvious because of unexpectedly reduced demand.

33.3.2   Water in the landscape

The relation of artificial water bodies and hydraulic structures to their surroundings is an important element of waterscape architecture. A very simple classification of landscape types can be obtained by considering them in relation to the river profile (Figure 33.1). This provides a starting point for looking at waterscape on a broad scale. Hydraulic structures can be exciting architecture in their own right.

Mountain headwaters are often viewed as the 'last remaining wilderness areas' which must be left untouched, but cities do need a water supply. Such landscapes do have the capacity to accommodate large structures like dams, so it may be better to exploit the dramatic possibilities of such structures rather than try to conceal them. In the gentler, populated landscapes downstream, waterside features have to be more consistent with conventional building, both in character and scale. Many old mills and their associated weirs have been so much part of the landscape for so long that their artificiality is almost forgotten. The capacity to accommodate drama rises again in hydraulic landscapes. In the Fens of Eastern England and in the Netherlands, for example, the structures associated with flood control are reminders of the very nature of existence in such parts—the perpetual struggle against the threat of inundation.

33.3.3   Properties of the water itself

The properties of water are not determined by its chemical and biological characteristics alone; hydrodynamics plays a part, producing an *emotional* scale, that is, frightening—angry—vigorous—bubbly—tranquil—sluggish. In standing waters, these states are determined by the wind speed and fetch at the site and, in running water, by the interaction of slope, bed particle size and water depth. The

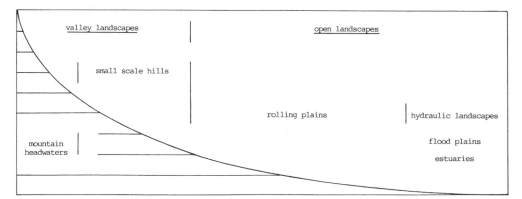

Figure 33.1   Landscape types in relation to the river profile.

prevalent nature of the water surface should be reflected in the architectural detail. Such details can influence the perception of a water body, whether it is treated sympathetically as a natural feature or simply as the input to an industrial plant. If the water is frequently angry, with turbulent white water, then erosion-resistant edges will be necessary. To meet the requirement of association—being comfortable with it—the edges must be seen to be strong. Large boulders of local stone would be appropriate whereas sheet piles, equally effective in terms of function, emphasize exploitation. It is noticeable that in earlier hydro-electric developments in Scotland, for example, considerable attention was paid to the architecture of the buildings housing generating and control plant, but that the smaller hydraulic structures and waterside features remain brutally functional.

33.4   Conclusions

For most people, freshwater quality is perceived as a total experience, combining both visual and environmental standards. Further, the pursuit of pseudo-naturalness may be misguided. It is not development in some form that is objected to, but bad development and bad architecture. The latter is usually vandalized. As scientists become more confident about scientific issues, they must be willing to contribute to the more complex cooperative design process.

References

Papanek, V. (1972). *Design for the Real World*. Thames and Hudson, London.

Smith, I. R. (1988). Ecology and design: an introduction. *Journal of Environmental Management,* **26,** 103–109.

34   THE CONSERVATION AND AMENITY VALUE OF FARM PONDS IN WALES

J. H. R. Gee, K. M. Lee, B. D. Smith and S. W. Griffiths

Summary

1. Conservation and amenity value were assessed in 51 new or restored farm ponds in Dyfed and Powys, mid-Wales, UK.

2. Colonization of new farm ponds by both aquatic macrophytes and macro-invertebrates appears to be rapid. After the first year, species richness is not significantly related to time elapsed since filling. Invertebrate species richness is positively correlated with both plant taxonomic and structural diversity.

3. Most of the ponds are well-designed and well-furnished with attractive vegetation. Nevertheless, it takes one or two decades for most ponds to acquire a semi-natural appearance.

4. New farm ponds rapidly acquire conservation interest and in time can achieve high quality as landscape features. However, many are of little amenity value to the general public, due to restricted access. Despite being close to public thoroughfares, the ponds scored poorly on an Amenity Visibility Rating. Less than one-quarter are open to the public for leisure activities such as fishing.

34.1   Introduction

Ponds provide habitat for a wide range of aquatic organisms, some of which are of considerable conservation interest. For instance, out of 42 species of endangered (Red Data Book category 1) freshwater invertebrates (excluding Diptera), 31 are associated with ponds (personal communication, Pond Conservation Group). The conservation benefit of ponds is not restricted to invertebrates or to fully aquatic organisms. Ponds on farms enhance both the numbers of species of breeding birds and their density (O'Connor and Shrubb, 1986; Lack, 1992).

In addition to conservation value, ponds may have public amenity value. This may simply derive from the pleasure that people gain from seeing a water body as part of a natural landscape. The landscape interest may be enhanced if the pond has some special historic significance. Part of the population may also benefit from access to ponds for leisure activities such as fishing, bird watching, swimming or boating.

Ponds are intrinsically ephemeral. Most existing ponds either were formed by geomorphic processes in the geologically recent history of the UK, or were man-made to provide water for stock, clay for construction or fish for consumption. When rates of pond creation fall below rates of pond loss (due to natural silting and encroachment of terrestrial vegetation, or to human interference such as land development) then the national stock of ponds is bound to fall. Between 1984 and 1990 about 12% of the ponds less than 1 ha in the UK were lost as aquatic habitats (Barr *et al.*, 1994). Over 50% of the ponds present in 1984 were on enclosed farmland, and 69% of the losses were from this land-use class.

Since it is inevitable that some ponds will be lost, protecting existing ponds will not be enough to maintain ponds as part of the landscape. Although it will be appropriate to protect ponds of special value, a continuing programme of pond creation will be essential. Pond creation (and restoration) are supported by grant aid from a number of bodies in the UK, including County Councils, National Parks Authorities and statutory conservation organizations, such as the Countryside Council for Wales (CCW). An estimated total of £150 K was allocated annually for pond creation between 1989 and 1992 in the Welsh counties of Dyfed and Powys alone. Despite this level of financial support, there is little documented evidence of the quality of the ponds created, in terms either of their conservation or amenity value. The purpose of this study was to record the conservation and amenity value of farm ponds in Dyfed and Powys. This chapter presents results relating to amenity value, together with summaries of the detailed results relating to conservation of water plants and invertebrates.

34.2 Methods

The methods used are described fully elsewhere (Gee *et al.*, 1994; Gee and Smith, 1995) and are described only briefly here. In 1992, a database of static water bodies was compiled from information provided by CCW, the National Rivers Authority (NRA), the County Councils (DCC and PCC), the Agricultural Development and Advisory Service (ADAS) and the Brecon Beacons and Pembrokeshire Coast National Parks. On the continuum of size from the smallest inland water body to the largest, there is no clear distinction between ponds and lakes. Those included in this study range in size from 0.01 ha to 16 ha (interquartile range 0.03–0.27 ha).

A questionnaire requesting information on the physical characteristics, surrounding land use, aquatic vegetation and animals, and uses of ponds was sent to about 400 pond owners listed in the database. About one third of pond owners returned a completed questionnaire. On the basis of this information 51 ponds were selected to include approximately equal numbers in each of eight age classes (1, 2, 3, 4, 5–6, 7–10, 11–24, >25 yr). As far as possible, in each age class there were equal numbers of ponds reputed by owners to be with or without fish. It should be noted that the ponds surveyed were to some extent self-selecting. It is not known whether these are representative of all Dyfed and Powys farm ponds in terms of quality. Since inclusion in the survey depended in part on the interest of the owner, it is possible that they are biased towards the better ponds.

In the summer of 1993, each pond was visited once by a survey team which completed a second, identical questionnaire on the basis of independent observations, made detailed observations of physical and chemical character-istics, surveyed emergent and submerged vegetation, and sampled aquatic macroinvertebrates.

In addition, the survey team made a number of observations relating to the amenity value of the ponds. Visibility of the pond from a public thoroughfare was judged on a five-point scale (0 = completely obscured from view, 4 = fully visible). The nature of the thoroughfare provided a rough measure of the number of people likely to benefit from sight of the pond. This was expressed on a four point access scale (1 = footpath, 2 = bridleway, 3 = minor road, 4 = road of A or B class). The sinuousness of the pond outline was scored on an arbitrary 5 point scale, on which rectilinear ponds scored 1 and ponds with smoothly curved and indented margins scored 5. Other landscape features were scored on binary scales: appearance artificial or natural, vegetation visually dominant or not domi-nant, plants with bright and obvious flowers present or absent, exotic plants present or absent, obvious pollution present or absent. In the same way a range of amenities were scored present or absent: fishing platforms, commercial exploi-tation, historical interest.

Three derived indices were calculated based on the information collected by the survey team. The vegetated area of the pond was estimated from the product of the mean length of 10 vegetation transects spanning the vegetated zone around the pond and the length of the pond perimeter. A Macrophyte Structure Index (MSI) for each entire pond was computed from the percentage cover values of emergent, floating and submerged vegetation. The MSI is similar to the structure evaluation number of de Lange and van Zon (1983) except that it omits the element accounting for the cover of filamentous algae. A related index (MSIT) was calculated based on cover values expressed in terms of area of the belt transects rather than the entire pond. Finally, a simple Amenity Visibility Rating (AVR) was calculated from the product of the visibility of the pond from a public thoroughfare and the access classification for the thoroughfare. Thus a pond invisible from a public thoroughfare scores 0, and a pond fully visible from a major road scores the maximum of 16.

34.3   Results

Only three of the ponds have an impermeable liner (butyl), the remainder being lined with natural materials, usually clay. Forty four of the ponds are connected by visible surface drainage to at least one other wetland habitat in which there is open water. There is a wide variety of terrestrial habitats within 100m of the ponds' margins, but improved pasture predominates.

As expected, there is a significant linear relationship between the natural logs of aquatic macrophyte species richness and total pond area (m^2); however, there is a closer relationship between log species richness and log of the area of the vegetated zone within the ponds (S $=$ 0.146A$^{0.161}$, $r^2 = 0.23$, $P < 0.001$). There is no relationship between the number of invertebrate taxa and total pond area, but there is a weak relationship with the area of the vegetated zone (S $=$ 2.13A$^{0.110}$, $r^2 = 0.095$, $P < 0.05$). Surprisingly, there is no relationship between either plant or invertebrate richness and pond age. A number of ponds had been planted by their owners, but there is no evidence that planted ponds contain more macrophyte species than those in which the aquatic vegetation has developed naturally.

No aquatic macrophyte species of great conservation interest were found. The majority of ponds are mesotrophic or eutrophic in character, with mean Trophic Ranking Scores (Palmer *et al.*, 1992) of about 8. The mean number of aquatic macrophyte species per pond is 13.8. Five Nationally Scarce invertebrate species were recorded, including two dragonflies and three beetles. The mean number of invertebrate taxa per pond is 20.8, but several of these were recorded only at generic or family level. Invertebrate richness increases with the number of plant species and the structural diversity of the vegetation (MSIT), but decreases with the percentage of open water. Among invertebrates, species richness is correlated positively with vegetation structure in the Odonata (MSI) and Hemiptera (MSI and MSIT).

More than half the ponds score 0 on the AVR (Figure 34.1a), and none achieves the maximum value. The lack of visibility is not due to extreme distance between the ponds and the nearest public thoroughfare: the median distance is between 50 and 100m (Figure 34.1b). Instead the low AVR values are due to ponds being hidden from public view by shrubs or trees, buildings, or the lie of the land. For about half the ponds the nearest public access was at least of minor road status. Although the ponds are generally sinuous in outline, with a modal value of four, only four of the ponds were not clearly identifiable from appearance as artificial. These are among the oldest ponds, three being over 25 years old and the fourth 11 years. In more than half the ponds (31/51) the aquatic vegetation is a dominant feature and about half include exotic plants (21/51) or plants with brightly coloured flowers (25/51). Only three of the ponds showed any visible sign of pollution, mainly in the form of traces of oil on the water surface.

Of the ponds stocked with fish (of 16 species), less than half are exploited commercially for fishing (11/26) and less than one third have fishing platforms (8/26). There is no strong evidence that stocking with fish has influenced the plant or invertebrate conservation value, but some dragonflies may have been affected. A boat is kept or used on 12 ponds.

Eight ponds have some claim to historical interest. Three of these are ponds that have been renovated recently, of which two are old mill ponds (one believed to date back as far as 1550) and one is a carp pond. The newly constructed ponds include one on the original site of a long house pond, one on the site of a clay pit, one at a site that had been a quarry then a rubbish dump, one at which the remnants of an old farmhouse garden and farmhouse foundations are discernible,

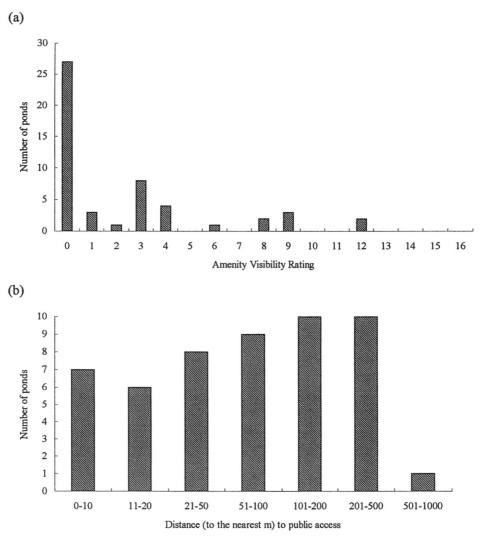

Figure 34.1   Frequency distributions of (a) Amenity Visibility Rating and (b) distances to the nearest point to which the public has access, for 51 farm ponds in Dyfed and Powys.

and a pond that was described by the owners as being the site of an old slurry pit.

34.4   Discussion

Pond quality can be assessed in terms of fitness for purpose. Among the purposes that may be served by newly created ponds are to provide habitat for an acceptable range of aquatic organisms and to enhance landscape to the benefit of the general public.

There is little doubt that the farm ponds created in Dyfed and Powys serve the first purpose, habitat creation, quite satisfactorily. There is no detectable relationship between taxonomic richness and pond age, suggesting that colonization of the ponds by both aquatic macrophytes and macroinvertebrates was rapid. Five out of six ponds in the youngest age class were at least 10 months old and the average age was 12.5 months. The rapidity of colonization may have been due to their construction in sites already prone to wetness and by the fact that most ponds are connected by surface drainage to existing aquatic habitats. Plant propagules may already have been present or have been transported readily from adjacent sources. Many aquatic insects can colonize by flight. Rapid colonization has been recorded over the first year even in new ponds without direct connection with other wetland habitat (Layton and Voshell, 1991; Christman and Voshell, 1993). No information was available relating to the terrestrial or wetland habitat that may have been destroyed in the process of pond creation, but this is a possible cost to balance against an aquatic conservation gain.

Although it is difficult to make direct comparisons with the results of surveys that have been carried out in other parts of Britain and which have used different survey techniques, the farm ponds of Dyfed and Powys are not conspicuously poor in species of aquatic macrophyte. Considered simply in terms of the number of species, the Dyfed and Powys ponds compare very favourably with ponds in Cheshire (Edmondson, 1974), Leicestershire (Jones, 1971) and Norfolk (Palmer, 1981), and with forestry ponds in Scotland (Jeffries, 1991). They also stand comparison with the floristically richer marl pit ponds in Lancashire, Cheshire and northern Wales (Day *et al.*, 1982). There are few comparable studies of macroinvertebrates. Boyle and Farooqi (1987) found rather greater diversity in most invertebrate groups in mid-Wales ponds, particularly Ephemeroptera, Plecoptera and Trichoptera, but this is likely to have been due to more intensive sampling in their survey and to the less eutrophic nature of the ponds. The positive correlation between species richness of invertebrates and the structural diversity of the vegetation suggests that an index such as MSIT has potential as an indicator of invertebrate conservation value. There are recent indications that macrophyte structure can also influence the diversity of macroinvertebrates in lowland rivers (Wright *et al.*, 1992).

The shape of newly created ponds is generally satisfactory. Pond owners and their contractors are sensitive to the need for a sinuous, indented pond outline, and most of the ponds have gently shelving margins. Although the ponds are well vegetated, often with visually appealing plants, only some of the oldest ponds have matured sufficiently to appear to be natural features. Most new ponds seem to take at least one or two decades to acquire a semi-natural appearance; after that period they may well become landscape features of high quality.

In considering landscape or amenity, it may be useful to distinguish quality from value. A pond of high landscape or amenity quality may be little valued by the general public if it is not accessible. The AVR scores show that few of the ponds can be seen easily from thoroughfares likely to be used by substantial numbers of people. The majority of ponds, though not far from a thoroughfare, are completely screened from public view. Their landscape quality is likely to be appreciated and valued mainly by the owner of the surrounding land. Whilst a substantial number of ponds have some provision for fishing or other leisure use, this also is mainly enjoyed by the family and friends of the pond owners. In these cases amenity and landscape quality may be high, but it is not realized as value to the population at large.

Acknowledgements

We are grateful to CCW for supporting this project and to many individuals in CCW, DCC, PCC, ADAS and the National Parks Authorities for their help. Without the interest and co-operation of the pond owners the study would not have been possible.

References

Barr, C. J., Howard, D. C. and Benefield, C. B. (1994). *Inland Water Bodies*. Department of the Environment, London.

Boyle, K. and Farooqi, M. (1987). *A Survey of the Invertebrate Fauna of Ponds in mid-Wales and an Attempt to Classify them based on their Faunal Assemblages*. University of Wales Institute of Science and Technology, Cardiff.

Christman, V. D. and Voshell, J. R. (1993). Changes in the benthic macroinvertebrate community in two years of colonization of new experimental ponds. *Internationale Revue der gesamten Hydrobiologie*, **78**, 481–491.

Day, P., Deadman, A., Greenwood, B. and Greenwood, E. (1982). A floristic appraisal of marl pits in parts of northwestern England and northern Wales. *Watsonia*, **14**, 153–165.

de Lange, L. and van Zon, J. C. J. (1983). A system for the evaluation of aquatic biotopes based on the composition of the macrophytic vegetation. *Biological Conservation*, **25**, 273–284.

Edmondson, T. (1974). Pond flora in Cheshire. *Field Naturalist*, **12**, 30–35.

Gee, J. H. R., Lee, K. M. and Griffiths, S. W. (1994). *The Conservation and Amenity Value of Farm Ponds*. The Countryside Council for Wales, Contract Science Report 44, Bangor.

Gee, J. H. R. and Smith, B. D. (1995). *The Conservation Value of Farm Ponds: Macroinvertebrates*. The Countryside Council for Wales, Contract Science Report 127, Bangor.

Jeffries, M. (1991). The ecology and conservation value of forestry ponds in Scotland, United Kingdom. *Biological Conservation*, **58**, 191–211.

Jones, R. (1971). A survey of the flora, physical characteristics and distribution of field ponds in North East Leicestershire. *Transactions of the Leicester Literary and Philosophical Society*, **65**, 12–31.

Lack, P. (1992). *Birds on Lowland Farms*. HMSO, London.

Layton, R. J. and Voshell, J. R. (1991). Colonization of new experimental ponds by benthic macroinvertebrates. *Environmental Entomology*, **20**, 110–117.

O'Connor, R. J. and Shrubb, M. (1986). *Farming and Birds*. Cambridge University Press, Cambridge.

Palmer, M. (1981). Relationship between species richness of macrophytes and insects in some water bodies in the Norfolk Breckland. *Entomologist's Monthly Magazine*, **117**, 35–46.

Palmer, M. A., Bell, S. L. and Butterfield, I. (1992). A botanical classification of standing waters in Britain: applications for conservation and monitoring. *Aquatic Conservation: Marine and Freshwater Ecosystems*, **2**, 125–143.

Wright, J. F., Blackburn, J. H., Westlake, D. F., Furse, M. T. and Armitage, P. D. (1992). Anticipating the consequences of river management for the conservation of macroinvertebrates. In: P. J. Boon, Calow, P. and Petts, G. E. (Eds), *River Conservation and Management*. John Wiley, Chichester, 137–149.

35 ASSESSING THE ECONOMIC VALUE OF FRESH WATERS

N. Hanley

Summary

1. This chapter outlines why fresh water as a resource has economic value. This value is conceptually and empirically much broader than that accounted for by markets, as it includes many 'non-market', environmental benefits. These benefits should properly be included in any assessment of the economic value of fresh water, yet their non-market nature makes their monetary valuation difficult.

2. The chapter discusses three techniques (contingent valuation, travel cost models and random utility models) for estimating such non-market values, and provides examples of their use in a water context. The use of monetary valuation within a cost-benefit analysis context is also discussed, again with reference to a case study.

3. Finally, the chapter notes that the use of non-market valuation techniques, in conjunction with conventional valuation methods, is likely to become more widespread given that governments are placing increasing emphasis on the use of cost-benefit analysis in environment policy appraisal.

35.1 Introduction

What determines whether a resource such as fresh water has economic value? What determines how this value changes when the quality of that resource changes? To answer these questions the ethical underpinnings of modern welfare economics must be confronted. Since the mid-nineteenth century, these have been built up around the principles of utilitarianism. Utilitarianism implies that ends count above means, and that the only 'end' of relevance to society in making decisions is the utility (happiness, satisfaction) that individuals get from the actions which follow from these decisions. Social welfare is thus the sum of individual utilities.

So, in asking the question 'what is the economic value of fresh water?', two separate questions 'how do members of society gain utility from fresh water?', and 'how much utility do they get?' are also implicitly being asked. Each of these questions is considered in turn below.

Individuals may derive utility from a freshwater resource (a river, for example) in a number of ways. Utility may be gained by those who go fishing, boating or swimming in the river, those who like to watch the wildlife that lives in and around the river, and those people who gain satisfaction from simply knowing that it is there. This last type of value has become known as a 'non-use' value, to be distinguished from 'use' values associated with *in situ* uses such as fishing and swimming. Another example of non-use value may occur where individuals derive utility from the existence of wilderness areas in northern Canada, even though they do not visit these areas. Such values, both use and non-use, may clearly change if the quality of a river changes. If river quality improves, then fishermen may be happier since their catch has gone up, or swimmers may be happier since they no longer risk catching an infection.

Other use values also exist for the river. If commercial fishermen catch trout in the river which are then sold on to restaurants in a nearby town, then fishermen, customers and restaurant owners benefit. If drinking water is derived from the river, then both householders and water companies benefit. Finally, river water might be used as an input to an industrial production process (such as brewing), generating profits for the company's shareholders. Again, these benefits may change when the quality of the river itself changes.

Finally, rivers (and habitats in general) can be thought of as providing indirect service flows which bring economic benefits to society. These service flows (sometimes referred to as environmental functions or ecosystem services) provide the basis for many of the use and non-use values described above. For a wetland, for example, these ecosystem service values include nutrient cycling, pollution abatement, flood regulation, sediment retention and shoreline stabilization (Barbier, 1989).

The second question posed above was concerned with *how much* utility society gets from fresh water. Economic values are usually measured in the market, an institution which brings about an equilibrium between supply and demand. The supply curve conveys information about the costs of producing commodities; the demand curve shows how much individuals are willing to pay for these goods. In equilibrium, marginal willingness to pay is equalized with marginal cost. Thus, economic value may be measured by looking at the market price. This is a very familiar concept: the value of an oilfield is often measured by multiplying the number of barrels the field is thought to contain by the price of oil on the world market. The net value is this amount minus the costs of production; that is, profits.

In certain cases (such as its role as a supply source for drinking water), fresh water can be similarly valued: for example, by tracing through the impact of a change in quality on water company profits. In many cases, however, such valuations are far more difficult to accomplish. What market can be used in order to value an improvement in riverside habitats which increases the conservation values of such areas? For many environmental resources, such as clean air, clean water and wildlife, no obvious market exists in which to value them. However, we know from preceding paragraphs that those aspects of such resources which generate positive utility have economic value, despite the fact that markets and market prices do not exist for them. Improving recreational fishing quality, or improving bird numbers, has economic value if it increases utility, but how can these changes be measured in monetary terms?

In deriving techniques to measure such 'non-market goods', economists have concentrated on the demand side of traditional market analysis, and sought to simulate what the demand for such goods (biodiversity, amenity uses) would be if a market did exist. These techniques have the advantage that even where some (perhaps nominal) fees are charged for use, as in some cases of recreational fishing, the additional benefit that users derive over and above these fees from being able to utilize the resource can be calculated. Value in this context is measured by willingness to pay: that is, preferences backed up by the ability to pay. Non-market valuation techniques may seek to measure people's maximum willingness to pay either to preserve an environmental asset at some quality level, or to bring about an increase in this quality level. Alternatively, people's minimum willingness to accept compensation to put up with an environmental loss, or to forego an environmental gain, may be sought. These two measures (payment and compensation) are not expected to be equal in most cases. Decisions over which measure to use may be based on assumptions about the allocation of property rights over environmental quality attributes.

Valuation techniques are divided into two groups. The first, direct valuation methods, seek to infer Willingness to Pay (WTP) directly from individuals, using structured questionnaires. The second, indirect valuation methods, attempt to trace individuals' preferences for environmental goods back to behaviour in related markets. In this chapter, one direct approach (contingent valuation) and one indirect approach (travel costs random utility models) are discussed, since these have dominated applications to freshwater quality. Other indirect methods include hedonic pricing and production-function based approaches. For a full description and critique of all of these valuation methods, see Hanley and Spash (1994).

35.2   The Contingent Valuation Method

The Contingent Valuation Method (CVM) is, in principle, very simple. In order to find out an individual's maximum WTP for an improvement in river water quality if a market existed, the researcher simply asks the respondent to 'tender' this amount in a survey. This involves establishing a hypothetical market situation, and seeking responses (in terms of WTP) contingent on the description of this market. The hypothetical market must contain both reasons for, and means of, paying for the goods. For example, in Scotland, householders could be told that in order to improve water quality off the Clyde coast, large improvements in sewage treatment were needed, and these could only be funded through higher council tax payments. Individuals may then be either simply asked the most they would pay as additional taxes for a carefully specified and described improvement in quality; or whether they would pay a given amount (£x) for the improvement. In this latter case, by varying £x across individuals, sufficient information can be gained to estimate the underlying distribution of WTP, by predicting the probability that an 'average' person will say 'yes' to a given x value (using logit or probit models). In either case, mean WTP can be measured across the sample, and thus a population, aggregate WTP identified.

Since its first use in Maine woodlands in 1963, CVM has been considerably developed, and is now in very widespread use by economists across the USA and Europe. A comprehensive account of the method is given in Mitchell and Carson (1989). Major factors underlying recent growth in the use of CVM in the USA have been Executive Order 12291, which required cost-benefit analysis of environmental programmes set up by the Environmental Protection Agency; and the acceptance by the USA courts system of the use of CVM in environmental litigation under the 1980 Superfund Act. Controversy still surrounds the technique, despite its widespread adoption by government departments (see Diamond and Hauseman (1994) for a summary of the case against CVM).

In the UK, CVM studies have been funded by many government departments and agencies, such as the Forestry Commission, Department of Transport, Ministry of Agriculture, Scottish Office and Scottish Natural Heritage. The National Rivers Authority (NRA) has also used the technique to assess improvements in water quality in several low-flow rivers in southern England, and to value amenity use of rivers by walkers (Green and Tunstall, 1991). In the USA, extensive use of CVM has been made in a freshwater context, notably by Smith and Desvouges (1986) and Mitchell and Carson (1989). These exercises have concentrated on valuing recreational benefits to fishermen, swimmers and boaters from improving water quality in rivers and lakes. Two CVM case studies are presented below: one of the Columbia River in the Pacific North West of the USA (Olsen *et al.*, 1991), and one of the River Darent in England (NRA, 1994).

35.2.1   Case study 1: Estimating recreational fishing benefits in the Columbia River

The Columbia River in the Pacific North West of America is one of the most important recreational fisheries in North America, especially for salmon and steelhead trout. Olsen *et al.* (1991) report the results of a CVM study of this fishery. Given that the Northwest Power Planning Council has large powers to invest in increases in fish stocks on behalf of the public, the authors model WTP for a doubling of salmon and steelhead stocks. Two samples from the general public ($n = 700$) and recreational fishermen ($n = 700$) were obtained. The payment (bid) vehicle used was additional electricity bills. For non-users, 29% of responses were genuine zero WTP and 16% were protests (zero bids given for reasons other than zero value). Mean WTP figures obtained were as follows: user— US\$6.18/month; non-user (no planned future use)—US\$2.21/month; non-user (some planned future use)—US\$4.88/month. These figures gave an aggregate WTP of US\$171 million per annum for a doubling of fish stocks. As may be seen, non-use values were an important part of this total value, whilst value figures varied across the three groups, in accordance with *a priori* expectations.

35.2.2 Case study 2: Low flow alleviation on the River Darent

The main benefits of low flow alleviation on the Darent are likely to accrue to local communities and visitors from increased use of the tourist and recreational aspects of the river. Other benefits include the economic and commercial development associated with enhanced landscapes, better educational uses of the river, and non-use values.

CVM was used to estimate WTP for two scenarios (NRA, 1994), both starting at a baseline of 100% extraction, giving extreme low flow conditions. The two scenarios were to maintain the current situation of 70% abstraction, and to improve low flow conditions to an ecologically acceptable position. The authors also address the problem of 'embedding'. Embedding occurs when WTP for one member of a class of resources (such as a particular river) is not significantly different from WTP for all members of the class together (that is, all rivers). This phenomenon may occur due to respondents' inability to understand correctly which resource is being valued within a CVM survey, or to respond more out of a desire to appear 'charitable' than with regard to their true WTP (Kahneman and Knetsch, 1992). To test for embedding, WTP was estimated for low flow alleviation on 20 rivers affected by low flow in England and Wales and then estimated for the River Darent alone. This ensures that respondents can distinguish between their valuations for many rivers and those for one river alone.

In total, 1418 personal interviews were conducted. These were divided between 325 local residents within 2km, 335 visitors, and 758 members of the general public, to estimate non-use values. Results showed that 72.3% of households had visited the River Darent at some stage during the previous year. On average, 92% of the general public were aware of the low flow problem, corresponding to 97% of residents and 72.3% of visitors. To alleviate low flows to an ecologically acceptable condition, mean WTP was £12.32 for residents, £9.76 for visitors and £12.92 for the general public. Residents' values are higher than those estimated for two other low flow rivers (the Misbourne and Wey), but there is no *a priori* reason why these values should be the same, since they refer to different rivers.

In conclusion, the River Darent survey showed that a large proportion of the population was willing to pay for maintaining current flows (that is, to prevent a deterioration in the *status quo*). A slightly smaller proportion was, in addition, willing to pay to alleviate low flows (that is, to improve the *status quo*). When aggregated, mean resident and visitor benefits (use-benefits) exceed £2 million per annum. In both scenarios, for the River Darent and for all affected rivers, the aggregated WTP of the general public far exceeds that of visitors or residents. The general public within 2 to 60km of the River Darent placed a valuation of £20,336,500 per annum on low flow alleviation.

35.2.3 Benefits transfer

Summarizing several river studies carried out using CVM at the Flood Hazard Research Centre, Green *et al.* (1994) suggest that valuations vary in a predictable and satisfactory way across different rivers, with mature, natural river corridors with abundant bird, fish and plant life attracting highest values. Mean values quoted range from £6.42 per visit for 'pristine' river corridors to £1.67 for canalized rivers. This raises the question as to whether CVM values obtained for a given quality change at one river can be applied to a similar quality change at a different river. Such 'benefits transfer' is seen by many regulators (such as the Environment Agency) as an attractive proposition, since CVM surveys are expensive to carry out. However, recent work on benefits transfer in Norway suggests that even in the case of very similar rivers undergoing very similar improvements, benefits transfer fails statistical tests of acceptability (Bergland *et al.*, 1995). Such findings reduce the usefulness of CVM in environmental management.

35.3   The Travel Costs and Random Utility Methods

The Travel Cost Model (TCM) was first used in the late 1950s, and has since become a popular means of estimating demand for outdoor recreation. The method works by using the costs of travel to such sites as a proxy for their price, and then deriving a 'quasi-demand curve' (a relationship between price and quantity) by statistically relating such costs to the frequency of visiting. For example, trips by recreational fishermen to river j might be thought to be determined according to:

$$VPA_j = f\{TC_j, Inc, TC_i, Qual_j\} \qquad (35.1)$$

where VPA are visits by any individual per annum, Inc is their income, TC_j and TC_i are travel costs to site j and to another, alternative site i; and $Qual_j$ is some index of water quality at site j relative to site i. Travel costs are assumed to comprise fuel, access and time costs (although the value of leisure time remains an awkward issue for economists). Data to enable the estimation of this equation can be collected from on-site surveys of users; it should be noted that the method is unable to estimate non-use values, since such preferences leave no mark on market transactions in this case. If the method is to be applied to many sites of a similar nature (e.g. all coarse fishing rivers in western England), then separate equations are specified for each site, and then estimated simultaneously.

Once Eq. (35.1) has been estimated, then mean WTP for a day visit to the site can be estimated by integrating under the quasi-demand curve. Alternatively (and of more relevance in this case), the effects of changes in water quality on trips can be predicted, and translated into an effect on aggregate WTP. The extent to which total WTP depends on various characteristics of the site can also be investigated; for example, Eq. (35.1) might be extended thus:

$$VPA_j = f\{TC_j\ Inc, TC_i, DO_j, SS_j, Crowd_j, SC_j\} \qquad (35.2)$$

where DO is dissolved oxygen, SS is some turbidity measure, Crowd measures congestion at the site, and SC is an index of the variation in species caught, all measured relative to some other site. Hanley and Ruffell (1993) discuss alternative means of incorporating characteristics in travel cost models.

The TCM has been widely employed in the USA and the UK. Smith and Kaoru (1990) subjected the results from TCM studies to meta-analysis—a technique of comparing the results gained from a particular method across different applications of this method—by using the design and results from each application to form a data set. They found that across 399 TCM studies, some 43% of the variation in WTP could be explained by observable differences, such as statistical techniques and the value given to leisure time. However, the sensitivity of TCM results to such value choices, and problems over the method's ability to handle both multi-purpose trips and multiple sites (see Bockstal *et al.*, 1991) have recently led researchers to concentrate on a related technique: the Random Utility Model.

The Random Utility Model (RUM) differs from the TCM in two principal ways. First, it assumes that the underlying utility functions are composed of two parts: one, deterministic, and in principle observable; the other, a random error term. Second, the model concentrates on site choice by a recreationalist, given a decision to visit a particular type of site. Thus, a RUM would predict which river site a fisherman would go to, given a decision to go fishing that day.

What determines these choices? Two factors are important: the cost of getting to the site, and the vector of characteristics describing the site. This vector could include the terms DO, SS, Crowd and SC from Eq. (35.2), but could be extended to many more variables. For example, Adamowicz *et al.* (1994), in a RUM application to improvements in flow conditions in the Highwood and Little Bow rivers in south-western Alberta, modelled site choice as dependent on 17 characteristic variables, including terrain, fish catch, fish size and water quality. Changes in any of these variables (assuming that they turn out to be statistically significant) can then be translated into predicted changes in visit rates and associated changes in WTP for a trip to a given site.

One major problem with both RUM and TCM approaches, however, is possible co-linearity between dependent variables (e.g. fish catch and water quality). Thus, attention is now turning to models which combine elements of both RUM and direct valuation methods, using a direct valuation method known as the Stated Preference Technique. These combined models can greatly reduce co-linearity problems, whilst still being based on actual rather than hypothetical behaviour. Case Study 3 gives an example of the RUM approach applied to water quality at bathing beaches near Boston, USA.

35.3.1   *Case study 3: Bathing water quality at beaches around Boston, USA*

Bockstal *et al.* (1987) estimated a Random Utility Model of choice of bathing site by recreationalists around Boston. Site choice was thought *a priori* to depend on the cost of visiting the site, and on the pollution levels in bathing water. A negative and significant relationship was found between choosing a given site and pollution indicators. These indicators were Chemical Oxygen Demand (COD), oil, faecal coliforms, and turbidity. For COD, a 10% reduction at all sites increased WTP by $2.95 per person per season; a 30% reduction gave an increase of $7.15. Given the large numbers of people using beaches in the area, this implies large economic benefits for water-quality improvement. Similar relationships were found between WTP and oil and coliforms.

35.4 Applying the Valuation Techniques in Context

Non-market valuation techniques, such as those outlined above, are applied in a variety of contexts. These include litigation for environmental damages in the USA, and in the application of cost-benefit analysis to either projects or policies having environmental impacts. In all of these cases where freshwater resources are concerned, economists require inputs from other scientists in order to predict changes in biological, physical and chemical characteristics of rivers and lakes resulting from policy/project choice, or actions by the private sector (such as increases in abstraction by farmers for irrigation purposes). Cost-benefit analysis can be used to assess the economic efficiency implications of policy/project choice, but where environmental impacts are involved CBA becomes more difficult in both theory and practice (Hanley, 1992). Still, economists argue that CBA provides a potentially useful tool in environmental management, which allows non-market environmental impacts to be recognized and given the same weight as conventional market-valued effects. A hypothetical example of such a CBA applied to a freshwater resource is given below in Case Study 4.

35.4.1 Case study 4: Applying CBA to freshwater management

This section concerns an illustrative, though fictitious, CBA of improved catchment management, which was produced as part of the 'Wild Rivers' initiative launched in 1995 by the World Wide Fund for Nature (WWF) (Scotland). The Wild Rivers initiative makes a biological, ecological and economic case for integrated catchment management aimed at producing more natural rivers and associated habitats (WWF (Scotland), 1995).

The fictitious River Cosbenan lies in south-west Scotland. It has a total catchment area of 20,000 ha, rising from sea level at the mouth to 1,500 m near the source. At present the river quality is Class 2 (see Pugh, this volume), with a poor run of salmon and sea trout. Land use in the catchment is mainly arable and dairy in the lowlands, and hill farming and forestry in the uplands, with some shooting estates for red deer and grouse in the higher hills.

At present, there are various problems associated with the river and associated catchment land use. There is some acidification in the upper reaches and considerable bank erosion in the middle and lower stretches. On the floodplain there have been some flood protection measures taken, but in the past decade high floods have breached these, causing damage to arable fields and flooding in lower parts of Invercosbenan, the town near the mouth of the river.

In order to develop the investment plan for the catchment, the catchment is divided into five areas:

Area 1.   A large shooting estate in the highest parts.
Area 2.   Hill farms on the west bank of the middle reaches.

Area 3.   Hill farms on the east bank of the middle reaches.

Area 4.   Arable farms in the lower reaches.

Area 5.   The town of Invercosbenan.

35.4.1.1   Proposed changes in catchment management: the Wild Rivers alternative

To Area 1: No change.

To Area 2: There are 10 farms here at present, with 250 sheep each on a mixture of improved in-bye and rough grazing. The proposal is to create a riparian strip, 100 m wide, along the main river, and 50 m wide along major tributaries. This would be fenced off and planted with native broadleaved trees. Each farm loses 25 ha of grazing because of this. This means that each farm reduces its sheep enterprise by 25 breeding ewes. Farmers lose out on lamb sales and headage payments.

To Area 3: There are 10 farms here, each of 250 ha, but these have all been bought up for afforestation. The proposal is to change this such that riparian strips are planted with native broadleaved tree species on the same basis as Area 2, but with an additional 25 ha of planting of broadleaves on each farm. No ditching occurs: all planting is by mounding. The net effects are thus no increase in coniferous tree cover; and an increase in broadleaved tree cover.

To Area 4: There are 20 farms here, each of 500 ha with arable ground used for cereals on the floodplain, and pasture for dairy cattle with some silage meadows higher up. The proposal is that a new flood wall is set back 200 m on either side of the main river and 50 m back from tributaries, and that this intervening ground is planted with broadleaves. Each farm loses 25 ha of arable production and 25 ha of pasture because of this. Farmers thus lose on cereals and dairying gross margins, but gain forest areas.

To Area 5: no change.

In addition, the following is assumed.

(a) River quality increases to Class 1 (see Pugh, this volume), notable for a good run of salmon and sea trout. This translates into a rise of 500 in total recreational fishing days per annum.

(b) An attractive new riverside walk is created in the washland forest, connecting with the town. This becomes usable immediately. It is estimated that 14,000 'recreational day walks' per annum are created.

(c) Wildlife diversity increases, with otters and kingfishers returning to the river within 10 years.

(d) Flooding is reduced in frequency on remaining cereal-growing land and in the town, from 1 year in 20 to 1 year in 100.

(e) Money must be spent on the new flood defences, but these have an expected lifespan of 100 years, whilst the old system breached every 20 years, requiring repair.

Given these circumstances, it is possible to construct a CBA of the proposals, in all cases comparing 'with' and 'without' scenarios. This gives the following benefits and costs. It should be noted that, in accordance with CBA practice, transfer payments such as subsidies for woodland planting, and the subsidy elements in agricultural profits, are excluded from the calculations: it is resource costs and benefits that count in CBA. The time frame of the project is taken to be 50 years. All costs and benefits are in real terms, and a discount rate of 6% (real) is assumed.

Major benefits. The major benefits are as follows:

B1. Improvement in fishing quality. An increase of 1,000 fishing days per annum, assumed to be worth £30 per day on the basis of the value of permits. *Present value: £466,800.*

B2. Value of the recreational walk through floodplain forest. Assume that a contingent valuation study has valued WTP for each day at £3 per person (this is comparable with existing UK estimates). Annual value of benefits is thus £42,000. *Present value: £653,520.*

B3. Reduction in expected flood damages. The last incident of flooding in the catchment incurred clean-up costs of £3.2 million in Invercosbenan; and a loss of agricultural incomes of £2.7 million. Assume that the average Producer Subsidy Equivalent of these losses was 0.2, then the resource cost of the farm losses is £2.16 million. The probability of serious flooding falls from 1 year in 20 to 1 year in 100. The reduction in expected damages is thus £278,000– £55,600 = £222,400 per annum. Assuming actuarially-fair insurance and risk neutrality, the reduction in insurance premiums each year will be equal to this amount. *Present value: £3.46 million.*

B4. Savings in flood defence repairs. These are assumed to be equal to £1 million in total, items which would have been saved in years 20 and 40 respectively. *Present value: £(311,800+97,220) = £409,020.*

B5. Non-use benefits of improved river quality, and for wildlife and landscape in uplands due to tree planting in riparian strips. These accrue to all residents of the region (50,000 people), and using recent CVM estimates from the UK are forecast to equal £12 per person per year. This gives annual benefits of £600,000. *Present value: £9.336 million.*

Benefits not included for simplicity include timber values of broadleaved woods; whilst all growth rates for benefits are assumed to be zero.

Major costs. The major costs are as follows:

C1. Loss in ewe production in Area 2. The farms lose 25 breeding ewes each, a total loss of 250 ewes. According to the Scottish Agricultural College hand-book, the gross margin on each ewe is around £3.85, giving an annual loss of £962. However, 30% of this amount is a transfer payment (as subsidies to sheep farmers), so the resource cost is only £674 per annum. *Present value: £10,487.*

C2. Loss in cereal production. It is assumed that winter barley is grown on the cereal area, and that the producer subsidy equivalent is 0.1. This implies a loss of a gross margin of £527 per ha across 500 ha in total, assuming a yield of 6.5 tonnes per ha. The resource cost of this loss is £237,150 per year. *Present value: £3.69 million.*

C3. Loss in dairy production. Here, 500 ha are lost in total. Assuming that each forage hectare supports 1.3 dairy cows, this implies a loss of 650 dairy cows. With a milk yield of 5,000 litres per annum, this means a reduction in total gross margins of £472,500; but with a producer subsidy equivalent of 50% the resource cost falls to £236,275. *Present value: £3.67 million.*

C4. Lost afforestation revenues, net of planting costs. Planting costs are assumed to be £1,000 per ha, including fencing; whilst a value at clearfell in year 50 of £6,500 per ha is predicted. Land costs are excluded to avoid double-counting in this case. A total of 2,500 ha of conifer planting is lost. Note that planting grants and annual subsidies are excluded, since these are transfer payments. *Present value: £882,212–£2.5 m = −£1,617,788.*

C5. Planting costs for broadleaved woodlands in riparian strips. A total of 750 ha (upland) plus 2,000 ha (lowland) is to be planted. Assuming planting costs of £1,000 per ha, this gives a total cost of £2.75 million in year 0. *Present value = £2.75 million.*

C6. Cost of new flood defence structure. This is estimated at £2 million in year 0. *Present value = £2 million.*

Results of the CBA. The results of the cost-benefit analysis are as follows.

Discounted benefits (£)
B1	466,800
B2	653,520
B3	3,460,000
B4	409,020
B5	9,336,000
TOTAL:	14,325,340

Discounted costs (£)
C1	10,487
C2	3,690,000
C3	3,670,000
C4	− 1,620,000
C5	2,750,000
C6	2,000,000
TOTAL:	10,500,487

Since the discounted value of total benefits is greater than the discounted value of total costs in this case, the project 'passes' the CBA test, *and thus will increase economic efficiency if it goes ahead.* Note, however, that farmers, in this case, may suffer income losses as a result.

35.5 Conclusions

This chapter has argued that water quality improvements have economic value, even if they do not show up in normal market transactions. Necessary conditions for economic value to exist are that (a) quality positively affects people's utility and/or (b) quality positively affects the production of goods which people value, either directly or indirectly. The value of changes in water quality can therefore be measured in economic terms by measuring changes in utility.

Given that utility itself is not observable, and that for many environmental goods such as clean water no market exists, economists must employ non-market valuation techniques to estimate these benefits. The principle valuation methods are contingent valuation, travel cost models, random utility models, hedonic pricing and production function-based approaches. Many academic studies now exist applying these techniques, which are starting to make their way into decisions by government agencies over environmental policy and management. Such decisions include, for example, whether to undertake expenditure on low-flow alleviation, and the planning and design of public forests. This use of non-market valuation techniques is likely to grow most quickly where regulators have some statutory duty to consider both the costs and the benefits which water quality improvements imply (for example, the Environment Agency in England and Wales and the Scottish Environment Protection Agency, both created under the 1995 Environment Act). Given the increasing emphasis being placed on such duties, it seems likely that environmental economists will be increasingly called on to help estimate the economic benefits of improved water quality.

Acknowledgements

Access to the River Darent study was granted as part of an NRA-sponsored research report on the use of CVM in benefits assessment. The author is grateful to the NRA for funding this research, and to an anonymous reviewer for helpful comments on an earlier draft of this chapter.

References

Adamowicz W., Louviere, J. and Williams, M. (1994). Combining revealed and stated preference methods for valuing environmental amenities. *Journal of Environmental Economics and Management*, **26**, 271–292.

Barbier, E. (1989). *The Economic Value of Ecosystems: Tropical Wetlands.* LEEC paper GK89-02, International Institute for Environment and Development, London.

Bergland, O., Magnussen, K. and Navrud, S. (1995). 'Benefit Transfer: Testing for Accuracy and Reliability'. Discussion Paper 03-95, Department of Economics, Agricultural University of Norway.

Bockstal, N., Hanemann, M. and Kling, C. (1987). Estimating the value of water quality improvements. *Water Resources Research,* **23**, 951–960.

Bockstal, N., McConnell, K. and Strand, I. (1991). Recreation. In: Braden, J. and Kolstad, C. (Eds), *Measuring the Demand for Environmental Quality.* Elsevier-North Holland, Amsterdam, 227–270.

Diamond, P. and Hausman, J. (1994). Contingent valuation: is some number better than no number? *Journal of Economic Perspectives,* **8**, 45–64.

Green, C. H. and Tunstall, S. M. (1991). The evaluation of river water quality improvements. *Applied Economics*, **23**, 1135–1146.

Green, C., Tunstall, S., Garner, J. and Ketteridge, A. M. (1994). 'Benefit Transfer: Rivers and Coasts'. Flood Hazard Research Centre, Middlesex University.

Hanley, N. (1992). Are there environmental limits to cost-benefit analysis? *Environmental and Resource Economics,* **2,** 33–59.

Hanley, N. and Ruffell, R. (1993). The valuation of forest characteristics. In: Adamowicz, W., Phillips, W. and White, W. (Eds), *Forestry and the Environment: Economic Perspectives.* CAB International, Oxford, 171–197.

Hanley, N. and Spash, C. (1994). *Cost-Benefit Analysis and the Environment.* Edward Elgar Publishing, Cheltenham.

Kahneman, D. and Knetsch, J. (1992). Valuing public goods: the purchase of moral satisfaction. *Journal of Environmental Economics and Management,* **22,** 57–70.

Mitchell, R. and Carson, R. (1989). *Using Surveys to Value Public Goods.* Resources for the Future, Washington DC.

National Rivers Authority (1994). *River Darent Low Flow Alleviation. Annex IV.* East Malling.

Olsen, D., Richards, J. and Scott, R. (1991). Existence and sport values for doubling the size of Columbia river basin salmon and steelhead. *Rivers,* **2,** 44–56.

Pugh, K. (This volume). Organizational use of the term 'freshwater quality' in Britain.

Smith, V. K. and Desvousges, W. H. (1986). *Measuring the Benefits of Water Quality Improvements.* Kluwer Nijhoff Publishing, Boston.

Smith, V. K. and Kaoru, Y. (1990). Signals or noise? Explaining the variation in recreation benefit estimates. *American Journal of Agricultural Economics,* **72,** 419–433.

WWF (Scotland) (1995). *Wild Rivers.* Aberfeldy.

36 Monetary Valuation of River Flows as an Element of the Landscape: A Case Study from the River Almond, Scotland

G. Edwards-Jones, C. Sloan and E. S. Edwards-Jones

Summary

1. Planned alterations to the regional sewage treatment system will prevent treated sewage effluent from entering the River Almond, Scotland. As a result, low flows along the river could decrease further by up to 85%.

2. In order to ascertain the public's perception of these planned changes in flows, a questionnaire and contingent valuation was undertaken in Almondell Country Park.

3. The results suggest that, on average, reductions in flows would decrease the utility derived from a visit to Almondell Country Park. Visitors to the park were willing to pay around £1 per visit as entrance fees if flows could be maintained at their preferred level.

4. The advantages and disadvantages of utilizing contingent valuation methodology to aid environmental decisions are discussed.

36.1 Introduction

Flow levels are known to affect the recreational and amenity value of rivers through their relationship with fish densities and catch rates (Johnson and Adams, 1988), boating (Brown *et al.*, 1990) and aesthetics (Brown and Daniel, 1991; Shelby *et al.*, 1992). Despite these documented relationships it remains difficult to incorporate changes in amenity values into analyses considering the consequences of changing flow levels. One option for incorporating non-market values into formal analyses is to express these values in monetary terms. While there is some debate about the philosophical and methodological problems associated with this approach (Sagoff, 1988) such transformations are well known in many areas of environmental management, including water resource management (Loomis, 1987; Dixon *et al.*, 1994; Edwards-Jones and Mitchell, 1995; Hanley, this volume).

Contingent valuation methodology (CVM) is the method most frequently used for estimating amenity values of rivers. This requires respondents to specify the monetary value they would pay in order to maintain/achieve some environmental objective (see Mitchell and Carson, 1989; Hanley, this volume) for further discussion of the technique). Loomis (1987) adopted this approach in order to value river recreation at different flow levels, and reported that the public's valuation of the recreational benefits increased with increasing flow up to a certain point, and then declined as flow increased further. Monetary valuation techniques have also been used to determine the aesthetic value derived from landscapes with different flow levels (Daubert and Young, 1981; Litton, 1984; Brown and Daniel, 1991). The general conclusions from these studies were that the aesthetic value of rivers was greatest at intermediate flow levels, and least at high and low levels. In this study, contingent valuation methodology (CVM) was used in order to estimate the social costs of a change to the flow regime of the River Almond, West Lothian, Scotland.

36.2 The Problem

The population of Lothian Region currently produces 15 000 t (dry weight) sewage sludge a year, 95% of which is dumped 16 km offshore. In order to meet the requirements of the EC Urban Wastewater Treatment Directive, the East of Scotland Water Authority is proposing to construct a sewage sludge incinerator on the site of existing sewage treatment works in Seafield, Edinburgh. In order to facilitate the transport of sewage to the incinerator from the neighbouring district of West Lothian, it has been proposed that a trunk sewer be constructed to divert flow from five existing treatment works to the new treatment works (Lothian Regional Council, 1994). Completion of the trunk sewer, which will be able to carry six times the average dry weather flow of each of the sewage works it serves, is planned by the year 2000.

Whilst Lothian Regional Council commissioned a full Environmental Impact Assessment (EIA) of the construction and operation of the Seafield incinerator, there was no legal requirement to conduct an EIA of the trunk sewer proposal, and none was commissioned. Independent modelling studies which evaluated the impact of altering the discharge from the five treatment works along the River Almond suggested that low flows in the river may decrease by up to 85% of present levels once the trunk sewer is operating (Harris, 1994). The potential impacts of the reduction in flows are unclear. For example, it is not certain whether or not the overall water quality of the river will improve, as the loss of dilution for remaining polluting inputs may obscure anticipated gains in water quality derived from the removal of sewage effluent. It is also unclear how the impact on instream flows will affect the amenity and recreation value of the river.

The amenity and recreation values of the river are a function of the direct uses derived from the river, such as boating, fishing and swimming, and the benefits derived from an appreciation of the area's landscape and ecology, of which the river is an integral part. The aim of this work was to investigate the importance of flow levels in the River Almond as an element of the landscape. This was achieved through measuring how changes in flow levels could effect the recreational experience of visitors to Almondell Country Park, West Lothian. No attempt was made to seek visitors' views on pollution levels in the river, nor the interaction between flows and pollution, although previous studies have shown pollution of fresh waters to be an important issue in Scotland (Edwards-Jones and Mitchell, 1995).

36.3   Methods

Almondell Country Park is approximately 16 km outside Edinburgh, and attracts an average of 137,000 visitors per annum. The majority of these visit the park for riverside recreation, largely walking and picnicking. A survey of visitors to the Country Park was conducted between March and September 1995. Visitors were approached on the riverside walkway and asked if they would be willing to participate in a survey. Those who agreed were asked to provide general socio-economic data about themselves and their perceptions of the river. They were then shown three illustrations depicting the river as it appeared from the site of the interview. These illustrations had flow rates corresponding to 100, 50 and 15% of present flows and provided all respondents with a similar information set, regardless of the state of the river at the time of interview. Whilst viewing these illustrations respondents were asked the following question:

> Lothian Regional Council are planning, in accordance with EU legislation, to remove the treated sewage effluent from the River Almond. As a result of the removal of sewage, the river flow will be reduced at Almondell Country Park during summer time. Please look at the accompanying illustrations showing different flow levels.
>
> Which of these scenarios do you most prefer?
> A   (100% flow)
> B   (50% flow)
> C   (15% flow)
>
> Say the river could be compensated for this loss of flow by storing water and then releasing it into the River Almond when flow was at its lowest, but the only way to fund this was to have an entrance fee to the park. How much would you be willing to pay in order to ensure that the river was always at your preferred level?

36.4   Results

Of the 179 respondents interviewed, 46% expressed a preference for the present flow level, while 31% and 23% favoured the 50% and 15% flow levels respectively. Of those who preferred the present flow levels, 79% were willing to pay an entrance fee to the park in order to maintain the flow at their preferred level. The willingness to pay for the present flow level ranged between 0 and £10, and

Table 36.1 Summary statistics of the amounts bid as an entrance fee to the park in order to maintain flows at the preferred levels. Protest bids are defined as occurring when the respondent refused to give a willingness to pay bid for reasons other than possessing a zero value for the good, e.g. disagreeing with the idea of valuing the environment, or the payment vehicle (here entrance fees).

Preferred flow level	Mean bid (£)	Standard deviation	Range of bid (£)	Protest bids	Sample size
100%	1.13	0.17	0–10	17	65
50%	0.82	0.70	0–2	13	42

averaged £1.13 (Table 36.1). This was slightly more than the average of £0.82 bid by those respondents who preferred the flow at 50% of present levels. Respondents who preferred the lowest flows of 15% of present levels were not included in the analysis.

36.5 Discussion

Contingent valuation has two advantages over most other methods for evaluating a project's environmental impacts. First, it enables respondents' values to be placed onto a common, quantified scale, and second, it provides some estimation of the impact a given environmental change may have on respondents' utility. While the theory here is similar to that adopted in some formal EIA methods (e.g. Dee *et al.*, 1973) CVM allows the expression of the public's preferences, rather than just those of 'experts'. In addition, the results of CVM give an indication of the monetary costs and benefits arising from any given environmental change. For publicly funded projects these may provide an estimate of the socially acceptable budget available for mitigating environmental costs.

Here, given that 46% of people who visit Almondell Country Park would pay around £1.13 per visit in order to maintain flows at present levels, a crude calculation (extrapolating that figure to the 137,000 people visiting the Park each year) would suggest that a minimum of £71,213 per annum could be raised from entrance fees alone in order to fund some form of flow enhancement scheme which would prevent the reduction in flows. However, given that on average 31% of respondents would pay an 82p entrance fee in order to see flows at 50% of present levels, defining the socially optimal flow level for the Almond from the CVM results alone is not a simple task.

Although CVM has been used widely to assess the value of flow regimes, its use in environmental management remains contentious. Not only are there ethical questions surrounding its use, but the actual framing of the questions and the provision of information are known to affect the willingness to pay bids (Mitchell and Carson, 1989). It has also been suggested that CVM is most reliable when used to value simple goods such as pollution levels, and that respondents' valuations become less reliable when they consider more complex goods, such as ecological communities (Edwards-Jones *et al.*, 1995). For this reason it remains unlikely that the results of CVM studies could be used alone in assessing options in environmental management projects. For example, in the present study, respondents were only asked to value the impact of flow levels on their recreational experience. They were not asked, and cannot be expected, to value the impact of flow rates on ecology, or the relationship between flow levels, pollution and ecology. While the public's opinion on these matters is important, it is unlikely that respondents could attain a sufficient level of understanding in an interview in order to be able to make a rational valuation of these goods.

So, if CVM is to be used in assessing a project's impact then analysts have two choices: either to ask respondents to value the overall impact of the project, which may result in the generation of imprecise values, or to ask respondents to value one or more easily defined and 'simpler' goods. The difficulty in the former situation is that assessing the overall impacts of a project is problematic when only some of the impacts are expressed in monetary terms. For this reason the setting of flow levels, and levels of other environmental attributes, will probably continue to depend on utilizing a range of techniques including EIA and participative conflict resolution.

36.6 Conclusions

The main conclusions of this study are that the public value instream flows, and that a reduction in the flow of the River Almond from present levels would, on average, reduce the utility derived from a visit to Almondell Country Park. Given these facts, it may be assumed that the utility derived from visitors to other parts of the river would also be reduced if flows were to fall. Reductions in the public's utility should be considered during a project's planning and analysis, and decision-makers should make any trade-offs between the costs and benefits arising from the project more explicit. In theory, the use of CVM should make this task simpler than when using other techniques such as EIA, but in reality several practical issues associated with its use remain unresolved.

References

Brown, T. C., Richards, M. T., Daniel, T. C. and King, D. A. (1990). Scenic beauty and recreational value: assessing the relationship. In: Vinning, J. (Ed.), *Social Science and Natural Resource Recreation Management*. Westview Press, Boulder, CO, 281–299.

Brown, T. C. and Daniel T. C. (1991). Landscape aesthetics of riparian environments: relationship of flow to scenic quality along a wild and scenic river. *Water Resources Research*, **27**, 1787–1795.

Daubert, J. T. and Young, R. A. (1981). Recreational demands for maintaining instream flows: a contingent valuation approach. *American Journal of Agricultural Economics*, **63**, 666–676.

Dee, N. J. K., Baker, N. L., Drobny, K. M., Duke, I. and Whitman, D. C. (1973). Environmental evaluation system for water resource planning. *Water Resources Research*, **9**, 523–535.

Dixon, J. A., Sura, L. F., Carpenter, R. A. and Sherman, P. B. (1994). *Economic Analysis of Environmental Impacts*. Earthscan, London.

Edwards-Jones, G. and Mitchell, K. (1995). Economic valuation of water pollution from Scottish farms. *Scottish Agricultural Economics Review*, **8**, 63–69.

Edwards-Jones, G., Edwards-Jones, E. S. and Mitchell, K. (1995). A comparison of contingent valuation methodology and ecological assessment as techniques for incorporating ecological goods into land-use decisions. *Journal of Environmental Planning and Management*, **38,** 215–230.

Hanley, N. (This volume). Assessing the economic value of fresh waters.

Harris, P. (1994). 'A Study of the Impact of Removing Sewage Pollution from the Almond River, Scotland'. Unpublished M.Sc. thesis, University of Edinburgh, Edinburgh.

Johnson, N. S. and Adams, R. M. (1988). Benefits of increased streamflow: the case of John Day River steelhead fishery. *Water Resources Research*, **24,** 1839–1846.

Litton, R. B. (1984). Visual fluctuations in river landscape quality. In: Popadic, S., Butterfield, D. I., Anderson, D. H. and Popadic, M. R. (Eds), *National River Recreation Symposium Proceedings*. Louisiana State University, Baton Rouge, 196–204.

Loomis, J. (1987). The economic value of instream flows: methodology and benefit estimates for optimum flows. *Journal of Environmental Management*, **24,** 169–179.

Lothian Regional Council (1994). *Planning Application: Proposed Sewage Sludge Incinerator, Seafield, Edinburgh*. LRC, Edinburgh.

Mitchell, R. C. and Carson, R. T. (1989). *Using Surveys to Value Public Goods: the Contingent Valuation Method*. Resources for the Future, Washington DC.

Sagoff, M. (1988). Some problems with environmental economics. *Environmental Ethics*, **10,** 57–64.

Shelby, B., Brown, T. C. and Taylor, J. G. (1992). *Streamflow and Recreation. General Technical Report* RM-209. Rocky Mountains Forest and Range Experimental Station, US Department of Agriculture, Fort Collins, CO.

PART FIVE
ACHIEVING IMPROVEMENTS IN FRESHWATER QUALITY

37 PROTECTING FRESHWATER QUALITY THROUGH LEGISLATION: ENFORCEMENT, INDUCEMENT OR AGREEMENT?

D. L. Howell and D. W. Mackay

Summary

1. This chapter examines the role of legislation in protecting and improving the quality of fresh waters in Britain (Scotland, England and Wales). It considers three main areas: pollution control, the management of physical alterations to fresh waters, and nature conservation.

2. These three aspects of freshwater quality are considered from three differing legislative perspectives: 'enforcement', 'inducement' and 'agreement'. In Britain, water-related prosecutions are rare outside the fields of pollution control and fishery protection, despite the existence of numerous other offences under water law. This variable prosecution activity is explored by comparing nature conservation and pollution control.

3. Conservation legislation tends to focus on protected areas and protected species, although statutes do promote conservation principles more widely in water management. In contrast, controls over pollution, abstraction and physical changes to fresh waters tend to have a broader geographical basis, although the importance of 'designated areas' is increasing in tackling issues such as diffuse-source pollution and water shortages.

4. In the past, different types of water quality legislation have been applied by various authorities in an often *ad hoc* manner. It is argued that the blend of statutory enforcement, inducement and agreement (and of voluntary action) must in future be a more conscious choice, with strategic and operational decisions being taken according to the principles of Integrated Catchment Management.

5. Freshwater specialists must continue to base their arguments for new legislation on strong technical reasoning, but these arguments will often fail unless they also acknowledge the human factors which influence legislators and their advisers. A more complete understanding of these factors is an urgent priority.

37.1 Introduction: the Purpose, Scope and Extent of Freshwater Legislation

Freshwater legislation is enacted for many purposes, usually reflecting (but rarely anticipating) some new demand or expectation placed on water resources by society. Statutes typically encompass the promotion of economic development and associated infrastructure; the protection and enhancement of public health and safety; nature conservation; or the promotion of public appreciation, enjoyment and recreational use of fresh waters. They usually set out government responsibilities (international, national, or local), establish new agencies, or provide mechanisms whereby the aims of governments and their agencies can be achieved. The process by which government wishes become law is a complex one, and the success of legislators is often only measurable long after the event, as new organizations and their policies are tested, and the judiciary puts particular aspects of law to the test.

Attempts to establish framework legislation (e.g. that setting out a government's general policy on water use, management and protection) can face formidable challenges in attempting to 'sweep up' all the various statutes that have gone before (often with an associated sectoral inflexibility and entrenchment of views). Such difficulties have been highlighted elsewhere, e.g. in France (Newborne, 1993), and the USA (Doppelt *et al.*, 1993), but there have also been some successes (e.g. Dutch Ministry of Transport and Public Works, 1989, cited by the Royal Commission on Environmental Pollution (RCEP, 1992) and by Luitens, 1995; see also other examples in Werritty, this volume). At present, the European Commission is addressing this challenge by seeking to promote a 'Water Framework Directive' (Commission of the European Communities, 1996) which would set a much wider context for water policy within the European Union than has hitherto been available. The proposed new Directive, based on the principles of the earlier proposed Directive on the Ecological Quality of Water (see Nixon and Juggins, 1995), would require the preparation of catchment management plans (Werritty, this volume), and would repeal or subsume a number of existing water Directives.

There is a large and complex body of water legislation in Britain. Of the areas being considered by this review, this is particularly the case with pollution prevention and control and, to a lesser extent, nature conservation. However, in contrast to pollution, other impacts of human activity on fresh waters are less well understood (such as changes to the physical structure or flow regime of watercourses) and have far less by way of legislation to limit their impact. This imbalance stems from the focus on chemical and microbiological aspects of water quality which originated in public health concerns in the nineteenth and early twentieth centuries (RCEP, 1992; Hammerton, 1994). British conservation legislation emanates from the deliberations of a number of committees set up to advise on national reconstruction following the debilitating effects of the Second World War (see Mackay, 1995 and Sheail, 1996 for more details). Reports submitted by these committees formed the basis of the National Parks and Access to the

Countryside Act 1949, and with it the concept of legally protected areas for nature conservation.

This chapter examines the role of legislation in supporting a number of different approaches to protecting water quality. These approaches can be summarized as 'enforcement', 'inducement' and 'agreement'. Here, 'enforcement' is regulatory activity carried out through legislation which ultimately carries penalties for uses of water which society regards as undesirable. 'Inducement' represents legislation which offers a net financial reward for actions with effects on water which society regards as desirable, or for preventing actions which society regards as undesirable. 'Agreement' represents a collaborative approach between a number of parties, often involving negotiation, persuasion, education, advice and perhaps even the threat of enforcement or the promise of inducement.

37.2 Chemical Aspects of Freshwater Quality—Pollution Prevention and Control

37.2.1 Point-source pollution

In Britain, the discharge consents procedures are the principal mechanism by which water pollution from point sources is controlled (National Rivers Authority (NRA), 1990; Hammerton, 1994; Mackay, 1994). The type of treatment required for a particular effluent is not usually prescribed by the consent conditions—in the majority of cases it is a simple statement of limits which must not be exceeded. Thus, the focus is on the character of effluents which dischargers introduce into the natural hydrological cycle, and on minimizing their effects on receiving waters. There is an ultimate sanction which allows the regulators to withhold consent to discharge, but that consent cannot be withheld 'unreasonably'. Any discharges made to fresh waters without a consent from the relevant authority are generally offences which can be punished by fines or, ultimately, a custodial sentence. Similar penalties can be applied in the case of consented discharges if the terms and conditions of the consent are breached.

An alternative enforcement mechanism available to the British authorities sets out regulations for the safe storage of potential pollutants. This has been used successfully to reduce pollution from stored agricultural materials such as silage, slurry and fuel oil. Here the emphasis is on containment to prevent any leakages or spillages, using storage facilities which must meet exacting construction standards, rather than the controlled release of pollutants within permitted limits. Any facilities not meeting these standards may render the owner liable to an enforcement notice, a fine, or both.

The British water pollution control authorities have been increasingly vigorous in their attempts to secure prosecutions for pollution offences. Where prosecutions are successful, such high-profile enforcement action can perform a valuable function. It publicizes the existence of legislation protecting water quality, and highlights the fact that good water quality is of sufficient value to society that on occasions it should be protected by legal action which punishes the offender and provides a deterrent against repeat offences. However, the Scottish judiciary has often proved reluctant to proceed with prosecutions, or to impose heavy fines when prosecutions are secured (Friends of the Earth Scotland, 1994). Smith (1993) highlighted the deterrent effect this has on the regulator, with reluctance to invest staff time in preparing a prosecution case if it is likely to fail, or to result in a derisory fine. Smith (1993) also noted a number of other important differences between Scotland, and England and Wales. In the latter, the Environment Agency (EA) is able to conduct its own prosecutions, and recover the costs of time spent in preparing and prosecuting a case. In Scotland, cases are conducted by public prosecutors (the 'Procurators Fiscal'), who may not be as familiar with the detail of pollution legislation as defence solicitors—who may be specialists in pollution law. In addition, there is no provision in Scotland for the Scottish Environment Protection Agency (SEPA) to recover the costs of staff time spent in court.

A warning letter, backed up by the threat of prosecution, can often be sufficient to deter potential future offenders. Prosecutions are generally pursued only in the case of persistent or negligent offenders, where there is evidence of deliberate misconduct, or where damage is so serious that a salutary lesson is needed. However, as Smith (1993) has pointed out, prosecutions *per se* do not improve water quality, although they may act as a stimulus to improve performance, or to agree a programme of effluent improvement. The British regulators have a long and fairly successful history of combining this enforcement approach, or the threat of it, with education and negotiation (agreement) to secure better-quality discharges and (thus) less polluted waters.

Most effort has been directed at reducing pollution from point-source discharges to rivers (in contrast to nature conservation, where most protected freshwater sites are standing waters—see Section 37.4.1.2 below). Despite a number of setbacks such as the declines in river quality in England and Wales during the 1980s reported by the National Rivers Authority (NRA, 1991a), the British system can claim a degree of success. In one of the European Environment Agency's first publications, Kristensen and Hansen (1994) compared recent river water quality in 20 European states. The data they reviewed suggested that Scotland, with 97% of its rivers of 'Good' quality (2% 'Fair' quality), was only outperformed by Iceland (99% Good, 1% Fair); other UK figures were presented for Northern Ireland (third place, 72% Good, 24% Fair), and for England and Wales (fourth place, 64% Good, 25% Fair). This review focused on performance in 1990, and subsequent data (e.g. NRA, 1995) point to further water quality improvements since then. However, growing concerns about the environmental presence and potential impact of oestrogenic analogues suggest that a more sophisticated approach to summarizing water quality data may be required if classifications are to enjoy public confidence in the future.

Recent work on standing waters (Moss *et al.*, this volume), has developed a 'hindcasting' technique whereby the degree of present-day pollution can be compared against a notional historical 'baseline' state, when pollution levels were much lower. Thus, for the first time in Britain, the quinquennial water quality surveys will be able to use a standard classification technique for reporting on the degree of pollution in standing waters, and some preliminary results from the 1995 survey are already available (Ferrier *et al.*, this volume; Fozzard *et al.*, this volume).

The way that standing waters receive and process pollutants differs from that of running waters, with factors such as flushing regime and the influence of sediments being particularly important in considering eutrophication. These differences can pose difficulties for pollution regulators in applying legislation which was perhaps designed far more with discharges to rivers in mind. Recent Scottish cases involving eutrophication concerns illustrate these points well. At Loch Leven (Bailey-Watts, 1994), discharge consent conditions have been tightened in the search for pollution reductions, and at Loch Shin (Highland River Purification Board, 1995) much debate has surrounded the need to constrain or even prevent new point-source phosphorus discharges. At both sites, catchment diffuse sources of phosphorus are important, and Loch Leven's enriched underlying sediments can release massive amounts of phosphorus into the water column.

The control of point-source pollution in Britain is notable for the lack of inducement as an element in the statutory 'toolkit', and in this respect, the contrast with nature conservation (see Section 37.4) is quite striking. The closest approximation to inducement is probably the charging systems operated by the pollution regulators, whereby they recover the costs incurred in determining and issuing consents, monitoring discharges and taking samples for enforcement purposes. The Royal Commission on Environmental Pollution (RCEP) examined this area in some detail (RCEP, 1992), and felt that the existing system could be reinforced to bring it even more in line with the 'polluter pays' principle as operated in France, Germany and The Netherlands, where there are greater financial incentives to reduce pollutant loadings. The RCEP's recommended system was set at levels where the most polluting discharges paid the highest charges—with the revenue funding research into improved methods of effluent treatment, and offering financial support for improvements in effluent treatment. Other recommendations included the need to examine tradeable permits as an option in pollution control. However, whilst the Government response to the RCEP's recommendations (Department of the Environment, 1995a) indicated a willingness to contemplate introducing economic instruments to control water pollution, no plans have yet emerged. During a period when controversy has surrounded the development of statutory Water Quality Objectives and Standards (Section 37.2.3), the water shortages during the 1995 drought (Section 37.3.1), and the upheavals associated with water industry reorganization, the Government's lack of progress in this area is perhaps understandable.

37.2.2 *Diffuse-source pollution*

As discharges from point sources are cleaned up, polluting inputs from diffuse sources are assuming a greater relative importance in Britain. Concerns over acidification, soil erosion and nutrient enrichment have led to suggestions for enhancing the self-purification capacity of receiving waters through the re-establishment of semi-natural vegetation in riparian buffer areas (Burt and Haycock, 1992; Forestry Commission, 1993; Wilson *et al.*, 1993; Hildrew and Ormerod, 1995). Measures to preserve the physical quality and habitat structure of fresh waters and adjacent wetlands are therefore assuming particular importance in limiting the effects of diffuse-source pollution (see Sections 37.3.2 and 37.4.2). As well as being diffuse, and hence by definition unsuitable for control by discharge consent, such inputs tend to be far more episodic in nature than point sources, rendering them more difficult to monitor effectively, and making it extremely unlikely that such pollution will be policed with sufficient certainty to bring prosecutions (enforcement). The regulatory approach is therefore more likely to be preventative and advisory, reliant on financial support and guidelines or codes of practice (inducement and agreement).

For example, the Forestry Commission issues grant aid for forest planting as long as the potential adverse diffuse-source impacts of forestry on fresh waters are minimized according to published guidance (Forestry Commission, 1993). Similar Government publications (e.g. Scottish Office, 1992) advise farmers on measures they can take to minimize the risk of water pollution arising from their activities; and financial compensation for lost agricultural production is paid to farmers offering voluntarily to alter land management practices in 'Nitrate Sensitive Areas' (Watson *et al.*, 1996).

However, there are some examples of activity more akin to enforcement. Provisions exist for the creation of 'Water Protection Zones', in which specific polluting activities can be restricted or banned; an application for such a zone in the Dee catchment on the English/Welsh border is awaiting a decision from Government. Similarly, 68 areas in Britain have been identified as 'Nitrate Vulnerable Zones' under the EC Nitrates Directive (91/676/EEC), and a degree of enforcement will be required to ensure that agricultural practices are altered in these areas in order to achieve the reductions in freshwater nitrate levels required under the Directive. Even here though, a modest amount of inducement is available, with farmers able to claim grant aid for improving waste handling facilities in the designated zones.

37.2.3 *Water quality objectives, water quality standards, and uniform emission standards*

The Water Act of 1989 enabled UK Ministers to establish statutory water quality classification schemes, with Water Quality Standards (WQSs) that must be achieved in order to meet a variety of use-related Water Quality Objectives (WQOs). Space limitations prevent a detailed examination of this area here, but recent British experience will be of great interest to those seeking an insight into the practicalities of using legislation to (in the terms of this book's title) 'define the indefinable'. In particular, the standards and use classes defined in the emerging proposals (see below) are echoed strongly in remarks by authors elsewhere in this volume (e.g. Hellawell, Pugh) regarding 'fitness for purpose'.

The strongest pressure to introduce these measures has been in England and

Wales, where declines in water quality detected by the 1990 water quality survey (NRA, 1991a) were attributed to pollution from the sewage treatment works owned and operated by the recently privatized water and sewerage utilities. The NRA's original plans to introduce statutory WQOs (NRA, 1991b) have taken some time to receive Government approval, but proposals were announced in early 1996 for testing such a scheme in eight pilot catchments in England and Wales. These proposals are currently subject to public consultation, but if they are implemented they will impose statutory requirements to improve water quality within a given timescale. This type of enforcement is typical of many EC Directives on water quality, but it is quite a departure from previous practice for the UK Government itself to set domestic water quality improvement targets. This goes at least some way to addressing the concerns of RCEP (1992) on the lack of such an approach in the past.

The delay in finalizing these proposals is due principally to financial and political constraints. The Government has been reluctant to expect the privatized utilities to undertake further investments in upgrading sewage treatment facilities (which would require increases in consumers' bills) when household bills have already been increased substantially to meet the costs arising from an investment backlog in water and sewerage infrastructure, and new demands arising from EC Directives. The ensuing debate about the costs and benefits of environmental improvements (e.g. Johnstone and Horan, 1994) culminated in EA and SEPA being required under the Environment Act 1995 to consider the costs and benefits of their regulatory activities. As Hanley (this volume) has noted, this duty is likely to provide a stimulus to the relatively new field of environmental economics, with debate about environmental and economic benefits more likely to intensify than to abate.

The WQO/WQS approach favoured in the UK is often contrasted with that of Uniform Emission Standards more favoured elsewhere in Europe, and differing preferences for the two approaches have been widely debated in considering the implementation of EC Directives. The former approach relies on setting quality standards for waters receiving discharges of a particular substance, and then setting varying discharge limits in order to achieve those standards; in the latter, uniform discharge limits for the release of individual substances are set according to the best available—but affordable—technology. Their relative merits have been debated elsewhere (e.g. Newson, 1995) and it is interesting to note that the European Commission (Commission of the European Communities, 1996) recommends combining both approaches in setting out its proposals for an EC Water Framework Directive.

In Scotland, there has been little pressure for the introduction of statutory WQOs. The preference has been to set non-statutory WQOs which correspond to Class 1 in most European classifications; that is, waters suitable for healthy salmonid fisheries. This more informal approach has been successful in securing considerable reductions in point-source pollution (Section 37.2.1), and the statutory route—with all its attendant bureaucracy and delay—has been regarded with some suspicion (Mackay, 1994). Mackay further suggests that, whilst statutory objectives and standards might be appropriate for cleaning up heavily polluted waters in England and Wales, they are less suitable for maintaining the very high water quality characteristic of much of Scotland. Moss *et al.* (this volume) are similarly sceptical, and have developed their proposals for a quality classification system for standing waters in a way which confronts both the difficulties of legislating for natural variation, and any temptation governments might have to relax standards whilst still claiming water quality achievements.

The need for WQOs and WQSs to take account of natural variations in water chemistry is also referred to by Trihadiningrum *et al.* (this volume), but of course the degree of pollution is only one aspect of freshwater quality influencing its suitability for different uses. In discussing similar issues in Denmark, Iversen *et al.* (1993) note that difficulties in achieving WQOs through pollution control measures alone led to legislative change which required improvements in the physical dimension of water quality as well, and the following section considers these aspects in more detail.

37.3 Physical Aspects—Flow Regimes and Physical Structure

37.3.1 Flow regimes

The issue of environmental damage arising from over-abstraction—or compensation flow regimes being set in an insensitive fashion—has been neglected in the past in the UK. This may be because the UK has traditionally regarded itself as having plentiful water resources. As has been noted elsewhere (Gilvear, 1994; Howell, 1994) flow regime is an aspect of fresh waters much neglected in Scotland, with little by way of statutory abstraction controls, and compensation flows downstream of abstractions and impoundments having been set some time ago on a fairly crude basis. Much more is now known about ecologically acceptable flow regimes, with research and modelling tools now reaching a quite intricate and sophisticated level (see Padmore, this volume).

These aspects of water quality have come to the fore in Britain since the late 1980s, with severe droughts bringing with them dried-up river beds, water rationing, and arguments about the costs and appropriateness of managing water demand vs. constructing new water supply schemes vs. controlling leakage from water mains. The accompanying rash of policy statements and consultation papers has yet to achieve any radical changes in the way water is abstracted, supplied and used, despite many calls for legislative and policy changes (e.g. RCEP, 1992; Gilvear, 1994; Howell, 1994; Petts *et al.*, 1995; RSPB, 1995) which have included the need for the following:

- More sensitivity to environmental concerns in setting and operating compensation flow regimes, especially in Scotland.
- A comprehensive abstraction control system in Scotland.
- Planning authorities to limit demands on water resources in considering their strategic plans and individual development proposals.

- The EA's compensation liabilities to be lowered where abstraction rates under 'licences of right' (see RSPB, 1995) need to be reduced on environmental grounds.
- Applications for 'drought orders' (to legalize additional abstractions during drought conditions) to be made before water supplies fall to crisis levels.

Government responses (e.g. Department of the Environment, 1995b) appear to favour inducement as the best means of tackling the root of these concerns, especially those which are drought-related, and continue to press the case for 'demand-side management' (cf. traditional supply-side management—see Guy and Marvin, 1996) outlined in response to earlier drought conditions (Department of the Environment, 1992). For example, water metering is central to proposals for reducing water demand (and hence environmental damage) during drought conditions such as those experienced during summer 1995. The recognition that freshwater quality ceases to exist if there is no water present prompted the NRA to take urgent action on a number of rivers with severe low flow problems, with innovative schemes being used in some cases to transfer water from catchments where water was in more plentiful supply (Petts *et al.*, 1995). Such initiatives for the most urgent examples fall within wider EA plans to set ecologically acceptable river flows as part of its catchment management planning programme (Werritty, this volume), accompanied by a vigorous policy of enforcement as regards setting abstraction licence conditions and monitoring compliance with them.

Bearing in mind these recent droughts—which have been primarily an English phenomenon—it is ironic that during the same period some parts of Scotland have suffered some of the worst flooding on record (Gilvear, 1994). It is of interest here to note that the legislation which created the new Scottish Water Authorities allows them to export water, but there are areas of Scotland where freshwater quality has suffered during recent droughts, so there is clearly no room for complacency.

37.3.2 *Physical structure*

Urban development and intensive agricultural cultivation are often associated with a whole range of activities which modify the physical architecture and behaviour of rivers (RSPB *et al.*, 1994). In England and Wales, the EA has supervisory responsibility for the vast majority of such works, a lot of which are carried out by its own staff. Taken together with the EA's responsibility to further and promote nature conservation, these statutory roles are used to protect the physical components of river habitat quality. However, they are far less explicit and powerful than those available for protecting natural chemical quality. Strong enforcement activity is less frequent, which perhaps reflects the traditional perception that a pollution incident is a more serious event than one entailing loss of physical habitat diversity. Agreement, in this case persuading those carrying out river works to do so in a sympathetic fashion, is far more of a feature in this area than inducement.

Notwithstanding the comments on riparian buffer zones in Section 37.2.2, the necessary focus of pollution control authorities on point sources has tended to mean that legislation and practice has concentrated on the polluting inputs them-selves (*pollutant* control), with rather less effort being devoted consciously to maximizing the self-purification capacity of the water body itself (*pollution* control). Furthermore, whilst the conservation and enhancement of physical habitat struc-ture has been a strong feature of river engineering works in England and Wales for some years (RSPB *et al.*, 1994), more emphasis has been placed on the desire to minimize direct damage to habitats arising from engineering works (Raven *et al.*, this volume) than on capitalizing on the greater ability of a diverse freshwater habitat structure to dilute, disperse, absorb and process pollutants. Early indi-cations from the EA are that these pollution control benefits, which are an important functional value of habitat diversity (O'Riordan, 1995), will be given much stronger emphasis in England and Wales in the future (P. Raven, personal communication).

In Scotland, river engineering is still dominated by traditional approaches, and, unlike in England and Wales, those authorizing or carrying out such works are still not explicitly required to do so in a manner which furthers conservation (Howell, 1994). This means that river engineering schemes tend to be designed and maintained in a way which reduces rather than enhances the self-purification capacity of the affected waters. However, the new pollution control agency (SEPA) is required by law to receive prior notification from anyone intending to carry out 'drainage works' (currently widely defined) in or near fresh waters. SEPA in turn offers its views on the extent to which these works may pose a pollution risk. Whilst SEPA has no powers of enforcement here (except in relation to the direct polluting effects of engineering activities), combining this requirement with its new duty to promote the conservation of aquatic wildlife may yet prove influential in shaping a move to a more sympathetic style of river engineering. Even if the only justification for maintaining or enhancing the natural physical diversity of watercourses is to render them less vulnerable to pollution, then perhaps the ends justify the means. The adoption of River Habitat Survey (Raven *et al.*, this volume) by SEPA is a positive sign in this respect.

37.4 Biological Aspects—Nature Conservation

37.4.1 Designated areas and sites

37.4.1.1 The founding legislation

The National Parks and Access to the Countryside Act of 1949 provided for three types of conservation designation in Britain: National Parks (although not in Scotland), National Nature Reserves (NNRs), and Sites of Special Scientific Inter-est (SSSIs). Whilst the primary purpose of NNRs and SSSIs was nature conser-vation, National Parks were also designed to protect special landscape qualities and provide opportunities for public enjoyment of open space. The merits and drawbacks of the National Park designation continue to attract much comment in Britain (see Bishop *et al.*, 1995), with particular controversy surrounding their continued absence in Scotland. Here, the Government favours a different mechanism (the 'Natural Heritage Area'—NHA), which is based more on agreement than enforcement. The NHA concept has yet to be tested in Scotland; however, its two possible testing grounds (the areas including and surrounding the Cairngorms, and Loch Lomond) have many fresh waters of international nature conservation value. The extent to which human use and enjoyment of fresh waters in these areas does not compromise their exceptional conservation importance will, therefore, be a key test of any NHA designation. The experience in areas such as the Norfolk Broads and the English Lake District will be crucial here in debating issues such as 'conservation primacy' (O'Riordan, 1995). As the conservation value of fresh waters in National Parks tends to rely heavily for its protection on the nature conservation measures described below (MacEwen and MacEwen, 1983; Stedman, 1993), National Parks will not be discussed further here.

37.4.1.2 Sites of Special Scientific Interest (SSSIs)

SSSIs have dominated British nature conservation policy, especially since the Wildlife and Countryside Act 1981 which bolstered their protection considerably, albeit at considerable financial cost (see below). The 1981 Act enables the three British conservation agencies to notify any area (and in the context of this paper, any fresh water) which is in their opinion of special scientific interest by reason of its fauna, flora or physiographical features. Boon (1991, 1994, 1995) has reviewed the application of this legislation to fresh waters, and a site-specific example from England is provided by Box and Walker (1994). Where SSSIs support features of European importance (e.g. under the EC Birds Directive, 79/409/EEC and the 'Habitats Directive'—92/43/EEC) a stricter degree of protection is provided where such sites receive designation under these Directives (see below).

The features of an SSSI which constitute its legally protected special interest are identified in the 'citation', which accompanies the letter informing an owner, occupier or statutory agency of the site's newly protected status. These features can be protected by a number of mechanisms, ranging from strict enforcement (e.g. compulsory purchase of land or water under threat; prosecution for unconsented activity damaging to the interest of the site, or Government orders preventing such damaging activities proceeding) to management agreement (e.g. compensatory, if permission is not granted to go ahead with activities which threaten the interest of the site, or positive, to try to encourage activities which guarantee that interest).

Very few prosecutions have been sought by the British conservation agencies for criminal damage to SSSIs—a fact which has attracted surprisingly little attention, even in quite detailed reviews of the extent of site damage (e.g. Adams, 1993). However, this lack of enforcement was noted with some concern by a recent Parliamentary enquiry (House of Commons Committee of Public Accounts, 1995).

The Committee considered that a higher-profile enforcement role was required, with more detailed statistics on site damage being published, and a less tentative approach to prosecutions, or to applications for so-called 'Section 29 Orders' (orders forbidding particular types of activity, obtained from the relevant Government Minister under section 29 of the Wildlife and Countryside Act 1981). The report, which focused on the situation in England, also welcomed plans (developed jointly with the conservation agencies in Scotland and Wales) for a more comprehensive approach to monitoring the condition of designated conservation sites. These points merit more detailed examination, as whilst the British pollution control agencies find their prosecution rates under close scrutiny (e.g. Friends of the Earth Scotland, 1994), far less attention has been devoted to the lack of prosecutions brought for damage to SSSIs. This contrast highlights the differing emphases on enforcement, inducement and agreement between British legislation for preventing pollution and for protecting and enhancing statutory conservation areas.

Citations have often been worded in very vague terms, making it very difficult to isolate the particular features which constitute a site's special interest. This in turn creates difficulties in monitoring site condition, or assessing the degree of damage arising from particular activities. Recent efforts have been made to improve the consistency and detail provided in these documents, and an assessment by Boon (1995) concluded that these efforts had resulted in much clearer citations for river SSSIs recently notified in England.

If site damage is to be detected, it is also necessary to know the complex of conditions on the site which support its features of protected special scientific interest, and the extent of change which is acceptable before that interest of the site is placed at risk. This implies a requirement for a detailed knowledge of structure, process and function, but these are areas of weakness in British freshwater conservation (Boon, 1995) although geomorphology is perhaps a little more advanced than ecology in this respect. An influential report by Rowell (1993) addressed the general issue of monitoring on SSSIs, and proposed a scheme which could be applied to all such sites (Figure 37.1). For any given feature of conservation interest, such as a rare fish population, an indicator of favourable condition can be identified (e.g. recruitment success) which will fluctuate naturally over time. Whilst recruitment remains favourable, there is no need for anything other than continued monitoring and benign maintenance management. However, a natural catastrophe, or damaging human activity (such as pollution), may force the population beyond the limit of acceptable change to a state where its condition is unfavourable (such as widespread recruitment failure). Such failures might continue at a constant rate, or the population may decline to partial or even total destruction. However, recruitment may also recover, either spontaneously or as a result of restoration efforts (such as improved effluent treatment). The change threshold can be used to inform SSSI management planning (historically not a particular strength of British conservation policy, although being addressed rapidly now) as well as for monitoring purposes in assessing site condition and reporting on the effect of damaging, possibly illegal, activities.

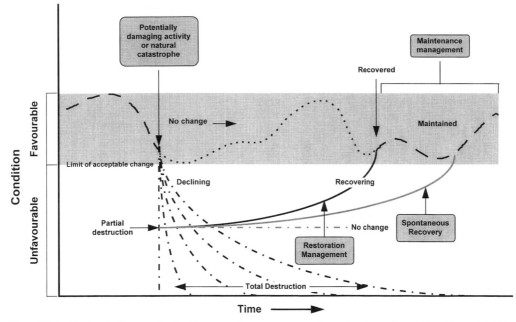

Figure 37.1   Rationale for monitoring features of nature conservation value (reproduced from Rowell, 1993, with permission). See text for fuller explanation.

For each SSSI, activities with the potential to damage the site's interest are notified to site owners, occupiers and relevant statutory authorities. Some activities of particular relevance to fresh waters are summarized in Table 37.1. The notification triggers a requirement to inform the conservation agency of plans to carry out such activities, and thereby apply for consent to proceed. If consent is not forthcoming, and the application is not withdrawn, the agency has the option of offering a management agreement (see below). Such agreements are designed to provide financial compensation on a 'profits foregone' basis—an independent assessor estimates the profits or savings that would have accrued to the owner or occupier had the operation (usually a development proposal, or change in

Table 37.1   Examples of operations potentially damaging to the special interest of fresh waters protected by SSSI notification.

- Dumping or spreading or discharge of any materials
- Changes in freshwater fishery production and/or management
- Changes in game and waterfowl management and hunting practice
- Killing or removal of any wild animal, including pest control
- Changing of water levels and tables and water utilization (including irrigation, storage and abstraction)
- Modification of watercourse structure, including banks and beds
- Management of aquatic and bank vegetation for drainage purposes
- Release into the site of any wild, feral or domestic animal, plant or seed
- Use of vehicles or craft likely to damage or disturb features of interest

management) gone ahead. The conservation agency in question is then required to pay from its own budget (from public funds) an equivalent sum as compensation for not allowing the operation to proceed (cf. similar procedures emerging in the USA—Gore, this volume). These procedures have attracted much criticism from a variety of quarters (Adams, 1993), and have prompted the conservation agencies to seek more positive and less costly ways of avoiding SSSI damage.

Of Scottish Natural Heritage's 1994–1995 budget of £41 million, approximately £3.3 million was spent on SSSI management agreements. However, agreements on SSSI fresh waters constitute a tiny proportion of this total figure, possibly because the role of other agencies in water management can remove the opportunity to seek compensation, because the profits foregone equation is more difficult to calculate in fresh waters than it is for terrestrial habitats and, simplest of all, because fresh waters—especially rivers—are under-represented in the SSSIs that have been notified, for reasons explained by Boon (1991, 1994) and Howell and Brown (1992).

It is also of interest to note here that so-called 'positive management agreements' are an increasingly important element. In Scotland, these have initially been targeted on northern peatland SSSIs, and a number of benefits are emerging from their adoption. As they focus on management beneficial to conservation interest, they accomplish more by way of environmental benefit than agreements which compensate landowners for merely not doing something damaging. They are also quicker to negotiate, they tend to be cheaper in the long term, and they have the benefit of creating a sense of partnership between landowner and public agency— an element often absent in the compensatory management procedures. A similar trend is apparent in England, where the 'Wildlife Enhancement Scheme' is used to promote positive management on SSSIs, and the 'Countryside Stewardship' scheme operated by the Countryside Commission has also proved to be successful, although its scope is not confined to SSSIs.

The power to approve or prevent operations such as those listed above in Table 37.1 does not rest solely with the conservation agency. In England and Wales, the EA has a number of equivalent consent or approval powers under legislation specific to water, and in Scotland, a variety of other authorities, including the Secretary of State, may be involved (see Howell, 1994 and other papers in Maitland *et al.*, 1994). In these circumstances, it may be more appropriate for these other authorities to carry out monitoring and enforcement, and agreements between the EA and English Nature over relative roles and responsibilities in this field are a feature of the river SSSI notification programme in England.

There are significant logistical problems involved in monitoring site condition— even if the appropriate monitoring techniques and protocols are available. SSSIs are widely dispersed, and an individual site could have several separate features of interest; in addition to fresh waters these might include a variety of wetland and terrestrial habitats (e.g. coastal, grassland, woodland, bog, moorland, fen, mountain plateau), as well as geological and geomorphological features. The bulk of the agencies' effort to date has therefore rested on the identification and notification of the sites concerned, then handling the subsequent casework arising from the notifications. As indicated above, this casework has often involved negotiating management agreements—and the agencies have struggled even to monitor compliance with the conditions of these, despite the fact that significant sums of public money are involved. Only very recently, some 15 years after the Wildlife and Countryside Act was passed, has the pressure eased sufficiently for the agencies to take stock and propose a monitoring programme for adoption throughout Britain.

Even if, despite all of the foregoing constraints, a monitoring system manages to detect illegally-caused damage to site condition, a final barrier confronts conservation agencies seeking prosecution for damage to statutory sites—that of a judiciary unfamiliar with environmental law. In this respect the situation resembles that encountered by the pollution control authorities in Scotland, although progress has been made with prosecutions under the species protection provisions of the 1981 Act (Section 37.4.3).

The challenge of expanding the river SSSI network is being spearheaded in England, where English Nature (1994) has published proposals to notify a representative series of 25 rivers. Scotland and Wales can be expected to follow suit, since the Government has decided that the 'Special Areas of Conservation' required under the EC Habitats Directive must first be notified as SSSIs, and several freshwater features requiring protection under the Directive have had sites proposed from throughout Britain (e.g. Table 37.2).

Table 37.2   Features for which Scottish fresh waters have been considered for designation under the EC Habitats Directive.

Habitats	*Species*
● Dystrophic lakes	● European otter *Lutra lutra*
● Lowland sandy oligotrophic lakes	● Atlantic salmon *Salmo salar*
● Upland oligotrophic lakes	● Sea lamprey *Petromyzon marinus*
● Hard oligo-mesotrophic lakes	● River lamprey *Lampetra fluviatilis*
● Naturally eutrophic lakes	● Brook lamprey *Lampetra planeri*
● Rivers with floating *Ranunculus* vegetation	● Freshwater pearl mussel *Margaritifera margaritifera*
	● Slender naiad *Najas flexilis*

Consideration of freshwater quality is central to the management of these sites, since the Directive requires them to contribute to the 'favourable conservation status' of the habitat or species across the EC. To do that will require a much clearer picture of the interplay of physical, chemical, biological and human factors which influences the 'quality' of a particular fresh water for a particular feature. For example, a better knowledge of the ecological requirements of protected species and habitats may be needed before stricter conditions can be set in discharge consents or abstraction licences.

Despite this very complex picture, prosecution is still seen as an option (albeit one of last resort) for punishing deliberate or malicious damage (as opposed to that due to accident or misunderstanding) and here at least the views of the conservation agencies are similar to those of the pollution control authorities. Evidence submitted to Parliament (House of Commons Public Accounts Committee, 1995) also suggests that warning letters are often used as an interim measure where there is evidence of damage to site condition. The rivers joining the SSSI complement in the 1990s will have their freshwater quality protected by complicated and often imprecise legislation and procedures. The lack of clear standards against which to assess site condition (Figure 37.1) means that strong enforcement activity such as prosecution is at present unlikely on the part of the conservation agencies, even if the wish was there in an area of environmental policy more traditionally dominated by inducement and agreement. Approaches such as River Habitat Survey (Raven *et al.*, this volume) and SERCON (Boon *et al.*, this volume) offer some scope for arriving at a far more quantitative assessment of freshwater quality for nature conservation than has been possible in the past— and for making such assessments more widely available than the traditional 'high priesthood' approach has permitted. The potential of these techniques, if widely adopted, to examine the relative successes of protected areas legislation and countrywide 'balancing duties', will be of particular interest here.

37.4.2 *Beyond designations— 'the wider environment' and 'balancing duties'*

As the previous sections suggest, perhaps the most complex body of British conservation law relates to formally designated protected areas. However, this legislation also provides opportunities for the conservation agencies to act on a much broader basis outside the designated areas in what is sometimes known as 'the wider countryside'. The first example of this is still dominated by SSSIs, and that is the extent to which activities outside them may damage their special interest. As their enforcement powers do not extend beyond the SSSI boundary, the conservation agencies rely on advice to, and persuasion of, others in such cases, whether the other parties have proposed activities which may be damaging, or have been approached for approval for such activities. They are thus likely to rely heavily on agreement in such cases. Agreements of a quite formal nature may be used, such as that forged between SNH, SEPA, Perth and Kinross District Council and the Scottish Agricultural College to promote improved catchment land-use practices in the hope of reducing the diffuse-source pollution load reaching Loch Leven.

Inducement is also a commonly used mechanism outside specially designated areas. The conservation and countryside agencies, and increasingly the Agriculture Departments, have large grant-aid budgets which are specifically geared to securing environmental improvements, especially in rural areas. Waterside habitats feature strongly in some of these incentive schemes, especially in the 'Countryside Stewardship' scheme initiated by the Countryside Commission in England, where funding commitments totalling millions of pounds over a 10-year period have been entered into in return for sympathetic management and restoration work in waterside landscapes.

Wide-ranging responsibilities—often called 'balancing duties'—apply to a range of public bodies with the potential to influence water quality. Thus, the Environment Act 1995 provides EA and SEPA with duties to promote the conservation of flora and fauna dependent on the aquatic environment, so far as is consistent with their other functions. In addition, the EA in England and Wales is required to further conservation in discharging its duties, e.g. in relation to river engineering, fishery management and abstraction control. Experience of such duties in England and Wales (Heaton, 1993; Howell, 1994; RSPB *et al.*, 1995, Raven *et al.*, this volume) has been very positive, and illustrates how a very simple legislative measure, properly applied, can accomplish a huge amount of environmental improvement. In contrast, the complexity and high resource implications of SSSI notification may have resulted in fresh waters (especially rivers) of SSSI *quality* declining through not receiving SSSI *protection*, thus hindering the contribution made by conservation legislation to freshwater quality in Britain. Aquatic habitats also pose particular problems in that damage to site condition may often arise 'off-site'. Recent assessments have indicated that eutrophication and acidification are areas of particular concern in this respect (Rimes *et al.*, 1994; Carvalho and Moss, 1995).

37.4.3   Species legislation

There are perhaps three principal aspects to the freshwater species legislation operated in Britain by the conservation agencies (see Boon *et al.*, 1992; Boon, 1994 for more details). These are: preventing the release of non-native species; providing special protection to rare and endangered species or populations; and the closely-related field of reintroducing species previously resident but now no longer present.

The control of unwanted non-native species is accomplished in legal terms by proposing their inclusion on lists of species which, subject to certain exceptions, cannot be released legally to the wild. Unfortunately, such species only tend to achieve this status once they have already become well-established in the wild, where they are often very difficult to eradicate. Relevant freshwater examples here include the aggressive alien riparian plant species, *Heracleum mantegazzanium* (giant hogweed—see Plate 3a) and *Fallopia japonica* (Japanese knotweed) which do much to detract from the quality of riparian areas in lowland Britain (de Waal *et al.*, 1995). A slightly better mechanism exists for fish, molluscs and crustaceans, through fishery legislation controlling the import and release to the wild of these taxa. This route is being used, again belatedly, in an attempt to prevent the proliferation of 'crayfish plague' in British rivers caused by the fungus *Aphanomyces astaci*. This is carried with immunity by the North American signal crayfish *Pacifastacus leniusculus* (see Plate 3c), but escapes of this commercially-reared species to the wild have passed the infection on to populations of the native Atlantic stream crayfish *Austropotamobius pallipes*, in which it has proved fatal (Holdich and Reeve, 1991).

Adding species to the 'protected' category does have the benefit of spurring the conservation agencies on to more research and, increasingly under the Government's

Biodiversity Action Plan (Department of the Environment *et. al.*, 1994), initiatives aimed at halting species decline, such as the proposal to reintroduce the vendace *Coregonus albula* to Scotland. These agencies have no powers to insist upon the reintroduction of species currently locally extinct, so they have to act by education and persuasion (agreement). This requirement is well illustrated by the need to reassure fishery proprietors in Scotland that dam-building activities of any reintroduced European beavers *Castor fiber* should not hamper upstream spawning migrations of salmonids (Macdonald *et al.*, 1995). The addition of the freshwater pearl mussel *Margaritifera margaritifera* to the list of British protected species (Young, 1991) has prompted investigations into a number of suspected illegal fishing offences, one of which reached court in Scotland, although no prosecution was secured.

Regrettably, all of these species protection provisions tend to have one thing in common—the difficulty in enforcing the legislation. This is due principally to the lack of monitoring effort highlighted above, but also to a lack of knowledge of species with often complex life cycles. In a few species groups there has been some high-profile enforcement activity, especially in relation to the robbing of birds' nests by egg collectors, and the illegal poisoning of birds of prey. In these cases, the police force—often aided by the general public through voluntary groups such as the RSPB—have played a strong role in securing the evidence required for the prosecution to proceed. A relevant freshwater example here is the osprey *Pandion haliaetus*, which was extinct in Britain but has recolonized Scotland very successfully, despite the occasional unwelcome attentions of egg collectors.

The advent of the EC Habitats Directive will provide a considerable boost to freshwater species conservation in Britain, not least because of the requirement to use a new designation (Section 37.4.1.2) to protect the habitats of species listed under the Directive (Table 37.2). This highlights one of the much wider benefits attributable to species legislation—in seeking to improve the lot of rare or endangered species, or reintroduce those which have become extinct, the need to provide good-quality habitat means that the benefits go far wider than just the individual species concerned. The potential wider benefits for freshwater quality of beaver reintroduction to Scotland (MacDonald *et al.*, 1995) illustrate this point particularly well.

37.5   Discussion and Conclusions

37.5.1   *Differing users of enforcement, inducement and agreement*

As the size or complexity of ownership of a water body or catchment increases, the strength of influence anyone can exercise over the various elements of freshwater quality (human, physical, chemical and biological) decreases (Figure 37.2). Influences range from the strongest—outright ownership—through others of decreasing force (including enforcement, inducement and agreement) which water owners will be familiar with and will experience to varying degrees. The effort for

Figure 37.2   Options in the management of freshwater quality through legislation (for fuller explanation see text).

protection of freshwater quality in Britain spans this range, but with different authorities having different emphases. The debates towards the next millennium will focus on where on this continuum is most appropriate for the nation's fresh waters as a whole, as well as in individual cases.

Management of freshwater quality in Britain is characterized by two distinct types of statutory agency, with differing styles of legislative approach. On the one hand, the pollution regulators (EA and SEPA) have inherited from their predecessors a great deal of experience in using enforcement (or the threat of it), to maintain and improve water quality. Here, despite scientific complexity and political controversy, quality can be determined objectively, and, with the support of a comprehensive monitoring network, is relatively easy to enforce by comparing field observations with preset numerical standards. Education, negotiation and persuasion (agreement) also feature strongly in their activities, and they have only recently begun to use specially designated areas to accomplish their statutory duties. Inducement is notably rare in these agencies' water quality management roles—they have no funds to disburse by way of encouragement to improve bad practice, they only occasionally resort to compensation provisions (e.g. in seeking to reduce rates of abstraction below existing approved limits), and their charging schemes are set on a cost recovery basis.

By way of contrast, the British countryside agencies (Scottish Natural Heritage, the Countryside Council for Wales, the Countryside Commission and English Nature), spend a great deal of time and money on specially designated areas, and this may increase as more rivers in particular become designated. Furthermore, these agencies carry out far less monitoring than the pollution regulators, and their enforcement activities very rarely lead towards prosecution. This may partly be because of difficulties in actually setting enforceable standards. Assessing the quality of fresh waters as landscape features, or as resources for nature conservation and recreation, relies on a far greater degree of subjective judgment, or even personal taste, than setting emission limits in a discharge consent. Whilst some elements of objectivity are being introduced in these areas (Boon *et al.*, this volume; Swanwick, this volume), a considerable increase in monitoring effort will be required if prosecutions are to feature more strongly in conservation policy in the future. The attractions of inducement as a means of improving water quality may in part be a reflection of these difficulties: much more money has been spent by the countryside agencies on agreements preventing activities which damage the environment, or encouraging positive improvements, than in monitoring and enforcement.

As has been noted elsewhere (Howell, 1994), Scotland lacks a single authority to take the lead in all of these areas of water policy, so decisions about enforcement, inducement and agreement rely heavily on several different agencies coming together in a partnership approach. This makes it more difficult to take forward sustainable approaches to water quality management—such as Integrated Catchment Management—in the way that the EA has done in England and Wales, but Werritty (this volume) suggests a way that this could still be accomplished in Scotland. New developments at a European level (e.g. the Habitats Directive; proposals for a Water Framework Directive) will require a far more widespread spirit of collaboration than has perhaps been the case in the past.

37.5.2   *The right blend—and the role of the public*

To succeed, these new developments will have to rely not on one or other of the three legislative mechanisms considered in this chapter, but on a combination of them all. The right blend of enforcement, inducement and agreement will vary depending on the location and the issues involved. Perhaps too often in the past the blend has been a last resort, or even a guess—what Luitens (1995) called 'management by accident'. Whatever blend of options emerges for a particular water body or catchment, it is important to ensure that it is a conscious, collective and well-informed choice, and that these options can be used to maximize all elements of water quality, with decisions being taken in the knowledge that there may be implications at a range of scales. The scale of the catchment, whether in its entirety or at the sub-catchment level, increasingly needs to feature in decisions on land use and water resource management (Werritty, this volume). The logic of this approach may appear self-evident to specialists in the fields of freshwater hydrology, geomorphology, chemistry and ecology. However, incorporating this logic into legislation, decision-making processes and water management priorities can be a considerable challenge.

With the millennium drawing to a close, there are numerous techniques for examining, describing and evaluating water quality—in its natural setting and in terms of the effects of human activities. However, the development of these techniques continues to outpace the ability of legislation to put them to best effect, and many water quality professionals—the authors included!—have expressed frustration at the lack of progress in this respect. If such calls for legislative change are to succeed, the balance of effort needs to shift towards tackling people's motivating forces. For example, the attitudes of water practitioners is but one of many factors which influence water quality legislation in its genesis, evolution and application (Figure 37.3). Stevenson (1995) has suggested that an understanding of key socio-political structures is a *more* challenging issue for conservationists than seeking to improve the science base, and analyses of British post-war country-side policy (e.g. Mackay, 1995; Sheail, 1996) show that an understanding of the prevailing pressures on civil servants is an essential prerequisite in endeavouring to ensure that specialist views on legislation reach the ears and desks of Ministers.

A less elitist, less technocratic approach, which seeks to share information with the public on whose behalf it is collected, and involve local people far more in decision-making processes, may also pay dividends, especially as it may avoid expensive, adversarial, enforcement activity. In the USA, recent experience in the catchment of the Tennessee River has highlighted the benefits of such public involvement (Ungate, 1996). Here, multidisciplinary 'Water Action Teams' within sub-catchments of the Tennessee are promoting a widespread programme of activities, including water quality assessments and aerial photography to isolate particular causes of pollution; public meetings, radio interviews, and use of volunteer labour to ensure that local communities are aware of the issues; and widespread riparian habitat restoration—again with the use of volunteers—as a means of improving the rivers' 'self-defence mechanisms'. Similar experience

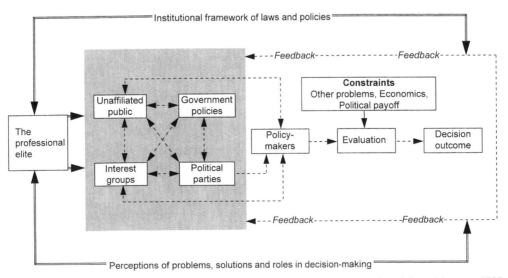

Figure 37.3 Factors affecting environmental decision-making processes (reproduced from Newson, 1995, with permission).

in Belgium (Mormont, 1996) highlights the benefits of actively seeking public involvement in, and support for, water quality improvement programmes, with the 'river contracts' procedures there operating with very little need for statutory reinforcement. In Britain, too, the images emerging from public perception and landscape studies (Tunstall *et al.*, this volume; Swanwick, this volume) suggest that in many respects the professional expert and the layperson are not far apart in their aspirations for freshwater quality.

The need to marshal economic arguments for environmental protection is increasingly compelling. Stevenson (1995) contrasts this need (which he sees as one primarily for the developing world) with the possibility of arguments in favour of nature conservation relying on appeals to aesthetics and science in the developed world. Concerns about recreation, nature conservation and landscape are characteristic of wealthy developed nations. In developing nations, it is more often the case that public health—adequate food, water, warmth and shelter—takes precedence. Human interactions with water continue to diversify and become more complex, with innovations in leisure pursuits, changes in patterns of leisure use, in irrigation and hydro-power technology, and a relentless demand for water, living space, energy, food and a dispersal route for pollution. Developing nations require political, institutional and fiscal structures which prevent freshwater quality deteriorating to the extent that it has done in many parts of the developed world.

This chapter has not attempted even the most superficial analysis of these latter human factors, but more analysis is undoubtedly needed. It will require a willingness to embrace those 'less scientific' disciplines which study human nature, as well as the understandable reliance on the familiar 'rigours' of studying the impacts on nature of human activity. Scientists seeking legislation to promote water quality—by whatever combination of enforcement, inducement and agreement— need to understand better the motivations of those who make legislation, those who apply it, and those to whom it applies. Greater public involvement in debates and action on freshwater quality should be a central part of this process. There is plenty to reflect on as the next millennium beckons!

Acknowledgements

We are especially grateful to Phil Boon for his patience in waiting for the final manuscript, and for his useful comments on an earlier version of the chapter. The assistance of Nikki Wood (who re-drew Figure 37.3) is also gratefully acknowledged. Our views have been informed by very useful discussions with our many colleagues in SNH and SEPA, but the opinions we express in this chapter are our own.

References

Adams, W. M. (1993). Places for nature: protected areas in British nature conservation. In: Goldsmith, F. B. and Warren, A. (Eds), *Conservation in Progress*. John Wiley, Chichester, 185–208.

Bailey-Watts, A. E. (1994). Eutrophication. In: Maitland, P. S., Boon, P. J. and McLusky, D. (Eds), *The Fresh Waters of Scotland: a National Resource of International Significance*. John Wiley, Chichester, 385–411.

Bishop, K. D., Phillips, A. A. C. and Warren, L. M. (1995). Protected for ever? Factors shaping the future of protected areas policy. *Land Use Policy,* **12,** 291–305.

Boon, P. J. (1991). The role of Sites of Special Scientific Interest (SSSIs) in the conservation of British rivers. *Freshwater Forum,* **1,** 95–108.

Boon, P. J. (1994). Nature conservation. In: Maitland, P. S., Boon P. J. and McLusky, D. S. (Eds), *The Fresh Waters of Scotland: a National Resource of International Significance.* John Wiley, Chichester, 555–576.

Boon, P. J. (1995). The relevance of ecology to the statutory protection of British rivers. In: Harper, D. M. and Ferguson, A. J. D. (Eds), *The Ecological Basis for River Management.* John Wiley, Chichester, 239–250.

Boon, P. J., Morgan, D. H. W. and Palmer, M. A. (1992). Statutory protection of freshwater flora and fauna in Britain. *Freshwater Forum,* **2,** 91–101.

Boon P. J., Holmes, N. T. H., Maitland, P. S., Rowell, T. A. and Davies, J. (This volume). A system for evaluating rivers for conservation (SERCON): development, structure and function.

Box, J. D. and Walker, G. J. (1994). Conservation of the Blythe, a high quality river in a major urban area in England. *Aquatic Conservation: Marine and Freshwater Ecosystems,* **4,** 75–85.

Burt, T. P. and Haycock, N. E. (1992). Catchment planning and the nitrate issue: a UK perspective. *Progress in Physical Geography,* **16,** 379–404.

Carvalho, L. and Moss, B. (1995). The current status of a sample of English Sites of Special Scientific Interest subject to eutrophication. *Aquatic Conservation: Marine and Freshwater Ecosystems,* **5,** 191–204.

Commission of the European Communities (1996). *European Community Water Policy.* Com(96)59 final. Brussels.

Department of the Environment (1992). *Using Water Wisely: a Consultation Paper.* London.

Department of the Environment (1995a). *Freshwater Quality: Government Response to the 16th Report of the Royal Commission on Environmental Pollution.* HMSO, London.

Department of the Environment (1995b). *Water Conservation: Government Action.* HMSO, London.

Department of the Environment *et al.* (1994). *Biodiversity: the UK Action Plan.* Command 2428. HMSO, London.

Doppelt, B., Scurlock, M., Frissell, C. and Karr, J. (1993). *Entering the Watershed: a New Approach to Save America's River Ecosystems.* Island Press, Washington.

English Nature (1994). *Conserving Rivers and their Wildlife.* Peterborough.

Ferrier, R. C., Owen, R., Edwards, A. C., Malcolm, A. and Morrice, J. G. (This volume). Hindcasting of phosphorus concentrations in Scottish standing waters.

Forestry Commission (1993). *Forests and Water Guidelines.* HMSO, Edinburgh.

Fozzard, I. R., Doughty, C. R. and Leatherland, T. M. (This volume). Defining the quality of Scottish freshwater lochs.

Friends of the Earth Scotland (1994). *Watered Down: Why the Law is Failing to Protect Scotland's Waters.* Edinburgh.

Gee, A. S. and Jones, F. H. (1995). The use of biological techniques in catchment planning. In: Harper, D. M. and Ferguson, A. J. D. (Eds), *The Ecological Basis for River Management.* John Wiley, Chichester, 475–489.

Gilvear, D. J. (1994). River flow regulation. In: Maitland, P. S., Boon, P. J. and McLusky, D. S. (Eds), *The Fresh Waters of Scotland: a National Resource of International Significance.* John Wiley, Chichester, 463–487.

Gore, J. A. (This volume). Water quality in the USA: evolving perspectives and public perception.

Guy, S. and Marvin, S. (1996). Managing water stress: the logic of demand side infrastructure planning. *Journal of Environmental Planning and Management,* **39,** 123–129.

Hammerton, D. (1994). Domestic and industrial pollution. In: Maitland, P. S., Boon, P. J. and McLusky, D. S. (Eds), *The Fresh Waters of Scotland: a National Resource of International Significance.* John Wiley, Chichester, 347–364.

Hanley, N. (This volume). Assessing the economic value of fresh waters.

Heaton, A. (1993). Conservation and the National Rivers Authority. In: Goldsmith, F. B. and Warren, A. (Eds), *Conservation in Progress.* John Wiley, Chichester, 301–320.

Hellawell, J. M. (This volume). The contribution of biological and chemical techniques to the assessment of water quality.

Highland River Purification Board (1995). *Annual Report for 1994.* Dingwall.

Hildrew, A. G. and Ormerod, S. J. (1995). Acidification: causes, consequences and solutions. In: Harper, D. M. and Ferguson, A. J. D. (Eds), *The Ecological Basis for River Management*. John Wiley, Chichester, 147–160.

Holdich, D. M. and Reeve, I. D. (1991). Distribution of freshwater crayfish in the British Isles, with particular reference to crayfish plague, alien introductions and water quality. *Aquatic Conservation: Marine and Freshwater Ecosystems,* **1,** 139–158.

House of Commons Committee of Public Accounts (1995). *Protecting and Managing Sites of Special Scientific Interest in England.* HMSO, London.

Howell, D. L. and Brown, A. E. (1992). River conservation in Scotland: legislative and organizational constraints. In: Boon, P. J, Calow, P. and Petts, G. E. (Eds), *River Conservation and Management*. John Wiley, Chichester, 407–424.

Howell, D. L. (1994). Role of environmental agencies. In: Maitland, P. S., Boon, P. J. and McLusky, D. (Eds), *The Fresh Waters of Scotland: a National Resource of International Significance*. John Wiley, Chichester, 577–611.

Iversen, T. M., Kronvang, B., Madsen, B. L., Markmann, P. and Nielsen, M. B. (1993). Re-establishment of Danish streams: restoration and maintenance measures. *Aquatic Conservation: Marine and Freshwater Ecosystems,* **3,** 73–92.

Johnstone D. W. M. and Horan, N. J. (1994). Standards, costs and benefits: an international perspective. *Journal of the Institution of Water and Environmental Management,* **8,** 450–458.

Kristensen, P. and Hansen, H. O. (Eds) (1994). *European Rivers and Lakes—Assessment of their Environmental State*. European Environment Agency Monographs No. 1. EEA, Copenhagen.

Luitens, J. P. A. (1995). The ecological basis for catchment management. A new Dutch project: the Water System Explorations. In: Harper, D. M. and Ferguson, A. J. D. (Eds), *The Ecological Basis for River Management*. John Wiley, Chichester, 453–473.

MacDonald, D., Tattersall, F. H., Brown, E. D. and Balharry D. (1995). Reintroducing the European Beaver to Britain: nostalgic meddling or restoring biodiversity? *Mammal Review,* **25,** 161–200.

MacEwen, A. and MacEwen, M. (1984). National Parks: a cosmetic conservation system. In: Warren, A. and Goldsmith, F. B. (Eds), *Conservation in Perspective*. John Wiley, Chichester, 391–409.

Mackay, D. (1995). *Scotland's Rural Land Use Agencies. The History and Effectiveness in Scotland of the Countryside Commission, Nature Conservancy Council, and Forestry Commission*. Scottish Cultural Press, Aberdeen.

Mackay, D. W. (1994). Pollution control. In: Maitland, P. S., Boon, P. J. and McLusky, D. S. (Eds), *The Fresh Waters of Scotland: a National Resource of International Significance*. John Wiley, Chichester, 517–529.

Maitland, P. S., Boon, P. J. and McLusky, D. (Eds) (1994). *The Fresh Waters of Scotland: a National Resource of International Significance*. John Wiley, Chichester.

Mormont, M. (1996). Towards concerted river management in Belgium. *Journal of Environmental Planning and Management,* **39,** 131–141.

Moss, B., Johnes, P. and Phillips, G. (This volume). New approaches to monitoring and classifying standing waters.

Newborne, P. (1993). Protection of the French water environment and riverine wetlands after the 1992 Water Law. *Water Law,* **4,** 98–102.

Newson, M. D. (1995). Planning, control or management? In: Newson, M. D. (Ed.), *Managing the Human Impact on the Natural Environment: Patterns and Processes*. John Wiley, Chichester, 258–279.

Nixon, S. and Juggins, P. (1995). *Ecological Quality of Water*. European Technical Workshop, Brussels, 10 and 11 May 1995. Report of Discussions, Findings and Recommendations. National Rivers Authority, Bristol.

NRA (1990). *Discharge Consents and Compliance Policy—a Blueprint for the Future*. London.

NRA (1991a). *The Quality of Rivers, Canals and Estuaries in England and Wales. Report of the 1990 Survey*. Bristol.

NRA (1991b). *Proposals for Statutory Water Quality Objectives*. Bristol.

NRA (1995). *The State of the Water Environment. Six Year Trends Report*. Bristol.

O'Riordan, T. (1995). Ecological basis for the management of recreation and amenity: the Norfolk Broads. In: Harper, D. M. and Ferguson, A. J. D. (Eds), *The Ecological Basis for River Management*. John Wiley, Chichester, 405–414.

Padmore, C. L. (This volume). Biotopes and their hydraulics: a method for defining the physical component of freshwater quality.

Petts, G., Maddock, I., Bickerton, M. and Ferguson, A. J. D. (1995). Linking hydrology and ecology. In: Harper, D. M. and Ferguson, A. J. D. (Eds), *The Ecological Basis for River Management*. John Wiley, Chichester, 1–16.

Pugh, K. (This volume). Organizational use of the term 'freshwater quality'.

Raven, P. J., Fox, P., Everard, M., Holmes, N. T. H. and Dawson, F. H. (This volume). River Habitat Survey: a new system for classifying rivers according to their habitat quality.

RCEP (1992). *Freshwater Quality*. HMSO, London.

Rimes, C. A., Farmer A. M. and Howell D. (1994). A survey of the threat of acidification to the nature conservation interest of fresh waters on Sites of Special Scientific Interest in Britain. *Aquatic Conservation: Marine and Freshwater Ecosystems*, **4**, 31–44.

Rowell, T. A. (1993). *Common Standards for Monitoring SSSIs*. Joint Nature Conservation Committee, Peterborough.

RSPB (1995). *Water Wise—the RSPB's Proposals for Using Water Wisely*. Royal Society for the Protection of Birds, Sandy.

RSPB/NRA/RSNC (1994). *The New Rivers and Wildlife Handbook*. Royal Society for the Protection of Birds, Sandy.

Scottish Office (1992). *Prevention of Environmental Pollution from Agricultural Activity. Code of Practice*. HMSO, Edinburgh.

Sheail, J. (1996). From aspiration to implementation—the establishment of the first National Nature Reserves in Britain. *Landscape Research*, **21**, 37–54.

Smith, H. (1993). Water pollution prosecutions—an effective policy for improvement? *Water Law*, **4**, 21–25.

Stedman, N. (1993). Conservation in National Parks. In: Goldsmith F. B. and Warren A. (Eds), *Conservation in Progress*. John Wiley, Chichester, 209–239.

Stevenson, A. (1995). The geography of conservation. In: Newson, M. D. (Ed.), *Managing the Human Impact on the Natural Environment: Patterns and Processes*. John Wiley, Chichester, 37–55.

Swanwick, C. (This volume). Landscape assessment of fresh waters.

Trihadiningrum, Y., Verheyen, R. F. and De Pauw, N. (This volume). The water pollution abatement programme in Indonesia.

Tunstall, S., Fordham, M., Green, C. and House, M. (This volume). Public perception of freshwater quality with particular reference to rivers in England and Wales.

Ungate, C. D. (1996). Tennessee Valley Authority's Clean Water Initiative: building partnerships for watershed improvement. *Journal of Environmental Planning and Management*, **39**, 113–122.

de Waal, L. C., Child, L. E. and Wade M. (1995). The management of three alien invasive riparian plants: *Impatiens globulifera* (Himalayan balsam), *Heracleum mantegazzianum* (giant hogweed) and *Fallopia japonica* (Japanese knotweed). In: Harper, D. M. and Ferguson, A. J. D. (Eds), *The Ecological Basis for River Management*. John Wiley, Chichester, 316–321.

Watson, N., Mitchell, B. and Mulamoottil, G. (1996). Integrated resource management: institutional arrangements regarding nitrate pollution in England. *Journal of Environmental Planning and Management*, **39**, 45–64.

Werritty, A. (This volume). Enhancing the quality of freshwater resources: the role of Integrated Catchment Management.

Wilson, H. M., O'Sullivan, P. E. and Gibson, M. T. (1993). Analysis of current policies and alternative strategies for the reduction of nutrient loads on eutrophicated lakes: the example of Slapton Ley, Devon. *Aquatic Conservation: Marine and Freshwater Ecosystems*, **3**, 253–268.

Young, M. R. (1991). Conserving the freshwater pearl mussel (*Margaritifera margaritifera* L.) in the British Isles and Continental Europe. *Aquatic Conservation: Marine and Freshwater Ecosystems*, **1**, 73–77.

38 THE WATER POLLUTION ABATEMENT PROGRAMME IN INDONESIA

Y. Trihadiningrum, R. F. Verheyen and N. De Pauw

Summary

1. The water pollution abatement programme in Indonesia has achieved some successes, although these are mainly of an institutional nature.

2. The techniques used in the current assessment approach are not sufficient for evaluating the sustainability of river uses.

3. Strong climatological and geological influences on river water quality in a number of regions require the establishment of water quality standards which take account of such natural variation.

4. An approach to the assessment of the ecological quality of rivers is described as an input for the development of the current nationwide Clean River Programme.

38.1 Introduction

Indonesia, inhabited by more than 200 million people, has experienced rapid industrial growth since the 1980s. The same period has seen the emergence of initiatives for managing water pollution at the national scale (Bapedal, 1994). The first phase was carried out during the period of the third and fourth five-year development programmes, 'Pelita III' (1979–1984), and 'Pelita IV' (1984–1989). During this period, water pollution problems increased in severity, although people's awareness of these problems, and the policy means and institutional tools to tackle them, were still very limited. Pollution control activities concentrated on improving public awareness, developing basic systems of water quality management, and problem-solving on urgent cases. In addition, some basic legislation was introduced and institutions with environmental responsibilities were established.

The second phase was the period of 'Pelita V' (1989–1994), which was characterized by the initiation of a Clean River Programme ('Prokasih') in 1989, the establishment and development of the Environmental Impact Management Agency ('Bapedal') in 1990, and the emergence of regulations of a more practical, operational nature. Prokasih is a nationwide water pollution control programme, with aims which include preventing the deterioration of water quality and increasing the functional uses of water sources, preparing the implementation of state regulations on water pollution control, and establishing regional institutions for water pollution control (Office of the State Minister for Population and Environment, 1990).

The following sections provide a critical evaluation of Prokasih in relation to water quality assessment and sustainable development concepts. The results of research work using an ecological assessment approach carried out in the Blawi river system in East Java province are also described.

38.2 Prokasih after Six Years of Activity

Up to the present time, the implementation of Prokasih has given priority to rivers used for drinking water production (Class B—see below) and subject to industrial pollution. According to Bapedal (1994), Prokasih has successfully reduced the industrial pollution load entering rivers and increased the institutional resources (regulations, human resources, budgets, etc.) devoted to tackling pollution problems. However, the need for clean water for various purposes will keep increasing because of the intensifying demands of population growth and associated economic activities. Further efforts are therefore required to improve river water quality.

Currently 27 rivers situated in 11 provinces (of a total of 27) are included in Prokasih. Some 1,386 factories are included in this programme, 549 of which are responding and undertaking efforts to reduce the organic load they discharge into rivers (Table 38.1) However, there is no obvious improvement in river water quality in the Prokasih rivers, in spite of the reduction in industrial organic waste inputs. In fact, monitoring data on most of the rivers show that water quality is declining (Bapedal, 1994), probably because of diffuse-source pollution, which has not been considered in Prokasih. The lack of sewage treatment facilities in most of the cities means that urban rivers receive a heavy burden of domestic wastes. Other diffuse pollution sources, such as agriculture, aquaculture, and general urban run-off, add to the water quality deterioration. For example, observations made in the Blawi river system (East Java) showed that eutrophication occurred as a result of domestic, agricultural, and aquacultural effluents, and the highest organic pollution level was observed in the most populous area (Trihadiningrum, 1995). This evidence emphasizes the importance of water quality deterioration caused by diffuse pollution sources.

Table 38.1 Reduction in BOD loading from Prokasih industries, 1989–1993 (Bapedal, 1994).

Year	BOD load $(t\,yr^{-1})$	% decrease
1989/1990	166,532	—
1990/1991	83,685	49.74
1991/1992	63,655	23.74
1992/1993	43,453	31.74

Prokasih applies water quality standards for functional uses, which are established in each province by the Governor. These comprise standards for drinking water (Class A), drinking water production (Class B), fisheries (Class C), agriculture (Class D), and drainage water (Class E), and each river is classified for a particular functional use by the local government. However, categorizing rivers according to functional uses has several limitations. First, people tend to use the river water in ways which differ from those for which it has been designated. For example, the Blawi River, which is designated for agriculture and drainage, is used by the riparian people for drinking water due to the lack of potable water distribution (Trihadiningrum, 1995). Second, water quality often does not meet the designated standards, because of pollution. Third, it does not provide a good measure of sustainable river use, because the assessment target is restricted to the condition for fulfilling a particular narrow human need.

The application of water quality standards for functional uses also has the limitation of not being able to include natural variation. For example, lowland rivers which are influenced by seawater intrusion cannot be classified into any designated class. Monthly monitoring data from the Lower Solo River (East Java province) carried out in 1991 showed that water quality varied between brackish and saline from July to October (dry season). This periodic high variation in salinity was beyond the range of the existing water quality standards. Furthermore, rivers of regions rich in humic acids—such as Kalimantan—should naturally have low pH and high iron and organic matter content. In contrast, rivers in regions rich in limestone (e.g. Java) should have neutral to slightly basic water due to high levels of calcium and bicarbonate ions.

The climatological and geological influences on water quality mentioned above require the establishment of particular water quality standards, to take account of this natural variety. This approach requires standards which may vary from one region to another. In Belgium, such standards are known as ecological water quality standards (Schneiders *et al.*, 1993), and these can explain how far the water quality differs from its natural state. Establishment of these standards, however, requires physical and chemical data from rivers with minimum human influence, which is not easy to determine in highly populated regions, such as Java.

Owing to the limited laboratory facilities in many provinces, the water quality variables which are monitored continuously are restricted to total suspended solids, COD and BOD. Provinces with better laboratory facilities are encouraged to monitor more water quality variables. However, even monitoring these extra variables may not be sufficient for indicating the 'real' water quality condition, particularly from the toxicological and ecological perspectives.

In principle, the ultimate goal of Prokasih should be based on the concept of sustainable development, which is stipulated in the Act of the Republic of Indonesia (UURI) No. 4/1982, concerning basic provisions for the management of the living environment, and UURI No. 5/1990, concerning living natural resources and ecosystem management. The objectives of the management of the living environment according to the first Act are: (a) to achieve harmonious relations between man and the living environment, (b) to control wisely the utilization of natural resources, and (c) to implement development for the interest of present and future generations. This concept is in accordance with the second Act, which states that the basic strategy for conserving living resources is to guarantee the continuation of ecological processes, to maintain genetic diversity, and to direct methods of utilizing living natural resources to ensure their sustainability.

The approach used for the achievement of the ultimate goal of natural resource conservation, which assures sustainability, is not mentioned explicitly in Prokasih. As a result, the water quality assessment method is not adequate for evaluating the sustainability of river uses. Therefore, it is necessary that the existing methodology applied in Prokasih be reviewed.

38.3 Ecological Assessment of Rivers: a Case Study from East Java

Ecological assessment of rivers, which includes the evaluation of environmental factors, has been developed by a number of researchers (e.g. Mitchell, 1990, cited in Barmuta and Marchant, 1992; Schneiders *et al.*, 1993; Boon *et al.*, this volume). These environmental factors should include as many variables as possible, and may include morphological features, flow rate, river bank and riparian vegetation, biocoenoses, etc.

A research study carried out between 1990 and 1995 in a lowland river system, located in Lamongan town, East Java, included ecological assessment of the river system. The main river Blawi has six tributaries, with the middle and upper parts surrounded by agricultural land, and the lower parts flowing through a productive aquaculture area. The environmental variables recorded in this study were physical aspects of river structure, and chemical water quality. Criteria for determining the river's structure and quality were based on the local situation, using the undisturbed river as a reference (Table 38.2), and the quality at each of 43 sampling stations was assigned an average score of the five variables observed. The chemical water quality variables were limited to the average of the Dutch Score (De Brabander, 1981), calculated from monthly data on BOD, dissolved oxygen, and ammonium. These variables were considered to be most relevant to the pollution sources, which mostly contributed organic matter. This research resulted in four groups of river segments each requiring different management responses (Figure 38.1).

Only the upper Gondang tributary, where population density is the lowest (less than 400 people km^{-2}), was close to its natural state and classified as being of very high ecological quality (G1). Elsewhere, the naturalness of the river segments decreased with increasing population density and land use. River reaches with high ecological quality (G2) were located in the upland agricultural area, which was characterized by little human influence on river structure and water quality. Those of moderate ecological quality (G3) were characterized by more intensive agriculture and denser human settlement than G2, with greater impacts on river structure and water quality. The lowest ecological quality (G4) was indicated by high turbidity due to intense erosion of the catchment area and river banks (G4a); straightened river banks and strong evidence of eutrophication in the very

Table 38.2 Criteria for determination of ecological values of 43 sites located in the Blawi River System (Trihadiningrum, 1995).

| *Variable* | *1 (very poor)* | *2 (poor)* | *Ecological value* | | |
			3 (moderate)	*4 (good)*	*5 (very good)*
Meandering feature.	No possibility for natural meanders to develop due to permanent structural changes.	Little possibility for natural meanders to develop due to: (a) a permanent structural change on one side of the river, or: (b) extensive channelization along the river.	Intensive non-permanent structural change is made locally.	Limited non-permanent structural change is made locally.	Natural meanders.
Bank vegetation.	No ground cover, permanent construction on both sides.	Permanent construction on one side.	Ground cover exists with some bare ground.	Moderate ground cover.	Undisturbed environment.
Riparian vegetation.	Absent; extensive construction.	Bare, pasture, cultivated land.	Narrow corridor of native or introduced vegetation.	Wide corridor of native or mixed native and introduced vegetation of >10 m width.	Undisturbed native vegetation extending >10 m.
Aquatic macrophytes (middle and lower rivers only).	0% cover, where no macrophytes available for shelter of aquatic fauna; or >80% cover, where macrophytes might cause high variation of dissolved oxygen concentration.	1–5% cover, where macrophytes are too limited for shelter of aquatic fauna; or 60–80% cover, where macrophytes might cause significant effect on dissolved oxygen concentration.	5–20% cover.	20–30% cover.	30–60% cover.
Erosion/sedimentation.	Extensive.	Significant.	Moderate.	Local erosion.	Stable, natural erosion/ sedimentation.

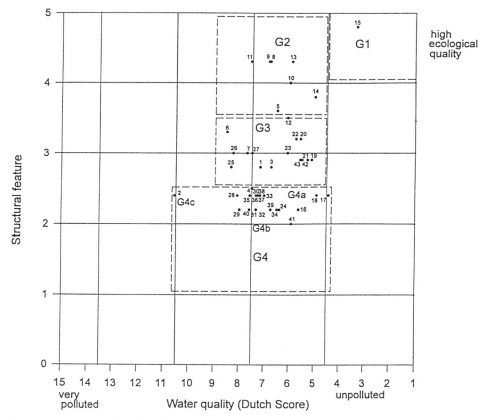

Figure 38.1   Ecological quality of 43 sampling sites in the Blawi River system (Trihadiningrum, 1995).

productive aquaculture area (G4b); and permanently channelized and polluted rivers (G4c). The latter (the middle Dapur tributary) was located in the most populous area (1,200 people km^{-2}).

Such an assessment approach not only provides water pollution data, but also valuable information for determining appropriate river conservation measures, which, if applied, will maintain the ecological quality of the river. A number of river conservation actions which are based on river naturalness are discussed elsewhere (e.g. Boon, 1992, 1996). In relation to Prokasih, considering that there is the potential for increased water pollution in the future, the current water quality assessment procedures should be reviewed, and extended towards a more ecological approach.

38.4   Conclusions

This chapter has highlighted several points which might be useful as inputs for developing Prokasih's activities in the future. It is clear that more effort should focus on diffuse pollution sources, and water quality assessment methods should be reviewed to ensure that they include variables relevant to the pollution sources. The existing water quality standards for functional uses need to be extended by establishing ecological water quality standards, as there are extreme climatological and geological influences on water quality in a number of regions. In order to maintain the sustainability of river uses, assessment methods should be developed so that river conservation measures can be identified and implemented.

References

Bapedal (1994). *Prokasih, Clean River Programme: Evaluating the Last Four Years and Looking to the Future*. Environmental Impact Management Agency (Bapedal), Jakarta.

Barmuta, L. A. and Marchant, R. (1992). Degradation of Australian streams and progress towards conservation and management in Victoria. In: Boon, P. J., Calow, P., and Petts, G. E. (Eds), *River Conservation and Management*, John Wiley, Chichester, 65–79.

Boon, P. J. (1992). Essential elements in the case for river conservation. In: Boon, P. J., Calow, P. and Petts, G. E. (Eds), *River Conservation and Management*, John Wiley, Chichester, 11–33.

Boon, P. J. (1996). The conservation of fresh waters: temperate experience in a tropical context. In: Schiemer, F. and Boland, K. T. (Eds), *Perspectives in Tropical Limnology*. SPB Academic Publishing, Amsterdam, 333–344.

Boon, P. J., Holmes, N. T. H., Maitland, P. S., Rowell, T. A. and Davies, J. (This volume). A system for evaluating rivers for conservation (SERCON): development, structure and function.

De Brabander, K. (1981). Beoordeling van de kwaliteit van oppervlaktewaters in België door middel van kwaliteits-indexen, *Water* (Belgium), **1**, November–December, 8–12.

Office of the State Minister for Population and the Environment (1990). *Prokasih, the Clean River Programme*. (In Indonesian). Kantor Menteri Negara Kependudukan dan Lingkungan Hidup, Jakarta.

Schneiders, A., Verhaert, E., Blust, G. D., Wils, C., Bervoets, L. and Verheyen, F. (1993). Towards an ecological assessment of water courses. *Journal of Aquatic Ecosystem Health*, **2**, 29–38.

Trihadiningrum, Y. (1995). 'Strategy Towards Water Quality Management of the Blawi River System in East Java, Indonesia'. Unpublished Ph.D. thesis. Department of Biology, Universitaire Instelling Antwerpen, Belgium.

39 ENHANCING THE QUALITY OF FRESHWATER RESOURCES: THE ROLE OF INTEGRATED CATCHMENT MANAGEMENT

A. Werritty

Summary

1. Freshwater resources are increasingly used and valued not just for consumptive purposes (public water supply, agriculture, forestry and industry) or for the release and dispersal of treated effluents. They also provide a source of hydro-electric power, sites for sport and water-based recreation, and locations where streams, lakes and wetlands can be appreciated in terms of visual amenity, or conserved on account of their biological and geomorphological interest.

2. Given this diversity of use, conflicts inevitably occur in terms of the total demand for water by these different sectoral interests. Integrated catchment management (ICM) provides a holistic framework within which these conflicting demands can potentially be reconciled.

3. Within Europe, ICM is being developed in a variety of formats in Portugal, Germany, France and the UK. Other countries where ICM has been developed over many decades include Australia, New Zealand and Canada. A critique of ICM theory and practice based on experience in these countries suggests that if it is to be successfully implemented many operational problems have to be overcome which may require radical changes in organizational culture.

4. This chapter includes an extended examination of catchment management planning in the UK, both in terms of formal procedures and informal schemes recently developed in a series of initiatives across Scotland. Whilst the general principles of ICM are well documented, adaptations are required as these principles are applied regionally and locally to enhance the quality of freshwater resources.

39.1   Introduction

With ever-increasing demands being made on finite water resources in many parts of the world, water quality issues are rapidly moving up the resource management agenda. Even in a country as well-endowed with water resources as the UK, water quality issues are attracting increasing attention (Institute of Hydrology, 1992; Department of the Environment, 1994). Water quality *sensu stricto* is determined partly by natural factors (e.g. climate, vegetation and lithology: Walling and Webb, 1981) but also by the consumptive uses to which water is put by society (agriculture, industry and domestic supply). The issues which then arise in the UK from this traditional definition of water quality include the domestic supply of drinking water; urban waste water treatment and disposal; acidification of upland waters; eutrophication of lowland waters; and the impact of excessive soil erosion and sedimentation.

However, this conventional definition of water quality issues has been greatly extended in the earlier chapters of this book to embrace a much wider agenda. Much water use is increasingly non-consumptive and the associated demands in terms of water quality extend far beyond the standard physical, chemical and biological criteria. As a result, water quality issues *sensu lato* now include the extent of physical modification of freshwater habitats, the use of such habitats for the conservation of wildlife, the role of rivers and lakes as landforms, the recreational use and value of fresh waters, and their role in terms of visual amenity and landscape appreciation. Water has thus become increasingly valued in its role as a physical, biological, geomorphological, recreational and aesthetic resource.

This chapter begins by exploring the conflicts that occur in the UK between competing water-user interests when water quality demands arise. It then outlines the goals of Integrated Catchment Management and its implementation within Europe, Australia, New Zealand and Canada, focusing particularly on recent developments within the UK. The chapter concludes with a discussion on how Integrated Catchment Management might enhance water quality in Scotland and elsewhere.

39.2   Water Quality and the Competing Demands Made on Freshwater Resources

Freshwater resources in the UK were traditionally exploited primarily to meet the consumptive demands of domestic customers, agriculture and industry. In many cases (notably in the case of drinking water) these demands included exacting physical and chemical criteria in terms of the quality of the water supplied (Department of the Environment, 1994). In order to meet these criteria, many public water supply reservoirs were historically located in unforested, non-agricultural catchments with minimal public access (Parker and Penning-Rowsell, 1980). More recently, as other activities have emerged which place different demands on water quality (e.g. water-based sports, large-scale commercial forestry, and visual appreciation of the natural heritage) potential conflicts have arisen in seeking to meet these new uses alongside the traditional requirement of supplying potable water. These conflicts have been especially acute as catchments providing water for public supply have become afforested (Greene, 1987), or reservoirs have been opened up to recreational water use (Parker and Penning-Rowsell, 1980). Another major consumptive use is the abstraction of water from surface or groundwater supplies to meet agricultural demands. This can generate severe seasonal water quality problems when baseflows are no longer adequate to sustain river biota. Such problems are further exacerbated when nutrient-rich waters (caused by excessive use of nitrate-based fertilizers) are flushed from the soil or discharged from ground waters (Foster *et al.*, 1986).

If the term 'water use' is extended to include many non-consumptive uses (e.g. the generation of hydro-electric power; maintaining rivers, lakes and wetlands such that they continue to support their indigenous biota; and the promotion of game fisheries) the potential for conflicting water quality demands increases significantly. The protection of the physical habitat for river, lake and wetland biota typically involves minimal interference with daily and seasonal fluctuations in water level or with the natural fluxes of sediment between bed and banks (Johnson *et al.*, 1992). These water quality demands for nature conservation are often in direct conflict with the use of water for hydro-electric power generation or proposals by commercial fishery operators to create artificial physical habitats to enhance the spawning of game fish (Campbell *et al.*, 1994; Johnson, 1994).

Finally, if waste disposal is included (i.e. the release of treated effluents into watercourses) as a further use to which fresh waters can be put, the conflict of interest in terms of water quality demands becomes potentially acute. Many stream biota are extremely sensitive to even modest levels of pollution, especially in terms of BOD and suspended solids (Newson, 1994). Their continued survival in many fresh waters requires vigilant monitoring and pollution control. Recreational use of such waters (including their enjoyment in terms of visual amenity) also necessitates the setting of stringent limits on discharge consents by the appropriate pollution control authorities. In the UK, these limits are determined on the basis of domestic legislation and, more recently, *via* Directives from the European Union, with the legislation being primarily targeted on controlling discharges at point sources (see Howell and Mackay, this volume). Whilst this represents a significant contribution to pollution control, especially in urban and industrialized areas, it fails to address the pollution that arises from diffuse sources (especially of nutrients and acid deposition). For such sources of pollution a catchment-based approach to monitoring and controlling land use would appear to offer the only solution (Mackay, 1994).

There are many merits in addressing water quality problems at the catchment scale rather than in terms of individual rivers, lakes and wetlands. First, such an approach explicitly acknowledges the hydrological cycle as a cascade in which fluxes of water, sediment, nutrients and pollutants steadily move downstream through a series of interconnected storages. Second, it focuses attention on the nature of the physical environment and the ways in which topography, lithology, vegetation, soil and land use collectively determine both flow regime and water quality. Third, it stresses the importance of embracing a 'holistic' approach to water quality issues, rather than addressing each question in terms which are site-specific or largely driven by narrow sectoral interests.

39.3   Integrated Catchment Management: Definitions and Applications

39.3.1   *The management of catchments*

The term 'Integrated Catchment Management' (ICM), and the related term 'catchment management planning', are only two attempts to specify the process whereby the management of a river and its surrounding catchment is undertaken in an increasingly holistic manner (Table 39.1). Downs *et al.* (1991) make a useful distinction between the term 'integrated' (where more than one sectoral interest is linked at both the strategic and operational levels) and 'holistic' (in which the drainage basin is conceived of as an ecosystem). The plethora of definitions in Table 39.1 makes it difficult to develop a standardized terminology, not least because of the country-specific nuances attached to each definition. This chapter will generally adopt definitions used in the UK but it will also incorporate terminology developed in other countries when appropriate.

The means whereby ICM is undertaken typically involves the development and implementation of a catchment management plan whose fundamental aim is 'to conserve, enhance, and, where appropriate, restore the total river environment through effective land and resource planning across the whole catchment area' (Gardiner and Cole, 1992, p. 401). When such catchment management plans are linked with local authority development plans and the asset management plans of water supply utilities, the resulting summation of these activities can be regarded as ICM (Gardiner, 1994). It is important to note that in the usage adopted in this chapter, catchment management planning is a component within the more all-embracing concept of ICM.

Catchment management leading to the development of ICM is now well established in many countries. However, there are many reasons for its development and implementation (Table 39.2). It is important to note that Gardiner and Cole's (1992) definition of catchment management planning explicitly targets the restoration of the *total river environment*. This principle is also implicit in the catchment management plans developed by the National Rivers Authority (NRA) across England and Wales in which 'the problems and opportunities resulting from water-related catchment uses are assessed and action is proposed *to optimize the future overall well-being of the water environment*' (NRA, 1993). This implies that catchment management plans should not be led by a common specific key issue. Different priorities will emerge in different catchments as a result of the review process. However, this purist view is not sustained across the many other examples of catchment management listed in Table 39.2. In many countries a key issue (often soil erosion, water quality or flood defence) initiated the process which ultimately

Table 39.1 Examples of terminology used to define various types of river and catchment management (adapted from Downs *et al.,* 1991, with permission from Springer-Verlag).

Term employed	Basin/area to which term relates
River basin planning	Gongola/Sokoto, Nigeria; Newfoundland, Canada
Integrated river basin development	Nile (esp. Sudan)
Integrated river management	Zambezi, Zambia and others
Basin-wide planning	Huang, China
Basin management	Acelhuate, El Salvador; Murray-Darling, Australia; Colorado, USA
River basin development	Han, China
Total catchment management	NSW, Australia
River basin management	Thames (Ontario), Canada; Alberta, Canada; Germany; Thames, England; elsewhere in England and Wales
Watershed management	Central Ontario, Canada
Comprehensive basin planning studies	Various, Canada
Comprehensive water quality management	Stratford/Avon, Ontario, Canada
Floodplain management	Hunter Valley, NSW, Australia
Integrated river basin management	Atchafalaya, USA
River basin management strategy	Tisza, Hungary
Catchment management	New Zealand

led to catchment management plans. In many instances these key issues have shaped (and in some cases dominated) the pathway taken by catchment management in different countries. Without denigrating the value and merits of this approach, such sectorally-driven catchment management tends not to result in ICM since it does not seek to encompass the total river environment as a functioning ecosystem. Using the distinction noted earlier (Downs *et al.,* 1991), it may involve integration across a number of sectoral interests, but it is not holistic. Thus the even-handed holistic approach in which no key issue is elevated to a special status over other issues has yet to emerge in many of the countries which aspire to implement ICM.

Table 39.2 Specific issues which triggered catchment management planning (Werritty, 1995).

Country	Specific issues
Australia	Soil erosion, salinization, floods
Canada (Ontario)	Floods
France	Irrigation, navigation, hydro-power
Germany	Water quality
New Zealand	Soil erosion, floods
Portugal	Water quality
UK (England and Wales)	Floods, conservation
USA (TVA)	Floods, soil erosion, navigation, hydro-power

39.3.2 Catchment management planning in Europe outside the UK

In many countries in Europe, water quality *sensu stricto* has historically been the key issue initiating catchment management plans. In some countries (e.g. Germany) this single sectoral interest has largely driven the agenda for water resource management. In other countries (e.g. France and Portugal) this single interest has broadened into a much wider agenda embracing much, if not all, of the river environment. In a few countries where ICM (or its equivalent) is being actively pursued, water quality is but one of a range of problems that are being addressed by catchment-wide planning. Each of these contrasting styles of catchment management within Europe is now examined.

In Germany, water quality *sensu stricto* has been the single sectoral interest driving the process of catchment management. Severe pollution problems caused by industrial production and population growth in the Ruhr area early this century resulted in catchment-based water associations being established in Nordrhein-Westfalen to enforce rigorous standards for wastewater disposal (Betlem, 1994). Reflecting this historical legacy, the focus of water management throughout Germany continues to be targeted on pollution control from point sources.

France developed a similar approach, based upon the principle of 'the polluter pays', in creating its *agences financières de bassin* in the 1960s. However, in response to increasingly stringent EC Directives, the focus has recently shifted from control of point sources to catchment management. Under the Water Act 1992, water is now seen as part of the common national heritage with its protection, utilization and development being part of the national interest. This legislation has the goal of 'balanced water management' which, as the following list demonstrates, provides yet another potential synonym for ICM:

- Protection and development of water resources.
- Protection from pollution of surface and groundwater sources.
- Preservation of ecosystems.
- Flood defence.
- Satisfactory reconciliation of conflicting usages, whilst retaining the resource in economic terms.

• Promoting human usage (where possible) in terms of agriculture, industry, power production, tourism, transport, recreation, etc.

Thus, water resource management in France has shifted markedly from being solely concerned with questions of a guaranteed supply (both in terms of quantity and quality) to the much larger question of the protection of aquatic ecosystems. Planning at the catchment scale has now become a crucial element in water management policy and the broader promotion of water quality (Betlem, 1994).

In Portugal, a severe deterioration in water quality *sensu stricto* was one of the environmental consequences of industrial expansion in the 1970s. This resulted in proposals for a complete restructuring of the water industry in 1986 which included the licensing of all water uses and planning and raising revenue on the 'polluter pays principle'. The resulting legislation (enacted in 1994) envisages the formulation of 15 river basin plans by 2002 and the National Water Plan two years later. Strategic water management will, for the first time in Portugal, be based on river basin plans. The Regional Development Plans will coordinate public sector investments, amongst which improvements in the treatment of wastewater, and the control of industrial pollution, irrigation and power generation will loom large. It is, however, important to note that neither the National Water Plan nor the 15 river basin plans will have the function of fully integrating social and economic considerations into water management (Betlem, 1994). Thus, these administrative structures are designed to create catchment management plans but not, as yet, ICM (see Gardiner's (1994) distinction noted above).

39.3.3 Catchment management planning in England and Wales

Within Europe, a strong case can be made that the NRA (now the Environment Agency) in England and Wales has made most progress in implementing a style of catchment management planning that could result in ICM being implemented if further legislation were forthcoming. Yet it is important to note (for the purposes of this chapter) that water quality *sensu stricto* was not the key issue which triggered catchment planning in the UK. For the pioneers in this field, flood defence and conservation were the key issues (Woolhouse, 1994). Following the replacement of the Regional Water Authorities by privatized utilities and a new regulatory agency (the NRA) in 1989, national guidelines for catchment planning began to emerge. Thus by 1991 the NRA had produced the following draft guidelines:

A Catchment Management Plan (CMP) will result from a multifunctional and multi-use appraisal of a catchment which:

• Takes account of functional strategies and objectives.
• Identifies present uses and defines:
   (a) future uses of water and associated land within the catchment.
   (b) future land use which influences the water environment.

   (c) future land drainage and flood defence activities, and sets appropriate standards for each, giving priority to statutory obligations.
- Identifies interaction and potential conflicts.
- Sets out an action plan to achieve the defined uses of water within the catchment, land use controls, land drainage and flood defence objectives.
- The action plan will allocate responsibility for that action and will provide an investment framework.

The former NRA's approach to producing a CMP (NRA, 1993) is outlined in Figure 39.1. Howlett (1994) suggested that this process adopted many of the principles and precepts of 'Agenda 21' proposed at the UN Conference on Environment and Development at Rio de Janeiro in 1992. In terms of developing water resources these principles included the involvement of local communities, the reconciliation of conflicting water use interests, the integration of water and land uses, the setting of standards relative to the carrying capacities of water systems, and the examination of issues within both the short term (action plans) and long term (visions) (see Woolhouse, 1994). Such is the theory, but how was this made operational and to what effect?

Some of the most innovative developments in terms of conceptualizing and implementing CMPs came from the former NRA in Thames Region (the Thames Water Authority before 1989) which began to formalize the process of public consultation in the 1980s leading to the publication of *River Projects and Conservation: A Manual for Holistic Appraisal* (Gardiner, 1991). More recent developments view the formulation of CMPs as one step within the much larger task of moving from single function investment to Integrated Catchment Planning (see Figure 39.2). Integrated Catchment Planning necessary to achieve 'Agenda 21' objectives, and in harmony with EC Directives on Environmental Assessment, can then be expressed by the following equation (Gardiner, 1994):

Asset Management + Catchment Management + Local Authority Development
Plan   Plan   Plans

= Integrated Catchment Planning/Total Catchment Planning.

where Asset Management Plans are the investment plans of the privatized water utilities. In this conceptualization the term 'Integrated Catchment Planning' appears to be equivalent to ICM or the Australian term 'Total Catchment Planning'. This pathway for delivering a sustainable development of water resources was, according to Gardiner (1994), an aspiration still to be fully achieved by the Thames Region of the NRA. Newson (1992), in his critique of catchment planning in the UK, comments that if CMP is to become the institutional vehicle for advancing holistic river basin development, then the methods pioneered by Gardiner and his colleagues in the Thames Region could well become a model template.

These developments (now superceded by Local Environment Agency Plans—Raven *et al.,* this volume) are undoubtedly an important step towards ICM within

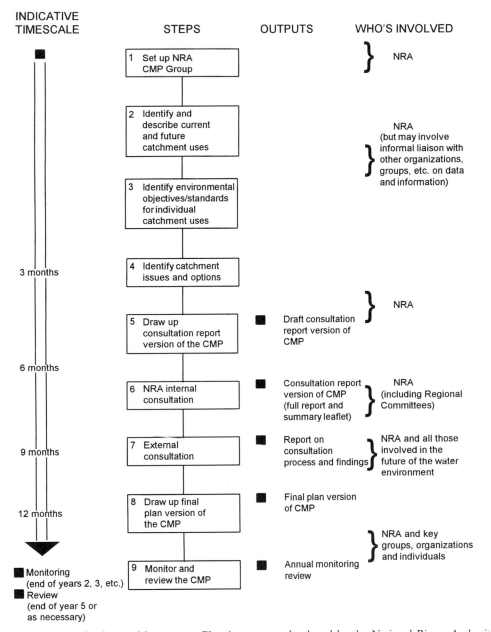

Figure 39.1 The Catchment Management Planning process developed by the National Rivers Authority (NRA, 1993).

the UK. However, links with the statutory planning process and conservation bodies, whilst improving, are as yet largely untested and the full implementation of ICM across England and Wales remains a somewhat distant goal. It is also important to appreciate that a different statutory framework exists in Scotland, where catchment planning has developed in a much more *ad hoc* and piecemeal manner.

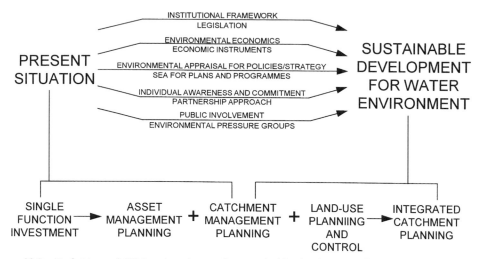

Figure 39.2 Definition of ICM and pathways for sustainable development for the water environment (Gardiner, 1994).

39.3.4 *Catchment management planning in Scotland*

Water resource management in Scotland is at present highly fragmented and lacks a comprehensive regulatory authority akin to that formerly provided by the NRA in England and Wales (Howell, 1994). Hitherto, pollution control has been provided by the 10 River Purification Authorities (RPAs), but responsibilities related to land drainage, flood protection, fisheries, nature conservation, water supply and sewerage have been variously distributed between the Scottish Office, the District Salmon Fishery Boards, Scottish Natural Heritage (SNH) and the local authorities. In April 1996 responsibilities for water supply and sewerage passed to three new Water Authorities, and the Scottish Environment Protection Agency (SEPA) took over responsibility for regulating pollution of the air, water and land. These changes are primarily administrative in nature and SEPA's regulatory remit will largely remain unaltered from that exercised by the RPAs. The Government, whilst committed to the sustainable development of Scotland's water resources, favours economic instruments coupled with exhortation and education rather than additional regulation in achieving this goal (Department of the Environment, 1994). Thus SEPA will not have a duty to implement proactive and integrated water management programmes (Werritty, 1995).

Given that the existing statutory agencies have no duty to promote ICM, many organizations (public, private and voluntary) have sought to promote a more holistic approach to water resource planning by other means. Some of these initiatives have arisen within the public sector (e.g. the Catchment Reviews on the Rivers Eden and Ythan by the Tay River Purification Board and the North East River Purification Board, respectively), whilst others have involved partnerships between the public and private sectors (e.g. the Water of Leith Action Plan: Edwards-Jones, this volume). Additional initiatives concerned primarily with enhancing salmonid fisheries (e.g. the West Galloway Fisheries Trust, the Tweed Foundation, and the Dee Salmon Action Plan) have arisen solely within the private sector. Further details on the precise nature of these initiatives and their current status is given in Werritty (1995). Many are still at a relatively early stage of development, but they have generally involved widespread consultation and have taken very seriously the need for a holistic and catchment-based approach. Particularly successful to date has been the Water of Leith Action Plan (Edwards-Jones, this volume). This highly urbanized watercourse in the west of Edinburgh, which had experienced severe environmental degradation over many years, is already showing identifiable improvements along the river corridor in terms of physical habitat, visual amenity and water pollution. It is clear from the development of these initiatives, and the returns from a questionnaire circulated to all the major potential stakeholders, that widespread support exists throughout Scotland for implementing some form of ICM (Werritty, 1995).

There are three potential models for implementing ICM in Scotland and thereby enhancing the quality of its freshwater resources (Werritty, 1995):

(a) *Centralized, multiple-function public agency ('top-down')*, whereby ICM is implemented *via* a large, centralized, multiple-function public agency such as SEPA. The merit of such a model would be the development of a coherent strategy across the whole of Scotland, a high degree of coordination (although this would often be driven by administrative direction from the centre i.e. the Scottish Office, SEPA or SNH) and economies of scale.

(b) *Local initiatives responding to public needs ('bottom-up')*; that is, ICM is implemented by diverse 'bottom-up' initiatives both by public agencies and voluntary bodies in response to publicly identified needs. This model has the merit of focusing on issues which command local concern and tapping into the enthusiasm of local activists, but it scarcely comprises a national strategy.

(c) *Strategic identification of issues made operational at the local level.* This is an intermediate model which would target a strategic issue (e.g. eutrophication) which is not just of local significance and seek to promote its resolution *via* concentrated action by a variety of stakeholders. This would require an external trigger—by SEPA, SNH or a Planning Authority—which would identify the key issues to be tackled locally by developing CMPs in catchments where the specific issue is a pressing concern.

Given the current level of support for ICM in Scotland, plus the recent legislation on water resource management, the third model based on strategic identification of issues made operational at the local level would seem to represent the optimal way forward. It provides a way of reconciling a national strategy for catchment management with action targeted upon issues that both generate public concern and will be owned by local communities (Werritty, 1995).

39.3.5   Catchment management planning outside Europe

Many countries outside Europe have also developed catchment planning and moved towards ICM in an attempt to resolve water resource problems. However, flood defence, soil erosion and water supply have been the key issues, with water quality *sensu stricto* still present, but generally much lower down the agenda. This section outlines the development of catchment management in Australia, New Zealand and Canada.

Catchment management in Australia dates back to the 1860s and the need to secure provision of potable water supplies. In the 1950s disastrous floods in New South Wales resulted in the creation of the Hunter Valley Conservation Trust. This was soon followed by the establishment of the Dandengong Valley Authority in Victoria, whose functions were designated as 'the improvement of lands within the catchment thereof and the prevention of flooding, pollution and other purposes' (Burton, 1988). Until recently, these were the only two state-based statutory catchment management agencies. However, the last decade has witnessed whole-catchment soil and water management programmes in which individual land-owners and government agencies have cooperated in catchment-based groups. The Warranbayne-Boho LandCare group initiated this development in the 1970s, since when this approach has been widely adopted as a community-based, 'bottom-up' method of catchment management. Today, LandCare Australia represents a major initiative in the field of ICM which permeates Australian policy-making at both federal and state levels. It provides the framework within which catchment management schemes are funded and affords a remarkable example of a 'bottom-up' initiative which, within two decades, has transformed land and water resource management in Australia (Werritty, 1995). Yet this programme has not been without its critics. In a recent review, Curtis and De Lacy (1996) observe that although LandCare represents an important contribution towards sustainable resource development, it may place too much responsibility upon individual landholders.

New Zealand's history of catchment management has a number of parallels with that of Australia in that it was also triggered by soil erosion and flood control problems. The Soil Conservation and Rivers Control Council was established in 1941 to conserve soil resources and prevent damage by erosion and flooding. However, comprehensive catchment-wide planning was slow to emerge because the regional catchment boards tended to be reactive rather than proactive (Erickson, 1990). Furthermore, it proved difficult to obtain joint support of upstream (soil erosion) and downstream (flood control) beneficiaries of such plans. In the late 1960s, increasing public concern over environmental quality, especially degraded fisheries and poor water quality, resulted in a new National Water and Soil Conservation Authority (NWSCA) being created within which a much wider range of sectoral interests were represented (local authorities, agriculture, industry, fisheries, wildlife conservation and land drainage). This was a commendable attempt at integrated water planning, but the over-centralized style of management, plus an inability in many of the technical staff to look beyond their narrow sectoral interest, resulted in the demise of the NWSCA in 1988 when its functions were dispersed or suspended (Erickson, 1990). More recent legislation has once again taken up the issue of the development of New Zealand's natural and physical resources under the aegis of promoting integrated environmental management (Scott, 1993).

In Canada, legislation in 1970 provided for an integrated approach to catchment management at the scale of large basins (e.g. the Okanagan basin in British Columbia and the Churchill-Nelson basin in north Manitoba). However, none proved successful, and by the end of the 1980s effective river basin management was only being undertaken at the provincial and local level (Gardiner *et al.*, 1994). The best-known example of a localized approach has developed in Ontario where the Conservation Authorities, which are municipal in origin, have the primary function of planning and managing flood control and erosion works. In 1987 a provincial review noted the absence of effective planning and conflict resolution mechanisms and recommended a better-focused approach. In the case of the Grand River Watershed, this improved coordination has taken the form of a Master Watershed Plan in which individual watershed plans drawn up by the Catchment Authorities have been combined with the Master Drainage Plan compiled by the municipalities. Although some of these plans contain untested or unproven concepts (e.g. buffer strips based on meagre environmental monitoring), Gardiner *et al.* (1994) regard Master Watershed Planning as a striking example of a 'bottom-up' as opposed to a 'top-down' initiative which has already demonstrated that it is possible to manage small catchments successfully and from this move on to groups of catchments and larger-scale planning.

39.4   A Critique of ICM Theory and Practice

This section is concerned with how the theory of ICM can be implemented, focusing especially on the organizational issues that inevitably arise. In developing this critique it is useful to distinguish three levels of analysis: normative, strategic, and operational. Whereas the normative level identifies *what ought to be done* and the strategic level *what can be done*, the operational level focuses on *what will be done* (Mitchell, 1990). This distinction between levels also partially explains why, despite widespread acceptance of the value of ICM, implementation has often been hesitant and unsystematic.

At the strategic level a *comprehensive* approach (identification of the broadest possible range of variables appropriate for ICM) is both appropriate and desirable. However, at the operational level this very comprehensiveness can result in inordinate delays in generating plans, which are often insufficiently focused. A partial solution is to retain the comprehensive approach at the strategic level (to ensure the widest possible perspective), but to operate a more focused *integrated* approach at the operational level, targeted on that subset of variables which generates the bulk of the management problems.

If ICM is to be implemented successfully the following problems have to be addressed:

- What are the specific goals and targets?
- What are the necessary conditions to achieve a successful outcome?
- What information is needed to underpin planning and management decisions?
- What are the respective roles of statutory agencies, individual landowners and communities?
- How can the process be truly participatory?
- How will the initiative be resourced?

In seeking to resolve these problems, several key issues emerge. First, there are two models for identifying goals and targets: collective identification of common goals by all participants followed by discussion as to how they can be achieved, or individual identification of goals which are subsequently reconciled collectively. Practical experience suggests that the former approach is more likely to result in successful implementation, as illustrated by the Water of Leith Action Plan (Scottish Wildlife Trust, 1993; Edwards-Jones, this volume). Second, it is important that the scope of the catchment management plan is well-defined and agreed by all participants to avoid imprecision and lack of clarity when moving from the strategic level, which is comprehensive, to the operational level, which is more selective and focused. Third, as Eddison (1985) has noted, major management problems often exist at the boundaries (between agencies or within departments) which have to be successfully resolved if truly integrated management is to be achieved.

In further developing a critique of ICM it is important to note that often, in practice, ICM is merely the amalgamation of management within a single organization which seeks to orchestrate all aspects of catchment activity. This can result in an overbearing 'top-down' structure which spawns a hierarchy of committees but little by way of practical results. In his critique of ICM practice in Australia, Burton (1988) argues that ICM is *not* about amalgamation, it is about planning and cooperation. It is not about doing everything at once, like a one-man band, instead it involves taking a holistic view, and tackling specific resource management problems within that context. Above all, the product of ICM should be improved catchment and river management practice, i.e. practices and not plans.

Also implicit in ICM is the recognition that water resources are both locally finite and vulnerable and thus of considerable significance to sustainable development. Furthermore, the development of water resources devoid of a holistic or integrated approach is likely to result in degradation of the resource, with inevitable socio-economic impacts. Despite this danger, the goal of ICM is often impeded by the existence of a highly fragmented and sector-driven style of water resource management. If ICM is to succeed, the statutory agencies have to will the means whereby land and water uses within the catchment can be harmonized to an agreed common set of objectives by all the stakeholders, including local communities. This means a weakening of sectoral management of water resources and its replacement by a multi-sectoral coordination in which the traditional goals and roles of individual agencies may have to be redrawn. This implies a high degree of institutional flexibility and a willingness to depart from former certainties. Such is the underlying philosophy behind ICM particularly well-exemplified by Gardiner (1991).

39.5 Conclusions

This chapter has sought to demonstrate how ICM can promote improved water quality in situations where there are conflicting demands on water use. Such a strategy, which has been developed in many parts of the world, has also yielded a framework for the sustainable development of water resources. The general principles that underpin ICM are now well-documented, but require adaptation as they are applied to each local situation.

In the case of Scotland, this involves taking note of the recent debate over the merits of applying ICM within the newly restructured water industry. That debate is still continuing, but there is no doubt that the majority of the potential stakeholders see ICM (suitably tailored to Scottish needs) as making a significant contribution to the improved management of the country's water resources. Before embarking on such a strategy, though, it is salutary to reflect on Boon's observation (1994) that the mere utterance of words like 'integration', 'sustainability' and 'holistic management' will not bring to an end all problems in promoting enhanced water quality in Scotland. Conflicts of interest are inevitable given the great variety of human uses of fresh waters (Maitland *et al.*, 1994). In Scotland one of these conflicts has arisen between those responsible for providing potable drinking water and landowners who wish to plant conifers in the catchments surrounding the water supply reservoirs (Greene, 1987). The exploitation of salmonid fisheries is also in potential conflict with conifer afforestation and with aquatic species conservation. Providing public access to water supply reservoirs for recreational purposes, such as water-based sports or the visual appreciation of the natural heritage, yields yet another potential source of conflict. Farmers seeking to abstract water for irrigation or involved in applying excessive amounts of nitrate-based fertilizers are also likely to generate conflict with conservationists and those promoting water-based recreation. In urban areas the use of watercourses to evacuate treated industrial and domestic wastes is often inimical to fishery interests, to the conservation of the natural heritage, and to recreation.

All these conflicts arise because of the variety of demands being made on water quantity and quality by diverse users. Many of these demands (e.g. in terms of forestry and agriculture), although exercised at some distance from the water, nevertheless have a direct impact on rivers and lakes. The theory of ICM (sensitively implemented to take into account local interests and agendas) provides one way of resolving these conflicts on the basis of bargaining, negotiation and compromise. Past experiences suggest that this is very demanding, not least because it requires each stakeholder to be willing to offer some compromise in terms of their sectoral interest. Yet without this commitment, plus strenuous efforts by the key players/stakeholders to negotiate an acceptable compromise, repeated chanting of the mantra of ICM will not yield success in terms of the sustainable development of freshwater resources.

References

Betlem, I. (1994). *River Basin Planning and Management*. RBA Centre for Comparative Studies on River Basin Administration, Delft University of Technology, Delft.

Boon, P. J. (1994). Nature conservation. In: Maitland, P. S., Boon, P. J. and McLusky, D. S. (Eds), *The Fresh Water of Scotland: a National Resource of International Significance*. John Wiley, Chichester, 555–576.

Burton, J. R. (1988). Catchment management in Australia. *Transactions of the Institution of Engineers, Australia, Civil Engineering*, **30,** 145–152.

Campbell, R. N., Maitland, P. S. and Campbell, R. N. B. (1994). Management of fish populations. In: Maitland, P. S., Boon, P. J. and McLusky, D. S. (Eds), *The Fresh Waters of Scotland: a National Resource of International Significance*. John Wiley, Chichester, 489–513.

Curtis, A. and De Lacy, T. (1996). Landcare in Australia: does it make a difference? *Journal of Environmental Management*, **46,** 119–137.

Department of the Environment (1994). *Sustainable Development: the UK Strategy*, HMSO, London.

Downs, P. W., Gregory, K. J. and Brookes, A. (1991). How integrated is river basin management? *Environmental Management*, **15,** 299–309.

Eddison, T. (1985). Managing an ecological system 5: reforming bureaucracy. *Australian Quarterly*, **57,** 148–153.

Edwards-Jones, E. S. (This volume). The River Valleys Project: using Integrated Catchment Planning to improve the quality of two Scottish rivers.

Erickson, N. J. (1990). New Zealand water planning and management: evolution or revolution. In: Mitchell, B. (Ed.), *Integrated Water Management: International Experiences and Perspectives*. Belhaven Press, London, 45–87.

Foster, S. D. D., Bridge, L. R., Geake, A. K., Lawrence, A. R. and Parker, J. M. (1986). *The Groundwater Nitrate Problem*. Hydrogeological Report 86/2, British Geological Survey, Wallingford.

Gardiner, J. L. (Ed.) (1991). *River Projects and Conservation: a Manual for Holistic Appraisal*. John Wiley, Chichester.

Gardiner, J. L. (1994). Sustainable development for river catchments. *Journal of the Institution of Water and Environmental Management*, **8,** 308–319.

Gardiner, J. L. and Cole, L. (1992). Catchment planning: the way forward for river protection in the UK. In: Boon, P. J., Calow, P. and Petts, G. E. (Eds), *River Conservation and Management*. John Wiley, Chichester, 397–406.

Gardiner, J. L., Thomson, K. and Newson, M. (1994). Integrated watershed/river catchment planning and management: a comparison of selected Canadian and United Kingdom experiences. *Journal of Environmental Planning and Management*, **37,** 53–67.

Greene, L. A. (1987). The effects of catchment afforestation on public water supplies in Strathclyde Region. *Transactions of the Royal Society of Edinburgh*, **78,** 335–340.

Howell, D. L. (1994). Role of environmental agencies. In: Maitland, P. S., Boon, P. J. and McLusky, D. S. (Eds), *The Fresh Waters of Scotland: a National Resource of International Significance*. John Wiley, Chichester, 577–611.

Howell, D. L. and Mackay, D. W. (This volume). Protecting water quality through legislation: enforcement, inducement or agreement?

Howlett, D. (1994). Freshwater and the Post-UNCED Agenda. *Environmental Politics,* **2,** 210–224.

Institute of Hydrology (1992). *Water and the Environment: the United Kingdom Statement*. UN International Conference on Water and the Environment, Dublin, January, 1992. Institute of Hydrology, Wallingford.

Johnson, F. G. (1994). Hydro-electric generation. In: Maitland, P. S., Boon, P. J. and McLusky, D. S. (Eds), *The Fresh Waters of Scotland: a National Resource of International Significance*. John Wiley, Chichester, 297–316.

Johnson, R. C., Piper, B. S., Acreman, M. C. and Gilman, K. (1992). *Flood Alleviation in Upper Strathspey. Environment Study*. Report to Nature Conservancy Council for Scotland. Institute of Hydrology, Wallingford.

Mackay, D. W. (1994). Pollution control. In: Maitland, P. S., Boon, P. J. and McLusky, D. S. (Eds), *The Fresh Waters of Scotland: a National Resource of International Significance*. John Wiley, Chichester, 517–529.

Maitland, P. S., McLusky, D. S. and Boon, P. J. (1994). Integrating development and conservation. In: Maitland, P. S., Boon, P. J. and McLusky, D. S. (Eds), *The Fresh Waters of Scotland: a National Resource of International Significance*. John Wiley, Chichester, 613–623.

Mitchell, B. (1990). Integrated water management. In: Mitchell, B. (Ed.), *Integrated Water Management: International Experiences and Perspectives*. Belhaven Press, London, 1–21.

Newson, M. (1992). *Land, Water and Development*. Routledge, London.

Newson, M. (1994). *Hydrology and the River Environment*. Clarendon Press, Oxford.

NRA (1993). *Catchment Management Planning: Guidelines August 1993*. Bristol.

Parker, D. J. and Penning-Rowsell, E. C. (1980). *Water Planning in Britain*. George Allen and Unwin, London.

Raven, P. J., Fox, P., Everard, M., Holmes, N. T. H. and Dawson, F. H. (This volume). River Habitat Survey: a new system for classifying rivers according to their habitat quality.

Scott, D. (1993). New Zealand's Resource Management Act and fresh water. *Aquatic Conservation: Marine and Freshwater Ecosystems,* **3,** 53–65.

Scottish Wildlife Trust (1993). *The Water of Leith Integrated Environmental Action Plan*. Edinburgh.

Walling, D. E. and Webb, B. W. (1981). Water quality. In: Lewin, J. (Ed.), *British Rivers*. Allen and Unwin, London, 126–169.

Werritty, A. (1995). *Integrated Catchment Management: a Review and Evaluation*. Scottish Natural Heritage Review, 58. Scottish Natural Heritage, Battleby.

Woolhouse, C. (1994). Catchment management plans: current successes and future opportunities. In: Kirby, C. and White, W. R. (Eds), *Integrated River Basin Development*. John Wiley, Chichester, 463–474.

40 THE RIVER VALLEYS PROJECT: USING INTEGRATED CATCHMENT PLANNING TO IMPROVE THE QUALITY OF TWO SCOTTISH RIVERS

E. S. Edwards-Jones

Summary

1. The River Valleys Project was initiated by the Scottish Wildlife Trust in order to identify and assess the potential benefits of a holistic approach to the assessment and management of river catchments. These benefits were perceived to be greater than those derived from historical management procedures undertaken on a functional basis by a range of organizations with limited inter-agency liaison.

2. The Project progressed via the consecutive development of integrated management plans for two rivers: first, for the river corridor of the Water of Leith, Edinburgh, and second, for the Almond Catchment, West Lothian.

3. The method adopted for the development of each plan involved the formation of a Project Group for each river with representation from all organizations and individuals with an interest in the river system.

4. Integrated Catchment Planning (ICP) has been shown to be a feasible and beneficial tool for resolving conflict and coordinating a holistic management programme in Scottish river catchments.

40.1 Introduction

It is frequently stated that the quality of Scottish fresh waters has improved substantially in the last 50 years (Hammerton, 1994; Mackay, 1994). Whilst this is true in terms of chemical water quality, the impact of engineering works, drainage and river regulation could be said to have resulted in a deterioration of the overall quality of Scottish river systems. Few of Scotland's rivers can now be regarded as entirely natural systems and all of the larger rivers have long since been modified and regulated (Gilvear *et al.*, 1995).

This deterioration may have been exacerbated by the difficulty of coordinating management when it is undertaken by a range of organizations, all implementing single-objective management at varying geographical scales. Such an institutional structure is unlikely to be able to predict and mitigate the damage to river systems that arises from cumulative and synergistic impacts of management activities and land-use changes. This is especially apparent when considering the rivers of lowland Scotland, where many flood embankment and channelization schemes have lacked a strategic approach and have not considered the downstream hydrological effects. Such schemes have reduced the time of travel of flood peaks and increased flood peaks downstream owing to the removal of floodplain storage (Gilvear, 1994). These hydrological effects may place downstream floodplain development at greater risk of flooding, thus necessitating further flood embankment construction to reduce the frequency of floodplain inundation. Howell (1994) details the increasing support for a more integrated approach to the management of Scottish water resources. The need for such an approach was emphasized for all high income countries, in 'Agenda 21', the action plan for the 1990s and twenty-first century, which arose from the United Nations Conference on Environment and Development in Rio de Janeiro, Brazil, in June 1992.

Integrated Catchment Planning (ICP) is a management tool which attempts to overcome the fragmentation of responsibilities amongst sectoral agencies. The rationale of ICP is that bringing statutory agencies and interest groups together to formulate management strategies for river systems generates a framework, which considers rivers as complex, dynamic systems. ICP takes account of the interactions between different management activities in the development of the management programme for the river system, the resultant programme minimizing both conflicts between activities and damage to the system itself. This systems approach allows each management activity and land-use change to be considered in the light of trends in environmental change, other management objectives, predicted cumulative impacts, and national policy objectives. Once established, the integrated catchment management framework allows trade-offs between impacts to be considered and priorities to be assigned to the components of river quality for each management activity. The formulation of a management strategy also forces consideration of those components of river quality that currently lie outside the statutory remits of the management agencies.

In England and Wales the National Rivers Authority (NRA) considered that the best way of arriving at sustainable solutions was to take an integrated approach to river management (NRA, 1993). The Environment Agency (EA) (the successor to the NRA) has adopted ICP as a means of fulfilling its remit which covers a range of activities including fisheries management, flood protection and the maintenance of water quality. In Scotland, where these responsibilities are split between a number of organizations, there has been a perception that the potential benefits that may accrue through the adoption of ICP may not outweigh the considerable effort involved. This attitude is reflected in the responses of potential 'stakeholders' in ICP to the questionnaire survey undertaken by Werritty (1995), which included adjectives such as 'impracticable' and 'unworkable' to describe ICP. There is also considerable uncertainty as to the best way to put such a system into practice given the current institutional structure, as discussed by Howell (1994).

The River Valleys Project was initiated by the Scottish Wildlife Trust in November 1992 to examine the feasibility and to identify the potential benefits of an integrated, holistic approach to the assessment and management of Scottish river catchments. The principal aims of the River Valleys Project were twofold: first, to investigate the potential improvements in river quality which could be achieved by the participation of all interested parties ('stakeholders') in the development of integrated catchment plans for two rivers in Lothian Region: the Water of Leith and the River Almond. Second, to develop a methodology for the participatory development of integrated catchment plans.

40.2 Methods

In phase one of the River Valleys Project, an integrated management plan was developed for the corridor of the Water of Leith. A series of steps were identified during this work and these steps were subsequently applied to the Almond catchment, with the aim of producing a full catchment plan:

(a) Identification and initial contact with all stakeholders in the management of the river system.
(b) Assessment of attitudes of stakeholders to the concept of integrated catchment plans, and the formation of a Project Group to work towards the development of an integrated catchment plan.
(c) Collation of all available data relating to the catchment.
(d) Production of a description of the resource in terms of the environment and existing uses.
(e) Assessment of the environmental, economic and social implications of the activities of all stakeholders.
(f) Identification of possible actions which might reduce impacts on the resource, reduce conflicts between uses, and enhance the resource (a preliminary report was produced at this stage).
(g) Identification of objectives for future management.
(h) Identification of management action to achieve objectives, including named agencies to assume responsibility for each action and setting time-scales for implementation.
(i) Implementation and monitoring, involving continued regular meetings of the Project Group.

These steps were initiated and coordinated by a Project Officer (the author of this chapter), who maintained regular contact with all members of the Project Group via correspondence, phone calls, and meetings. A number of techniques were used in steps (e)–(h) to ensure the participation of all members of the Project Group, including topic workshops, the collaborative production of summary

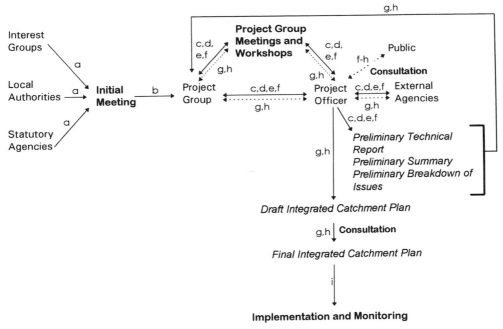

Figure 40.1   Steps in the development of an integrated catchment plan for the River Almond. Descriptions of each step (a–i) in the process are provided in the text.

reports and regular full Project Group meetings. Figure 40.1 illustrates the cyclical nature of steps (a)–(i). The process was designed to ensure that decisions and outcomes at each stage were reviewed in the light of information made available during subsequent stages.

40.3   The Water of Leith

The Water of Leith flows north-eastwards from its source in the Pentland Hills, through the City of Edinburgh to the Forth Estuary at the port of Leith. The total length of the main stream is 31.7 km, draining a catchment of 122 km^2. The catchment encompasses a wide range of land-use types and more than 40% of it is urban. Despite this predominantly urban catchment, much of the river valley retains a rural atmosphere. It is the most significant semi-natural corridor running through the centre of the city and is a popular area for informal recreation for the people of Edinburgh (Edwards-Jones, 1993).

A wide range of initiatives to improve the quality of the Water of Leith resulted from the implementation of the Plan. For example:

- A detailed landscape assessment was undertaken and a strategy prepared for the future management of the landscape.
- The angling permit system was revised to enable the collection of improved fisheries data, and a series of electro-fishing surveys were carried out.
- A number of initiatives were established to improve the prevention of rubbish

dumping and clearance of rubbish within the valley, an issue for which no-one had previously taken responsibility.

- The public were encouraged to become actively involved in river management through 'Running Your River', whereby community groups were given the opportunity to adopt their stretch of the Water of Leith. This enabled them to communicate their concerns directly to the Project Group and to undertake a range of management activities in accordance with the overall management strategy.

- Improved communication between the management agencies through the Project Group framework enabled the Group members to obtain up-to-date information on any situation and to provide a coordinated response, whether it was to a potentially serious pollution event or to inaccurate representation by the media.

It is unlikely that any of these initiatives would have taken place in the near future, if at all, without the development of the Integrated Environmental Action Plan. The Water of Leith Plan is on target in terms of implementing its management activities; however, no formal analysis of the socio-economic or environmental benefits has been undertaken to date.

40.4 The River Almond

The River Almond rises in the Cant Hills, between Edinburgh and Glasgow, and flows in a north-easterly direction to the Forth Estuary at Cramond, on the western outskirts of Edinburgh. The total length of the main stream is approximately 50 km, draining a catchment of 375 km^2. The catchment is mainly rural although there are several areas of high population and rapid economic growth along its banks, such as Livingston New Town. There has been a significant amount of coal mining activity throughout the catchment. The last deep coal mine (Pol-kemmet), closed in 1985, but open-cast coal mining still continues in the upper catchment. Oil was extracted from shale deposits in the Pumpherston and Addi-ewell district, but this industry has also now ceased. This history of land use has a legacy of severe water quality problems which are now in conflict with the river's increasing role as an area for recreation and leisure (Edwards-Jones, 1995).

The Almond Project Group has reached the halfway mark (Figure 40.1) with the production of a preliminary report (Edwards-Jones and Pollard, 1995). The priority issues identified are those of poor water quality and low flows. Gaps in the available data are preventing an assessment of the available management options in some areas, and funding is being sought for further studies. In its continuing discussions the Project Group will set objectives and identify further steps for the future management of the river which will form the River Almond Catchment Plan. Mechanisms are being set in place to involve the large number of riparian landowners in the development of the management plan, with the aim of improving river quality through appropriate riparian management.

40.5 Conclusions

The River Valleys Project has demonstrated the feasibility of ICP for Scottish rivers and established that one mechanism for achieving this is through the voluntary participation of stakeholders, coordinated by a Project Officer.

The key components of the Project's approach included the involvement of all stakeholders in the development of the plans. A wide range of statutory agencies and interest groups were represented on the Project Groups, ensuring that all issues relating to river management were identified and considered. Local communities were asked to contribute to the development of the plans *via* liaison with the Project Officer. This community consultation process involved a series of public lectures by the Project Officer to a range of community organizations, and subsequent discussion between these organizations and the Project Officer regarding the concerns of the local communities with respect to the rivers.

The development of the Water of Leith Integrated Environmental Action Plan demonstrated that consensus could be reached between the many stakeholders involved in river management, at the scale of the river corridor. The conflict resolution techniques adopted for the Water of Leith were then applied to the Almond catchment in the development of a full integrated catchment plan, which addressed all elements of the catchment influencing the river.

The direct outcomes of ICP for the Almond catchment will be twofold—first, the establishment of a long-term management team, encompassing all stakeholders; and second, the integrated catchment plan itself, a holistic management programme to ensure the future overall quality of the river system.

The indirect benefits of the ICP process, identified to date, are:

- An increased awareness of the many component parts of river management and their complexity.
- The identification of the responsibilities of management agencies, voluntary groups and the public, and the potential partnership between them.
- Clearing channels of communication between management agencies, preventing duplication of effort and minimizing conflicts of interest.
- Pooling information concerning the catchment, revealing gaps in the information base.
- Identifying clear management objectives.
- Assigning priorities to the components of the system at different locations.
- A more clearly defined relationship between the agencies responsible for management and the public.
- The establishment of an infrastructure for the generation of good ideas to solve complex problems.
- Creating opportunities for organizations to cooperate with each other and encouraging the initiation of collaborative projects.

The resultant integrated catchment plan will include a work programme addressing all aspects of river quality, each with an assigned responsible agency and target timescales. The management team (Project Group) will be responsible for monitoring both the implementation of the management programme and its effectiveness in improving river quality. Although the Almond Catchment Plan is still being developed, the development process has already yielded benefits that would not have come about without the ICP initiative (B. D'Arcy, personal communication). For example, clauses have been included in the recent Bathgate Local Plan to address the potential problem of pollution from urban run-off arising from future development in West Lothian. This is an issue that would not have been addressed without the liaison between the Local Authority Planning Departments and the River Purification Board, which was initiated through the development of the Almond Catchment Plan.

Acknowledgements

The Scottish Wildlife Trust would like to thank Scottish and Newcastle plc; City of Edinburgh District Council, Department of Planning; UK2000; Scottish Wildlife Trust, Lothians Branch; West Lothian District Council, Department of Planning; Livingston Development Corporation; Central Scotland Countryside Trust; and Scottish Natural Heritage for supporting the River Valleys Project.

References

Edwards-Jones, E. S. (1993). *The Water of Leith: Integrated Environmental Action Plan*, Scottish Wildlife Trust, Edinburgh.

Edwards-Jones, E. S. and Pollard, P. (1995). *Integrated Management of the Almond Catchment—Preliminary Report*, Scottish Wildlife Trust, Edinburgh.

Gilvear, D. (1994). River flow regulation. In: Maitland, P. S., Boon, P. J. and McLusky, D. (Eds), *The Fresh Waters of Scotland: a National Resource of International Significance*. John Wiley, Chichester, 463–487.

Gilvear, D., Hanley, N., Maitland, P. and Peterken, G. (1995). *Wild Rivers—Phase 1: Technical Paper*. WWF Scotland, Aberfeldy.

Hammerton, D. (1994). Domestic and industrial pollution. In: Maitland, P. S., Boon, P. J. and McLusky, D. (Eds), *The Fresh Waters of Scotland: a National Resource of International Significance*. John Wiley, Chichester, 347–364.

Howell, D. L. (1994). Role of environmental agencies. In: Maitland, P. S., Boon, P. J. and McLusky, D. (Eds), *The Fresh Waters of Scotland: a National Resource of International Significance*. John Wiley, Chichester, 577–611.

Mackay, D. W. (1994). Pollution control. In: Maitland, P. S., Boon, P. J. and McLusky, D. (Eds), *The Fresh Waters of Scotland: a National Resource of International Significance*. John Wiley, Chichester, 517–529.

NRA (1993). *NRA Conservation Strategy*. Bristol.

Werritty, A. (1995). *Integrated Catchment Management: a Review and Evaluation*. Scottish Natural Heritage Review, 58. Scottish Natural Heritage, Battleby.

41 THE USE OF ECOLOGICAL INFORMATION IN THE SELECTION OF PRIORITY ZONES FOR RIVER CONSERVATION AND RESTORATION IN FLANDERS

A. Schneiders, C. Wils and R. F. Verheyen

Summary

1. This chapter summarizes the methodology used in producing policy maps as guidelines for integrated water management in Flanders.

2. The ecological evaluation of 240 sub-catchments resulted in a priority map of Flanders, in which four priority levels are distinguished. The evaluation integrates data on water quality, morphological characteristics and aquatic communities for the watercourses, and land-use plans, biological valuation maps and ecological infrastructure maps for the surrounding areas. As an example the results are discussed for the River Nete, part of the River Scheldt basin.

3. Different quality objectives were assigned to the watercourses of the selected sub-catchments. In some watercourses nature conservation is the principal objective; in others it is their role in maintaining connectivity with the stream network which is important. The assignment of objectives resulted in a policy map for Flanders.

41.1 Introduction

Most of the catchment areas in Flanders have a low ecological value: the run-off is very high due to human constructions, most rivers are straightened, numerous watercourses have a poor water quality, etc. To restore the ecological variety of watercourses in Flanders and to make it possible for them to function as a hydrological network, priority should be given at the level of whole catchment areas.

In the proposed EC Directive on the Ecological Quality of Water (see Preface), some watercourses should be designated for reaching 'high' ecological quality, which is the highest or most natural quality level. For a densely populated area such as Flanders this level can only be reached in small, mostly upstream parts of some catchments. 'Good' ecological quality, describing the 'minimal' quality level, according to the same Directive, should be reached in nearly all catchments. 'Good' ecological quality is the quality compatible with the normal functioning of the ecosystem, including the necessity of sustaining self-purification capacity (Anonymous, 1994). In addition to the EC Directive there is a need to define different ecological quality levels between 'good' and 'high' and to determine priority levels for river conservation and restoration (Schneiders *et al.*, 1993, 1996). This chapter describes methods for developing policy maps that can form a starting point for water management planning in Flanders. These are for use by the Flemish Authority responsible for Water Management, and for the Flemish Minister of the Environment.

41.2   Methodology

41.2.1   Selection of priority zones

Figure 41.1 illustrates the method used to set up policy maps for an efficient, integrated water management system. The first step is to collect all ecological information available throughout Flanders, and store it in a digital form in a Geographical Information System (GENAMAP) linked with an ORACLE database. The second step is the processing of data to assess the ecological value of each sub-catchment. Flanders is divided into 240 small catchment areas. In the evaluation of sub-catchments objective ecological information is combined with statutory regulations and political initiatives related to nature conservation.

Data on the biological, physical and chemical components of water quality together with structural features such as meanders and pool-riffle sequences provide a good overall view of the present and potential ecological value of the river system. The aquatic communities are examined at a number of sampling points. Evaluation of the fish fauna is based on the population structure of the fish community and on the presence or absence of pollution-sensitive species such as brook lamprey (*Lampetra planeri*), bullhead (*Cottus gobio*), dace (*Leuciscus leuciscus*) and spined loach (*Cobitis taenia*). Some of these species are also very vulnerable to a reduction in the structural diversity of the channel, and populations are quite often isolated in upstream parts of the river system. Aquatic vegetation is evaluated with reference to the number of species combined with their sensitivity to pollution (Wils *et al.*, 1994). The biological valuation map gives an overall picture of the typology, the biological value and the sensitivity to desiccation and eutrophication of the surrounding vegetation (De Blust *et al.*, 1994). All this ecological information is combined with information on catchment land-use. The land-use plans determine the legal designation: which parts must be preserved as nature reserves, which for agricultural uses, urban development, recreation, industries, and so on. River channels in nature reserve areas are often well preserved, and can reach the 'high' ecological quality level more easily than those in industrial or urban areas. The legal designation under the EC Directives for

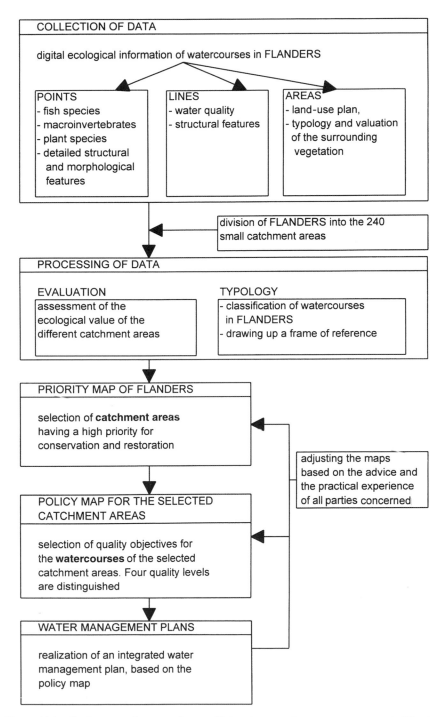

Figure 41.1   Setting up policy maps for an efficient integrated water management in Flanders.

bathing water (No L31-5/2/76), water for freshwater fish (No L222-1/8/78), water for shellfish (No 281-10/11/79) and drinking water (No L229-30/8/80), partly determines the quality level that can be reached in a watercourse (Johnson and Corcelle, 1989). Although the present quality level of a watercourse is not always consistent with the objectives of its legal designation, the human uses of watercourses often reflect their priority for purification programmes.

The 'Green Main Structure' (GMS) is an example of a political initiative related to nature conservation. It is a policy plan of the ecological network for Flanders with four spatial categories: *core areas* having at present a high nature value, *nature development areas* in which restricted efforts at ecological engineering allow the development of valuable biotopes, *ecological corridors* to facilitate the movement of species between those areas (these can also include areas with a dense network of small biotopes), and *buffer zones* (De Blust *et al.*, 1995). The assessment in our study is based on the percentage and the proportion of these categories for each catchment.

The method for calculating an appraisal score per catchment for each selected criterion is illustrated in Figure 41.2. In the first step, different evaluation criteria are selected. The values of each criterion are divided into classes, and depending on the percentage of each class and the weight assigned to each class, an appraisal score is calculated for each catchment area. Based on the scores of all criteria, all catchment areas are compared and priority zones are selected.

Parallel with the evaluation of each catchment, a typology for Flemish watercourses has been established. This is based on a classification and ordination of geomorphological, hydrometric, physical and chemical characteristics combined with biotic data, and provides the information necessary to ensure that all types of watercourses are represented in the hydrological network.

Appraisal scores are used to select catchment areas as priority zones for river conservation and restoration, resulting in a 'priority map' (Figure 41.1). Four priority levels are distinguished:

Priority I   The sub-catchment deserves the highest priority for the production of an integrated water management plan. Most of the watercourses already reach a 'high' ecological quality level. Nature conservation will be one of the most important goals in the catchment area.

Priority II   The sub-catchment has a high priority for the production of an integrated water management plan. Some watercourses already reach a 'high' ecological quality level and/or relict populations of pollution-sensitive species are found. Nature conservation is an important goal in the catchment area.

Priority III   The sub-catchment has a moderate priority for the production of an integrated water management plan. Many watercourses have a 'high' potential ecological value, or rare types of watercourses are found, or the sub-catchment forms an entity with sub-catchments

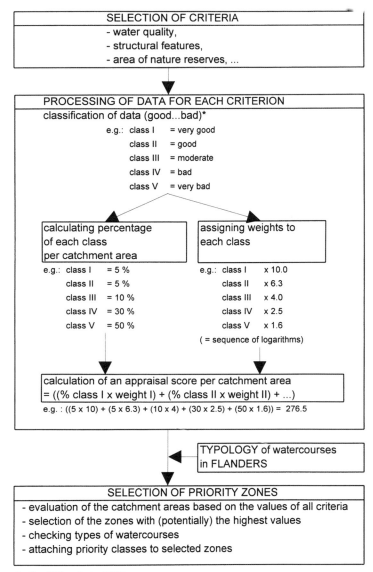

Figure 41.2 Calculation of appraisal scores for the evaluation and selection of priority zones for water management planning.

of priority I or II. Interweaving of agricultural uses and nature conservation is often an important goal.

Priority IV The sub-catchment has no priority for river restoration programmes. The mean ecological quality is low. Extensive water treatment programmes are necessary to reach basic quality standards.

Catchments are assigned to one of these four levels, based on the current and potential ecological value of the river channel, the ecological value of the river corridor, and the legal designation of the watercourse and the surrounding area. At least one watercourse of each type should be selected within the priority map. The large river types, such as the lower reaches of lowland rivers and tidal river systems, often enclose different sub-catchments. These rivers are evaluated and selected as a whole, with no regard to their lateral branches. The selected sub-catchments should form an entity. Islands of upstream river systems with a 'high' ecological value isolated from each other by barriers of water quality or structural features are not desirable. Therefore, downstream river systems, even when they have a low ecological quality, can sometimes be included in the priority map with priority III. For sub-catchments with priority IV, the general principles of environmental protection and sustainable use must remain. Nature conservation must be treated as an integral part of the planning and implementation of development activities (Anonymous, 1987).

41.2.2   *Selection of quality objectives*

In a third step, quality objectives are ascribed to the watercourses of the selected catchment areas. In the policy map of Flanders four quality levels have been formulated:

Class I   Conservation of watercourses reaching 'high' ecological quality. Nature conservation is the principal objective.

Class II   Restoration of watercourses with potentially 'high' ecological quality. Nature conservation should become the principal objective.

Class III   Watercourses which should be restored to an intermediate quality level (between 'high' and 'good' ecological quality). Nature conservation is an important subsidiary function. Integrating agricultural uses and nature conservation is often an important goal.

Class IV   Watercourses with a connecting function which should reach at least 'good' ecological quality.

41.3   Case Study of the River Nete

The catchment of the River Nete (situated in the River Scheldt basin) is divided into 21 sub-catchments, located in the north-east of Flanders. Table 41.1 summarizes the appraisal scores of the most important criteria. The highest priority (I) is given to protecting the high water quality and populations of vulnerable fish species in the upstream parts (zones 500, 530, 532); priority II is assigned to most of the sub-basins of the Kleine Nete. Watercourses in the lower parts of the catchment have a low ecological value, but serve an important connecting function by allowing species to migrate throughout the whole river basin. They are assigned priority III to ensure the restoration of the hydrological network as a whole. In the downstream part of the Grote Nete (zone 513) the land-use plan seems to encourage nature conservation with 33% described as 'green' areas; also the GMS gives a high score (Table 41.1). Nevertheless, restoring the connection between

Table 41.1   Summary of the ecological valuation of the sub-catchments of the River Nete.

ZONE	water quality	structural features	vulnerable fish species	'green' areas	GMS	functional uses	PRIO	main watercourse
530	722	386	11	34	291	F	I	Kleine Nete
532	530	295	8	16	208	F	II	Kleine Nete
500	620	459	3	22	392	F	I	Grote Nete
502	514	335	2	29	265	F	II	Grote Nete
531	404	265	1	17	262	/	II	Kleine Nete
540	402	278	/	21	263	/	II	Aa (KN)
541	392	283	1	23	259	/	II	Aa (KN)
550	404	463	1	25	347	F	II	Abeek (KN)
551	394	425	3	21	273	F	II	Molenbeek (KN)
552	290	315	/	15	175	F	III	Kleine Nete
501	398	435	/	23	292	/	III	Grote Nete
510	410	284	/	16	306	F	III	Grote Nete
511	158	398	/	19	247	/	III	Grote Laak (GN)
512	267	351	/	18	252	/	III	Grote Laak (GN)
513	158	269	/	33	549	F	III	Grote Nete
514	167	310	/	21	287	/	III	Grote Nete
520	158	263	/	6	277	/	III	Grote Nete
521	267	264	/	5	32	F	III	Wimp (GN)
522	180	258	/	10	170	/	III	Grote Nete
560	233	310	/	5	113	F	III	Nete
561	213	285	/	7	75	F	III	Nete

very bad   very good

ZONE: number of the sub-catchment of the River Nete. Water quality: appraisal score for the water quality in each catchment area (129–1,000). Structural features: appraisal score for the structural features in each catchment area (129–1,000). Vulnerable fish species: number of sampling points where species very sensitive to pollution occur. 'Green' areas: areas within the land-use plan identified as important for nature conservation (% of the catchment area) (0–100%). GMS: appraisal score for the Green Main Structure (= map of the ecological network) (0–1,000). Functional uses: F = watercourses which are designated under the EC Directive on freshwater fish (OJ No L222 14/8/1978) are present. PRIO: priority level I, II or III for the development of an integrated water management plan. KN = Kleine Nete. GN = Grote Nete.

the river and its surrounding valley is very difficult due to river embankment, so priority level III is assigned.

41.4   Priority Map of Flanders

Priority zones have been assigned to the 240 sub-catchments of Flanders, using the approach described for the River Nete (see Plate 7c).

Many sub-catchments in the north-east and east of Flanders, belonging to the basins of the Nete and the Meuse, are given a high priority level, as they have the highest ecological values. In addition, for both statutory and ecological reasons, the sub-catchments of the River Meuse have more potential for river restoration. In the south of Flanders many spring brooks with a high ecological value occur but their quality declines very quickly farther downstream. Attention should be given to improving water quality and restoring physical structure in these sub-catchments, and so improve the integrity of the hydrological network. The Polders along the coast mainly contain man-made water systems, and the highest priority is given to those sub-catchments containing semi-natural creeks. In the Polders there will always be a difficult balance to maintain between agricultural uses and nature conservation.

Three large rivers, enclosing different sub-catchments, are selected as a whole and assigned priority II:

- The tidal river system of the Scheldt in the central part of Flanders, owing to the rarity of the river type with a range from fresh to brackish tidal systems, and to the high potential value of some parts. The whole tidal system is also designated by the government of Flanders as an Ecological Impulse Area. These are zones where the local and federal government cooperate closely with the private sector to realize nature conservation and nature development projects, and to support initiatives in river restoration.
- The River Meuse, at the border with the Netherlands, as the only representative of its type and its high potential value.
- The River IJzer, on the western side of Flanders, with a large natural floodplain. This river system has also been designated as an Ecological Impulse Area.

41.5   Use of the Policy Maps

The aim of the priority map, together with the ensuing policy map for the selected catchment areas, is to restore the 'natural' diversity of biotic communities in Flanders as quickly as possible. Both maps should be seen as a way of opening a wide-ranging discussion on integrated water management planning and river restoration programmes in Flanders. Following consultation and the participation of all interested parties within the existing river basin committees, maps can be modified and translated into detailed plans for management and action.

References

Anonymous (1987). *Our Common Future. The World Commission on Environment and Development*. Oxford University Press, Oxford, 348–351.

Anonymous (1994). 'Proposal for a Council Directive (EEC) on the Ecological Quality of Water'. Submitted by the Commission on 8/7/1994 (94/C 222/6-15).

De Blust, G., Paelinckx, D. and Kuijken, E. (1994). Up-to-date information on nature quality for environmental management in Flanders. In: Klijn, F. (Ed.), *Ecosystem Classification for Environmental Management*. Kluwer Academic Publishers, The Netherlands, 223–249.

De Blust, G., Paelinckx, D. and Kuijken, E. (1995). The Green Main Structure for Flanders. The development and implementation of an ecological network. *Landschap*, **3,** 89–98.

Johnson, S. P. and Corcelle, G. (1989). *The Environmental Policy of the European Communities*. International Environmental Law and Policy Series. Graham and Trotman, London, 25–108.

Schneiders, A., Verhaert, E., De Blust, G., Wils, C., Bervoets, L. and Verheyen, R. F. (1993). Towards an ecological assessment of watercourses. *Journal of Aquatic Ecosystem Health*, **4,** 29–38.

Schneiders, A., Wils, C., Verheyen, R. F. and De Pauw, N. (1996). Ecological water quality objectives, a useful frame of reference for ecological impact assessment. *European Water Pollution Control*, **6,** 8–16.

Wils, C., Schneiders, A., Bervoets, L., Nagels, A., Weiss, L. and Verheyen, R. F. (1994). Assessment of the ecological value of rivers in Flanders (Belgium). *Water Science and Technology*, **30,** 37–47.

42 DEFINING THE QUALITY OF FRESH WATERS: THEME AND VARIATIONS

P. J. Boon and D. L. Howell

Summary

1. This chapter explores the main theme of the book, and focuses on the variation in ideas expressed in the responses to a questionnaire issued to all delegates attending the conference on which the book is based.

2. More than 80% of respondents considered that pollution status, physical modification, catchment land use, and biological and geomorphological nature conservation value should be included in any broad definition of freshwater 'quality'. A smaller proportion (but well over half) felt that landscape, recreation, economic, and cultural attributes should also be considered.

3. Most respondents (90%) thought that more rigorous methods should be devised for assessing 'quality', and 80% considered that the indices derived should be kept separate.

4. It was generally felt (by 80% of respondents) that the term 'water quality' should be used only when referring to pollution status. Many responses included proposals for other terms to describe the broader concept of 'quality', but there was no clear consensus.

5. A majority of staff from the water regulatory agencies considered it appropriate to classify nature conservation as a 'use' in fresh water. Those from conservation bodies more often said it should be thought of as an intrinsic philosophy underlying water resource management.

6. Recommendations are made on the breadth of freshwater quality assessment, the requirement for new evaluation techniques, the need for clarity in terminology, and the role of nature conservation in managing water resources.

42.1 Introduction

This book represents perhaps the first attempt at examining in detail what the word 'quality' means when applied to fresh waters. It has probed current uses of the term, and has described some of the many new techniques being developed to enable a more comprehensive approach to quality assessment.

Most contributions in this volume have been written from the perspective of the developed world, many from within the UK. A different picture would have emerged, of course, if this publication had been produced entirely by authors from developing countries. When water for human use is often in short supply, and even essential amenities cannot be provided for all, freshwater conservation is unlikely to be motivated by perceptions of recreational or aesthetic value, or even by concerns for protecting biodiversity. Indeed, O'Keeffe (this volume) states that in South Africa, where 30% of the population do not have access to adequate supplies of drinking water, and over 50% lack basic sanitation, government conservation policy is directed more at sustainable development and less at preservation. This chapter takes the analysis of such geographical and socio-economic aspects no further but re-examines, largely from a British standpoint, some of the fundamental questions raised throughout the book: 'Does the assessment of 'quality' in fresh water need to be broadly based?' 'Should all aspects of quality be assessed by means of a single index?' 'What role does nature conservation play in the wider arena of water resource management?' 'Are the terms currently used to describe aspects of freshwater quality clear and unambiguous, and does terminology matter anyway?'

Books like this often end with a summary chapter, where threads are pulled together, and patterns identified and interpreted chiefly from the editors' perspective. This chapter is rather different, in that it presents a synthesis of a wide cross-section of 'expert' opinion. Immediately after the conference on which this book is based, all delegates were sent a short questionnaire seeking their views on the main topics discussed in the programme. The responses represented the personal views of individuals with professional expertise in the subject area, rather than official views of the organizations for whom they worked. Approximately 50% (128) of the forms were completed and returned, and the results were analysed. To see whether opinions varied according to professional background, respondents were assigned to one of five groups, the first two representing the water regulatory authorities in England and Wales, and in Scotland, respectively:

(a) National Rivers Authority (NRA; now the Environment Agency).
(b) River Purification Boards (RPBs; now the Scottish Environment Protection Agency).
(c) Statutory and voluntary conservation bodies.
(d) Research institutes, universities, and environmental consultants.
(e) Delegates not obviously affiliated to the preceding four categories, and including those from overseas.

(Results from group (e) contributed to the overall analysis, but were not used in inter-group comparisons.)

An analysis of responses forms the basis for the chapter and increases the number of individuals contributing views on freshwater quality to this volume. Access to such a wide body of opinion allows some general conclusions to be reached on the central theme of the book, and sheds light on some of the variation in ideas surrounding this topic.

42.2 Freshwater Quality: Inclusive or Exclusive?

The first question examined whether 'quality' should be a comprehensive, all-embracing concept, or whether it should be more restricted:

- 'When trying to define the environmental quality of freshwater systems, which of the following features (ideally) should be assessed?'

The results are given in Table 42.1, and strongly support the view that descriptions of freshwater 'quality' should be inclusive. The first five attributes listed relate principally to the ecological and geomorphological quality of fresh waters and their catchments. These five received broad support from more than 80% of respondents. The other four introduce very different elements of 'quality' and relate more to the immediate and direct values and benefits which fresh waters provide for society. The proportion of respondents voting to include these was lower than for the first five, but still ranged from about one-half to three-quarters.

The analysis of responses showed few differences between groups. However, it is worth noting that NRA staff voted unanimously to include both the 'extent of physical modification' and 'geomorphological nature conservation value', compared with RPB staff, where the two figures were 79% and 71% respectively. Perhaps this demonstrates the greater emphasis on these aspects in England and Wales exemplified through new developments such as River Habitat Survey (Raven

Table 42.1 The percentage of respondents in support of assessing the attributes listed when defining the environmental quality of freshwater systems.

Areas of assessment	*All* (n = 128)	*NRA* (n = 12)	*RPB* (n = 24)	*NRA/RPB* (n = 36)	*Conserv.* (n = 31)	*Univ./Res* (n = 41)
Water quality/pollution status	98	92	100	97	97	98
Extent of physical modification	90	100	79	86	97	80
Catchment land use	82	75	75	75	87	83
Biological nature conservation value	95	100	96	97	97	90
Geomorphological nature conservation value	82	100	71	81	97	71
Landscape and aesthetic value	74	75	67	69	87	68
Recreational value	58	58	63	61	65	54
Economic value	48	42	50	47	55	46
Cultural/historic value	59	50	42	44	74	61

NRA = National Rivers Authority; RPB = River Purification Boards; Conserv. = Statutory and voluntary conservation bodies; Univ./Res = Universities/Research institutes/Environmental consultants; All = categories listed+unclassified response.

et al., this volume) as well as the lesser degree of physical modification in Scottish rivers compared with those in the rest of the UK.

Evidence from surveys of public attitudes in the UK suggests that the professional views expressed in this questionnaire may be closer to those of the general public than sometimes thought (Smith, this volume; Tunstall *et al.,* this volume). For example, far from preferring manicured and highly managed river corridors, most people value the 'naturalness' of winding channels, unmodified banks, and diverse vegetation. Their perception of 'quality' encompasses landscape and aesthetic character, wildlife, and recreational opportunity: described by Smith (this volume) as a 'total experience'.

Several chapters in this book describe broad-based approaches to quality assessment (Boon *et al.*, Moreira *et al.*, Schneiders *et al.*), but should the breadth of quality measurements be encapsulated in a single index, or should each aspect be kept clearly separate? Recent work in Germany on river evaluation (Braukmann and Pinter, 1995) proposes an assessment of three main areas—chemistry, biology, and morphology—all of which are then amalgamated into one overall score for 'ecological quality'. The questionnaire dealt with more than just 'ecological quality' and asked respondents to consider the full range of quality attributes identified in the previous question:

- 'Is it desirable to work towards one index of freshwater quality that incorporates the values you have ticked or listed in Q1, or should there be separate assessments?'

Figure 42.1 shows that 80% of those replying believe it is undesirable to try to

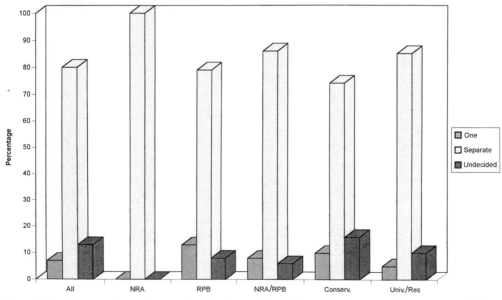

Figure 42.1   The percentage of respondents in favour of one index of freshwater quality, or separate indices. (For an explanation of the six groups, see legend to Table 42.1.)

amalgamate everything in one quality index, although some felt that an all-embracing index might help impart information more simply to planners or to the general public.

42.3   Objectivity in Quality Assessment

At the heart of this theme of quality assessment lies the whole notion of objectivity. Is 'freshwater quality' such an elusive concept, so much a matter of individual perception or organizational position, that it defies definition?

42.3.1   'Quality' vs. 'value'

One of the prerequisites of defining anything is to have clear terminology. This has been discussed from time to time throughout the book (e.g. Maitland, O'Keeffe, Pugh), and the questionnaire also invited comments on the subject. In the responses to these questions, the main area seen as unclear is the distinction between the words 'quality' and 'value'. Comments such as 'Both quality and value imply subjective measures', and 'You can measure 'quality' in an objective way, but value will always resist repeatable assessments' illustrate well some of the confusion that seems to exist. Some people are clearly reticent to use the word 'value' at all, because 'value opens up a whole new can of worms'.

Maitland (this volume) suggests that dictionary definitions of 'quality' (with reference to water) fall into two categories: those which relate to the nature and concentration of substances in water (an objective statement of 'condition'), and those in which waters are placed in a hierarchy, perhaps from 'good' to 'bad' (a subjective statement usually related to human use). He concludes that both uses of the word 'quality' are valid but users should state which meaning is intended. This point is illustrated by comparing the preferred habitat of a young salmon (*Salmo salar*)—flowing water, high oxygen content, little decaying organic matter—with that of a rat-tailed maggot (*Eristalis tenax*)—stagnant water, low oxygen content, large amounts of decaying organic matter. The fishery manager's perception of the 'quality' of both waters ('good' and 'bad' respectively) is naturally quite different from the broader ecological view in which the 'quality' of both areas is seen to be 'good' in terms of the communities inhabiting them. The need to avoid confusion in this area, and to ensure that 'like is compared with like' emerges strongly in chapters elsewhere in this volume (Boon *et al.*, Moss *et al.*, O'Keeffe, Raven *et al.*) It is hoped that the new techniques for quality assessment discussed in these chapters should do much to dispel any such confusion in the future.

Many aspects of freshwater 'quality' listed in Table 42.1 fall into Maitland's second category, and even those that could be considered as more 'objective' are still overlain with value judgements. A case in point is the recent proposal for an EC Directive on the Ecological Quality of Water (see Preface), which described categories such as 'high ecological quality' and 'good ecological quality' with reference to descriptors such as pollution status, physical habitat structure, and biotic diversity. The distinction between 'quality' and 'value' ceases to be a real issue if there is acceptance (as one respondent wrote) that:

> the higher up the scale of 'quality' (a water body) is for most of the features listed in Q1, the higher its overall value to society.

The questionnaire addressed these problems of terminology in two ways. First, respondents were asked:

- 'In the interests of clarity, should the term "water quality" be used chiefly with reference to the "health" or pollution status of rivers and lakes, and an alternative term be sought to describe the broader concept of "quality"?'

Most agreed with this proposal (80% voting 'Yes') (Figure 42.2). The pattern of response was similar in all groups, although respondents from the NRA gave the greatest support for using the term in its restricted sense. Second, various other terms were proposed for describing the broader area of 'quality', and respondents were asked to select one from the list or to propose a different term. The results show a spread of support for all 10, but with more than 50% choosing either 'Freshwater environmental quality' or 'Freshwater environmental value' (Table 42.2). A further 24 terms were offered by respondents as alternatives (Table 42.3) of which 14 include the word 'quality', three 'value', three 'status', two 'integrity', and one each the words 'health' and 'condition'. The preference for terms which refer to 'freshwater environments' may indicate that many people are searching for words that will adequately describe the breadth of the subject: it is not just

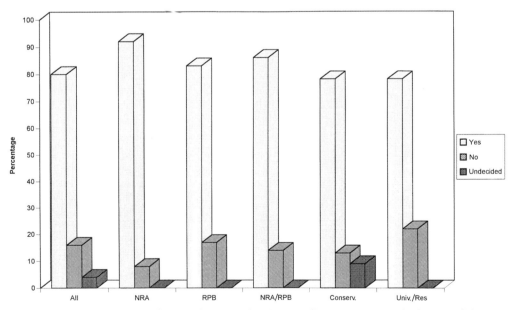

Figure 42.2 The percentage of respondents agreeing (yes) or disagreeing (no) with the use of the term 'water quality' being restricted to the 'health' or 'pollution status' of rivers and lakes. (For an explanation of the six groups, see legend to Table 42.1.)

Table 42.2   The numbers of votes given by respondents for terms which might be used in a comprehensive description of freshwater quality.

Proposed terms	All	NRA	RPB	NRA/RPB	Conserv.	Univ./Res.
Freshwater quality	6	0	2	2	3	0
Freshwater value	8	1	0	1	2	3
Freshwater environmental quality	30	3	5	8	11	6
Freshwater environmental value	19	1	5	6	3	7
Inclusive freshwater quality	2	0	1	1	1	0
Inclusive freshwater value	1	0	0	0	0	1
Composite freshwater quality	5	0	1	1	0	2
Composite freshwater value	6	0	1	1	1	2
Total freshwater quality	9	0	1	1	2	6
Total freshwater value	5	0	0	0	2	2

Table 42.3   Alternative terms to those listed in Table 42.2, proposed by respondents for use in the comprehensive description of freshwater quality.

Absolute quality	Environment quality	Freshwater environment quality
Basin quality	Environmental quality	Freshwater environment value
Catchment quality	Environmental value	Freshwater habitat quality
Ecological health	Environmental water quality	Freshwater status
Ecological quality	Freshwater condition	Freshwater system quality
Ecological water quality	Freshwater ecosystem integrity	Principal use quality
Ecosystem integrity	Freshwater ecosystem quality	Status
Ecosystem quality	Freshwater ecosystem status	Total water value

about 'ecosystems' or 'habitats' but about other aspects as well which together amount to a comprehensive picture of environmental quality or value.

42.3.2   Nature conservation: art or science?

In his introduction to the principles of conservation evaluation, Usher (this volume) uses the phrase 'the search for objectivity'. Indeed, nature conservation is perhaps the best example of where quality assessment requires far greater rigour. In Britain over the last 20 years, the principles set out in *A Nature Conservation Review* (Ratcliffe, 1977) have been put into practice when selecting particular areas meriting special conservation measures (Boon, *et al.*, this volume; Lassière and Duncan, this volume). Yet it has not always been clear whether practitioners see this exercise as a branch of art or of science. One definition of 'art' is 'the application of skill to subjects of taste'; of 'science' 'a branch of study concerned either with a connected body of demonstrated truths or with observed facts systematically classified' (Onions, 1973). To some extent, it can always be argued that conservation evaluation is more art than science, inasmuch as the criteria often used (naturalness, diversity, and so on) essentially reflect the tastes of society.

Perhaps some future civilization might consider straight, concrete-lined river channels as the pinnacle of conservation value, but it is unlikely. So if society places importance on conserving biodiversity, or preserving what little remains of natural or quasi-natural areas of the countryside, then greater emphasis must be placed on developing ways of applying those criteria more rigorously and repeatably. This has been the motivation for systems such as SERCON (Boon, *et al.*, this volume) and System Aqua (Willén *et al.*, this volume).

Of course, there are very good practical reasons why conservation evaluation cannot be allowed to remain merely a matter of taste, where one opinion is as valid as the next. Management decisions must be made, such as where to invest money on rehabilitation or enhancement, and when catchment development proposals are put forward, planners need some basis for decision making. For example, in 1989, the Nature Conservancy Council (NCC) formally objected to a proposed fish farm development on the River Hull, a Site of Special Scientific Interest in northern England. Ecological evidence was given at a public inquiry by scientifically qualified witnesses (Boon, 1992). The NCC's witness stated that:

> The River Hull is nationally important because it is the only northern example of a chalk stream which retains much of its former interest

whereas the witness for the appellant concluded:

> There are no particular species or assemblages which would characterize this particular site, in relation to ... countrywide criteria which render it of singular national importance.

The same river, the same evidence—but different interpretations of the criteria used for evaluation. Whether what is needed is better described as 'greater objectivity' or 'greater rigour' is not especially important; what matters is that generally accepted conservation criteria can be applied consistently so that practical decisions are made on a firmer basis.

The views expressed through the questionnaire on this matter were quite clear. Respondents were asked:

- 'Is it desirable to devise more rigorous and repeatable methods for assessing any or all of the features listed in Q1, rather than relying simply on "expert opinion"?'

Ninety per cent of respondents said 'Yes' (Figure 42.3), with very few differences between groups.

42.4 The Position of Nature Conservation in Water Management

Fundamental to the assessment of nature conservation value is the way that nature conservation itself is perceived alongside other elements of water management. Over the last 50 years, nature conservation in Britain has become a clearly circumscribed activity, both within formal government structures and non-statutory organizations, rather than an attitude permeating interactions between society and

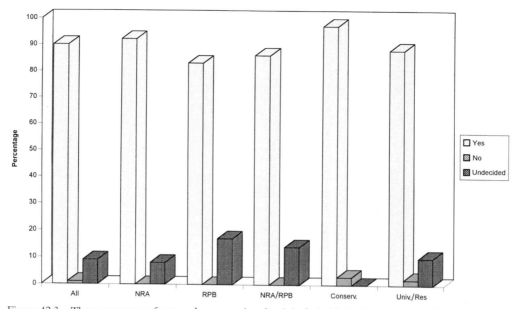

Figure 42.3 The percentage of respondents agreeing that it is desirable (yes) or not desirable (no) to devise more rigorous and repeatable methods for quality assessment. (For an explanation of the six groups, see legend to Table 42.1.)

environment (Boon, 1994). For example, when the NRA was established in England and Wales in 1989, it was given statutory responsibilities both in 'furthering' nature conservation when carrying out its other duties (such as land drainage and flood defence), and (as a 'free-standing' duty) in 'promoting' nature conservation. This in turn influenced organizational structure, with a division devoted to fisheries, conservation and recreation.

Without doubt, these statutory and organizational changes have proved immensely valuable in focusing attention on the importance of nature conservation, and in funding related research. On the other hand, there has been a growing tendency to see conservation as merely another competing 'use' alongside other uses such as water supply or recreation. This is well illustrated by the proposals in England and Wales for a new, statutory scheme of Water Quality Objectives, in which a category termed 'Special Ecosystem Use' will comprise rivers whose principal 'use' is considered to be nature conservation, and where protection will be afforded through setting standards for levels of soluble reactive phosphorus.

Should nature conservation be considered as a 'use' in fresh water, or is it something altogether more fundamental? This issue was explored by asking the question:

- 'Is it appropriate to define nature conservation as a "use"?'

A total of 47% of respondents to the questionnaire felt that it was appropriate to define nature conservation as a use, compared with 41% who did not (Figure

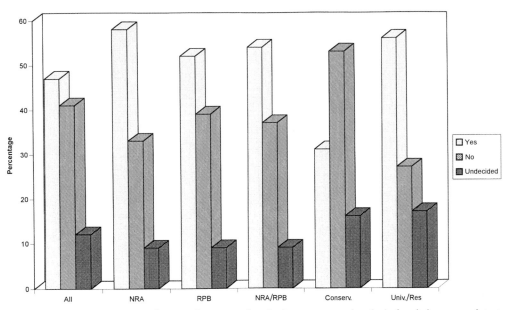

Figure 42.4   The percentage of respondents agreeing (yes) or not agreeing (no) that it is appropriate to define conservation as a 'use'. (For an explanation of the six groups, see legend to Table 42.1.)

42.4). When the results for each group are compared there are some interesting differences, in particular between those from the water regulatory agencies and those from the conservation bodies. In the former group, 58% voted 'Yes' and 33% 'No'; the situation was reversed in the latter group with respective percentages of 31 and 53. It is perhaps surprising that with the NRA's statutory role in nature conservation, the percentage (of an admittedly small sample) voting 'Yes' was not higher. It is also interesting to note that although the Scottish RPBs lacked the strong statutory conservation duties of the NRA, RPB staff nonetheless returned a response very similar to those from the NRA.

Most respondents voting 'No' offered their own alternative perceptions of nature conservation. These were broadly similar, and included phrases such as:

> A function of the system rather than a use
> A method of managing the water resource
> An intrinsic quality
> An *a priori* component of sustainable development
> A philosophy which underpins and imposes some constraints on uses.

Several people pointed out that while it may not be desirable to consider nature conservation as a use, it may be the only pragmatic way of ensuring that it is taken seriously—'the end justifies the means'.

42.5   Conclusions and Recommendations

(a) 'Freshwater quality' is a term that has long been used, albeit mainly when describing the chemical or pollution characteristics of water itself. There is now an increasing awareness that 'quality' assessments must incorporate far more. With reference to freshwater *ecosystems*, assessment must address physical, chemical and biological attributes, and must extend from the water out into the catchment. Where the emphasis is primarily on human use of fresh waters, quality assessments should encompass all aspects valued by society: e.g. landscape, recreation and culture.

(b) Most elements of freshwater quality imply some measure of value to a greater or lesser extent. Although some flexibility will always be needed when matters of taste are involved, planners and decision makers require more rigorous techniques for assessing value and for comparing one area with another. Semi-quantitative scoring methods provide one useful way of presenting information in a relatively simple form, and (when used properly) allow such comparisons to be made easily. Work is needed on developing new assessment techniques for many of the quality aspects discussed in this book, but it is vital not to 'dilute' or mask information by attempting to combine indices into some form of global quality index.

(c) The field of freshwater assessment is smothered with an array of terms. It is probably unrealistic to expect that a common vocabulary can be agreed, but at least when terms such as 'quality', 'value', or 'status' are used the meaning should be clear from the context, or should be specifically defined. The term 'water quality' has become almost synonymous with 'pollution status' and for the sake of clarity its use should be restricted to this single meaning. When a comprehensive assessment is referred to, the evidence presented here suggests that a term such as 'freshwater environmental quality' might be preferable. Whichever term is chosen its meaning must be clear.

(d) The important role of nature conservation in the wider field of aquatic resource management needs due emphasis, whilst at the same time recognizing that there may be some practical benefits in classifying nature conservation as a 'use'. The threefold aim of the World Conservation Strategy (IUCN, 1980)—to maintain essential ecological processes and life-support systems; to preserve genetic diversity; to ensure sustainable utilization of species and ecosystems—while necessarily anthropocentric, provides a good basis, together with more recent global declarations (such as Agenda 21), for freshwater conservation and management into the next century.

References

Boon, P. J. (1992). Channelling scientific information for the conservation and management of rivers. *Aquatic Conservation: Marine and Freshwater Ecosystems*, **2**, 115–123.

Boon, P. J. (1994). Nature conservation. In: Maitland, P. S., Boon, P. J. and McLusky, D. S. (Eds), *The Fresh Waters of Scotland: a National Resource of International Significance*. John Wiley, Chichester, 555–576.

Boon, P. J., Holmes, N. T. H., Maitland, P. S., Rowell, T. A. and Davies, J. (This volume). A system for evaluating rivers for conservation (SERCON): development, structure and function.

Braukmann, U. and Pinter, I. (1995). *Concept for an Integrated Ecological Evaluation of Running Waters*. Landesanstalt für Umweltschutz Baden-Württemberg, Karlsruhe.

IUCN (1980). *World Conservation Strategy*. Gland.

Lassière, O. L. and Duncan, W. M. (This volume). Assessing the conservation value of standing waters.

Maitland, P. S. (This volume). 'Freshwater quality': the use of the term in scientific literature.

Moreira, I., Saraiva, M. G. and Pinto, P. (This volume). Assessing the conservation value of a Mediterranean river basin (Sado, Portugal).

Moss, B., Johnes, P. and Phillips, G. (This volume). New approaches to monitoring and classifying standing waters.

O'Keeffe, J. (This volume). Methods of assessing conservation status for natural fresh waters in the Southern hemisphere.

Onions, C. T. (Ed.) (1973). *The Shorter Oxford English Dictionary*. Clarendon Press, Oxford.

Pugh, K. (This volume). Organizational use of the term 'freshwater quality' in Britain.

Ratcliffe, D. A. (Ed.) (1977). *A Nature Conservation Review*. Cambridge University Press, Cambridge.

Raven, P. J., Fox, P., Everard, M., Holmes, N. T. H. and Dawson, F. H. (This volume). River Habitat Survey: a new system for classifying rivers according to their habitat quality.

Schneiders, A., Wils, C. and Verheyen, R. F. (This volume). The use of ecological information in the selection of priority zones for river conservation and restoration in Flanders.

Smith, I. R. (This volume). Waterscape architecture.

Tunstall, S., Fordham, M., Green, C. and House, M. (This volume). Public perception of freshwater quality with particular reference to rivers in England and Wales.

Usher, M. B. (This volume). Principles of nature conservation evaluation.

Willén, E., Andersson, B. and Söderbäck, B. (This volume). System Aqua: a biological assessment tool for Swedish lakes and watercourses.

INDEX